ADVANCES IN LIPID RESEARCH

Volume 12

CONTRIBUTORS TO THIS VOLUME

Piero P. Foà
Beatrix Fourcans
Barbara V. Howard
William J. Howard
Mahendra Kumar Jain
Gilbert A. Leveille
Leon A. Lipshaw
Sergio Muntoni
Dale R. Romsos
P. S. Sastry
Elspeth B. Smith

Advances in Lipid Research

Volume 12

Edited by

Rodolfo Paoletti

Institute of Pharmacology
Milan, Italy

David Kritchevsky

The Wistar Institute
Philadelphia, Pennsylvania

1974

ACADEMIC PRESS • New York and London
A Subsidiary of Harcourt Brace Jovanovich, Publishers

ACADEMIC PRESS, INC.
111 Fifth Avenue, New York, New York 10003

United Kingdom Edition published by
ACADEMIC PRESS, INC. (LONDON) LTD.
24/28 Oval Road, London NW1

LIBRARY OF CONGRESS CATALOG CARD NUMBER: 63-22330

ISBN 0-12-024912-X

PRINTED IN THE UNITED STATES OF AMERICA

CONTENTS

The Relationship Between Plasma and Tissue Lipids in Human Atherosclerosis

Elspeth B. Smith

Lipid Metabolism in Cultured Cells

Barbara V. Howard and William J. Howard

Effect of Diet on Activity of Enzymes Involved in Fatty Acid and Cholesterol Synthesis

Dale R. Romsos and Gilbert A. Leveille

Role of Phospholipids in Transport and Enzymic Reactions

Beatrix Fourcans and Mahendra Kumar Jain

The Composition and Possible Physiologie Role of the Thyroid Lipids

Leon A. Lipshaw and Piero P. Foà

Glycosyl Glycerides

P. S. Sastry

Inhibition of Fatty Acid Oxidation by Biguanides: Implications for Metabolic Physiopathology

Sergio Muntoni

LIST OF CONTRIBUTORS

Numbers in parentheses indicate the pages on which the authors' contributions begin.

PIERO P. FOÀ, *Department of Research, Sinai Hospital of Detroit, Detroit, Michigan* (227)

BEATRIX FOURCANS, *Department of Chemistry, Indiana University, Bloomington, Indiana* (147)

BARBARA V. HOWARD,* *Department of Biochemistry, School of Dental Medicine, Department of Microbiology, School of Medicine, University of Pennsylvania and the Clinical Research Center, Philadelphia General Hospital, Philadelphia, Pennsylvania* (51)

WILLIAM J. HOWARD, *Department of Medicine, School of Medicine, University of Pennsylvania and the Clinical Research Center, Philadelphia General Hospital, Philadelphia, Pennsylvania* (51)

MAHENDRA KUMAR JAIN,† *Department of Chemistry, Indiana University, Bloomington, Indiana and Department of Chemistry and Health Sciences, University of Delaware, Newark, Delaware* (147)

GILBERT A. LEVEILLE, *Department of Food Science and Human Nutrition, Michigan State University, East Lansing, Michigan* (97)

LEON A. LIPSHAW, *Department of Research, Sinai Hospital of Detroit, Detroit, Michigan* (227)

SERGIO MUNTONI, *Department of Pharmacology and Chemotherapy, University of Cagliari; Second Division of Medicine, and Center for Metabolic Diseases and Arteriosclerosis, SS. Trinità Hospital of Cagliari, Cagliari, Italy* (311)

---

* Present address: Clinical Research Center, Philadelphia General Hospital, Philadelphia, Pennsylvania 19104.

† Present address: Department of Chemistry and Health Sciences, University of Delaware, Newark, Delaware, 19711.

Dale R. Romsos, *Department of Food Science and Human Nutrition, Michigan State University, East Lansing, Michigan* (97)

P. S. Sastry, *Department of Biochemistry, Indian Institute of Science, Bangalore, India* (251)

Elspeth B. Smith, *Department of Chemical Pathology, University of Aberdeen, Aberdeen, Scotland* (1)

PREFACE

The current volume of *Advances in Lipid Research* brings together topics which range across the field of lipid metabolism. As in the past, the chapters in this book represent the most advanced knowledge in the specific areas represented.

The opening review is devoted to a discussion of the relationships between plasma and tissue lipids and atherosclerosis. Understanding the dynamics of exchange of plasma lipoproteins with aortic tissue is the basis of understanding the etiology of this disease and, hopefully, the approaches to therapy. A relatively recent research tool, but one which has already shown great utility, is the study of metabolism using cultured cells.

The second paper of this book is devoted to a discussion of lipid metabolism in cultured cells. Cell systems hold promise of understanding mechanisms of lipidoses and may aid in their diagnosis. All phases of lipid metabolism are discussed in this review. Research on dietary effects on lipid metabolism has progressed beyond descriptions of the lipid content of blood and tissues. The "what" of various regimens is known and we are now asking "how?" The third article describes the influences of various dietary components on the specific enzymes of fatty acid and cholesterol biogenesis. This discussion includes enzyme induction, synthesis, and degradation. Membrane function, especially the metabolic behavior of one important membrane component, is discussed in the fourth paper. This article is devoted to an exposition of the role of phospholipids in transport and enzymic reactions. This discussion includes membrane fluidity and aspects of lipid-protein interactions. Thyroid hormone exerts specific effects on cholesterol and bile acid metabolism. It has been implicated, via these effects on lipids, in the etiology of atherosclerosis. The lipids of the thyroid gland, however, have never been fully investigated. The fifth review is devoted to a discussion of thyroid lipids and their physiologic role. Thyroid lipids are primarily triglycerides; their synthesis and hydrolysis may aid in the regulation of glucose metabolism by this gland. The designation "glycolipid" covers a variety of structures. A newcomer to this area is the class of glycolipids known as glycosyl glycerides. These compounds are found in plants, bacteria, and in animal tissues. The chemistry and biological function of glycosyl glycerides is discussed in the sixth article. The last paper is devoted to the physiopathology of the biguanidines, a class of oral hypoglycemic agents whose relationship to carbohydrate and lipid metabolism is only now being established.

RODOLFO PAOLETTI
DAVID KRITCHEVSKY

CONTENTS OF PREVIOUS VOLUMES

Volume 3

Volume 6

Volume 7

Volume 8

Volume 9

Volume 10

Volume 11

The Relationship Between Plasma and Tissue Lipids in Human Atherosclerosis

ELSPETH B. SMITH

Department of Chemical Pathology, University of Aberdeen, Aberdeen, Scotland

I. Introduction

A high level of plasma cholesterol has emerged as an important risk factor in all epidemiological studies on the incidence and prevalence of ischemic heart disease. However, in man the relationship between plasma cholesterol levels and the extent and severity of atherosclerosis and the cholesterol content of the arterial wall has not emerged clearly. This probably arises from at least two causes. First, it is difficult to obtain information on plasma cholesterol levels during life in subjects coming to autopsy; consequently, the few studies that are published are based on institutionalized patients of advanced age (Paterson *et al.*, 1956, 1963); second, the atherosclerotic lesions found in arteries of middle-aged or older humans are extremely heterogeneous, ranging from accumulation of lipid, particularly cholesterol ester, with very little increase in connective tissue components to a massive hyperplasia of collagen and smooth muscle cells with only slight accumulation of lipid. The balance between the different types of lesion is clearly influenced by many factors including age, sex, and race (McGill, 1968), but the influence of plasma lipid levels is not clear.

There is, however, a close correspondence between the detailed lipid composition of the S_f 0–12 (LD) lipoprotein of plasma and the composition of extracellular lipid in samples of intima with defined histological characteristics (Smith *et al.*, 1967, 1968; Smith and Slater, 1972a). There is also a substantial amount of electrophoretically and immunologically intact LD-lipoprotein in the human aortic intima, and its concentration in normal intima is highly correlated with the level of the subject's plasma cholesterol during the week before death (Smith and Slater, 1972b, 1973a,b). From the analysis of the cholesterol esters in topographically and morphologically defined fractions isolated by microdissection, Smith and Slater (1972a) concluded that most of the cholesterol in the main "atheroma" lipid pool of large plaques in human aorta is derived directly from plasma LD-lipoprotein and not from disintegration of fat-filled cells. This suggests that in humans, the entry of LD-lipoprotein, its retention within the intima and the precipitation of lipid from it may be key factors in atherogenesis.

This is the aspect of the problem which will be discussed in this paper; several reviews on other aspects of arterial lipids have already appeared in *Advances in Lipid Research* (Clarkson, 1963; Zemplényi, 1964; Day, 1967; Wissler and Vesselinovitch, 1968; Adams, 1969; Whereat, 1971), and in particular Portman (1970) has published a most comprehensive review on esterified fatty acids and cholesterol. No attempt will be made to cover the same ground as these papers or to emulate their completeness.

II. Relationship Between the Chemical and Morphological Characteristics of Lipid in Human Aortic Intima

A. Morphology of Normal Intima and Atherosclerotic Lesions

Much of the confusion and apparent disagreement in atherosclerosis research has undoubtedly arisen either from failure to differentiate between different types of lesion or because the same name has been applied to tissue samples which are not in fact comparable. In the hope of avoiding further confusion and repetitive descriptions in the text the morphological characteristics of the intimal samples are briefly described below.

1. *Normal Intima*

In children of the first decade and in virtually all experimental animals the normal intima consists of a single layer of endothelial cells separated from the internal elastic lamina by a very thin subendothelial layer containing small amounts of fine collagen and elastic fibers and glycosaminoglycans (GAG). In man by the third decade, the subendothelial layer is invariably thickened, and contains several layers of smooth muscle cells and bundles of collagen fibers. This "diffuse intimal thickening" increases progressively with age; its significance was recently reviewed by Geer and Haust (1972). All samples of "normal" intima in adult humans have some degree of diffuse intimal thickening, and this is an important difference from normal intima in experimental animals. From the fourth decade onward, two upper (luminal) layers can be distinguished in the aorta—a superficial layer containing collagen and smooth muscle cells in which elastin cannot be demonstrated by the Verhoeff stain and a deeper layer which lies between this and the first intact medial elastic lamina and contains numerous fragmentary elastic laminae (Taylor, 1953; Smith, 1974). It is not clear whether this layer should be regarded as intima or media. In young subjects, very little lipid can be demonstrated by sudan staining, but from about age 30 onward there is an increasing accumulation of fine, extracellular, perifibrous, sudanophilic droplets. These have a diameter of 0.5–1.5 μ and seem to be particularly associated with the fragmentary elastic laminae in the deep layer of the intima (Smith *et al.*, 1967).

2. *Fatty Infiltration*

Arteries stained macroscopically for fat (Holman *et al.*, 1958) generally show areas of intense, focal staining corresponding with fatty streaks, nodules, or plaques. They may also show patches of more diffuse sudanophilia that correspond to microscopic collections of extracellular lipid droplets, slightly coarser than the perifibrous lipid droplets of normal intima, which are scattered through an otherwise rather normal intima; fine sudanophilic droplets may also be found in the smooth muscle cells. These areas of "fatty infiltration," which can only be detected in unstained arteries if the lipid infiltration is unusually massive, probably occur more commonly in the coronary arteries than in aorta; they are frequently described as "fatty streaks," but microscopically their morphology is quite different from the lesion containing numerous fat-filled cells which is the typical aortic fatty streak of the second decade. The confusion arising from using the same term for lesions of different morphology, and probably also different etiology, is reflected in the controversy as to whether the fatty streak is the precursor of the fibrous plaque.

3. *Fatty Streaks*

Macroscopically, in unstained arteries, typical juvenile fatty streaks appear as slightly raised whitish or pale yellow spots, 2–3 mm in diameter, and generally occurring in clusters. In the aorta, they frequently occur in lines between the orifices of the intercostal arteries. They are found at all ages after birth, reaching a maximum extent about age 20 (Holman, 1961). Microscopically, the lesions contain clusters of cells filled with *large* lipid droplets. These fat-filled cells may be confluent, or slightly separated from each other; they may occur at any depth in the intima but are most frequent in the superficial (luminal) layers and are found rarely, if at all, in aortic media. In the human, they are probably mainly smooth muscle cells and "ovoid foam cells" (Geer and Haust, 1972) of uncertain origin. In the author's opinion, fatty streaks must be defined on the microscopic basis that most of the lipid is within fat-filled cells.

4. *Raised Fatty Nodules and Fatty Plaques*

In larger fatty streaks and nodules, extracellular lipid may accumulate between and beneath the fat-filled cells, and this process is probably extended to produce macroscopically raised, yellow "fatty" plaques. Microscopically there is a thin "cap" consisting mainly of fat-filled cells overlying an "atheroma pool" of amorphous, extracellular lipid. It appears that in the human aorta this type of structure is not commonly found in large lesions. Smith and Slater (1972a) found that in larger macroscopically "fatty" plaques, the fat-filled cells were generally embedded in a fairly thick, fibrous cap overlying the atheroma lipid center.

5. *Gelatinous Thickenings and Plaques*

Macroscopically, these lesions have a characteristic translucent appearance, often slightly pinkish, and on stripping or cutting the intima has a "gelatinous" texture. Microscopically, they are very ill-defined, the only consistent finding being a loose structure with wide gaps between the smooth cells and rather thick collagen bundles. Lipid is variable, ranging from virtually no staining, through intense diffuse sudanophilia or heavy perifibrous lipid to accumulation of extracellular "atheroma" lipid in deep layers. It seems probable that these lesions are the precursors of fibrous plaques; fibrous plaques frequently have gelatinous peripheries that seem to be their growing points. The literature on this type of lesion has recently been reviewed by Haust (1971) and Geer and Haust (1972). They appear to correspond to the "focal intimal edema" described by German workers, or the insudation lesions described for example, by More and Haust (1957).

6. *Fibrous Plaques*

These are sharply raised lesions that macroscopically appear pearly white in both stained and unstained arteries. Microscopically, there is a thick, compact, collagen cap that may show very little lipid staining or patches of normal or abundant perifibrous lipid, generally in the deeper layers; occasionally, there are scattered smooth muscle cells containing a few fat droplets or Nile-blue-positive granules (Smith and Slater, 1972a). In some fibrous plaques, lipid staining is low throughout the whole depth, but more characteristically, there is a pool of amorphous atheroma lipid in the deep layers. This consists of a mass of fine, extracellular lipid droplets or granules, which may be interspersed with coarser droplets and "cholesterol crystals," and which extends down to the internal elastic lamina and sometimes into the upper media. Plaques complicated by ulceration, calcification, hemorrhage, or thrombosis will not be discussed in this paper.

B. Concentration and Composition of the Lipids

The amount and composition of lipid differs greatly between intima and media, and between normal intima and the different types of lesion described above; consequently, only studies on defined tissue samples will be discussed.

1. *Normal Intima*

In normal intima there is a progressive increase in the concentration of most lipid classes with age (Smith, 1965a) and morphologically this is correlated with increasing numbers of perifibrous lipid droplets that are particularly, but not exclusively, associated with fragmentary elastic laminae in the deeper layers (Smith *et al.*, 1967). Total phospholipid, free cholesterol, and triglyceride increase very slowly, approximately 0.2 mg/100 mg defatted dry tissue per decade for each group, but from about age 20 upward, cholesterol ester increases at about 5 times this rate. Thus, although cholesterol ester is a minor component of normal intimal lipid up to about age 30, it becomes the main component above age 40.

The original data suggested that cholesterol ester was very low until the rapid increase starts in the second decade, and this has now been examined in more detail; results on aortic samples from 32 subjects aged 6 months to 39 years, in which at least 60% of the tissue appeared to be intima, are shown in Fig. 1. Ester cholesterol remains almost constant at a level of about 0.4 mg/100 mg defatted dry tissue over the first two decades, but over the third and fourth decades it rises steeply ($r = 0.863$, $p \ll 0.001$) at a rate of 0.63 mg per decade. This is in contrast to free cholesterol which rises continuously over the whole period at a rate of 0.17 mg per decade ($p < 0.001$). The ratio free cholesterol/phospholipid shows no significant change from a mean value of 0.45 ± 0.11, which is very close to a 1:1 molar ratio; this relationship seems to be maintained up to age 60. This suggests that free cholesterol and phospholipid are linked, either in the membranes of the cell, or in a liquid

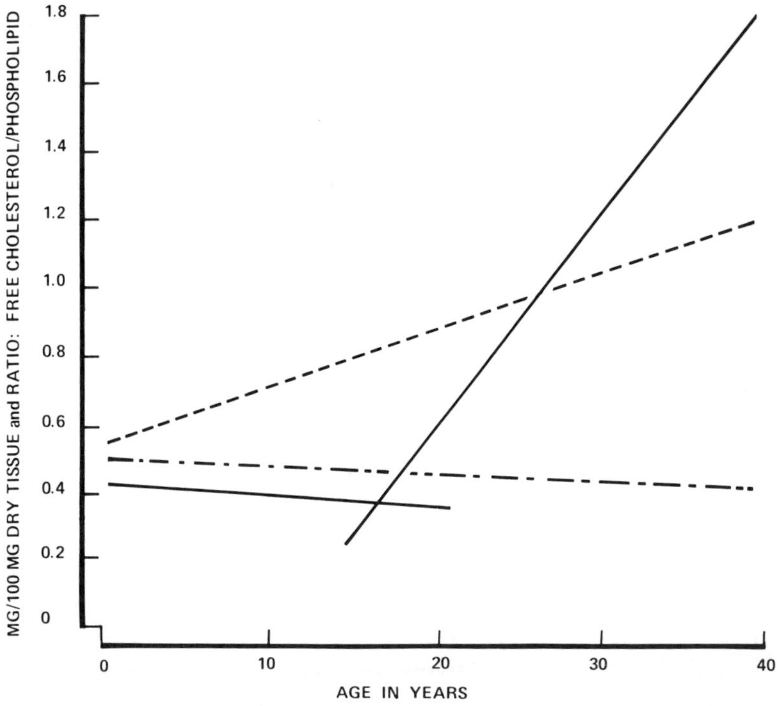

FIG. 1. Regression lines for the relation between free and esterfied cholesterol concentrations and age in normal intima from 32 subjects, aged 6 months to 39 years. For esterified cholesterol, separate regressions have been calculated for 6 months to 20 years and 15 to 39 years. The ratio of free cholesterol/phospholipid is also shown. (Esterified cholesterol ——; free cholesterol — — —; ratio: free cholesterol/phospholipid —·—·—.)

crystalline lattice (Small, 1970). By contrast, the increase in ester cholesterol, starting in the 15–20 age range seems to be an independent process, which may be related to the amount of intact plasma low density (LD) lipoprotein in the intima, and this will be discussed later. Eisenberg *et al.* (1969) found a continuous increase in cholesterol ester in preparations that included most of the media; in the young age-groups, the contribution of the intima would be negligible. In ascending aorta and arch from children aged 1 month to 10 years, Day and Wahlqvist (1970) found comparable concentrations of free cholesterol, but much less ester cholesterol. Their published photograph suggests that their preparations contained at least 80% media, and the ester cholesterol concentration is similar to that found in intima-media preparations in this laboratory.

In addition to the rapid increase in the concentration of cholesterol ester with age, there is a change in the cholesterol ester fatty acid pattern, so that with increasing age the whole composition of normal intimal lipid approaches the composition of the LD-lipoprotein of adult plasma (Smith, 1965; Smith *et al.*, 1967). Intimal lipid composition in three age groups is compared with isolated plasma S_f 0–12 lipoprotein in Table I. The cholesterol esters in the youngest age groups are particularly characterized by a high proportion of C_{16} acids and a low proportion of 18:2 (linoleic) acid; there are also higher proportions of both long and short chain minor components, and of 18:0 (stearic) acid. These findings are in close agreement with Day and Wahlqvist (1970), and with the findings of Portman and Alexander (1966) on Rhesus monkeys. It appears that this type of fatty acid pattern is also characteristic of the serum cholesterol esters in newborn and very young children (Zöllner *et al.*, 1966; Zee, 1968). Day and Wahlqvist (1970) found a high ratio of 18:1/18:2 acids up to 1 year, but in the 1–5 year age-group the ratio fell to unity, and in the 5–15 age-group reached the adult level of 0.75; the "intimal" ratio also fell, and between 1 and 10 years of age, it was about twice the plasma ratio. The authors conclude that all this cholesterol ester is derived from plasma.

Our results seem more complex—the constancy of the ester cholesterol concentration during the first two decades suggest that this may represent "endogenous" cholesterol ester and that plasma cholesterol ester does not accumulate until about age 20 when the concentration starts its steep and linear rise (Fig. 1). If this is correct, the cholesterol ester fatty acid pattern might be expected to remain constant over the first two decades, when the concentration remains constant, and then to change rapidly toward the pattern found in serum when the concentration starts to rise. However, using the proportion of linoleic acid (18:2) in the

Table I

Composition of the Lipid in Normal Intima (Perifibrous Lipid Only)

	Intima with perifibrous lipid			Plasma S_f 0–12 lipoprotein
	Age 6 mo.–20 yr	Age 40–59	Age over 70	
No. of samples	10	33	13	22
Total lipid (mg/100 mg tissue)[a]	4.3	10.8	16.0	—
Percentage of total lipid				
Cholesterol ester	16.7 ± 6.8[c]	42.1 ± 5.7	57.2 ± 7.9	58.2 ± 2.2
Free cholesterol	17.6 ± 3.7	13.0 ± 2.3	10.5 ± 1.1	11.5 ± 1.0
Phospholipid	42.7 ± 7.5	29.3 ± 3.6	17.2 ± 4.8	20.0 ± 1.5
Triglyceride	23.0 ± 10.5	15.4 ± 6.1	15.1 ± 5.7	10.2 ± 2.6
CEFA[b]				
Percentage 18:2 in 18:1 + 18:2 fraction	39.5	58.0	58.7	66.0
Percentage of total				
14:0	3.4 ± 2.1	1.7 ± 0.8	1.2 ± 0.7	1.0 ± 0.3
16:0	23.6 ± 6.7	14.5 ± 1.5	13.7 ± 1.7	13.7 ± 3.2
16:1	9.4 ± 2.7	5.5 ± 2.5	6.3 ± 1.8	4.2 ± 0.6
18:0	7.1 ± 3.9	1.5 ± 1.8	0.8 ± 0.5	2.5 ± 1.0
18:1	27.2 ± 6.5	28.0 ± 4.4	27.4 ± 4.5	24.1 ± 3.1
18:2	17.8 ± 9.9	38.6 ± 7.0	40.0 ± 7.3	46.8 ± 6.6
20:3	0.7 ± 0.6	1.0 ± 0.5	0.9 ± 0.4	trace
20:4	3.3 ± 2.3	5.3 ± 1.0	5.2 ± 1.2	5.2 ± 1.2
Minors	7.1	3.9	4.5	2.5
Ratio: free cholesterol/phospholipid	0.41	0.44	0.61	0.57

[a] Defatted dry tissue.
[b] Cholesterol ester fatty acid.
[c] ± Standard deviation.

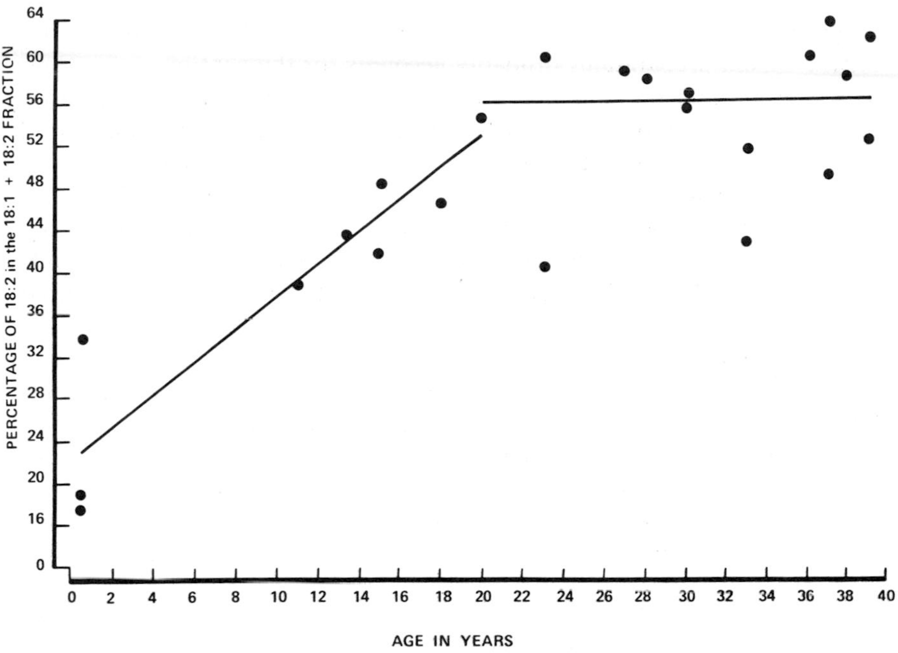

FIG. 2. Relation between age and the percentage of linoleic (18:2) acid in the 18:1 + 18:2 fraction of the cholesterol ester fatty acids from normal intima (23 subjects, aged 6 months to 39 years).

18:1 + 18:2 fraction as an index, it can be seen in Fig. 2 that the reverse happens: the percentage of 18:2 rises rapidly during the first two decades when the concentration is constant, but between ages 20 and 39 it appears to have reached a maximum of 56.5 ± 5.8% linoleic acid and shows no significant increase in older age groups although the concentration of cholesterol ester increases rapidly. Thus during the first two decades, the arterial cholesterol ester seems to be in equilibrium with the plasma cholesterol ester, although there is no net accumulation. If this amount of cholesterol ester were present in the form of contaminating or reversibly-bound plasma lipoprotein, it could be measured by quantitative immunoelectrophoresis (Smith and Slater, 1972b), but in the first decade we have failed to detect any intact LD-lipoprotein, and in the second decade, the amount of lipoprotein found could account for only about one-third of the ester cholesterol.

Total phospholipid increases linearly with age in normal intima. Smith (1965a) found no significant change in the ratio lecithin/sphingomyelin with age in intima, but in media there was a marked increase in the proportion of sphingomyelin between ages 15 and 55. The use of intima + media preparations probably accounts for the continuous increase in the proportion of sphingomyelin with age found by Eisenberg *et al.* (1969). These authors find that aortic lecithinase increases about 5-fold between the first and tenth decades, whereas sphingomyelinase decreases slightly; it seems important that this work should be extended to pure intimal preparations where the proportion of sphingomyelin does not apparently increase, and the tissue is in contact with substantial amounts of plasma LD-lipoprotein. Arterial phospholipids were expertly reviewed by Portman in 1970.

Triglycerides also increase slowly with age in normal intima (Table I) but in lesions they generally increase less than the other lipid components (Tables I, II, and VI; Böttcher, 1961; Insull and Bartch, 1966) and consequently have not aroused much interest. Earlier reports that they occur in significantly higher concentration in coronary arteries than in aorta (Böttcher *et al.*, 1960; Böttcher, 1961) have not been confirmed (Abdulla *et al.*, 1969; Panganamala *et al.*, 1974).

2. *Fatty Infiltration*

There appears to be little information on this rather ill-defined lesion which may resemble a fatty streak by macroscopic staining. Day and Wahlqvist (1970) compared normal with lesion in children aged 1 month to 10 years and the only consistent difference was in the percentage of the cholesterol esterified; the lesion contained approximately twice the proportion of esterified cholesterol in all age groups. In this laboratory, 19 samples containing a mixture of abundant perifibrous lipid and occasional scattered cells containing fat droplets showed an increase of 44% in total cholesterol, compared with normal intima and a cholesterol ester fatty acid pattern intermediate between normal intima and fatty streaks.

3. *Fatty Streaks* (as defined in Section II,A,3)

Typically, lesions in which most of the lipid is within fat-filled cells contain a high proportion of cholesterol ester of very characteristic fatty-acid pattern (Smith, 1965a; Geer and Guidry, 1964; Smith *et al.*, 1967). Lipid patterns in fatty streaks in which the numerous fat-filled cells are either scattered or in confluent groups are shown in Table II, where they are compared with fat-filled cells isolated by microdissection from the caps of large atheromatous plaques. The maximum divergence from the plasma pattern occurs in the fatty streaks containing groups of confluent fat-filled cells. These lesions were found in a remarkably restricted age-group; 8 of the 10 subjects were aged 38–47 and the remaining two subjects were aged 19 and 51. There is no significant difference in the

Table II

Composition of the Lipid in Fatty Streaks and Isolated Fat-Filled Cells

	Fatty streaks		Fat-filled cells from caps of plaques	
	Scattered fat-filled cells	Confluent fat-filled cells	Small and scattered	Large and confluent
No. of samples	15	10	8	21
Total lipid (mg/100 mg tissue)	38.7 ± 7.2	40.0 ± 8.7	45.1 ± 7.4	115.6 ± 15.6
Percentage of total lipid				
Cholesterol ester	64.1 ± 7.6	68.7 ± 5.8	62.9 ± 3.5	65.9 ± 2.6
Free cholesterol	13.1 ± 2.9	10.1 ± 2.9	16.5 ± 2.0	14.1 ± 1.4
Phospholipid	16.2 ± 3.0	14.8 ± 2.2	14.6 ± 2.0	13.4 ± 1.4
Triglyceride	6.6 ± 1.1	6.4 ± 2.7	7.2 ± 1.4	6.5 ± 1.6
CEFA				
Percentage 18:2 in 18:1 + 18:2 fraction	24.4 ± 5.1	18.6 ± 3.5	24.3 ± 8.8	29.6 ± 6.8
Percentage of total				
16:0	13.6 ± 3.3	10.7 ± 3.1	With the very small samples obtained from microdissection the 14:0 to 18:0 and 20:3 and 20:4 acids are not reliable	
16:1	6.7 ± 1.4	7.7 ± 1.5		
18:0	2.5 ± 1.5	2.0 ± 1.6		
18:1	47.6 ± 5.3	52.4 ± 4.3		
18:2	15.2 ± 4.5	12.1 ± 3.0		
20:3	4.0 ± 1.6	5.0 ± 1.7		
20:4	3.9 ± 1.9	3.6 ± 1.4		
Ratio: free cholesterol/phospholipid	0.81	0.68	1.1	1.05

composition of the lipids in fatty streaks and fat-filled cells dissected from the caps of large plaques.

The ratio free cholesterol/phospholipid is approximately twice the ratio in normal intima, but there appears to be no significant difference in the composition of the phospholipids from fatty streaks and adjacent normal intima (Smith, 1965a). Lang and Insull (1970) have divided fatty streak lipids into droplets and residue; 95% of the droplet lipid was cholesterol ester, and the ratio free cholesterol/phospholipid was 1.7, approximately 4 times the ratio in normal intima, but in the residue, the ratio was close to that for normal intima. The fatty acid composition of the droplet cholesterol esters was very similar to the fatty streaks with confluent fat-filled cells shown in Table II. The composition of the phospholipids in both fractions was rather markedly different from that found by Smith, but the proportion of sphingomyelin in the droplets was significantly lower than in the residue.

4. *Small Raised Fatty Nodules and Plaques*

The lipid composition is highly correlated with the detailed morphology of the lesion (Smith *et al.*, 1968). With increasing amounts of amorphous atheroma lipid in the deep layers of the lesion, there is a marked increase in the proportion of free cholesterol, decrease in proportion of ester cholesterol, and change in the cholesterol ester fatty acid pattern. These changes are illustrated in Table III, which shows the lipid composition in a series of small lesions obtained from a single aorta. The concomitant increases in the amount of amorphous lipid, in the proportion of free cholesterol, and in the proportion of cholesterol linoleate suggest that formation of the amorphous lipid may involve breakdown of fat-filled cells with the release of cholesterol esterases that catalyze preferential hydrolysis of cholesterol oleate.

In an attempt to demonstrate hydrolysis we incubated minced or homogenized intima for periods between 14 and 20 hours and compared the proportions of free cholesterol and of oleic and linoleic acids in the cholesterol ester fatty acids in control (frozen) and incubated samples (E. B. Smith and R. S. Slater, unpublished). An increase in free cholesterol greater than 5% occurred in only 8 of 42 tissue samples (19%), comprising no samples of normal intima, 3 of 9 fatty streaks and nodules (33.3%), 1 of 5 gelatinous thickenings (20%) and 4 of 24 large plaques (16.7%). For the remaining tissue samples, the mean difference in the proportion of free cholesterol was only 1.5%, and in the proportion of linoleic acid was less than 1%. For the 8 samples which showed significant change, the mean rate of hydrolysis, expressed as micrograms of cholesterol per milligram of defatted dry tissue per hour is shown in

Table III

Series of Small Plaques From a Case with Myocardial Infarction (male, aged 48)[a]

	Cholesterol (mg/100 mg tissue)[b]			P-Lipid (mg/100 mg tissue)	Ratio: Free cholesterol / Phospholipid	CEFA: % of total			
	Total	Free	% free			18:1	18:2	20:3	20:4
Superficial layer of large fat-filled cells (FFCs); very little extracellular lipid	18.1	4.1	22.7	5.7	0.7	55.0	15.9	2.0	1.1
Large FFCs at all levels; definite extracellular lipid in deep layers	20.8	6.2	29.8	6.9	0.9	47.4	20.1	4.4	3.6
Large FFCs at all levels; small area of "amorphous lipid" at center	24.7	7.0	28.6	6.2	1.1	44.3	21.1	4.9	3.7
As in previous lesion; larger area of "amorphous lipid"	30.7	11.2	36.5	11.0	1.0	39.6	24.2	4.0	4.9
Slightly more collagen in cap; large area of "amorphous lipid"	26.9	11.9	44.1	10.8	1.1	37.2	27.4	3.0	4.4

[a] Data from Smith *et al.* (1968).
[b] Lipid-extracted dry tissue.

Table IV

HYDROLYSIS OF ENDOGENOUS CHOLESTEROL ESTER

Age and sex	Time after death (hr)	Fatty streaks and nodules: Rate of hydrolysis (μg cholesterol/mg dry tissue/hr)	Fatty streaks and nodules: % increase of free cholesterol	Large plaques: Rate of hydrolysis (μg cholesterol/mg dry tissue/hr)	Large plaques: % increase of free cholesterol	Gelatinous thickening: Rate of hydrolysis (μg cholesterol/mg dry tissue/hr)	Gelatinous thickening: % increase of free cholesterol
59, F	3½	—	—	—	—	0.08	5.5
57, M	4	0.12[a]	9.2	0.32	5.0	—	—
		0.44[b]	13.5	—	—	—	—
57, M	4½	0.67	21.8	1.09	8.1	—	—
69, F	13	—	—	8.80	12.3	—	—

[a] Scattered fat-filled cells only.

[b] Confluent fat-filled cells + amorphous lipid.

Table IV. Significant change in fatty acid pattern occurred in only one sample in which the proportion of linoleate fell by 6.8%; this is the *opposite* direction from the change required to transform the lipid in fat-filled cells into "amorphous" type extracellular lipid. These rates of hydrolysis are lower than the rates calculated from the data of Patelski *et al.* (1967) for pig aorta tissue slices (approximately 20 μg/mg dry tissue per hour) but mainly higher than the rates calculated from the data of Howard and Portman (1966) for rat and monkey aorta (0.002–0.012 μg/mg dry tissue per hour). Exogenous substrates were used by both these investigators.

5. *Large Plaques Containing Numerous Fat-Filled Cells*

The obvious interrelationship between morphology, free cholesterol and cholesterol ester fatty acid pattern, and the failure to demonstrate a hydrolytic mechanism that could account for this, led to an attempt to localize the position in the lesion at which the chemical change occurs. Smith and Slater (1972a) dissected thick cryostat sections into topographically and histologically defined fractions and analyzed the lipids in each fraction. Large plaques were required to obtain sufficient lipid, and it became clear that in human aorta, the typical fatty streak with masses of fat-filled cells and little increase in collagen does not frequently lead to the formation of large atheromas. With only one exception, the "fatty" plaques that were large enough for microdissection had relatively thick collagen caps in which the numerous fat-filled cells were embedded. The lipids in adjacent layers of such plaques, proceeding from the luminal surface downwards, are shown in Table V.

There appears to be no significant change in composition when fat-filled cells start to disintegrate (fractions 1–2) and might be expected to release lysosomal enzymes. At the cap/amorphous lipid junction (fraction 2–3), there is a significant increase in proportion of free cholesterol, but no significant change in cholesterol ester fatty acid composition. Between the upper and middle layers of the amorphous lipid (fractions 3–4) the proportions of free cholesterol increase and of oleic acid decrease—this is the only region of the plaque in which the idea of cholesterol oleate hydrolysis is supported. Between the middle and bottom layers of the amorphous lipid (fractions 4–5) there is a *decrease* in the proportion of free cholesterol and a further significant decrease in the proportion of cholesterol oleate. It is clear from Table V that increase in the proportion of the cholesterol which is free does not necessarily occur in the same region of the plaque as decrease in cholesterol oleate. Furthermore, there is no significant correlation between free

Table V

COMPARISON OF THE LIPIDS IN ADJACENT LAYERS OF LARGE PLAQUES CONTAINING NUMEROUS FAT-FILLED CELLS IN THE CAP[a]

Fraction number	No. of pairs of samples	Cholesterol (mg/100 mg tissue)		Cholesterol	Ratio: Free cholesterol / Phospholipid	CEFA: % 18:2 in 18:1 + 18:2 fraction
		Total	Free	% free		
1. Intact fat-filled cells in cap	4	38.4	10.0	26.0	1.3	30.1
2. Mixture of intact and disintegrating fat-filled cells		55.1	21.0	38.1	2.1	33.7
	Difference:	$p = 0.3$	$p = 0.05$	$p = 0.08$	$p = 0.05$	$p = 0.2$
2. Mixture of intact and disintegrating fat-filled cells	5	65.2	22.7	34.9	1.9	32.7
3. Disintegrating fat-filled cells mixed with amorphous lipid		138.2	76.6	55.4	2.2	43.1
	Difference:	$p = 0.09$	$p = 0.01$	$p = 0.01$	$p = 0.4$	$p = 0.1$
3. Disintegrating fat-filled cells mixed with amorphous lipid	6	130.7	56.5	43.2	1.4	44.7
4. Upper and middle amorphous lipid free from fat-filled cells		155.9	80.9	51.9	2.2	55.2
	Difference:	$p = 0.6$	$p = 0.03$	$p = 0.03$	$p = 0.1$	$p = 0.015$
4. Upper and middle amorphous lipid free from fat-filled cells	5	172.3	87.0	50.5	2.2	57.9
5. Lower amorphous lipid		83.5	35.3	42.3	1.5	64.1
	Difference:	$p = 0.1$	$p = 0.01$	$p = 0.02$	$p = 0.025$	$p = 0.01$

[a] Each layer is compared with that immediately below it in the same plaque.

cholesterol and cholesterol ester fatty acid pattern within any layer of the plaques (Smith and Slater, 1972a); in the cap/amorphous lipid junction area, where maximum hydrolysis might be expected, there is a slight *increase* in oleate and decrease in linoleate, results in line with the tentative findings in the hydrolysis experiments. In the lower amorphous lipid layer, cholesterol linoleate (18:2) accounts for 64% and cholesterol oleate (18:1) for 36% of the 18:1 + 18:2 cholesterol ester fraction; this is similar to the proportion in the cholesterol ester in plasma S_f 0–12 lipoprotein (66% cholesterol linoleate). The proportion of cholesterol oleate increases in each successive layer through the plaque from base to surface, where in the intact fat-filled cells, it accounts for 70% of the 18:1 + 18:2 fraction. In the absence of evidence of preferential cholesterol oleate hydrolysis it seems probable that linoleate-rich cholesterol ester enters directly from the plasma, and "dilutes out" the oleate-rich cholesterol ester derived from the fat-filled cells. In the lowest layer of the amorphous lipid it appears that all the cholesterol ester is derived from plasma; in the top layer where the amorphous lipid just under the cap is mixed with disintegrating fat-filled cells, it can be calculated from the fatty acid distribution that about 60% of the cholesterol ester is derived from the fat-filled cells and 40% directly from plasma.

6. *Gelatinous Lesions*

These lesions are frequently found in the human aorta, and appear to be early stages in a sequence leading to fibrous plaques. In the smaller thickenings, sections stained for fat typically show only a diffuse sudanophilia or very fine perifibrous lipid droplets on the thick collagen bundles. In larger lesions there may be areas of abundant, coarser perifibrous lipid that most frequently occur in the deep-lying central area where the collagen fibers may lose their linear arrangement and form a network. In the majority of these lesions no fat-filled cells can be detected, and the lipids (Table VI) are similar to the lipids of plasma LD-lipoprotein with a high proportion of linoleic acid (18:2) in the cholesterol esters. Table VI also shows the lipids in three layers of a plaque with a gelatinous cap overlying a central pool of amorphous "atheroma" lipid; no fat-filled cells could be detected in any layer. The proportion of linoleic acid remains extremely high, and there is a striking fall in the proportion of phospholipid in both layers of the amorphous lipid. The proportion of free cholesterol is only slightly increased in the upper layer of the amorphous lipid, but is almost doubled in the lower layer, suggesting that there is either hydrolysis of ester or preferential retention of free cholesterol.

Table VI
Composition of the Lipids in Gelatinous Lesions

	Gelatinous thickenings		Layers of a gelatinous plaque		
	Diffuse sudanophilia or weak PFL[b]	Very abundant PFL	Cap	Upper layer of "amor-phous"	Lower layer of "amor-phous"
No. of samples	13	5			
Total cholesterol (mg/100 mg tissue)[a]	4.4 ± 0.4	16.0 ± 5.2	4.9	48.0	79.5
% of cholesterol free	27.1 ± 1.9	20.8 ± 1.7	27.0	29.0	51.6
Percentage of total lipid					
Cholesterol ester	46.7 ± 3.5	63.8 ± 4.7	52.3	60.0	44.5
Free cholesterol	13.0 ± 1.1	12.4 ± 0.1	11.7	14.6	28.4
Phospholipid	29.2 ± 3.5	16.4 ± 5.9	23.5	12.8	11.5
Triglyceride	11.1 ± 1.2	7.5 ± 1.0	12.5	12.6	15.6
CEFA: percentage 18:2 in 18:1 + 18:2 fraction	64.7 ± 1.2	64.9 ± 0.2	69.0	62.5	55.2
Ratio: free cholesterol/phospholipid	0.47 ± 0.04	0.65 ± 0.14	0.51	1.14	2.46

[a] Lipid-extracted dry tissue.
[b] Perifibrous lipid.

Table VII

"White" Fibrous Plaques Containing No, or Very Few, Fat-Filled Cells

		Cholesterol (mg/100 mg tissue)				
	No. of samples	Total	Free	% free	Ratio: Free cholesterol / Phospholipid	CEFA: % 18:2 in 18:1 + 18:2 fraction
Fine perifibrous lipid only						
Whole depth of plaque	7	5.8 ± 2.6	1.5 ± 0.8	25.7 ± 3.4	0.5 ± 0.1	62.8 ± 2.2
Plaque in two layers	3					
Upper		3.3 ± 0.6	0.9 ± 0.3	28.2 ± 6.1	0.4 ± 0.3	61.7 ± 2.0
Lower		6.3 ± 1.2	1.5 ± 0.4	24.4 ± 6.8	0.5 ± 0.3	63.0 ± 1.9
Layers through plaque with amorphous lipid center						
Surface of cap	10	2.7 ± 0.2	1.3 ± 0.2	46.9 ± 3.2	0.5 ± 0.1	58.2 ± 3.0
Deep layer of cap	7	8.4 ± 1.6	2.7 ± 0.5	33.6 ± 3.6	0.6 ± 0.1	64.7 ± 3.3
Upper amorphous lipid	10	62.1 ± 7.4	26.1 ± 4.1	42.3 ± 2.6	1.3 ± 0.1	60.8 ± 1.2
Lower amorphous lipid	7	88.4 ± 12.5	47.4 ± 8.6	51.6 ± 2.3	2.1 ± 0.4	58.2 ± 2.3

7. *Fibrous Plaques*

The composition of the lipid appears to be more closely related to the detailed morphology of the lipid itself than to the overall morphology of the plaque. Thus perifibrous lipid seems to have similar characteristics whether it is located in the loosely structured gelatinous lesions or in the close fibrous tissue of fibrous plaques (Tables VI and VII), whereas the histologically "amorphous" lipid shows marked changes in the proportion of free cholesterol and the ratio of free cholesterol/phospholipid (Table VII). A striking increase in the proportion of sphingomyelin in the phospholipids with increasing severity of atherosclerosis has been

Table VIII

PHOSPHOLIPID PARAMETERS IN TISSUES WITH LIPID OF DEFINED MORPHOLOGY

	Ratio: Free cholesterol / Phospholipid	Ratio: Sphingomyelin / Lecithin
S_f 0–12 Lipoprotein	0.57	0.9
Tissues with perifibrous lipid		
Normal intima	0.45	0.9
Gelatinous lesions		
Light PFL[a]	0.46	—
Abundant PFL	0.65	—
'White' fibrous lesions		
Whole depth	0.55	0.9
Upper layers	0.43	—
Lower layers	0.54	—
Cap of plaques with underlying amorphous lipid	0.63	1.1
Amorphous lipid		
Fibrous plaques		
Whole amorphous lipid	1.67	5.1
Upper layers	1.27	—
Lower layers	2.05	—
Plaques with numerous fat-filled cells in the cap		
Upper layers	2.00	3.1
Lower layers	1.55	9.0
Lipid within fat-filled cells		
Fatty streaks	0.74	0.9
Fat-filled cells from caps of plaques	1.05	1.0

[a] Perifibrous lipid.

reported by many workers (Weinhouse and Hirsch, 1940; Buck and Rossiter, 1951; Steele and Kayden, 1955; Smith, 1960, 1965a; Böttcher and van Gent, 1961); this appears to be particularly associated with the amorphous lipid fraction (Smith *et al.*, 1968). Table VIII summarizes data obtained in this laboratory on the ratios, free cholesterol/total phospholipid and sphingomyelin/lecithin in intimal samples containing lipid of defined morphology. For samples from all sources containing perifibrous lipid, values for free cholesterol/total phospholipid lie between 0.43 and 0.65, and for sphingomyelin/lecithin at about unity; these values are close to the values found for plasma LD-lipoprotein. In samples of amorphous lipid, free cholesterol/total phospholipid increases 3-to 5-fold and sphingomyelin/lecithin increases 3-to 9-fold. Lipid within fat-filled cells shows some increase in the proportion of free cholesterol, but no change in the proportions of sphingomyelin and lecithin.

Thus it appears that amorphous lipid is not merely a massive accumulation of perifibrous lipid, but that it has undergone specific chemical changes. Smith and Slater (1972a) examined the relationship between the percentage of the cholesterol that was free and the cholesterol ester fatty acid composition in successive layers of fibrous plaques (Fig. 3). In the lower layer of the amorphous lipid (Table VII, last line) there is a significant correlation between increase in percentage of the cholesterol that is free and increase in percentage of cholesterol oleate (18:1) in the 18:1 + 18:2 cholesterol ester fraction ($r = 0.901$, $p \ll 0.001$; slope $b = 0.924$, $p < 0.005$). In the upper layer of the amorphous lipid there

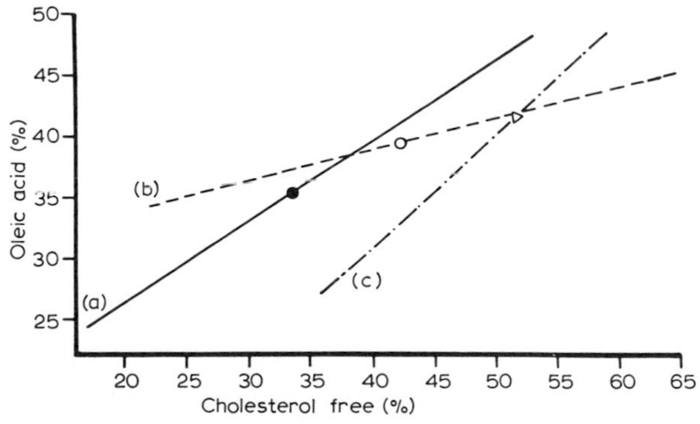

FIG. 3. Regression lines showing the increase in proportion of oleic acid (18:1) in the 18:1 + 18:2 fraction of the cholesterol ester fatty acids with increase in proportion of free cholesterol. Successive layers isolated from large fibrous plaques by microdissection. (a) Lower layers of the fibrous cap. (b) Upper layers of the amorphous lipid (just under the fibrous cap). (c) Deep layers of the amorphous lipid. From Smith and Slater (1972a).

is little variation in the proportion of cholesterol oleate and although the overall range of free cholesterol is large (26–61%), most of the samples (7 of 10) lie within the range 38–48% cholesterol free. In the adjacent deep layers of the fibrous cap there is again a significant correlation between the proportion of cholesterol oleate and the proportion of cholesterol free although the slope is not as steep ($r = 0.738$, $p = 0.02$; $b = 0.668$, $p < 0.01$). The meaning of these linked changes is not clear, but they could be indicative of preferential hydrolysis of cholesterol linoleate; this would be compatible with our preliminary incubation experiments and with the findings of Bowyer *et al.* (1968). However, these workers used exogenous substrates and because of the difficulties of uniform presentation, observed differences in rates of hydrolysis of different cholesterol esters must be interpreted with caution.

III. Concentration of Plasma LD-Lipoprotein in Normal Intima and Lesions

It has been known for many years that plasma constituents are present in the artery wall; conventional immunoelectrophoresis (Grabar and Williams, 1953; Grabar, 1959) of extracts has demonstrated β-lipoprotein and virtually all plasma components (Ott *et al.*, 1958; Gerö *et al.*, 1961; Tracy *et al.*, 1961; Klimov *et al.*, 1974). Investigators have demonstrated LD-lipoprotein by immunofluorescent microscopy in normal intima and lesions of various types (Kayden *et al.*, 1959; Watts, 1963; Kao and Wissler, 1965; Woolf and Pilkington, 1965; Choi, 1966; Knieriem *et al.*, 1967; Walton and Williamson, 1968). In a valuable series of studies More, Haust, and their colleagues have also demonstrated albumin and HD-lipoproteins and compared their distribution with fibrinogen/fibrin in normal intima, fatty streaks, and gelatinous lesions (reviewed by Haust, 1968, 1971). In this laboratory we attempted to obtain *quantitative* measurements of the amount of lipoprotein in extracts of intima. VLD-and LD-lipoprotein fractions were separated by preparative ultracentrifugation and analyzed for cholesterol, and for intact lipoprotein by radial immunodiffusion (Smith and Slater, 1970). Substantial amounts of LD-lipoprotein were found in most tissue samples, but we were unable to demonstrate immunologically intact VLD-lipoprotein although the ultracentrifuge fraction contained a large amount of cholesterol. Unequivocal demonstration of VLDL is difficult because of immunological cross reactions with both LDL and HDL. The low proportion of triglyceride found in both normal intima and lesions suggests that it probably does not enter the intima intact in any quantity. French (1963) and Schoefl and French (1968) have published pictures of chylomicra on the endothelium which in some instances appear to be undergoing lysis.

Recently Smith and Slater (1971, 1972b) have developed a method for the measurement of immunologically and electrophoretically intact plasma constituents in very small tissue samples by electrophoresis directly from the minced tissue into an antibody-containing gel. This is a development of the technique of Ressler (1960); the antibody-antigen complex precipitates as a rocket-shaped peak with an area proportional to the concentration of antigen (Clarke and Freeman, 1966). By use of different antisera, aliquots of individual tissue samples have been assayed for LD-lipoprotein and albumin (Smith and Slater, 1972b) and fibrinogen (Smith *et al.*, 1973). The assays can be performed with less than 1 mg defatted dry tissue so that the entire sample of intima can lie within 2 or 3 mm of the histological control sections, and different layers of normal intima, and different layers and regions of lesions can be compared (Smith and Slater, 1973a,b). After electrophoresis the tissue samples are recovered, the residual lipids (not mobile in the electric field) extracted and measured, and the defatted dry weight of the tissue determined. The results obtained using this technique are discussed in the following section.

A. Concentration of LD-Lipoprotein in Normal Intima

1. *Relationship to the Patient's Serum Cholesterol Level*

In 30 subjects coming to autopsy in whom there were areas of normal intima in the descending thoracic or upper abdominal regions of the aorta, blood samples were obtained during the week before death, so that a direct comparison could be made between the lipoprotein levels in intima and serum. The samples of intima were assayed together with 10 μl standard lipoprotein preparation and 10 μl of the patient's own serum on the same immunoelectrophoresis plate; this allows quantification of intimal lipoprotein in two ways—an absolute measure of lipoprotein concentration in terms of the standard lipoprotein preparation, and quantification in terms of the volume of the patient's own serum or plasma from which the lipoprotein was derived. In 24 subjects, aged 29–69, with no history of hypertension, the absolute amount of lipoprotein in the intima is very highly correlated with the patient's serum cholesterol level during the week before death; the regression is shown in Fig. 4a ($r = 0.971$; $p \ll 0.001$). However, when the lipoprotein is expressed in terms of the volume of the patient's own plasma from which it was derived

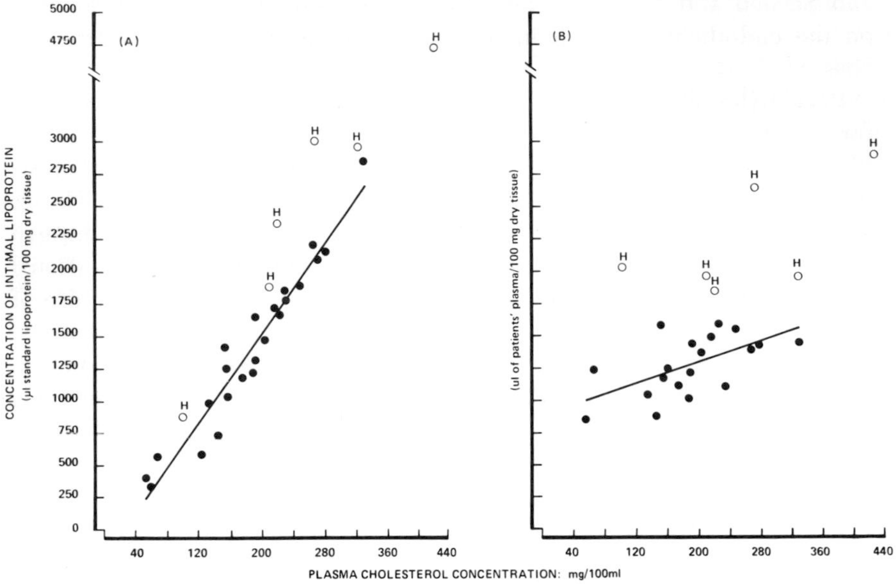

FIG. 4. Relation between the concentration of LD-lipoprotein in normal intima and the subject's serum cholesterol level during the week before death. (A) Expressed as volume of standard lipoprotein preparation. (B) Expressed as the volume of the patient's own plasma from which the lipoprotein has been derived. Hypertensive patients (open circles marked H) are not included in the regression calculations.

(Fig. 4b) the correlation with serum cholesterol level is much lower ($r = 0.589$). In addition to the 24 normotensive subjects, there were six known hypertensives from whom normal intima and blood samples were available; these have not been included in the calculation of the regression lines, but are shown on Figs. 4a and b as open circles marked H. The volume of plasma from which the intima lipoprotein was derived is significantly higher in the hypertensive than in the normotensive group (mean normotensive 1349 ± 95 μl (SEM) patient's plasma /100 mg defatted dry intima; mean hypertensive 2166 ± 154 μl /100 mg; $p < 0.001$).

An average 1 cm^2 sample of "normal" intima with a thickness of 200 μm contains lipoprotein derived from about 20 μl of the patient's own plasma; thus, very surprisingly, the LD-lipoprotein is at approximately the same concentration in the intima as in the plasma. Smith and Slater (1972b) found that increasingly vigorous washing *increased* the apparent concentration of arterial lipoprotein, so this similarity in concentration does not arise from massive surface contamination.

These findings suggest the concept that lipoprotein from a rather constant amount of plasma is retained in the intima; if the plasma has a low cholesterol level the amount of intimal lipoprotein will be low, whereas if the plasma has a high cholesterol level the amount of intimal lipoprotein will be high. Since hypertension increases the amount of plasma in the intima, the effect of hypertension and hypercholesterolemia on intimal lipoprotein will be additive, and this parallels the findings of the Framingham study on the relationship between serum cholesterol, blood pressure level, and ischemic heart disease (Dawber *et al.*, 1962).

In the lipoprotein assay, the immunoelectrophoresis plates are stained

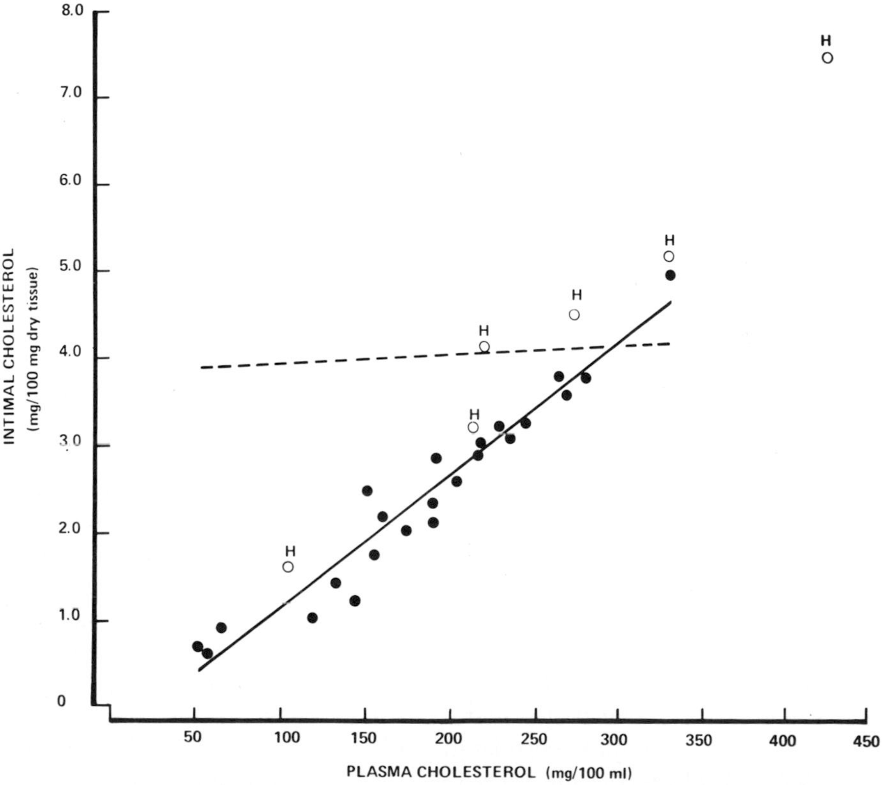

FIG. 5. Relation between the concentration of intact lipoprotein cholesterol (——) in the intima (calculated from the standard lipoprotein) and the patient's serum cholesterol level. Hypertensive patients (open circles marked H) are not included in the regression calculation. The regression line for the residual cholesterol left in the tissue after electrophoresis is also shown (– – – –).

for lipid with oil red O, and the lipoprotein antibody peaks derived from nearly all intimal samples have the same intensity of staining as the plasma lipoprotein standard. In preliminary experiments in which the immunopeaks from tissue samples and the patient's serum were cut out of the agarose and their cholesterol contents compared, the mean concentrations of cholesterol per unit area of immunopeak derived from tissue and the patient's serum were not significantly different. It therefore appears valid to assume that the intimal lipoprotein has the same composition as serum lipoprotein, and on this basis, the concentration of lipoprotein cholesterol in intima has been calculated (Fig. 5). For every 100 mg/100 ml increase in serum cholesterol, the lipoprotein-bound cholesterol in normal intima increases by 1.5 mg/100 mg dry tissue; residual (electrophoretically immobile) tissue cholesterol shows no correlation with plasma cholesterol or intimal lipoprotein levels.

2. *Relationship to Age*

Because of the high correlation between intimal and plasma lipoprotein levels, the effect of age can only be examined in terms of volumes of the patient's plasma in the intima. There is a small increase of 113 μl/100 mg defatted dry tissue/decade over the age range 29 to 69 years ($p = 0.03$); this amounts to about 0.1 mg ester cholesterol compared with the total ester cholesterol increase of about 0.7 mg/decade previously found, so that intact LD-lipoprotein accounts for about 10% of the age-related increase in cholesterol ester. The two studies are not, however, strictly comparable because the original cholesterol measurements were taken on intimal samples stripped in a single layer on the first *intact* elastic lamina (Smith *et al.*, 1967), whereas the lipoprotein measurements were made on the upper (luminal) layer of the intima, stripped on the first *fragmentary* elastic lamina (Smith and Slater, 1972b). In these upper intimal samples, the total residual cholesterol increases at a slower rate with a wide scatter (0.55 mg/decade, $p = 0.04$). In 17 samples, analyses are also available on the lower layer, in which the concentration of lipoprotein is only about 16% of the concentration in the upper layer, and which contains the fragmentary elastic laminae. In this layer, residual cholesterol is highly correlated with age ($r = 0.795$), increasing at a rate of 0.99 mg/decade ($p = 0.001$). Thus the age-related increase in total cholesterol occurs mainly in the region of the fragmentary elastic laminae, a result in agreement with many histological observations and other chemical studies (Kramsch and Hollander, 1973; Smith, 1974).

The relationship between serum cholesterol and intimal lipoprotein concentrations (Fig. 4a) seems to be maintained down to age 29, but in the two younger subjects, from whom blood samples were obtained, the intimal lipoprotein was much lower. In a girl aged 8 years, with serum cholesterol of 94 mg/100 ml, no lipoprotein could be detected in the intima although very large tissue samples were used; no lipoprotein was found in another child of 8 with unknown serum cholesterol. In a boy aged 14, with serum cholesterol of 290 mg/100 ml, the intima contained 150 μl standard LP per 100 mg tissue, which is only 6% of the expected level; comparable concentrations were found in two boys aged 17 with unknown serum cholesterol levels. Thus it appears that in the first and second decades, there is very little lipoprotein in the intima and this observation agrees with the findings of Kao and Wissler (1965) using immunofluorescent microscopy. It is not clear whether this indicates that the endothelium is not as "leaky," or that a certain minimum thickness of subendothelial connective tissue is required for accumulation of measurable amounts of lipoprotein.

B. Distribution of LD-Lipoprotein in Lesions

Because of the close relationship between intimal lipoprotein concentration, blood pressure, and serum cholesterol levels the concentration of lipoprotein in the lesions has little meaning unless it is related to adjacent normal intima or, if distribution within plaques is examined, to other areas of the same plaque.

1. *Change in Concentration of LD-Lipoprotein in Lesions*

In Table IX the overall concentration of lipoprotein in different types of lesion is presented as a percentage of the concentration in normal intima from the same aorta. In fatty streaks the concentration of lipoprotein is very low, only about a quarter of the normal level; this is a constant finding and confirms previous results on extracts (Smith and Slater, 1970). In intima which is gelatinous, but not thickened beyond normal limits, lipoprotein is increased about 50%; in definite gelatinous thickenings it is doubled and in the periphery of plaques it is increased between 2- and 4-fold. The larger plaques shown in the lower part of the table were analyzed in two layers, and the results have been recombined to give an estimate of the overall lipoprotein concentration. The group of fibrous plaques which have not accumulated lipid still show a marked increase in lipoprotein. Only the fibrous plaques with dense collagenous caps and an underlying pool of amorphous "atheroma" lipid show a fall in lipoprotein concentration. Thus with the exception of the fatty streaks, all lesions which might be regarded as "developing," show increases in lipoprotein concentration.

Table IX

CONCENTRATIONS OF LD-LIPOPROTEIN AND "RESIDUAL CHOLESTEROL" IN LESIONS[a]

	No. of samples	Percentage of the normal level: Concentration of lipoprotein	Percentage of the normal level: Concentration of residual cholesterol
Lesions analyzed in a single layer			
Fatty streaks (containing numerous fat-filled cells)	14	28 ± 5	1319 ± 268
Gelatinous normal	12	142 ± 10	83 ± 12
Gelatinous thickenings	21	196 ± 13	138 ± 19
Gelatinous periphery of plaques	19	363 ± 36	133 ± 24
Reconstituted from lesions analyzed in two layers			
White fibrous plaques (<15 mg/100 mg tissue residual cholesterol)	15	170	95
Plaques with amorphous lipid centers			
Gelatinous	12	221	629
White fibrous	10	55	902

[a] Expressed as percentage of the level in normal intima from the same aorta.

2. *Distribution of Lipoprotein in Different Layers*

The distributions of lipoprotein and residual cholesterol between different layers of normal intima and lesions are summarized in Fig. 6, which shows spatial as well as chemical relationships. In samples divided into two layers, the concentration of LP in the lower layer is expressed as a percentage of the concentration in the upper layer, and shown below each column. The height of the columns represents thickness of the intima in micrometers; the broken line at zero represents the first fragmentary elastic lamina, thus samples below this line contain fragmentary elastic laminae, whereas in samples above the line no elastic tissue could be detected by the Verhoeff stain. In groups 1–4, the upper strip plane was on the first fragmentary elastic lamina and the lower strip plane on the first intact elastic lamina. In groups 5–12, the bottom strip plane was on the first fragmentary elastic lamina and elastin could not be demonstrated by the Verhoeff stain in any of the tissue layers. Groups 1–3 represent normal intima grouped by the thickness of the upper layer; the proportion of lipoprotein in the lower layer remains rather constant at about 16% of the concentration in the upper layer in spite of increasing distance from the lumen. Group 4 samples are of normal thickness but gelatinous; the concentration of lipoprotein in the lower layer is 38% of

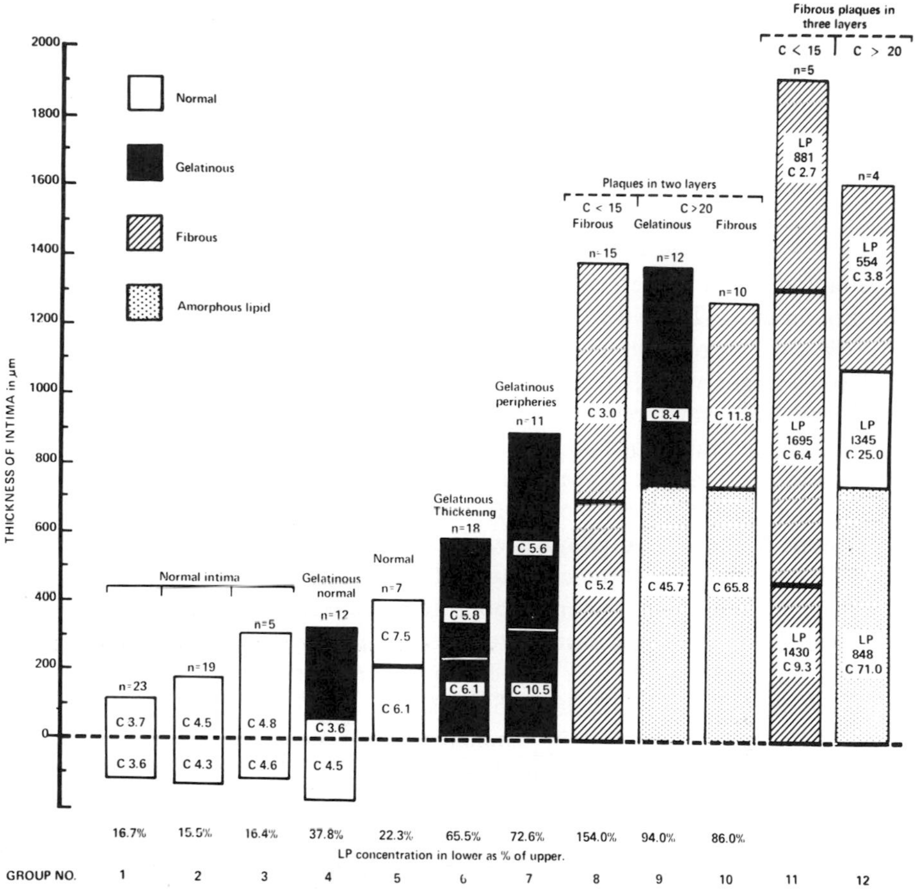

FIG. 6. Distribution of LD-lipoprotein (LP) and residual cholesterol (C) in different layers of normal intima and lesions. The height of the columns represents the thickness of the intima in micrometers, with zero on the first fragmentary elastic lamina (heavy dashed line). Strip planes are represented by horizontal lines. Residual cholesterol in milligrams per 100 mg tissue (C) is shown within each layer. For groups 1–10, the concentration of lipoprotein in the lower layer is expressed as percentage of the concentration in the upper layer, and is shown below each column. For groups 11 and 12 (stripped in 3 layers), the concentration of lipoprotein in microliters per 100 mg tissue (LP) is shown within the columns. Groups 1–3 are normal intimas classified by the thickness of the upper layer: (1) Less than 151 μm; (2) 151–250 μm; (3) 251–350 μm. The maximum concentration of residual cholesterol in any layer is used to classify plaques into low-lipid (less than 15 mg/100 mg dry tissue) and high-lipid (more than 20 mg/100 mg dry tissue) groups.

the concentration in the upper layer, thus there is a great increase in permeability.

In group 5, the *lower* strip plane is on the first fragmentary elastic lamina and the upper strip plane is about the middle of the collagenous intima; the intimas are thick with slightly raised residual cholesterol (C) but otherwise appear normal. The lipoprotein concentration in the lower layer is 22% of the concentration in the upper.

In the gelatinous thickenings and gelatinous peripheries of plaques (groups 6 and 7), there is a great increase in the overall concentration of lipoprotein (Table IX) and the proportions in the lower layers rise to 65% and 73%, respectively.

Group 8 are white, fibrous plaques containing only perifibrous lipid and with maximum residual cholesterol less than 15 mg/100 mg. The overall concentration of lipoprotein is slightly greater than normal (Table IX), and the increase occurs mainly in the *lower* layer where the concentration is 154% of the concentration in the upper layer.

Groups 9 and 10 are plaques with amorphous "atheroma" lipid in the deep layers. In group 9 the caps are gelatinous, suggesting that the lesions may be "developing." Overall lipoprotein concentration is high at 220% of normal and is evenly distributed between the gelatinous cap and the "early" amorphous lipid in the lower layer (residual cholesterol 45.7 mg/100 mg). In group 10, dense fibrous caps overlie amorphous atheroma lipid; the overall lipoprotein concentration is only 55% of normal and again it is fairly evenly distributed between the two layers.

Groups 11 and 12 are very thick plaques that have been dissected into three layers; the actual concentrations of lipoprotein are shown within each layer. In both the low and high lipid groups, the maximum concentration of lipoprotein occurs in the middle layer which, in the high lipid group, comprises the junction of the cap with the amorphous lipid; the lowest concentration of lipoprotein is in the surface layers of the fibrous cap.

The concentration of lipoprotein in the upper layer of the media—immediately below the first intact elastic lamina—has been examined in 12 samples. The highest level of 58 μl standard LP/100 mg (16% of the concentration in the whole intima) was found under a patch of fatty infiltration in which half the intima contained numerous fragmentary elastic laminae. No lipoprotein was detected in media underlying the six samples of normal intima or one of the fatty streaks; in the remaining three fatty streaks the mean concentration was 4% of the concentration in the whole intima. In the media underlying one fatty plaque, the concentration of lipoprotein was 10% of the concentration in the lower layer of the intima and 5% of the concentration in the upper layer. Although the numbers are very small, these results lend no support to the idea that filtration through the media is a normal route of egress for plasma LD-lipoprotein.

It is clear from the results summarized in Fig. 6 that the pattern of distribution of lipoprotein within the intima is highly complex; presumably the net amount found in any layer is the resultant of differing rates of ingress and egress, of reversible and irreversible binding, and of lipoprotein destruction; however, certain patterns seem to emerge. In normal intima the highest concentration of lipoprotein is in the upper (luminal) half, but in all the gelatinous lesions there is not only a large increase in the concentration of lipoprotein, but a very great increase in its permeation into the deep layers. From the analysis of whole plaques with atheroma centers (Smith and Slater, 1973a), it was thought that low concentrations of lipoprotein were associated with amorphous lipid, but from the last four groups in Fig. 6, it is clear that this is not true. The concentration of lipoprotein is approximately the same in the cap and underlying lipid pool both in gelatinous plaques with a very high lipoprotein content and in fibrous plaques with a low lipoprotein content. In the plaques analyzed, in three layers the distribution of lipoprotein is the same in plaques with low lipid (group 11) and high lipid (group 12). Thus it appears that low levels of lipoprotein are not specifically associated with high concentrations of extracellular lipid. The concentration of lipoprotein appears to be more dependent on topographical position in the lesion and the state of the connective tissue.

IV. Quantitative Relationship Between Plasma Constituents in Intima

The increased concentration of LD-lipoprotein in lesions could result from increased endothelial permeability, increased "binding" of lipoprotein or a combination of both, and studies on the relative and absolute concentrations of other plasma constituents should give some indication of the mechanisms involved. The fluorescent antibody technique is difficult to quantify, but Haust (1968) found albumin in small amounts in the superficial layers only in normal intima, whereas in early lesions it permeated into the deep layers; she was unable to demonstrate fibrin in normal intima, but it was present in all the fatty streaks examined, and in "white, fibrous plaques" where large amounts were demonstrated in the atheromatous "core" which showed only small, scattered deposits with the PTAH stain (Haust *et al.*, 1964). Kao and Wissler (1965) showed that LD-lipoprotein and fibrinogen (or fibrin) paralleled each other in a large number of tissue samples, but they were unable to demonstrate albumin in the unfixed tissues, and small amounts of HD-lipoprotein were found in only 18 of the 46 samples that contained LD-lipoprotein.

A. LD-Lipoprotein, Albumin, and Fibrinogen in Normal Intima and Lesions

The quantitative immunoelectrophoretic technique has been used to measure the amounts of LD-lipoprotein, albumin, and fibrinogen in aliquots of the same tissue sample, and they have all been found in substantial amounts in normal intima and lesions. Both albumin and lipoprotein can be assayed against the patient's own serum, giving a direct measure of the "volumes of plasma" from which each is derived. In normal intima, LD-lipoprotein is derived from approximately seven times as much plasma as albumin, which means that their actual concentrations are about the same. Unfortunately samples of the patient's *plasma* are rarely available and the fibrinogen level of most patients is not known. Consequently a ratio is calculated in terms of absolute concentrations of lipoprotein cholesterol and fibrinogen. About 60% of the fibrinogen/fibrin-related antigen (FRA) in the intima can be clotted with thrombin and is presumably intact fibrinogen; the remainder appears to be split products (Smith *et al.*, 1973). The changes in concentration in lesions compared with normal intima from the same aorta are shown in Table X. In fatty streaks containing numerous fat-filled cells, LD-lipoprotein is *reduced* to only 22% of the normal level, but very surprisingly, albumin and FRA also show a small reduction to 60–70% of the normal level. In gelatinous thickenings, LD-lipoprotein and FRA are both increased to more than twice the normal level while albumin shows a rather smaller increase. In the gelatinous periphery of plaques there is a further small increase in albumin and much greater increases

Table X

Comparison of the Concentrations of LD-Lipoprotein, Albumin, and 'Fibrinogen' in Lesions[a]

	Concentration in lesion as percentage of normal		
	Lipoprotein	Albumin	Fibrinogen
Fatty streaks	23	69	62
Gelatinous thickenings	225	177	255
Gelatinous periphery of plaques	352	220	425

[a] Expressed as percentage of the concentration in normal intima from the same aorta.

Table XI

RATIOS OF LIPOPROTEIN TO ALBUMIN[a] AND OF LIPOPROTEIN CHOLESTEROL TO FIBRINOGEN IN UPPER AND LOWER LAYERS OF NORMAL INTIMA AND LESIONS

	Lipoprotein/albumin		Lipoprotein cholesterol/ fibrinogen	
	Upper	Lower	Upper	Lower
Normal intima	7.4	4.3	1.9	2.9
Gelatinous thickenings	10.8	8.4	1.5	2.3
Gelatinous periphery of plaques	10.4	18.5	1.9	1.7
White fibrous plaques (residual cholesterol < 15 mg/100 mg tissue)	9.0	16.9	1.3	1.2

[a] In terms of volumes of the patient's serum.

in LD-lipoprotein and FRA. The finding that all components increase suggests that in the gelatinous lesions there is a general increase in permeability, but a greater retention of lipoprotein and fibrinogen than of albumin.

The ratios of LD-lipoprotein to albumin and to FRA in the upper and lower layers of normal intima and lesions are summarized in Table XI. In the lower layers of gelatinous lesions and the fibrous plaques with low lipid, in which there is a particularly marked increase in the proportion of LD-lipoprotein there is a 4 fold increase in the ratio of LD-lipoprotein to albumin; only small changes occur in the upper layers. By contrast, the ratio of LD-lipoprotein cholesterol to FRA *decreases*. It could be argued that the results are distorted by fibrinolytic activity with release of "split products" in the deep layers, but Smith *et al.* (1973) found a rather high proportion of thrombin-clottable "fibrinogen" in the lower layers of plaques, and the high level of fibrinogen is compatible with the findings of Haust *et al.* (1964). If there is some mechanism for the specific binding of lipoprotein it appears to act equally upon fibrinogen.

B. RATIOS OF CONSTITUENTS IN PLASMA AND INTIMA AND MECHANISMS OF ENTRY AND RETENTION

There is a remarkable change in the ratios of plasma constituents between the plasma and intimal compartments. The changes in the relationship between albumin, LD-lipoprotein, and fibrinogen are summarized in Table XII. Compared with plasma there is a 7-fold decrease in albumin relative to lipoprotein in normal intima, and a 14-fold decrease

Table XII
PLASMA CONSTITUENTS IN INTIMA[a]

	Concentration in plasma (mg/100 ml)	Ratios in plasma and intima		
			Intima	
		Plasma	Normal	Gelatinous
Albumin	4000	14	2	1
LD-lipoprotein	300	1	1	1
Fibrinogen	300	1	⅓	½

[a] From Smith (1974).

in gelatinous lesions; fibrinogen shows a 3-fold decrease in normal intima, but is only half the plasma ratio in gelatinous lesions. These changes are the reverse of the changes found in capillary transudates, and highlight the problems of lipoprotein passage through or across the endothelium, and of its retention in the intima.

1. *Entry of LD-Lipoprotein into the Intima*

Plasma proteins cross the *capillary* endothelium at rates that are inversely proportional to their molecular weights, so that albumin is the largest component of transudates and LD-lipoprotein, with a molecular weight of 2×10^6, is present in trace amounts only (Dangerfield *et al.*, 1960). Experimental studies on the permeability of endothelia were extensively reviewed by French (1966) and in general, it appears that albumin also crosses arterial endothelium more rapidly than lipoprotein. Our finding (Fig. 4b) that the volume of plasma from which the LD-lipoprotein in the intima is derived remains fairly constant, and that there are constant relationships between lipoprotein and albumin, and lipoprotein and fibrinogen suggests that "whole plasma" may enter the intima and that the change in the ratios of plasma components in intima results from physical interactions affecting their rates of egress. This would imply either that the endothelium is "totally leaky" or that whole plasma is engulfed in pinocytotic vesicles. Recent studies lend support to this latter idea; there appear to be much tighter cell junctions in arterial than in capillary endothelium (Hess and Staubli, 1968; Schwartz and Benditt, 1972; Hess, 1973) and proteins apparently cross the endothelium in pinocytotic vesicles. Stein and Stein (1973) found that horseradish peroxidase (M.W. 40,000; diameter 40 Å) appeared to cross the endothelium entirely in vesicles when at low concentration, but at high concentration, some peroxidase appeared within the cell junctions, an observation in agreement with Florey and Sheppard (1970). Schwartz and Benditt (1972) also found horseradish peroxidase in vesicles, some of which appeared to open into the cell junctions. Ferritin (diameter 110 Å) and lactoperoxidase (M.W. 82,000) do not appear to enter the junctions, and cross the endothelial cells in vesicles (Florey and Sheppard, 1970; Stein and Stein, 1973). By analogy, Stein and Stein suggest that HD-lipoprotein (diameter approximately 100 Å) and LD-lipoprotein (diameter 200 Å) will also cross *intact* arterial endothelium in vesicles. In perfusion experiments with protein-labeled VLD-, LD-, and HD-lipoproteins they found very little penetration of the endothelium by VLD-, whereas both LD- and HD-lipoprotein appeared in and under the endothelium, but penetrated only the most superficial layers of the media. By contrast, apo-HDL (M.W. about 16,000) was uniformly distributed throughout the media. Schwartz and Benditt (1972) found that horseradish peroxidase had penetrated all layers of the vessel wall within 20 minutes. Adams *et al.* (1968) found labeled albumin, γ-globulin, and cholesterol in all layers of the rabbit aorta 1–4 days after injection. Thus all these different approaches give remarkably concordant results; if whole plasma, with the possible exception of VLDL, is transported in vesicles and the smaller proteins then pass on through the media, the high ratio of lipoprotein to albumin could be explained. The rapid transport of lipoprotein across the endothelium of these normal experimental animals suggest that the failure to detect measurable amounts of LD-lipoprotein in young children springs from the absence of a subendothelial connective tissue layer in which it can accumulate. There is, however, one aspect of the problem about which we have no information, and that concerns the condition of the endothelium in the "normal" middle-aged human artery. Areas of increased permeability and cell turnover have been demonstrated in the aortas of rats and rabbits perfused with dye *in situ* (Björkerud and Bondjers, 1972) and in the aortas of young normal pigs, administered dye *in vivo* (Bell *et al.*, 1972; Caplan and Schwartz, 1973) and it is possible that the endothelium overlying diffuse intimal thickening and gelatinous lesions is "totally leaky." Since Caplan and Schwartz find different results of dye-uptake experiments *in vivo* and in excised aortas it is difficult to see how the problem can be investigated in human vessels.

2. *Binding of LD-Lipoprotein in the Intima*

Mucopolysaccharides or glycosaminoglycans (GAG) have been implicated in atherogenesis for many years, but more recent *quantitative* studies indicate a decrease in concentration with increasing severity of atherosclerosis (reviewed by Smith, 1974) and their precise role, if any, is very difficult to interpret. GAG *in vitro*, including preparations from arterial intima, form complexes with LD-lipoproteins at concentrations that are comparable to the concentration in intima (about 3 mg/cm^3) (Amenta and Waters, 1960; Gerö *et al.*, 1961; Bihari-Varga and Végh, 1967; Srinivasan *et al.*, 1970; Iverius, 1972). Thus it seems reasonable to postulate that such complexes will be formed in the arterial wall; Bihari-Varga *et al.* (1968) using thermal decomposition, find evidence of complexes in whole intimal tissue, and Srinivasan *et al.* (1972) report extraction of complexes from "fatty streaks" that have not been defined morphologically. However, Iverius (1972) considers that only dermatan sulfate (chondroitin sulfate B) will form stable complexes at physiological pH and ionic strength. From the scanty and discordant information available on distribution of different GAG in arterial wall (see Smith, 1974) it appears that this is a very minor component, and decreases in lesions.

Data from this laboratory on concentrations of LD-lipoprotein, total GAG, and "deposited" cholesterol in fatty streaks and gelatinous thickenings are summarized in Table XIII; lipoprotein and GAG were not determined on the same tissue samples, but the samples are believed to be comparable. In fatty streaks, LD-lipoprotein falls to about a quarter of the normal level, GAG increases by about 16%, and deposited cholesterol increases about 13-fold and is mainly within fat-filled cells. It is difficult to believe that a 16% increase in GAG could increase *cellular* uptake of cholesterol more than 10-fold, and it is also difficult to understand what role GAG could be playing in the massive reduction in LD-lipoprotein found both by electrophoresis directly from the tissue into an antibody-containing gel, and by saline extraction and radial diffusion (Smith and Slater, 1970, 1972b). It has been reported that GAG-lipoprotein complexes have a high electrophoretic mobility at pH 8.6 and that the lipoprotein retains its antigenic properties (Gerö *et al.*, 1961;

Table XIII

CHANGES IN THE CONCENTRATIONS OF INTACT LD-LIPOPROTEIN, GLYCOSAMINOGLYCANS (GAG), AND "DEPOSITED" CHOLESTEROL IN EARLY LESIONS

	Percentage of the normal level	
	Fatty streaks	Gelatinous thickenings
LD-lipoprotein	28% (14)[a]	196% (17)
Total glycosaminoglycan	116% (19)	91% (7)
Deposited cholesterol	1319% (14)	138% (17)

[a] Number of samples.

Srinivasan *et al.*, 1970); therefore, even if a complex is formed which does not dissociate at pH 8.6, it should be measurable in the immunoelectrophoretic system. There is some tentative support for the suggestion that lipoprotein may be destroyed at the surface of cells that are taking up cholesterol (Robertson, 1968); this could account for the low level of intact lipoprotein found in intima containing fat-filled cells, and the slight increase in GAG could be secondary to their increased metabolic activity.

In the gelatinous lesions the 40% increase in "deposited" cholesterol is mainly in the form of fine perifibrous lipid droplets and diffuse sudanophilia. The concentration of LD-lipoprotein is doubled, but the concentration of GAG is *decreased* by 10%, making it difficult to postulate that the increase in lipoprotein results from increased complex formation; furthermore, fibrinogen increases to the same extent as lipoprotein (Table XI). Lindner (1972) also reports a decrease in GAG in edema lesions, but finds an increase in the glycoprotein fraction. It is clear that there is no simple relationship between intimal lipoprotein, GAG, and deposited cholesterol, but it is not clear that an hypothesis of specific binding of lipoprotein is required. If albumin is able to pass through the media with minimal hindrance, whereas LD-lipoprotein is virtually unable to enter the media, an area of leaky endothelium allowing increased inflow of whole plasma might be expected to produce a greater increase in lipoprotein than in albumin. *Reduced* levels of GAG, which all investigators find in advanced fibrous plaques (Smith, 1974) might allow more rapid penetration of lipoprotein into the deep layers of the intima.

V. Relationship Between LD-Lipoprotein and the Lipid "Deposited" in Intima

A. Comparison of Lipoprotein and Intimal Lipids

1. *Extracellular Lipid in Normal Intima*

In normal intima of young children, phospholipid is the major component and most cholesterol is in the free (unesterified) form; the predominant fatty acids in the small cholesterol ester fraction are palmitic and oleic. By the eighth decade, diffusely thickened but otherwise lesion-free intima, with lipid only in the perifibrous form, contains four times as much lipid of a composition very similar to the S_f 0–12 lipoprotein of plasma (Table I). Because of its composition we have assumed that the additional lipid is derived directly from plasma LD-lipoprotein

(Smith *et al.*, 1967). Calculations of the resultant lipid composition, if varying amounts of LD-lipoprotein are added to the lipids of a child's intima broadly support this idea, although the calculated mixture contains more free cholesterol and phospholipid than is actually found.

The most rapid accumulation of cholesterol with age occurs in the lower layers of the intima, where it increases at a rate of 0.1 mg/100 mg dry tissue per annum. In this layer the concentration of intact lipoprotein cholesterol is about 0.5 mg, so this would represent "deposition" or "irreversible binding" of about 20% per annum of the available lipoprotein pool; in the upper, collagenous layer of the intima, cholesterol accumulates at only half the rate, representing 1–2% of the larger lipoprotein pool. There seems to be no correlation between the concentrations of intact LD-lipoprotein and of residual (electrophoretically immobile) cholesterol in normal intima, suggesting that this "deposited" cholesterol is no longer able to equilibrate with plasma cholesterol. This idea seems to be at variance with the apparently rapid equilibration between plasma and intimal cholesterol oleate and linoleate during the first two decades (Fig. 2). However, the "constant concentration" cholesterol ester of the first two decades (Fig. 1) may be in a different pool (Wilson, 1970)—possibly the cell membrane—from the cholesterol ester that accumulates as fine extracellular droplets from the third decade upwards. It is in the third decade that the adult level of lipoprotein in the intima is reached.

2. *Intracellular Lipid in Fatty Streaks*

In all aortic fat-filled cells (Table II) and the fat-filled cells of adrenal cortex and skin xanthomas (Dailey *et al.*, 1960; Jepson *et al.*, 1965; Baes *et al.*, 1968; Smith, 1971; Smith and Slater, 1973b; Fletcher, 1973) the cholesterol esters have a highly characteristic fatty acid pattern in which there is a very high proportion of oleic acid and low proportion of linoleic acid, thus differing radically from plasma cholesterol esters. This seems to be the characteristic pattern in which cells esterify cholesterol (Blomstrand *et al.*, 1964) compared with the high linoleate plasma pattern arising from lecithin–cholesterol acyl transferase (LCAT) activity (Glomset, 1962, 1968). Thus the cholesterol ester in fat-filled cells could only be derived from plasma cholesterol ester by very elaborate differential hydrolysis, and there is no conclusive experimental evidence in support of this idea. There is, however, much evidence that arterial intima, including isolated foam cells, synthesize fatty acids (reviewed by Whereat, 1971) and esterify them with cholesterol (Lofland *et al.*, 1965; Day and Wilkinson, 1967; St. Clair *et al.*, 1968, 1969, 1970; Day and Wahlqvist, 1968; Day and Tume, 1970). Oleic acid seems to be a major product of synthesis and of incorporation into cholesterol ester (St. Clair *et al.*, 1969, 1970). By contrast, cholesterol is synthesized only to a small, and probably not significant extent in older and atherosclerotic arteries (reviewed by Dayton and Hashimoto, 1970) and there is much evidence, some of which will be presently discussed, that it is mainly derived from plasma. The finding that there is a consistently low level of intact LD-lipoprotein in the vicinity of fat-filled cells therefore suggests that they break down the lipoprotein and from it derive cholesterol which is then esterified in the cellular pattern. Fatty streaks containing confluent fat-filled cells accumulate about 20 mg cholesterol/ 100 mg tissue; they would thus need to "process" the lipoprotein from 10–15 ml normo-cholesterolemic plasma if all the cholesterol in the lipoprotein were used. If one assumes that a human fatty streak takes 6 months to develop, the cells would have to utilize lipoprotein from 100 μl plasma per day, which is less than 10% of the normal intimal lipoprotein level, and would be unlikely to produce the 70% decrease observed. This implies either that the cells are accumulating cholesterol much more rapidly, or that only part of the lipoprotein cholesterol is utilized. We do not know if there is hydrolysis and reesterification of the ester fraction, or if only the free cholesterol of the lipoprotein is utilized. If only free cholesterol were utilized there should be a disproportionately low free cholesterol and high ester cholesterol in the tissue surrounding the fat-filled cells. Lang and Insull (1970) fractionated fatty streaks into lipid droplets and tissue residue; in the residue there were normal proportions of free and ester cholesterol, and a normal free cholesterol/phospholipid ratio. This provides some indirect evidence that both free and ester cholesterol are utilized. Peters *et al.* (1973) have found "light lysosomes" containing large amounts of cholesterol in cholesterol-fed rabbits, but these seemed to be associated with rather low levels of esterase activity. Portman and Alexander (1972) have described "light microsomes" which increased early during the development of atherosclerosis and had a high ratio of free cholesterol to phospholipid, and high proportion of sphingomyelin in the phospholipid.

3. *Extracellular Lipid in Fibrous Plaques*

In the gelatinous and fibrous lesions containing only perifibrous lipid (Tables VI and VII) all the parameters of lipid composition are very similar to LD-lipoprotein; the concentration of lipoprotein is approximately double the concentration in normal intima (Table IX), and intact lipoprotein can account for half the total cholesterol in the lesion. In plaques with a gelatinous cap overlying an amorphous "atheroma" lipid core, intact lipoprotein accounts for about half the total cholesterol in the cap, but only 12% of the cholesterol in the amorphous lipid, and the proportions are lower in the "white" fibrous plaques (Fig. 6). From plaques divided into three layers (Fig. 6, groups 11 and 12) it is clear that there is considerable variation in lipoprotein concentration between the layers with the maximum level in the mid-zone. However, variation in the relative proportions of the lipid present, as intact lipoprotein and as deposited residual lipid, cannot account for the large differences in the percentage of the cholesterol that is free, or in the changing ratio of free cholesterol/phospholipid. Disappointingly, these analyses seem to give no clue to the mechanism of lipid deposition from the lipoprotein.

4. *Relationship Between Cholesterol and Phospholipid*

An intriguing feature of the lipid accumulating in fibrous lesions is a progressive increase in the ratio of free (or total) cholesterol to phospholipid. Since it appears that the cholesterol is derived directly from LD-lipoprotein, any increase above the mass ratio of 0.57 found in the lipoprotein, must indicate that lipoprotein phospholipid is being removed.

In normal intima, free cholesterol/phospholipid remains remarkably constant over the first six decades at a mass ratio of 0.4–0.5, which is close to a 1:1 molar ratio. It is only in the eighth decade, where total cholesterol increases above 8 mg/100 mg tissue, that the ratio reaches or slightly exceeds the ratio in LD-lipoprotein.

Fleischer and Rouser (1965) report 1:1 as the molar ratio in plasma membrane. Regardless of the morphology of the surrounding tissue, this ratio seems to be maintained in all tissue samples in which total cholesterol does not exceed approximately 8 mg/100 mg tissue and the lipid, when demonstrated by light microscopy, is in the form of fine, perifibrous droplets (Table VIII). The ratio of cells to connective tissue elements differs greatly between normal intima with 25% collagen, gelatinous lesions with 30% collagen, and fibrous plaques with more than 40% collagen (Smith, 1965b, 1974), so this apparent maintenance of the plasma membrane ratio may be fortuitous and instead reflect a physicochemical relationship (Small, 1970). In samples in which the lipid is morphologically extracellular the ratio increases as soon as the cholesterol rises above about 8 mg/100 mg tissue—increases of up to 3-fold where there is no marked change in the proportion of the cholesterol which is free, and of up to 5-fold where there is a large change in free cholesterol. Thus it appears that at least two-thirds of the incoming phospholipid in the lipoprotein must be eliminated, and since there is active phospholipid synthesis in the arterial wall the proportion eliminated may be even higher. Phospholipid metabolism in the arterial wall was extensively reviewed and discussed by Portman in 1970 and will not be recapitulated here.

It may, however, be of interest to examine the relationship between the ratios of free cholesterol/total phospholipid and of sphingomyelin/lecithin in Table VIII. In all samples with "normal" amounts of perifibrous lipid, the ratio of free cholesterol/phospholipid is about 0.5 and sphingomyelin/lecithin about 1.0; the sphingomyelin/lecithin ratio is about 1.0 in fat-filled cells. It is only in the amorphous lipid, where the very large amount of cholesterol ester appears to be derived directly from LD-lipoprotein, that there are substantial increases in both ratios. This would be compatible with extensive hydrolysis of lecithin (Eisenberg *et al.*, 1969) and suggests that the large amount of sphingomyelin that accumulates in amorphous lipid is derived mainly from LD-lipoprotein.

5. *Accumulation of Plasma-Type Lipid in Other Tissues*

The accumulation with age, of lipid showing characteristics of LD-lipoprotein composition, has been observed in a number of connective tissues (Andrews, 1962; Broekhuyse and Kuhlmann, 1972; Broekhuyse, 1972; Crouse *et al.*, 1972; Smith and Slater, 1973b). Crouse *et al.* (1972) showed large increases in cholesterol in biceps and psoas tendons over the age range 20–80 years, with a mean of about 1 mg/100 mg dry tissue in the 60–80 age group; the largest increase was in esterified cholesterol, which increased to between a half and a third of the total cholesterol. More detailed studies have been reported on the sclera and cornea of the eye; over the age range 3–68 years, Broekhuyse (1972) found slow, linear increases in free cholesterol and total phospholipid and a much more rapid increase in cholesterol ester, giving curves very similar to aging aortic intima; there was a progressive increase in the proportion of sphingomyelin.

In this laboratory we have compared lipids in other connective tissues with artery wall; in Achilles tendon and ligamentum flavum, lipid can be seen microscopically as very fine sudanophilic droplets lying between the bundles of collagen or elastin—the elastic ligament appears to have no greater affinity for lipid than the collagenous tendons. In the sclera of the eye, lipid appears as rather coarser droplets lying between the connective tissue fibers; in this tissue, cholesterol ester concentration is most precisely correlated with age ($r = 0.99$), increasing from 0.9 mg/100 mg dry tissue at age 51 to 3.1 mg at age 83 (Smith and Slater, 1973b). The lipids in sclera and cornea are very similar both in concentration and composition, and the lipid patterns in all the connective tissues examined are comparable to aortic intima: 30–35% of the cholesterol free, 55–60% cholesterol linoleate in the oleate + linoleate fraction, and a sphingomyelin/lecithin ratio close to unity. The only consistent difference is a higher free cholesterol/phospholipid ratio that may reflect the small number of cells in these tissues. Thus it is clear that the age-related accumulation of perifibrous lipid droplets, which appears to be derived from LD-lipoprotein, is not confined to the artery wall.

B. Lipoprotein Concentration and Dynamic Studies on Influx and Efflux

1. *Exchange of Free Cholesterol Between Lipoproteins and Membranes*

Since the measured concentration of plasma LD-lipoprotein in intima must be the resultant of influx, efflux, reversible binding, and irreversible binding or destruction, it tells us nothing about the rate of entry. A high concentration could arise from increased endothelial permeability, an increase in "reversible binding" producing a decreased rate of efflux, or reduction in the rate of lipoprotein destruction. There have been numerous studies on the uptake of isotopically labeled lipoprotein by arterial wall in attempts to disentangle these factors.

The majority of investigators have used isotopically labeled cholesterol that has been incorporated into the lipoprotein either *in vitro* or *in vivo*. However, it seems probable that interpretation of results obtained with this system are complicated by the rapid exchange of the free cholesterol in the lipoprotein with free cholesterol in the tissue. This exchange was first demonstrated with red cell membrane (Hagerman and Gould, 1951; Eckles *et al.*, 1955; Gould *et al.*, 1955[1]) and is now known to occur with a large range of other membranes including mitochondria, intestinal microvilli, liver plasma membrane, muscle sarcolemma, and microsomes (Graham and Green, 1967); it also occurs between different lipoprotein fractions (Roheim *et al.*, 1963). The problem of quantitative interpretation of apparent uptake in the presence of this exchange were discussed by Gould *et al.* (1963). In 1966, papers indicating that the passage of labeled cholesterol into the artery wall was not an energy-requiring process were published by both Hashimoto and Dayton and by Newman and Zilversmit. Both groups found that the entry of free cholesterol was much greater, relative to its concentration in plasma, than the entry of esterified cholesterol, and both concluded that at least part of the free cholesterol might be transferred by physicochemical exchange. Newman and Zilversmit (1962) published data from an experiment in which rabbits were fed a high cholesterol diet containing cholesterol-4-^{14}C so that uptake of plasma cholesterol could be observed

[1] See also Ashworth and Green (1964).

during atherogenesis. From their results, the increment of cholesterol in the aorta can be calculated, and the expected number of counts compared with the observed counts. At 21 days, the counts in the free cholesterol fraction were greater than the counts predicted from the observed cholesterol increment, suggesting that between 25% and 40% of the free cholesterol represented exchange with preexisting tissue cholesterol.

2. *Measurement of Isotope in Human Arteries*

Several investigators have administered tracer doses of labeled cholesterol to terminal patients and measured the isotope in the artery wall at autopsy (Rabinowitz *et al.*, 1960; Field *et al.*, 1960; Chobanian and Hollander, 1960; Gould *et al.*, 1963); Scott and Hurley (1970) administered LD-lipoprotein labeled with radioactive iodine in the peptide, so that problems of cholesterol exchange were avoided. In "normal appearing" intima, Field *et al.* (1960) found no cholesterol-^{14}C at 2.5 days after feeding, traces only at 18 days, and substantial amounts from 27 days upwards. From the number of counts in the wall and the counts per 100 ml of plasma (unfortunately individual plasma and intimal cholesterol values were not given), a crude estimate can be made of the "volume of plasma" in the intima. Although the plasma specific activity ranged from 268 to 67 counts/minute/mg cholesterol, the three subjects examined at 27, 38, and 88 days gave quite similar results of 1000 ± 300 μl/100 mg dry intima when the calculation is based on ester cholesterol, and 1700 ± 200 μl when based on free cholesterol. The figure from cholesterol ester is entirely compatible with the "volumes of plasma" that we have found by direct measurement of lipoprotein (page 24), and suggests that there is complete equilibration between plasma and intimal lipoprotein in 3 to 4 weeks. The difference between the estimates based on ester and free cholesterol could be taken to indicate that about 40% of the free cholesterol counts represent exchange with tissue cholesterol, which is close to the proportion estimated from the experimental data of Newman and Zilversmit (1962).

Scott and Hurley (1970) presented their data as a ratio of counts per gram of tissue to counts per milliliter of plasma; from the results of Smith and Slater (1972b, 1973a) it appears that the concentration of lipoprotein in the upper layers of the intima is about equal to the concentration in plasma, but for "intima plus inner media" preparations the concentration would only be 30–40% of the plasma concentration, thus a ratio of 0.3–0.4 should indicate equilibrium. In Scott and Hurley's published curves, the ratio rises rapidly and by day 15—their longest time interval—the ratio had reached 0.3, suggested equilibration in 2 to 3 weeks. Thus the results of these two human studies are in close agreement, and compatible with our concentration data.

Unfortunately, there seems to be no adequate data on lesions; Field *et al.* (1960) found about three times as many counts for both free and ester cholesterol in "plaques" as in normal intima, whereas Rabinowitz *et al.* (1960) found fewer counts in plaques; results expressed as specific activity are confusing because of dilution by preformed deposits of cholesterol.

3. *Experimental Studies on Cholesterol Influx and Efflux*

Hashimoto and Dayton (1966) found a much greater influx of free cholesterol than of ester cholesterol into normal rat aorta *in vitro;* their results can be used to calculate the "volume of plasma" in the whole aorta and give figures of 16 μl when based on ester cholesterol and 140 μl when based on free cholesterol. Dayton and Hashimoto's (1966) results on uptake *in vivo* are again 16 μl when based on ester cholesterol, but only 60 μl when based on free cholesterol, which is a ratio of 3.7. It seems possible that the exchange reaction is accelerated, or the uptake of whole lipoprotein reduced under *in vitro* conditions, but this idea is not supported by results from other laboratories. Thus data from Newman and Zilversmit (1966) give ratios of 2.4 and 3 after oral administration of labeled cholesterol 2 days before sacrifice, compared with 1.6 and 3.3 after *in vitro* incubation with labeled plasma, and the results of Day *et al.* (1970) give ratios of 1.8 both after feeding and *in vitro;* both these groups used atherosclerotic rabbits.

There is now much experimental evidence indicating that severity of atherosclerosis greatly influences influx of free and ester cholesterol; unfortunately, valuable information has been lost through the failure of investigators to define the morphology of the lesions with which they work. Schwenk and Stevens (1960) fed a moderate cholesterol diet to rabbits for 12 weeks, substituting feeding with cholesterol-^{14}C for one week at different times during the experiment. Radioactivity incorporated during the first week had virtually disappeared by week 12, but radioactivity incorporated during week 7 showed no decrease over the next 5 weeks. Newman and Zilversmit (1962) found increases in both influx and net accumulation with increasing time of cholesterol feeding, and Bell *et al.* (1970) found that rates of both influx and efflux were proportional to the aortic cholesterol concentration. Lofland and Clarkson (1970) fed atherosclerotic pigeons labeled cholesterol for periods up to 30 days, sacrificing them at intervals between 18 and 122 days. The aortas were divided into normal areas, "fatty streaks," and plaques; counts per gram of wet tissue increased about 4-fold between normal intima and plaques for free cholesterol, and 25-fold for ester cholesterol; the ratio, free/ester counts fell from 4.8 in normal intima to 0.7 in plaques. The influx pattern in the plaques would thus be compatible with the idea of greatly increased permeability to whole lipoprotein. Unfortunately, inasmuch as the pigeon "fatty streaks" seem to differ greatly from human fatty streaks, increase in lipid concentration is relatively small and 70% of the cholesterol is free, they shed no light on one of the most striking characteristics of the human lesion—the low concentration of intact lipoprotein.

VI. Conclusions

In atherosclerosis research there are almost as many methods of approach as there are research workers. The experimental systems have ranged from man through a host of experimental animals to tissue cultures. Results are expressed in every conceivable way. Superficially, the field appears to be hopelessly confused and results frequently contradictory. However, after this attempt to effect some sort of synthesis between the lipids accumulating in arterial tissue and the plasma lipoproteins from which they, at least in part, are derived, the author is left with the feeling that the available data are more often compatible than incompatible.

The accumulation of cholesterol ester with the characteristics of plasma cholesterol ester in aging normal intima and in plaques, is compatible with the demonstration of plasma lipoproteins in artery wall by immunofluorescent microscopy. This has led in turn, to the quantitative measurement of intimal lipoprotein, and the concentration estimated by immunoelectrophoresis is remarkably corroborated by the uptake of radioactive cholesterol ester. The immunoelectrophoretic assay shows that the concentration of lipoprotein in normal intima is highly correlated with plasma lipoprotein level, and radioisotope studies suggest complete equilibration between plasma and intimal lipoprotein in two to three weeks. In "early" fibrous lesions the amount of intact lipoprotein is greatly increased providing, particularly in hypercholesterolemic subjects, a substantial reservoir of lipoprotein from which lipid could be "deposited."

There is, however, no information on the nature of this "deposition." It is not even clear if the apoprotein is still attached to the perifibrous and amorphous lipid droplets or if it is the removal or destruction of the apoprotein that causes the lipid to precipitate. It is in this area that information is now particularly needed to explain the accumulation of pathological amounts of lipids derived from plasma lipoproteins in arterial tissue.

Acknowledgments

The experimental work in the author's laboratories was supported by grants from The British Heart Foundation and The Medical Research Council, and the names of co-workers will be found in the reference list. I am particularly indebted to Mr. F. C. Pain who helped to prepare this manuscript.

References

Abdulla, Y. H., Adams, C. W. M., and Bayliss, O. B. (1969). *J. Atheroscler. Res.* **10,** 149.
Adams, C. W. M. (1969). *Advan. Lipid Res.* **7,** 1.
Adams, C. W. M., Virág, S., Morgan, R. S., and Orton, C. C. (1968). *J. Atheroscler. Res.* **8,** 679.
Amenta, J. S., and Waters, L. L. (1960). *Yale J. Biol. Med.* **33,** 112.
Andrews, J. S. (1962). *Arch. Ophthalmol.* **68,** 264.
Ashworth, L. A. E., and Green, C. (1964). *Biochim. Biophys. Acta* **84,** 182.
Baes, H., van Gent, C. H., and Pries, C. (1968). *J. Invest. Dermatol.* **51,** 286.
Bell, F. P., Lofland, H. B., and Stokes, N. A. (1970). *Atherosclerosis* **11,** 235.
Bell, F. P., Somer, J. B., Craig, I. H., and Schwartz, C. J. (1972). *Atherosclerosis* **16,** 369.
Bihari-Varga, M., and Végh, M. (1967). *Biochim. Biophys. Acta* **144,** 202.
Bihari-Varga, M., Simon, J., and Gerö, S. (1968). *Acta Biochim. Biophys.* **3,** 375.
Björkerud, S., and Bondjers, G. (1972). *Atherosclerosis* **15,** 285.
Blomstrand, R., Gürtler, J., and Werner, B. (1964). *Acta Chem. Scand.* **18,** 1018.
Böttcher, C. J. F. (1961). *In* "Drugs Affecting Lipid Metabolism" (S. Garattini and R. Paoletti, eds.), p. 54, Elsevier, Amsterdam.
Böttcher, C. J. F., and van Gent, C. M. (1961). *J. Atheroscler. Res.* **1,** 36.
Böttcher, C. J. F., Boelsma-van Houte, E., ter Haar Romeny-Wachter, C. C., Woodford, P. F., and van Gent, C. M. (1960). *Lancet* **ii,** 1162.
Bowyer, D. E., Howard, A. N., Gresham, G. A., Bates, D., and Palmer, B. V. (1968). *Progr. Biochem. Pharmacol.* **4,** 305.
Broekhuyse, R. M. (1972). *Biochim. Biophys. Acta* **280,** 637.
Broekhuyse, R. M., and Kuhlmann, E. D. (1972). *Exp. Eye Res.* **14,** 11.
Buck, R. C., and Rossiter, R. J. (1951). *Arch. Pathol.* **51,** 224.
Caplan, B. A., and Schwartz, C. J. (1973). *Atherosclerosis* **17,** 401.
Chobanian, A. V., and Hollander, W. (1960). *Clin. Res.* **8,** 179. (Abstr.)
Choi, J. H. (1966). *Fed. Proc., Fed. Amer. Soc. Exp. Biol.* **25,** 665. (Abstr.)
Clarke, H. G. M., and Freeman, T. (1966). *Protides Biol. Fluids, Proc. Colloq.* **14,** 503.
Clarkson, T. B. (1963). *Advan. Lipid Res.* **1,** 211.
Crouse, J. R., Grundy, S. M., and Ahrens, E. H. (1972). *J. Clin. Invest.* **51,** 1292.
Dailey, R. C., Swell, L., Field, H., and Treadwell, C. R. (1960). *Proc. Soc. Exp. Biol. Med.* **105,** 4.
Dangerfield, W. G., Smith, E. B., Kinmonth, J. B., and Taylor, G. W. (1960). *J. Clin. Pathol.* **13,** 76.
Dawber, T. R., Kannel, W. B., Revotskie, N., and Kagan, A. (1962). *Proc. Roy. Soc. Med.* **55,** 265.
Day, A. J. (1967). *Advan. Lipid Res.* **5,** 185.
Day, A. J., and Tume, R. K. (1970). *Atherosclerosis* **11,** 291.
Day, A. J., and Wahlqvist, M. L. (1968). *Circ. Res.* **23,** 779.
Day, A. J., and Wahlqvist, M. L. (1970). *Exp. Mol. Pathol.* **13,** 199.
Day, A. J., and Wilkinson, G. K. (1967). *Circ. Res.* **21,** 593.
Day, A. J., Wahlqvist, M. L., and Campbell, D. J. (1970). *Atherosclerosis* **11,** 301.
Dayton, S., and Hashimoto, S. (1966). *Circ. Res.* **19,** 1041.
Dayton, S., and Hashimoto, S. (1970). *Exp. Mol. Pathol.* **13,** 253.

Eckles, N. E., Taylor, C. B., Campbell, D. J., and Gould, R. G. (1955). *J. Lab. Clin. Med.* **46**, 359.
Eisenberg, S., Stein, Y., and Stein, O. (1969). *J. Clin. Invest.* **48**, 2320.
Field, H., Swell, L., Schools, P. E., and Treadwell, C. R. (1960). *Circulation* **22**, 547.
Fleischer, S., and Rouser, G. (1965). *J. Amer. Oil. Chem. Soc.* **42**, 588.
Fletcher, R. F. (1973). *Nutr. Metab.* **15**, 97.
Florey, H., and Sheppard, B. L. (1970). *Proc. Roy. Soc., Ser. B* **174**, 435.
French, J. E. (1963). *In* "Biochemical Problems of Lipids" (A. C. Frazer, ed.), B.B.A. Library, Vol. 1, p. 296. Elsevier, Amsterdam.
French, J. E. (1966). *Int. Rev. Exp. Pathol.* **5**, 253.
Geer, J. C., and Guidry, M. A. (1964). *Exp. Mol. Pathol.* **3**, 485.
Geer, J. C., and Haust, M. D. (1972). "Smooth Muscle Cells in Atherosclerosis," Monographs on Atherosclerosis, Vol. 2. Karger, Basel.
Gerö, S., Gergely, J., Jakab, L., Székely, J., and Virág, S. (1961). *J. Atheroscler. Res.* **1**, 88.
Glomset, J. A. (1962). *Biochem. Biophys. Acta* **65**, 128.
Glomset, J. A. (1968). *J. Lipid Res.* **9**, 155.
Gould, R. G., LeRoy, G. V., Okita, C. T., Kabara, J. J., Keegan, P., and Bergenstal, D. M. (1955). *J. Lab. Clin. Med.* **46**, 372.
Gould, R. G., Wissler, R. W., and Jones, R. J. (1963). *In* "The Evolution of the Atherosclerotic Plaque" (R. J. Jones, ed.), p. 302. Univ. of Chicago Press, Chicago, Illinois.
Grabar, P. (1959). *Methods Biochem. Anal.* **7**, 1.
Grabar, P., and Williams, C. A. (1953). *Biochim. Biophys. Acta* **10**, 193.
Graham, J. M., and Green, C. (1967). *Biochem. J.* **103**, 16c.
Hagerman, J. S., and Gould, R. G. (1951). *Proc. Soc. Exp. Biol. Med.* **78**, 329.
Hashimoto, S., and Dayton, S. (1966). *J. Atheroscler. Res.* **6**, 580.
Haust, M. D. (1968). *Progr. Biochem. Pharmacol.* **4**, 429.
Haust, M. D. (1971). *Hum. Pathol.* **2**, 1.
Haust, M. D., Wyllie, J. C., and More, R. H. (1964). *Amer. J. Pathol.* **44**, 255.
Hess, R. (1973). *Atherogenesis: Initiating Factors, Ciba Found. Symp. N.S.* No. 12, p. 59.
Hess, R., and Staubli, W. (1968). *In* "Atherosclerosis" (F. G. Schettler and G. S. Boyd, eds.), p. 49. Elsevier, Amsterdam.
Holman, R. L. (1961). *Amer. J. Clin. Nutr.* **9**, 565.
Holman, R. L., McGill, H. C., Strong, J. P., and Geer, J. C. (1958). *Amer. J. Pathol.* **34**, 209.
Howard, C. F., and Portman, O. W. (1966). *Biochim. Biophys. Acta* **125**, 623.
Insull, W., and Bartch, G. E. (1966). *J. Clin. Invest.* **45**, 513.
Iverius, P.-H. (1972). *J. Biol. Chem.* **247**, 2607.
Jepson, E. M., Billimoria, J. D., and Maclagan, N. F. (1965). *Clin. Sci.* **29**, 383.
Kao, V. C., and Wissler, R. W. (1965). *Exp. Mol. Pathol.* **4**, 465.
Kayden, H. J., Segal, B. C., and Hus, K. C. (1959). *J. Clin. Invest.* **31**, 1.
Klimov, A. N., Denisenko, A. D., and Magracheva, E. Ya. (1974). *Atherosclerosis* **19**, 243.
Knieriem, H. J., Kao, V. C., and Wissler, R. W. (1967). *Arch. Pathol.* **84**, 118.
Kramsch, D. M., and Hollander, W. (1973). *J. Clin. Invest.* **52**, 236.
Lang, P. D., and Insull, W. (1970). *J. Clin. Invest.* **49**, 1479.
Lindner, J. (1972). *Verh. Deut. Ges. Inn. Med.* **78**, 1166.

Lofland, H. B., and Clarkson, T. B. (1970). *Proc. Soc. Exp. Med. Biol.* **133**, 1.
Lofland, H. B., Moury, D. M., Hoffman, C., and Clarkson, T. B. (1965). *J. Lipid Res.* **6**, 112.
McGill, H. C., ed. (1968). *Lab. Invest.* **18**, 463.
More, R. H., and Haust, M. D. (1957). *Amer. J. Pathol.* **33**, 593.
Newman, H. A. I., and Zilversmit, D. B. (1962). *J. Biol. Chem.* **237**, 2078.
Newman, H. A. I., and Zilversmit, D. B. (1966). *Circ. Res.* **18**, 293.
Ott, H., Lohss, F., and Gergely, J. (1958). *Klin. Wochenschr.* **36**, 383.
Panganamala, R. V., Geer, J. C., Sharma, H. M., and Cornwell, D. G. (1974). *Atherosclerosis* (in press).
Patelski, J., Waligora, Z., and Szulc, S. (1967). *J. Atheroscler. Res.* **7**, 453.
Paterson, J. C., Cornish, B. R., and Armstrong, E. C. (1956). *Circulation* **13**, 224.
Paterson, J. C., Armstrong, R., and Armstrong, E. C. (1963). *Circulation* **27**, 229.
Peters, T. J., Takano, T., and de Duve, C. (1973). *Atherogenesis: Initiating Factors. Ciba Found. Symp., N.S.* No. 12, p. 197.
Portman, O. W. (1970). *Advan. Lipid Res.* **8**, 41.
Portman, O. W., and Alexander, M. (1966). *Arch. Biochem. Biophys.* **117**, 357.
Portman, O. W., and Alexander, M. (1972). *Biochim. Biophys. Acta* **260**, 460.
Rabinowitz, J. L., Myerson, R. M., and Wohl, G. T. (1960). *Proc. Soc. Exp. Biol. Med.* **105**, 241.
Ressler, N. (1960). *Clin. Chim. Acta* **5**, 359.
Robertson, A. L. (1968). *Progr. Biochem. Pharmacol.* **4**, 305.
Roheim, P. S., Haft, D. E., Gidez, L. I., White, A., and Eder, H. A. (1963). *J. Clin. Invest.* **42**, 1277.
St. Clair, R. W., Lofland, H. B., and Clarkson, T. B. (1968). *J. Lipid Res.* **9**, 739.
St. Clair, R. W., Lofland, H. B., and Clarkson, T. B. (1969). *J. Atheroscler. Res.* **10**, 193.
St. Clair, R. W., Lofland, H. B., and Clarkson, T. B. (1970). *Circ. Res.* **27**, 213.
Schoefl, G. I., and French, J. E. (1968). *Proc. Roy. Soc., Ser. B* **169**, 153.
Schwartz, S. M., and Benditt, E. P. (1972). *Amer. J. Pathol.* **66**, 241.
Schwenk, E., and Stevens, D. F. (1960). *Proc. Soc. Exp. Biol. Med.* **103**, 614.
Scott, P. J., and Hurley, P. J. (1970). *Atherosclerosis* **11**, 77.
Small, D. M. (1970). "Surface Chemistry of Biological Systems," p. 55. Plenum, New York.
Smith, E. B. (1960). *Lancet* **i**, 799.
Smith, E. B. (1965a). *J. Atheroscler. Res.* **5**, 224.
Smith, E. B. (1965b). *J. Atheroscler. Res.* **5**, 241.
Smith, E. B. (1971). *Advan. Exp. Med. Biol.* **16A**, 81.
Smith, E. B. (1974). *Advan. Exp. Med. Biol.* **43**, 125.
Smith, E. B., and Slater, R. S. (1970). *Atherosclerosis* **11**, 417.
Smith, E. B., and Slater, R. S. (1971). *Biochem. J.* **123**, 39P.
Smith, E. B., and Slater, R. S. (1972a). *Atherosclerosis* **15**, 37.
Smith, E. B., and Slater, R. S. (1972b). *Lancet* **i**, 463.
Smith, E. B., and Slater, R. S. (1973a). *Atherogenesis: Initiating Factors, Ciba Found. Symp. N.S.* No. 12, p. 39.
Smith, E. B., and Slater, R. S. (1973b). *Nutr. Metab.* **15**, 17.
Smith, E. B., Evans, P. H., and Downham, M. (1967). *J. Atheroscler. Res.* **7**, 171.
Smith, E. B., Slater, R. S., and Chu, P. K. (1968). *J. Atheroscler. Res.* **8**, 399.
Smith, E. B., Slater, R. S., and Hunter, J. N. (1973). *Atherosclerosis* **18**, 479.

Srinivasan, S. R., Lopez-S, A., Radhakrishnamurthy, B., and Berenson, G. S. (1970). *Atherosclerosis* **12,** 321.

Srinivasan, S. R., Dolan, P., Radhakrishnamurthy, B., and Berenson, G. S. (1972). *Atherosclerosis* **16,** 95.

Steele, J. M., and Kayden, H. J. (1955). *Trans. Ass. Amer. Physicians* **66,** 249.

Stein, Y., and Stein, O. (1973). *Atherogenesis: Initiating Factors, Ciba Found. Symp. N.S.* No. 12, p. 165.

Taylor, H. E. (1953). *Amer. J. Pathol.* **29,** 871.

Tracy, R. E., Merchant, E. B., and Kao, V. C. (1961). *Circ. Res.* **9,** 472.

Walton, K. W., and Williamson, N. (1968). *J. Atheroscler. Res.* **8,** 599.

Watts, H. F. (1963). *In* "The Evolution of the Atherosclerotic Plaque" (R. J. Jones, ed.), p. 117. Univ. of Chicago Press, Chicago, Illinois.

Weinhouse, S., and Hirsch, S. (1940). *Arch. Pathol.* **29,** 31.

Whereat, A. F. (1971). *Advan. Lipid. Res.* **9,** 119.

Wilson, J. D. (1970). *J. Clin. Invest.* **49,** 655.

Wissler, R. W., and Vesselinovitch, D. (1968). *Advan. Lipid Res.* **6,** 181.

Woolf, N., and Pilkington, T. R. E. (1965). *J. Pathol. Bacteriol.* **90,** 459.

Zee, P. (1968). *Pediatrics* **41,** 640.

Zemplényi, T. (1964). *Advan. Lipid Res.* **2,** 235.

Zöllner, N., Wolfram, G., Londong, W., and Kirsch, K. (1966). *Klin. Wochenschr.* **44,** 380.

Lipid Metabolism in Cultured Cells[1]

BARBARA V. HOWARD[2,3] AND WILLIAM J. HOWARD[4]

[1] This review was aided by Grants RR-107 and AM-14526 from the National Institutes of Health.

[2] Address correspondence to: Clinical Research Center, Philadelphia General Hospital, Philadelphia, Pennsylvania 19104.

[3] Department of Biochemistry, School of Dental Medicine, Department of Microbiology, School of Medicine, University of Pennsylvania and the Clinical Research Center, Philadelphia General Hospital, Philadelphia, Pennsylvania.

[4] Department of Medicine, School of Medicine, University of Pennsylvania and the Clinical Research Center, Philadelphia General Hospital, Philadelphia, Pennsylvania.

I. Introduction

Since the subject of lipids in cell cultures was last reviewed in this series (Rothblat, 1969), the studies involving lipid metabolism in cell cultures have progressed both in depth and in scope. In considering basic questions of lipid biochemistry, advances have been made in understanding the mechanisms of uptake of lipids into cells, and in the investigation of pathways of lipid metabolism and their regulation. In addition to these basic advances, the thrust in this field is now also directed toward the study of lipids and their function in cultures of differentiated cells, and toward the application of the methodology to clinically oriented problems.

This review will consider basic studies of lipid metabolism in cells in culture and the major expansions that the field has taken into areas of differentiated cells and clinical problems. Most of the studies cited in this review were reported between 1969 and 1973. This chapter is limited to animal cells and does not include studies on the changes in lipid metabolism in cell cultures induced by viral infection. This latter topic has been recently reviewed (Blough and Tiffany, 1973).

II. Methodology

A consideration of the methodology of cell culture and lipid chemistry is beyond the scope of this chapter and the reader is referred to recent texts by Kruse and Patterson (1973) for the former and by Johnson and Davenport (1971) for the latter. It is pertinent at the start, however, to emphasize the advantages and the disadvantages of the cell culture system.

Cell culture is a useful system for biochemical studies because it provides a source of large, homogeneous populations of cells. Experimental conditions can be more easily manipulated to allow quantitative experiments. Moreover, cells are isolated from the hormonal and other superimposed physiological regulations of cells *in situ*.

On the other hand, one must consider that there is a constant selection and, therefore, a genetic drift in the population being studied. The mode of culture and the choice of artificial medium can be sources of variation in the enzymology and metabolism of cultured cells (de Luca, 1966). Moreover, variations in metabolism occur with changes in cell density and with the cell cycle (Griffiths, 1972). Finally, since the cells grow in suspension or in monolayer cultures, they lack the anatomic organization and spatial regulation which exists *in vivo*.

One aspect of methodology which must be considered is the use of lipid-free medium. Cell culture media generally contain serum or other biological fluids as necessary supplements. Therefore, the study of uptake or the regulation of lipid metabolism often necessitates the development of serum-free or lipid-free media, and these conditions often impose limitations on cell growth (Table I). One approach has been the use of chemically-defined synthetic culture media. These media are usually extremely complex and are only applicable to the most hardy, established cell lines. Often the generation time obtained is quite high, and in most cases, sublines of the cells must be selected before growth occurs (Takaoka and Katsuta, 1971). Since in most cases the growth promoting factors in serum are protein in nature (Temin *et al.*, 1972), the other approach has been to supplement the medium with serum proteins from which part or all of the lipid has been removed. Some culture media simply utilize defatted serum albumin (Maca and Connor, 1971). Another method consists of removing the lipoproteins from the serum by flotation (Holmes *et al.*, 1969; Watson, 1972). The resultant lipoprotein-poor serum (LPPS) is relatively free of sterols and glycerides, but contains albumin and free fatty acids. The most widely used method is the supplementation of medium with delipidized serum protein, that is, serum from which the lipid has been extracted, usually by the method of Albutt (1966). This has been useful for both established and fibroblast lines, and the generation time of the cells cultured in this medium has been similar to that in serum-supplemented medium (Rothblat *et al.*, 1971; Dunbar, 1972). Finally, a defined medium including methocel has been described for the suspension culture of L-cells (Lengle and Geyer, 1972). Although the generation time obtained was 72 hours, lipid composition was found to be normal under these conditions.

Table I

Types of Lipid-Free Media in Use for Studies of Lipids in Cell Culture

Medium	Characteristics	Type of cell	References
Synthetic + lipoprotein-poor serum	Contains albumin-bound free fatty acid; applicable mainly to studies of cholesterol metabolism	Diploid fibroblasts HTC cells	Holmes *et al.* (1969); Watson (1972)
Synthetic + albumin	Requires adaptation of cells to this medium	Mouse fibroblasts	Maca and Conner (1971)
NCTC 135 without fat soluble vitamins	Requires adaptation of cells to this medium	L-2071	Raff (1970); Howard and Bailey (1973)
Synthetic + delipidized serum protein	Applicable to wide range of cells; adaptation not usually necessary	L-5178Y WI-38 Skin fibroblasts Ehrlich ascites	Rothblat *et al.* (1968) Rothblat *et al.* (1971) Jacobs *et al.* (1973) Dunbar (1972)
Synthetic + cellulose derivatives	For suspension cultures	LS cells Littlefield strain L	Birch and Pirt (1971) Lengle and Geyer (1972)
DM-120	Extensive period of adaptation required	10 cell lines including rat liver, L and HeLa	Takaoka and Katsuka (1971)
Synthetic + glycoprotein supplements	Supplements probably contain lipids	Mammary-tumor lines	Lasfargues *et al.* (1973)

III. Fatty Acids

A. Fatty Acid Uptake

The uptake of fatty acids has been extensively studied in Ehrlich ascites tumor cells *in vivo* and *in vitro,* and this topic has been recently reviewed by Spector (1971). The initial step in fatty acid utilization is a rapid binding to sites on the cell membrane. This occurs by rapid, reversible adsorption followed by entry into a nonexchangeable cellular pool. The main factor that regulates the uptake of fatty acids by these cells is the fatty acid/albumin molar ratio. The rate of uptake increases with increasing fatty acid chain length and is decreased by increasing the degree of fatty acid unsaturation. This rate is also increased by decreasing the pH and by the addition of calcium ions.

Recent work on the uptake of fatty acids has centered around the mechanism of entry of fatty acid into the nonexchangeable cellular pool. When fatty acid methyl esters (Kuhl and Spector, 1970) or the analog hexadecanol (Spector and Soboroff, 1972) were used, these compounds were both incorporated into the exchangeable and nonexchangeable pools, as determined by their availability for release to a medium containing albumin. The data, therefore, support the hypothesis that fatty acids enter the cellular metabolic pool by a nonenzymatic process such as diffusion. Cellular utilization of free fatty acids has also been studied using free fatty acids complexed to plasma lipoproteins (Spector and Soboroff, 1971). In these studies, the mechanism of uptake involved the transfer of fatty acids from low density lipoprotein to the cell surface and then to intracellular lipid pools in a manner similar to that observed for free fatty acids bound to albumin. These investigations clearly indicate that fatty acids which naturally occur complexed to lipoproteins, or which are released after action of lipoprotein lipase, are also available for uptake by cells.

B. Metabolism of Fatty Acids

It had been established earlier that fatty acids taken up by the cell can be oxidized and esterified to form intracellular triglyceride stores (Geyer, 1967; MacKenzie *et al.*, 1967). Recently, there has been an attempt to localize the site and pathway of fatty acid synthesis in cultured cells. Pedersen *et al.* (1972) have presented evidence that the predominant pathway for fatty acid synthesis in Ehrlich ascites tumor cells *in vitro* is the cytoplasmic CO_2/HCO_3 dependent path. Incorporation of ^{14}C

acetate into fatty acids was investigated in a particle-free supernatant fraction of the cells. It was dependent on an NADPH regenerating system and CO_2 tension, and a stimulatory effect of glucose on this system was observed. These studies indicate the usefulness of cell cultures for elucidating the role and interaction of cofactors in fatty acid synthesis.

The effect of B_{12} deficiency on fatty acid metabolism has also been investigated. The data of Barley *et al.* (1972) indicate that as the intracellular B_{12} concentration decreases, cells make increasing amounts of unbranched fatty acids with 15 and 17 carbon atoms. This process utilizes propionyl-CoA for fatty acid biosynthesis, since the cells are unable to metabolize propionic acid via B_{12}-requiring methylmalonyl-CoA mutase. These experiments point to the possible importance of fatty acid metabolism in B_{12} deficiency diseases.

C. Control of Fatty Acid Synthesis

Cell cultures are particularly useful for studying the regulation of lipid biosynthesis. In addition to avoiding the complex physiological interactions imposed on cells *in vivo*, cell culture systems allow the investigation of both short and long–term regulatory mechanisms. Jacobs *et al.* (1973) have investigated the regulation of fatty acid biosynthesis in human skin fibroblast cultures. An elevation in the activity of the enzyme acetyl-CoA carboxylase was observed in cells cultured in lipid-deficient medium, as compared to control cells cultured in serum-supplemented medium. They determined, by equivalence point assays using antibody against acetyl-CoA carboxylase, that this increase was the result of elevated enzyme synthesis. When the time course of induction and repression of enzyme activity was studied, the changes in the enzyme occurred over a two to three-day period after alteration in exogenous fatty acid supply. However, when acetate incorporation into fatty acid was determined after cells were transferred to and from serum-supplemented medium, an 8-fold increase in activity was observed within 7 hours, and the time course of inhibition was even more rapid. These results indicated a regulation of acetyl-CoA carboxylase occurred in the pathway of fatty acid biosynthesis, but that additional points of control might also be operative.

Howard and Bailey (1973) have studied the enzyme acetyl-CoA synthetase in L cells cultured in the presence and absence of exogenous serum lipid. A 4- to 6-fold increase in enzyme activity was observed in cells cultured in lipid-free medium, as opposed to the level in cells cultured in serum-supplemented medium. A rapid time course of stimulation and inhibition of enzyme activity was observed upon change in exogenous lipid supply; moreover, the stimulation and inhibition of enzyme activity seemed insensitive to inhibitors of macromolecule synthesis. These studies point to a possible regulatory role for this enzyme in the biosynthesis of fatty acid from acetate in cultured cells.

Raff (1970) has studied the regulation of fatty acid synthesis in L cells using ^{14}C glucose as a precursor. Removal of exogenous lipids caused an increase in glucose incorporation into fatty acids after a 6-hour lag period. This stimulation was sensitive to cycloheximide, suggesting that the site of control operative in this case is at the enzyme acetyl-CoA carboxylase in a manner similar to that observed by Jacobs *et al.* (1973). Since glucose is metabolized directly to acetyl-CoA, it bypasses the step of acetate activation. Nevertheless, the question of what controls are operative in the regulation of cellular fatty acid biosynthesis requires further study, and it remains to be elucidated which enzyme is rate-limiting and functionally most significant.

An interesting question can be raised concerning a possible regulatory effect of serum on fatty acid synthesis. It has been reported by Williams and Avigan (1972) that acetate incorporation into fatty acids and sterols is stimulated in fibroblasts cultured in the presence of solvent-extracted serum. Bailey and Keller (1971) have observed that when cells are transferred to hyperlipoproteinemic serum which has an elevated lipid content, there is an increase in fatty acid synthesis that is diverted primarily to the esterification of cholesterol. It remains to be determined in both of these studies whether the effect of the serum is a primary one or simply due to a perturbation of cell lipid transport or flux.

D. Polyunsaturated Fatty Acids

Animals maintained on fat-free diets develop deficiency symptoms that can be cured by the administration of certain polyunsaturated fatty acids referred to as essential fatty acids (EFA). The function of these compounds at the cellular level can be conveniently examined using cell cultures. Earlier studies with some cell lines indicated an EFA requirement for growth and normal function (Gerschenson *et al.*, 1967; Ham, 1963; Harary *et al.*, 1967). In contrast to these findings, there have been recent reports that a large number of cells cultured in lipid-free medium can grow and metabolize normally and contain no detectable amounts of essential fatty acids in the cell lipids. Ten cell lines were cultivated in lipid-free medium by Takaoka and Katsuta (1971). Essential fatty acids were not found in these cultures; the content of monounsaturated fatty acid increased, and growth parameters and mitochondrial function were unimpaired. In addition, L cells cultured in a number of essential fatty acid-free media have been reported to grow adequately in the absence of polyunsaturated fatty acids (Lengle and Geyer, 1972; Geyer, 1967; Evans *et al.*, 1965).

Bailey and Dunbar (1971, 1973) have studied essential fatty acid requirements in Ehrlich ascites cells cultured *in vitro* and in essential fatty acid-deficient mice. In both situations, the EFA-deficient cultures had normal growth rates and their morphological appearance both by light and electron microscopy is indistinguishable from controls. Respiratory and mitochondrial functions were not significantly different from controls. Cells cultured *in vitro* contained no EFA and those *in vivo* contained the unusual polyunsaturates eicosatrienoic (20:3) and docosatrienoic (22:3) acid. These workers concluded that EFA were not essential for the function of individual cells and that the requirement for essential fatty acids *in vivo* is related to their role as precursors of the prostaglandins.

IV. Glycerides

A. Uptake of Glycerides

Although free fatty acids are often the primary source of cultured cell lipids (Howard and Kritchevsky, 1969b; MacKenzie *et al.*, 1967), several studies have indicated that exogenous glycerides are also used by cells. Bailey *et al.* (1959) demonstrated by early balance studies a depletion of triglycerides by densely growing MBIII cells. MacKenzie *et al.* (1970), in fractionating serum to determine the localization of lipogenic activity, observed some intracellular triglyceride accumulation in response to the exposure of the cells to the serum fraction with density less than 1.063 and the fraction with density between 1.063 to 1.21. Triglyceride accumulation has been studied directly in L cells (Bailey *et al.*, 1973). The cells were able to take up triglycerides although the rate of accumulation was less than that of free fatty acids or monoglycerides (Fig. 1). When doubly-labeled triglycerides were used to study the mechanism of uptake, some lipolytic activity was observed in fetal bovine serum. However, the majority of the triglycerides were taken up intact and converted to phospholipid without prior hydrolysis. Essentially similar results have been reported by Spector and Brenneman (1973) who studied the uptake of triglycerides from very low density lipoproteins (VLDL) by Ehrlich ascites tumor cells. Their data indicated that the majority of the uptake did not result from adsorption or incorporation of whole VLDL mole-

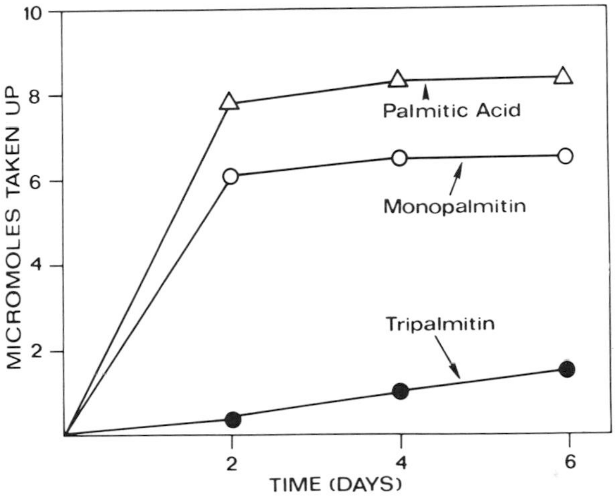

FIG. 1. Relative incorporation of fatty acid, monoglyceride, and triglyceride by L cells. From Bailey *et al.* (1973). L-929 cells were grown to confluency in Minimal Essential Medium (Eagle) supplemented with 5% delipidized fetal calf serum containing either [carboxyl-^{14}C] tripalmitin, [carboxy-^{14}C] monopalmitin, or sodium [$^{14}C_1$] palmitate. Each lipid was added at a concentration of 5 μg/ml of medium. Radioactivity was determined at the indicated times in medium and extracted cell lipids.

cules. Moreover, only approximately 10% of the triglyceride was hydrolyzed before uptake.

A major problem in lipid uptake studies concerns the method of combining the radioactive or nonradioactive lipid with protein to produce a functionally native configuration (Rothblat, 1972). It is interesting to note that the studies performed on triglyceride accumulation in L cells, when the glycerides were dissolved in ether and added to delipidized serum protein, and the studies with the Ehrlich ascites cells, when triglycerides were added to VLDL by exchange on Celite, yielded similar results and led to the hypothesis of similar mechanisms.

The uptake of monoglycerides by cells in culture has been studied recently by Lynch and Geyer (1972). Cells incubated with *rac*-glycerol-1-oleate in a medium containing 10% horse serum formed cytoplasmic lipid particles containing primarily glycerol trioleate. This accumulation could be accounted for by the utilization of fatty acid liberated by the action of a serum esterase present in the medium. When this esterase was inhibited, 70% of the monoglyceride was incorporated into the cells intact. The rate of accumulation in both cases was similar, and in both cases the monoglyceride was converted intracellularly to triglyceride and phospholipid.

B. Metabolism of Glycerides

The earlier work on lipid metabolism in cultured cells indicated that triglyceride droplets were a storage form for exogenous fatty acids which accumulated and were not required for energy or phospholipid synthesis. There seemed to be no cellular mechanism to limit the uptake of fatty acids or prevent the overproduction of intracellular triglycerides (Rothblat, 1969). Geyer and Neimark (1959) had also established that glycerol triolein and glycerol tripalmitin could be converted to CO_2 by cell lines, establishing that triglycerides can serve as a source of free fatty acids to meet the energy requirements of the cell. During studies of lipases in L cells, Lengle and Geyer (1973) found that 80% of the lipolytic activity in these cells was associated with a lipase with a pH optimum of 6.5. This lipase, associated with the soluble fraction of the cell, has been extensively characterized and does not fit the criteria usually used to differentiate the three classic lipases (pancreatic, hormone-sensitive, and lipoprotein lipase). Two other minor lipases were also observed in the cells. The total lipolytic activity measured in the cells was found to be sufficient to account for the rate of removal of intracellular lipid droplets in growing L cells and for the exchange of acyl groups observed between lipid droplets (Schneeberger *et al.*, 1971).

Although several alternative pathways exist for glyceride assembly and interconversions in animal cells (Spector, 1972) this question has not been extensively investigated in cell cultures. Agranoff and Hajra (1971) have studied the acyl-dihydroxyacetone phosphate (DHAP) pathway for glycerolipid synthesis in Ehrlich ascites cells. Their data indicate that a significant fraction of the glycerides and phospholipids in these cells is synthesized via esterification of DHAP followed by reduction of the keto group. The data of Bailey *et al.* (1973) suggest that triglycerides are converted to phospholipids via a 1,2-diglyceride intermediate, rather than by the acylation of 1-glycerol-3-phosphate, suggesting that this pathway may play a role in glyceride metabolism of cultured cells. The data of Lengle and Geyer (1973) showed a rapid acylation of monoglyceride via 1, 3-diacylglycerol which was subsequently converted to 1, 2-diglyceride. This observation demonstrates a potential transacylation capability in cultured cells.

V. Sterols

Cholesterol is probably the most extensively studied lipid in cell culture, and cholesterol metabolism in cultured cells has been recently reviewed (Rothblat, 1972). To prevent duplication, therefore, the results of studies conducted during the last four years will be summarized in the present chapter with the exception of two topics: the regulation of sterol biosynthesis, and the action of sterols other than cholesterol in cultured cells. In brief, the intracellular sterol pool is the result of three processes—uptake, excretion, and *de novo* synthesis. The rate of uptake and excretion are the function of exogenous sterol/protein and sterol/phospholipid ratios (Rothblat *et al.*, 1968; Burns and Rothblat, 1969). It is proposed that β-lipoproteins regulate uptake and α-lipoproteins regulate excretion. The cell's primary response to changes in flux is at the level of synthesis. Sterol synthesis is efficiently regulated and responses in synthetic rates are rapid (Sokoloff and Rothblat, 1972). Sterol esters are also taken up by cells, but the rates of incorporation may be slower, in the case of some cells such as the L cell, than that of free sterol. Cellular metabolism of cholesterol esters consists primarily of the hydrolysis and liberation of the fatty acids, which then serve as carbon and energy sources, and cholesterol which enters the sterol pool (Rothblat, 1972).

An interesting investigation of the effect of hyperlipemic rabbit serum on sterol accumulation has been reported by Bailey and Keller (1971). They observed a 4-fold increase in cellular levels of cholesterol and a 20-fold increase in cholesterol esters when cells were transferred to medium supplemented with this serum. This accumulation is probably related to the increased cholesterol/protein ratio in the serum. Moreover, a significant proportion of the cholesterol was converted to cholesterol ester, often accompanied by increased fatty acid synthesis. This indicates a coordination of sterol and fatty acid metabolism which might play a significant role in cellular responses to increased exogenous lipid supply.

A. Regulation of Cholesterol Biosynthesis

There has been considerable interest in the regulation of cholesterol biosynthesis in cultured cells. Although differences in levels of cholesterol biosynthesis are observed in livers from cholesterol-fed and fasted animals, no stimulation or inhibition of sterol synthesis is observed when cholesterol is added to cell-free preparations (Sabine, 1973). In addition, there have been reports of a deficiency in the feedback inhibition of cholesterol biosynthesis in tumors exposed to exogenous cholesterol (Siperstein and Fagan, 1966). These studies have stimulated the investigation of the regulation of cholesterol biosynthesis in tumor cells in culture (see Section XI).

Bailey (1967) was the first to observe that there is an inhibition of the incorporation of glucose and acetate into cholesterol of L cells cultured in serum-supplemented as opposed to serum-free medium. No inhibition of cholesterol synthesis was observed when mevalonic acid was used as a precursor, suggesting that the regulation of the process occurred at the level of the enzyme β-hydroxy-β-methylglutaryl (HMG)-CoA reductase. A similar regulatory point has been observed in response to changes in exogenous lipid supply in diploid fibroblast lines (Avigan *et al.*, 1970; Rothblat *et al.*, 1971), their transformed derivative (Rothblat *et al.*, 1971) and a hepatoma line (HTC) (Watson, 1972). The site and mechanism of regulation has been studied by Watson (1973). He found alterations in HMG-CoA reductase activity which corresponded temporally to the regulation of cholesterol synthesis from acetate and ^3H_2O in HTC cells when the exogenous cholesterol supply was altered. The stimulation of the enzyme regulating sterol synthesis was completely eliminated by cycloheximide, indicating a protein synthesis-dependent regulation of the enzyme was occurring (Kirsten and Watson, 1973).

The data of Howard and Bailey (1973) concerning the possible regulation at the level of acetate activation would apply to cholesterol synthesis when acetate is used as a precursor. Watson, however, observed a similar time course in the regulation of cholesterol biosynthesis using either ^{14}C acetate or ^3H_2O. Therefore, the relative importance of this regulatory site for cholesterol biosynthesis in these cells remains to be elucidated. The nature of the compound active in the inhibition of cholesterol synthesis has been studied only with respect to the whole cell response. In this case, the regulatory compound seems to be cholesterol, either free or bound to lipoproteins (Rothblat and Buchko, 1971; Watson, 1973). There is no information, however, concerning the existence of an intracellular cholesterol complex or derivative which influences sterol biosynthesis. A stimulatory effect by serum protein on cholesterol biosynthesis has been reported (Avigan *et al.*, 1970; Williams and Avigan, 1972). This stimulation was observed using both ^3H_2O and ^{14}C acetate as precursors, and the data suggest that the effect is not simply due to depletion of intracellular sterol pools. Moreover, a sterol carrier protein has been reported active in cholesterol synthesis in liver (Ritter and Dempsey, 1973). These observations indicate the importance of further studies concerning the nature of the intracellular effectors of induction and repression of sterol synthesis in cultured cells.

B. Metabolism of Sterols Other than Cholesterol

It has been reported that the principal sterol synthesized by L cells is desmosterol (Rothblat *et al.*, 1970). Cholesterol was not detected in these cells when they were grown in a sterol-free medium; this is probably a result of sterol Δ^{24}-reductase loss. When L cells were fused with different human cells that synthesize cholesterol, the lipids were reductase positive (Croce *et al.*, 1974), and the gene for reductase activity appeared to be localized on the F-20 chromosome. This is the first, hopefully of many, applications of the methodology of genetics to the study of lipid metabolism in cell cultures.

The role of other sterols in the metabolism of cholesterol by cultured cells has also been studied. Wilton (1971) has described the biosynthesis of cholesta-8, 14-dien-3β-ol by Chang liver cells in culture, indicating that cholesterol synthesis in these cells occurs via removal of the Δ-methyl group before reduction of the double bond at the 4 position. Comparative studies have been conducted on the metabolism of a number of steroids and sterols in cell cultures (Rothblat and Buchko, 1971). Cholesterol, desmosterol, lathosterol, 7-dehydrocholesterol, and cholestanone reduced *de novo* sterol synthesis and produced only limited toxicity when present in the medium at high concentrations. Significant cellular toxicity is observed when cells are grown in the presence of coprostanol and Δ-4-cholestenone. No effect on either cell growth or sterol biosynthesis is produced by cholestanol, β-sitosterol, stigmasterol, campesterol, ergosterol, cholesteryl oleate, or cholestane. However, Avigan *et al.* (1970) have shown that stigmasterol, β-sitosterol, and cholestanol, when present in the incubation medium at concentrations 5–40 times greater than in the aforementioned experiments, can affect sterol biosynthesis in skin fibroblast cultures. Direct studies have been conducted on the cellular metabolism of cholesterol, cholestanol, and β-sitosterol (Rothblat and Burns, 1971). The rate of cellular uptake of cholesterol was found to be greater than that of cholestanol, and β-sitosterol was accumulated at a much lower rate. No metabolic products arose from any of these sterols. Failure to elicit feedback could be due to a lower rate of uptake in the case of β-sitosterol. In the case of cholestanol, when concentrations of sterol were adjusted to yield equal intracellular sterol levels, no difference in feedback was observed (Rothblat, 1973). These studies with various sterols indicate a potentially valuable approach to the elucidation of mechanisms involved in sterol uptake and feedback regulation.

VI. Phospholipids

Phospholipid metabolism is of central importance to cells because of their occurrence in membranes and, therefore, their relation to cell division. Yet progress in the field of phospholipid metabolism has been slow because of the complexity of the phospholipid subclasses and the difficulty of the methodology. Studies have been initiated on phospholipid metabolism and on phospholipid uptake by cells. There have also been some attempts to explore the cellular function of these compounds.

A. Uptake of Phospholipids

There have been few studies of phospholipid uptake by cells in culture. There is some indirect evidence that cultured cells can take up phospholipids. Bailey *et al.* (1959) observed a 50% depletion of serum phospholipid by dense cultures of MBIII cells and the data of MacKenzie *et al.* (1970), suggest that glycerides or phospholipids from serum lipoproteins act as precursors for the cell's polar lipids. The mechanism of the cellular uptake of phospholipids remains to be elucidated. Peterson and Rubin (1969, 1970) have shown that chick embryo fibroblasts continuously release phospholipid into the growth medium and reabsorb them; they also observed exchange of phospholipid between membrane structures of adjacent cells. Moreover, these phospholipid transfers, as examined by autoradiography, appeared to represent intact phospholipid molecules. Other evidence for uptake of intact phospholipid by mammalian cells comes from studies of red blood cells (Reed, 1968; Marcus and Cass, 1969). The mechanism of cellular uptake of phospholipids in cultured cells has not been studied directly. Elsbach (1965) has demonstrated the incorporation of phospholipids by alveolar macrophages by phagocytosis, and Patriarca *et al.* (1972) have established that microbial phospholipids can be engulfed and utilized by granulocytes. It is an open question, however, whether phagocytosis plays a significant role in the uptake of phospholipids by cells in culture, and the observations of Peterson and Rubin (1969, 1970) previously described, would suggest that direct lipoprotein-cell membrane interactions are operative.

B. Phospholipid Biosynthesis

There are three main paths for phosphatide synthesis in mammalian cells: the *de novo* path via phosphatidic acid, the incorporation of fatty acids onto lysophosphatide, and a condensation of two lysophosphatide molecules (see review by Spector, 1972). Studies of phospholipid synthesis in cultured cells by Pasternak and Bergeron (1970) suggest that the *de novo* pathway predominates. The recent work of Gallagher *et al.* (1973) suggests that acyltransferases also influence phospholipid turnover via the monoacyl-diacylphosphoglyceride pathway (see Section VI,C). Finally, Agranoff and Hajra (1971) have reported a significant occurrence of the acyl-DHAP pathway for glycerolipid biosynthesis in

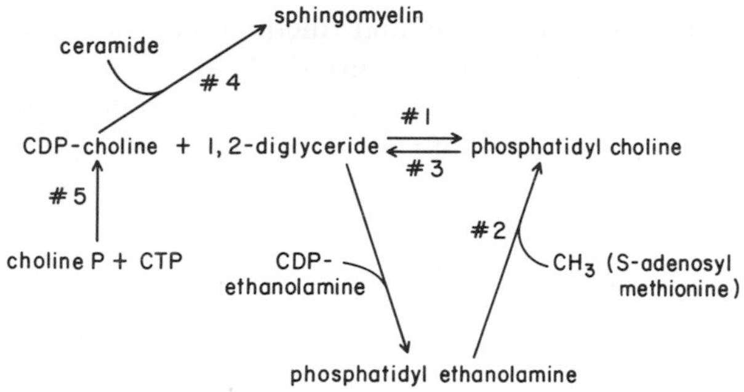

FIG. 2. Pathways for interconversion of phospholipid subclasses in cultured cells. The numbers indicate pathways referred to in Sections VI,B,C and IX,G of the text.

Ehrlich ascites cells. In this route, phospholipids are synthesized by reduction of the keto group of acyl-DHAP followed by a second acylation that yields phosphatidic acid.

There have been direct studies on the routes of phosphatidyl choline synthesis in cell cultures. Plagemann (1971) has established that choline is incorporated into phosphatidyl choline of rat hepatoma cells via conversion to cytidine diphosphate (CDP) choline (Fig. 2, #1). An alternative pathway for phosphatidyl choline synthesis in mammalian cells, via phosphatidyl ethanolamine (Fig. 2, #2), utilizes the methyl donor S-adenosyl methionine (Bremer and Greenberg, 1960). The relative importance of this pathway in cultured cells is not clear. The early work of Donisch and Rossiter (1965) indicated that there is significant synthesis of phosphatidyl choline via methylation of phosphatidyl ethanolamine in Ehrlich ascites tumor cells. However, Rytter and Cornatzer (1972) have studied this pathway for synthesis of phosphatidyl choline in HeLa, KB cells, and Ehrlich ascites cells using choline-^{14}C and ethanolamine-^{14}C; they concluded that the methylation pathway for the synthesis of phospholipids had a low activity in their cells. On the other hand, Sinclair (1971) has observed that this pathway occurs in Ehrlich ascites tumor cells. These workers also reported that phosphatidyl choline synthesis is reversible (Fig. 2, #3), yielding CDP-choline from phosphatidyl choline. More studies are required of lecithin synthesis in various cell types to resolve this conflict.

Sphingolipid synthesis has also been studied in cultured cells. Diringer *et al.* (1972) studied sphingomyelin synthesis in SV40-transformed mouse cells using choline-^{32}P and -^{3}H, and their data indicate that sphingomyelin is synthesized via transfer of phosphoryl choline from lecithin to sphingosine. This observation could be explained by the work of Sinclair (1971). Using Ehrlich ascites tumor cells, Sinclair observed the transfer of radioactive label from ethanolamine and methionine into sphingomyelin. Therefore, he proposed that this occurred via the methylation pathway from phosphatidyl ethanolamine to phosphatidyl choline (Fig. 2, #2), followed by the direct removal of CDP-choline from phosphatidyl choline (Fig. 2, #3), which could then participate directly in the synthesis of sphingomyelin (Fig. 2, #4). Their studies, in addition to elucidating pathways for sphingomyelin synthesis, point to the possible importance of separate pools of phosphatidyl choline in cell cultures.

C. Turnover of Phospholipids and Regulation of Synthesis

The turnover of phospholipids has been the concern of a number of investigators who are interested in phospholipid metabolism in cell cultures. Pasternak and Bergeron (1970) have studied the turnover of phospholipids using long pulses of radioactive precursor in cells cultured in the presence of serum. Their results indicate two classes of phospholipids, "the unstable," consisting primarily of phosphatidyl choline, and a "stable" class containing most of the sphingomyelin. They calculated the half-life of phosphatidyl choline to be 18–24 hours in mastocytoma cells. This figure agrees with the data of Plagemann (1971) who studied phosphatidyl choline turnover in Novikoff rat hepatoma cells. However, when short pulses (approximately 1 hour or less) of two labeled phospholipid precursors, glycerol-2-^{3}H, and acetate-^{14}C were used (Gallagher *et al.*, 1973), the results indicated a half-life of 2 to 2½ hours for certain phospholipids in BHK21 cells and chick embryo fibroblasts. Also, when studied using short pulses of radioactive precursors, the turnover rates of all phospholipids were not the same (Blough and Tiffany, 1973). These workers report turnover rates as low as 7½ minutes for some phospholipids and their data indicated that there are multiple turnover rates, not only between phospholipid classes, but also within each class. These workers postulate that the monoacyl-diacyl phosphoglyceride cycle is important in this rapid turnover process. The significance of these rapid turnover rates awaits further studies.

Almost all of the phospholipids that exist in cells are associated with cell membrane structures; it is now clear that membrane structures are intimately involved with DNA replication in mammalian cells (Mizuno *et al.*, 1971; Hanaoka and Yamada, 1971) indicating a possible role for phospholipids in the regulation of cell division. It is, therefore, of interest to study phospholipid synthesis during the cell cycle and to attempt to coordinate phospholipid metabolism with cell division. Bossmann and Winston (1970) have examined the synthesis of glycolipids, glycoproteins, lipids, and proteins in synchronized L-5178Y cells. Lipids and glycolipids were found to be synthesized and excreted primarily in the G_2 and M phases of the cell cycle; however, none were synthesized in G_1 and S phases. On the other hand, phospholipids are found to be synthesized throughout the cell cycle in neoplastic mast cells (Bergeron *et al.*, 1970) and the phospholipid content of these cells doubles during the S phase. The rate of phospholipid synthesis was found to begin to increase during G_1 in these cells (Warmsley and Pasternak, 1970). Thus phospholipid metabolism undoubtedly varies with the cell cycle, but present studies do not reveal a consistent pattern nor a direct relation to DNA synthesis.

A more consistent pattern emerges from a variety of studies that demonstrate a stimulation of phospholipid turnover following the initiation of cell division. These studies are summarized in Table II. Some of the studies have been performed on cultured lymphocytes (see Section IX,A). Resch and Ferber (1970) monitored choline-^{14}C, oleate-^{14}C, and acetate-^{14}C incorporation into phospholipids of stimulated lymphocytes. After treatment with three different stimulators of mitosis, they observed a 2- to 3-fold stimulation of general lipid biosynthesis. In addition, there was a 33-fold stimulation of acetate incorporation into phospholipids, suggesting that the stimulation of phospholipid synthesis was associated with early changes in the membrane that occur upon mitogenic stimulation. In further studies of cultured lymphocytes stimulated by phytohemagglutinin (PHA) (Nelson and Scribney, 1972), phosphorylcholine-glyceride transferase (Figure 2, #1) was found to be rate-limiting in the synthesis of lecithin. The changes in phospholipid synthesis that occurred following the stimulation of mitosis could be correlated with changes in this enzyme. The regulation seemed to occur at the level of new enzyme synthesis, since cycloheximide and actinomycin D inhibited this response. Finally, Lucas *et al.* (1971) reported a stimulation of phosphate incorporation into phosphatidyl inositol in lymphocytes by PHA that correlated with stimulation of DNA synthesis and induction of agglutination. They concluded that the stimulation of phosphatidyl inositol synthesis was a direct consequence of mitogenic stimulation.

In monolayer cultures of established cell lines, recent studies associate phospholipid metabolism with cell population density and contact inhibition. Cunningham (1972) has examined phospholipid patterns in growing, density-inhibited and serum-stimulated 3T3 cells. He found that there was no change in total ^{32}P incorporation into phospholipids after confluency. Upon stimulation of cell division, there were rapid increases in the turnover of all phospholipids within the first 2 hours. Diringer and Koch (1973) have reported pulse-chase experiments on mouse fibroblasts using glycerol-^{3}H and-^{32}P that revealed a decreased

Table II

STUDIES WHICH SHOW ALTERATIONS OF PHOSPHOLIPID TURNOVER UPON CELL STIMULATION

Cell	Stimulant	Phospholipid stimulated	Reference
Lymphocytes	Mitogenic stimulants	All phospholipids	Resch and Ferber (1970)
Lymphocytes	Phytohemagglutinin	Phosphorylcholine-glyceride transferase	Nelson and Scribney (1972)
3T3	Serum	All phospholipids	Cunningham (1972)
Lymphocytes	Phytohemagglutinin	Phosphatidyl inositol	Lucas *et al.* (1971)
Mouse embryo fibroblasts	Low population density	Phosphatidyl inositol and phosphatidyl ethanolamine	Diringer and Koch (1973)
3T3	Serum	Phosphatidyl inositol	Pasternak (1972)

turnover of phosphatidyl inositol and an inhibition of phosphatidyl ethanolamine synthesis in densely packed cells, as opposed to cutures of low population density. This data correlates with a study by Pasternak (1972) that showed that phospholipid turnover, especially that of phosphatidyl inositol, is stimulated when the contact inhibition of confluent 3T3 cells is removed by serum.

While various aspects of phospholipid metabolism seem to increase upon stimulation of division in cultured cells, the most consistent observation is a rapid enhancement of phosphatidyl inositol turnover (Lucas *et al.*, 1971; Diringer and Koch, 1973; Pasternak, 1972). Similarly, enhanced phosphoinositide turnover is observed upon stimulation of nervous and secretory tissue *in vivo*. The *in vivo* studies have been correlated by Lapetina and Mitchell (1973) who propose the occurrence of a phosphinositide cycle. This involves a cleavage of phosphatidyl inositol to diglyceride and cyclic inositol phosphate (myoinositol-1,2-cyclic phosphate). Cell culture studies should prove useful for the elucidation of the function of this compound and the metabolic significance of phosphoinositide turnover.

D. Role of Phospholipids in Cell Membranes

There is very little phospholipid in cells that is not associated with membrane, indicating a primary role of phospholipids in cell membrane function. Recent developments in methodology have allowed the isolation, and thus the characterization of various membrane components of cultured cells (Warren *et al.*, 1966). Several recent reports on cell membrane lipid composition are summarized in Table III. The lipid composition of cell membranes is similar to total cell lipid except there is an enrichment of the phospholipid and sterol components. Sokoloff and Rothblat (1973) have determined cholesterol/phospholipid molar ratios of the surface membrane fractions of L cells under different culture conditions. They found that although cell phospholipid is constant, cholesterol can vary more than 2-fold, depending on exogenous cholesterol supply. Renkonen *et al.* (1972) have separated cell membranes into three types based on their composition; the endoplasmic reticulum, nuclear and outer cell membranes are one class, the inner mitochondrial membrane comprises the second class, and the plasma membrane is the third.

In addition to studies discussed in Section VI,C on phospholipid turnover, which most certainly are related to membrane function, there have been other isolated studies on the role of phospholipids in the membranes of cultured cells. Goshima (1971) has reported that the beating

Table III
STUDIES OF LIPID COMPOSITION OF MEMBRANES IN CULTURED CELLS

Cell	Lipids studied	Reference
L-929	Neutral lipids, phospholipids, and fatty acids of plasma membrane compared to whole cell	Weinstein (1968)
Chick embryo fibroblasts	Phospholipids in plasma membrane compared to whole cells	Quigley *et al.* (1971)
Rat liver parenchyma	Phospholipids, sterols, and sialic acid of density gradient fractions of plasma membrane	Perdue *et al.* (1971b)
Chick embryo fibroblasts	Phospholipid, sterol, and sialic acid of density gradient fractions of plasma membrane	Perdue *et al.* (1971a)
BHK-21	Cholesterol, phospholipids, fatty acids, of plasma membrane and endoplasmic reticulum	Renkonen *et al.* (1971, 1972)
Hamster kidney	Fatty acids from phospholipids of total cell membrane	Laine *et al.* (1972)

of myocardial cells in monolayer culture is inhibited by phospholipase C and restored by lysophosphatides. Croce *et al.* (1971) has described the action of lysolecithin in concentrations of 100–1000 μg/ml on the stimulation of hybrid formation by cells in culture; these studies indicate that lysolecithin favors the micellar arrangement of lipid in membranes and therefore, aids in cell fusion. Another study of the effect of lysolecithin on cell membrane metabolism (Reporter and Raveed, 1973) indicated lysolecithin interferes with metabolism and turnover of membrane phospholipids. In this case, however, it resulted in inhibition of the natural fusion of cultured myoblasts.

VII. Lipid Ethers

There has been a great deal of interest recently in the alkyl and alk-1-enyl derivatives of glycerides and phosphatides (see the recent review by Snyder and Snyder, 1974). The pathway for biosynthesis of these compounds has been studied both in whole animals and in cultured cells (Hajra, 1970; Agranoff and Hajra, 1971). The lipids ethers are synthesized via acyl-dihydroxyacetone phosphate. After DHAP is esterified in the 1 position, the acyl residue is exchanged with alcohol, and after reduction, the resulting alkyl-glycerolphosphate is acylated in the 2 position. Alk-1-enyl ethers are formed from intact alkyl-acyl-phosphoglycerides by dehydrogenation (Wood *et al.*, 1970).

A high level of glyceryl ethers were observed in L-M cells, a line derived from L cells (Anderson *et al.*, 1969). Relatively high levels of glyceryl ethers were also observed in the diploid line WI-38 and in a number of other established lines of normal and tumor origin (Howard and Bailey, 1972). In this study, the levels of glyceryl ethers were found to correlate with decreased levels of the enzyme α-glycerolphosphate dehydrogenase. A decrease in this enzyme possibly leads to the increased production of these compounds because changes in the activity of this enzyme could influence the concentration of dihydroxyacetone phosphate. The acylated derivative of DHAP serves as the precursor of these lipid ethers.

VIII. Studies of Drugs and Inhibitors of Lipid Metabolism in Cultured Cells

Investigation of the action of drugs and inhibitors on lipid metabolism may have two purposes. The first is to determine the toxic action of a drug on cellular metabolism. The second objective is to develop specific inhibitors of lipid metabolism that can be used as tools for further biochemical studies. To date, most of the studies fall into the former category, although the hope is that the information gained may be applicable to further investigations.

Suss *et al.* (1971) have investigated the influence of the carcinogen, croton oil, on lipid metabolism in HeLa and L cells. Autoradiographic studies have indicated that this drug localizes in the plasma membrane. They found a 3-fold stimulation of choline-^{3}H incorporation into phospholipid upon treatment with croton oil. These workers proposed that the localization of the drug in the membrane leads to a stimulation of phospholipid turnover that possibly has a subsequent effect on cell division. Studies with the antitumor terephthalanilides on P388 cells (Yesair *et al.*, 1971) indicate the active derivatives of these drugs also inhibit cell lipid biosynthesis from acetate. In addition, a drug-phospholipid complex occurred in the cells with a greater proportion occurring in the case of inactive forms of these drugs.

The effects of the anesthetic halothane have been studied in cultures of HTC cells (Ishii and Corbascio, 1971). At a time when exposure to halothane produces only a slight reduction in DNA and protein synthesis, a marked increase in lipid synthesis was detected, as measured by acetate-^{14}C incorporation. No preferential accumulation of acetate was found in any of the neutral or phospholipid fractions examined, and it appears that the primary effect of halothane is the acceleration of transfer of acetate into the hepatoma cells.

The effect of steroid hormones on cultured cells has also received some attention. The steroid hormones have been observed to effect changes such as altered permeability in cellular membranes. Dell'Orco and Melnykovych (1970) noted immediate inhibition of ^{32}P incorporation into the lipids of Henle cells upon treatment with prednisolone. This inhibition occurred during the entire cell cycle, but there was no significant alteration in the distribution of the radioactive label into the phospholipid subclasses. This effect upon phospholipid metabolism preceded any effect on permeability or other actions of the hormone. These studies have been extended to the investigation of choline metabolism in L-5178Y cells upon treatment with glucocorticoids (Story and Melnykovych, 1973). In these experiments, prednisolone inhibited incorporation of choline-^{14}C into lipids. Inhibition of choline incorporation was less in cells selected for increased resistance to the steroid. It is, therefore, possible that some steroid hormones may be specific inhibitors of phospholipid synthesis.

Finally, various inhibitors of macromolecule synthesis have been used in cell culture studies to investigate the relationship between phospholipid metabolism and cell division. The presence of 2 m*M* thymidine in the growth medium leads to the cessation of cell division, but allows the continuation of phospholipid synthesis in P815Y mast cells (Bergeron, 1971). FUdR, however, inhibited both cell division and phospholipid synthesis. These workers concluded that phospholipid and DNA synthesis were, therefore, not linked in these cells. This hypothesis requires further study with other inhibitors of macromolecule synthesis. However, it does indicate a promising method of approach to this problem.

IX. Studies of Lipids in Differentiated Cells in Culture

Most cells in tissue culture are dedifferentiated in the sense that they do not have the morphological characteristics or biochemical functions of specialized tissues. Although the culture originates from a specific organ, there is a loss of the specific functions characteristic of that organ during serial propagation, probably due to selective overgrowth by connective tissue fibroblasts. There may also be phenotypic changes in the

Table IV
Some Studies of Lipids in Differentiated Cell Cultures

Origin of cells	Types of studies	Reference
Corneal epithelium	Accumulation of lipid inclusions	Klintworth and Hijmans (1970)
Mammary epithelium	Synthesis and excretion of triglyceride	Maragoudakis (1971)
	Variation in chain length of glyceride fatty acids with age in culture	Kinsella (1972)
	Effect of hormones on triglyceride excretion	Dils *et al.* (1972)
Skin fibroblasts	Metabolism of testosterone in genital and nongenital cultures	Pinsky *et al.* (1972)
	Phospholipid metabolism	Long and Yardley (1970)
Adipose explants	Lipid synthesis from glucose	Smith (1972)
Primary bone cells	Lipid synthesis from glucose and glycerol	Dirksen *et al.* (1970)
Myoblasts	Phospholipid hydrolysis	Norris and Reporter (1970)
	Effect of lysolecithin	Reporter and Raveed (1973)
Glial cells	Glycosphingolipid biosynthesis	Snyder *et al.* (1970); Dawson *et al.* (1971)
Frontal lobe explants	Incorporation of fatty acids into glycerolipids	Menkes (1972)
Adrenal tumor cells	Steroid biosynthesis	Yasumura *et al.* (1966); Schimmer (1969)
Testicular tumor cells	Steroid biosynthesis	Steinberger *et al.* (1970); Inano *et al.* (1972)
Aorta explants and fibroblasts	Sterol biosynthesis	Avigan *et al.* (1972)
	Effect of chondroitin polysulfates on sterol synthesis	Murata and Furukashi (1969)
	Lipid accumulation	Nicolosi *et al.* (1972); Chen and Dzoga (1973)

cultured cells or an inadequate environment for expression of differentiated functions.

Most of the studies on lipid metabolism in cells in culture have been performed on mixoploid lines. These have undergone a transformation with respect to the original culture (see Section XI) and are adapted toward indefinite proliferation *in vivo*. Specific mixoploid cell lines have few distinguishing characteristics, and the various mixoploid lines resemble each other more than their tissue of origin. These cell lines have proven very useful for the study of basic cell lipid metabolism. There is no doubt, however, that organ specific differentiation involves several aspects of lipid metabolism, and it would be useful to be able to examine the specific effects of differentiation on lipid metabolism using cell culture systems.

There has recently been an emphasis on establishing cell lines in culture that maintain differentiated function. The culture methods include animal passage, cloning, specific enzymatic digestion, and the selective removal of fibroblasts (Kruse and Patterson, 1973). The following is a review of studies on lipid metabolism that have been performed using these differentiated cell cultures. They are summarized in Table IV.

A. Lipids in Lymphoblastoid Cell Lines

Cell lines have been developed from human peripheral blood leukocytes (Eisinger, 1973). Although diploid in chromosome number, these lines are somewhat dedifferentiated in that they lose some of the characteristics of leukocytes and are capable of indefinite proliferation. Lipid composition of these cultures has been reported by Gottfried (1967, 1971). Lipid content and distribution seems similar to other established cell lines, although he observed increased phosphatidyl choline, decreased sphingomyelin, and decreased cholesterol content with prolonged cultivation *in vitro*. These cells, especially early in the culture period, can be stimulated to divide by compounds such as phytohemagglutinin, and the relationship of phospholipid turnover to mitogenic stimulation has been investigated in these cells. These studies are included in Section VI,C because of their close relationship to studies of other serum-stimulated cell lines.

B. Lipids in Epithelial Cells

Although some mixoploid cell lines are epitheloid in morphology, the aim has been the development of differentiated epithelial lines from various tissues. Shapiro *et al.* (1969) have established cultures from lens epithelium. Induction of lipid storage has been studied in cells from the cornea in culture (Klintworth and Hijmans, 1970). Intracellular lipid accumulates in these cells following growth in medium containing normal serum and the extent of accumulation was directly related to the quantity of serum in the medium. The intracellular lipid droplets were triglyceride in nature and seemed to arise from serum free fatty acid in a manner similar to that described for established cell lines (see Section III).

Borek *et al.* (1969) have established a line of epithelial cells from rat liver. These cells have the morphological characteristics of liver cells, are diploid, and are able to manufacture serum proteins. Therefore, they may be very useful for the study of lipoprotein synthesis *in vitro*. Methods have also been developed for the isolation of liver parenchymal cells (Capuzzi *et al.*, 1971) and lipid metabolism has been assayed in these cells. However, they have not been maintained in serial culture. Culling *et al.* (1973) have cultivated epithelial cells isolated from the gastrointestinal tract; however, no metabolic studies have been performed in these cells.

Cell cultures have recently been established from mammary glands (Maragoudakis, 1971; Kinsella, 1972) that synthesize and secrete lipids related to milk production. Maragoudakis has observed the synthesis of cellular and secretory lipids, primarily triglycerides, from acetate or glucose via malonyl-CoA. Synthesis was most active in newly explanted cells and was subject to inhibition by drugs that are inhibitors of acetyl-CoA carboxylase. Kinsella (1972) has followed the secretory pattern of mammary cells with age in culture. Initially, large amounts of triglyceride with fatty acids of 10 carbon chain length, characteristic of milk production, are found. Then the concentrations of these fatty acids decrease, and fatty acids of longer chain length and more phospholipids are synthesized. It appears that the change in the secretion of phospholipids and fatty acids of longer chain length represents a functional dedifferentiation in these cells. An attempt has been made to maintain the secretion of triglycerides containing medium chain fatty acids (C_8–C_{12}) by the use of lactogenic hormones (Dils *et al.*, 1972). He found that the initial treatment of the cells with insulin and corticosterone, followed by treatment with prolactin, led to the maintenance of a high rate of synthesis of C_8 to C_{12} fatty acids.

C. Lipids in Cultures from Skin

Skin fibroblast cultures have been used as a model for the investigation of specific problems of skin metabolism. The question that must be asked, however, is to what degree do these cultured skin fibroblasts maintain normal *in vivo* skin functions. Pinsky *et al.* (1972) has found differences between human genital and nongenital skin in regard to their capacity to metabolize testosterone, and these differences persisted throughout the life of the cell strain. Studies of phospholipid metabolism in cultured guinea pig skin have shown that phospholipid synthesis decreased when glucose was omitted from the medium (Long and Yardley, 1970). There was a decrease in phosphatidyl ethanolamine, an increase in phosphatidyl inositol, and phosphatidyl serine and phosphatidyl choline remained constant in these cells. These investigators proposed, therefore, that the keratinization of skin observed during starvation might be related to depletion of phospholipid.

D. Lipids in Adipose Cells in Culture

Although isolated adipocytes have been used extensively for lipid studies (Rodbell *et al.*, 1968), there have only been recent attempts to establish them in culture. Smith (1972) has studied the incorporation of glucose and the release of glycerol in explants of adipose tissue. Synthesis and turnover of lipids, as measured by glucose incorporation and glycerol release, increased for 7–8 days. Glucose was incorporated primarily into triglyceride, and insulin led to an increase in this incorporation. A correlation could be made between the size of the cells and these parameters. These studies demonstrate that cultured adipocytes could be a useful tool for both metabolic and morphologic studies of adipose tissue function.

E. Lipids in Bone Cell Cultures

Dirksen *et al.* (1970) have studied lipid metabolism in primary cultures of bone cells. Inclusion of glucose-^{14}C and glycerol-^{14}C into the medium of these cultures resulted in the lipids labeled primarily in the glycerol portion of the molecule. When ATP was added to this system, there was a stimulation of neutral lipid synthesis and an inhibition of phospholipid synthesis.

F. Lipids in Cultured Muscle Cells

Cultures derived from rat muscle have yielded monolayers of myoblasts which fuse *in vitro* to form syncytia resembling multinucleated muscle fibers *in vivo*. Hydrolysis of phospholipid esters was localized in these cells by autoradiography (Norris and Reporter, 1970). The hydrolysis occurred primarily in lysosomal vesicles; however, none occurred at the site of fusion, raising the question of how the membrane can be reorganized without breakdown of phospholipids. On the other hand, treatment of myoblasts with lysolecithin (Reporter and Raveed, 1973) interfered with phospholipid turnover and prevented cell fusion.

G. Lipids in Cultures from Brain

Several cell lines have been established from neuroblastomas and glial tumors. These have been used mainly for the study of glycosphingolipids. Snyder *et al.* (1970) report that glial cells in culture have less than 10% of the gangliosides found in normal brain. The predominant ganglioside measured in these cultures was G_{M3},[5] and there was a decrease in polysialyl gangliosides. Dawson *et al.* (1971) have observed the same pattern in glial tumor lines. The predominant glycosphingolipid in these tumor lines was G_{M3} and no other gangliosides of higher chain lengths were present. When these workers studied a neuroblastoma line, however, G_{M3} was absent and their were significant amounts of G_{M2}, G_{M1}, G_{D2}, and G_{D1a}. The studies, therefore, suggest that glial cells probably differ from neurons in their ganglioside content, although the loss of polysialyl gangliosides could simply be due to the culture conditions. The only studies of the metabolism of neutral lipids and phospholipids in brain cells in culture have been performed by Menkes (1972) using frontal lobe explants. ^{14}C-labeled stearic, palmitic, and lignoceric acids were incorporated into both neutral lipids and phospholipids in these cells, and the biosynthesis of all major subclasses of phospholipid occurred during the period of culture. In addition, these cells demonstrated significant elongation and desaturation of fatty acids.

H. Hormone Production in Cultured Cells

Some of the earliest and most successful examples of differentiated function in cell cultures concern the establishment of hormone-secreting and hormone-responsive cell lines. In the area of lipid metabolism, the significant examples are those cell lines that secrete steroid hormones. These fall into two categories. The first consists of adrenal tumor cell lines; the second category refers to interstitial and Leydig cells derived from testicular tumors.

There are now available several isogenic adrenal tumor cell lines with differing degrees of competence in the pathways of adrenocorticotropic hormone-stimulated steroidogenesis (Yasumura *et al.*, 1966; Schimmer, 1969). Hormone production and release in response to trophic stimulation and the role of cyclic nucleotides in this process has been exten-

---

[5] Nomenclature according to Svennerholm (1963).

sively studied and these investigations are beyond the scope of this chapter (see reviews by Sato *et al.*, 1970; Schimmer, 1972). These cell lines produce primarily Δ3,4-ketosteroids. The biosynthetic pathway has not been well-studied.

Steroid bioconversions have been more thoroughly investigated in testicular cell lines. The activity of 21-hydroxylase was lost or inactivated during *in vitro* culture of interstitial tumor cells. The enzyme activities related to androgen biosynthesis were maintained in the tumor cells, and when pregnenolone-^{3}H was added to the culture medium, it was converted to progesterone, testosterone, androstendione, and related derivatives, but not to any adrenal corticoid (Inano *et al.*, 1972). The opposite pattern was observed in Leydig cell cultures. Young cultures were able to convert progesterone to androgens; older cultures showed loss of the specific enzymes (17 α-hydroxylase and 17–20 lyase). There was an apparent progressive increase in the activity of 20 α-hydroxysteroid dehydrogenase in the Leydig cell cultures (Steinberger *et al.*, 1970).

I. Use of Cultures from Aorta to Study Atherosclerosis

One of the most interesting applications of studies on differentiated cells concerns the use of cultures derived from aorta for the purpose of investigating atherosclerosis. The accumulation of lipids in the arterial wall during atherosclerosis is derived primarily from serum cholesterol. However, local metabolic factors seem to be involved in the accumulation of cholesterol (Newman and Zilversmit, 1962). Moreover, local biosynthesis within the arterial wall appears to provide the source of triglycerides and phospholipids in these lesions (Newman *et al.*, 1961). Culture systems which preserve the differentiated functions of aorta could be very useful for the study of the etiology of this disease. Avigan *et al.* (1972) have established fibroblast cultures from aortic intima. They observed a stimulation of ^3H_2O and acetate-^{14}C incorporation into sterols and fatty acids upon treatment with solvent-extracted serum. They view this as evidence that aorta cells can be stimulated to overproduce lipid. Murata and Furukashi (1969) have studied the effect of chondroitin polysulfates on lipid synthesis in newly explanted chick aorta cells. They observed an inhibition of lipid synthesis that was most effective in the reduction of sterol and neutral lipid biosynthesis. This suppressive effect was related to the sulfur content of the added chondroitin polysulfate. These findings support *in vivo* observations of the antilipemic and antiatherosclerotic activities of chondroitin polysulfates.

Cell culture systems have also been used to investigate factors that influence susceptibility and resistance to atherosclerosis. Nicolosi *et al.*

(1972) observed the accumulation of lipids, primarily cholesterol esters and hydrocarbons (possibly squalene), in cells cultured from the thoracic aorta of White Carneau (atherosclerosis-susceptible) pigeons. This accumulation was not observed in cultures of aorta from Show Racer (atherosclerosis-resistant) varieties. The pattern of lipid accumulation observed in the cultures from the susceptible animals paralleled the lipid accumulation observed in muscular foci at the beginning of plaque formation. These workers proposed, therefore, that these cultures reflect a pattern of metabolic differences that predispose to atherosclerosis. Finally, Chen and Dzoga (1973) have studied the accumulation of lipids in cells from aortic media incubated in hyperlipemic rabbit serum. Cholesterol ester content increased to 5 times the original value and cholesterol increased 2-fold. No increase was noted in cultures incubated in control serum. This latter study presents a model system for the study of the response of lipid metabolism in the aorta to the presence of altered lipoprotein structure.

X. Use of Cell Cultures for the Study of Lipidoses

The pathological chemistry of nine heritable lipid storage diseases is now well-established and there is clear evidence that all of the lipid storage diseases are caused by an attenuation or lack of a specific hydrolytic enzyme required for the disposal of a normal tissue lipid metabolite (Brady, 1972). Most of the enzyme defects or deficiencies associated with these inborn errors in metabolism are ubiquitous in their tissue distribution and are, therefore, manifest in cells in culture, derived from biopsy of skin or other sites. The use of cell cultures for the study, diagnosis, and the investigation of possible treatment for these disorders is one of the best examples of the potential application of cell culture to the studies of clinical problems. This subject has recently been extensively reviewed (Nitowski, 1972; Mellman and Cristofalo, 1972). The following summary of these studies is intended to demonstrate the potential uses of cell culture for the study of lipid metabolic diseases.

Chronologically, the first successful application of tissue culture techniques to the study of lipid disorders was accomplished by Brady *et al.* (1965) who demonstrated in skin fibroblast cultures from patients with Gaucher's disease, a deficiency of β-glucocerebrosidase and an accumulation of ceramide glucoside similar to that observed *in vivo.* Cultures of splenic tissue are also useful in the diagnosis of Gaucher's disease, as these cells characteristically show an elevation of acid phosphatase (Perona *et al.*, 1968).

Uhlendorf *et al.* (1966) have studied cell cultures of patients with Niemann–Pick disease. They demonstrated that tissue cultures derived from bone marrow and skin of these patients have 2 to 3 times the sphingomyelin and cholesterol content of cultures derived from normal individuals. Subsequently, the accumulation of these lipids was determined to be due to the decrease in the enzyme sphingomyelinase and this has been observed both in cultured skin fibroblasts (Sloan *et al.*, 1967) and also in cultures of fetal cells obtained by amniocentesis (Epstein *et al.*, 1971). Thus, the culture of amniotic fluid can be used for the successful prenatal diagnosis of this disorder.

Metachromatic leukodystrophy (MLD) represents several closely related disorders in which myelin degeneration is associated with accumulation of cerebroside sulfate. A defect in the enzyme arylsulfatase A can be detected in skin fibroblasts of these patients and the occurrence of early and late onset variants of MLD can be explained on the basis of an inverse correlation observed between the amount of residual enzyme activity in the fibroblast cultures and the rate of progression of clinical symptoms (Porter *et al.*, 1971). Moreover, arylsulfatase A can be concentrated from urine and then added to fibroblasts from MLD patients, resulting in the hydrolysis of sulfatide at a rate up to 50% of normal values. This enzymatic replacement is a possible basis for future therapy of these diseases (Weismann *et al.*, 1971).

Tay-Sachs disease has been one of the most publicized lipidoses to which cell culture methodology has been applied. This disease is characterized by deposits of ganglioside G_{M2} in brain as a result of a lack of hexosaminidase A. These phenomena have been observed in skin fibroblast cultures from individuals with Tay-Sachs disease. Moreover, heterozygotes can be readily identified, and the prenatal diagnosis of fetuses with this disorder can be made (O'Brien *et al.*, 1971).

The study of G_{M1} generalized gangliosidosis in cell cultures has progressed to the point of yielding clues as to the mechanisms of this enzymatic defect. There are two forms of this disease that can be clinically differentiated. However, a decrease in β-galactosidase occurs in both types. Temperature and pH curves of the two enzymes *in vitro*, however, indicate that the enzymes are different (Pinsky *et al.*, 1970). This indicates that there is a separate defect for each type of this disease.

Clues concerning the enzymatic defect resulting in Fabry's disease have recently become available through studies of cells cultured from patients with this disorder. It had been determined earlier that fibroblasts from these patients, displayed a deficiency in the activity of α-galactosidase (Romeo and Migeon, 1970). Studies, however, examining the residual α-galactosidase activity in cells from patients with Fabry's disease, as compared to normal controls, indicate that two different isozymes of this enzyme may occur. The α-galactosidase in Fabry's cells differs from the normal enzyme in heat stability, electrophoretic mobility, and inhibition by myoinositol (Wood and Nadler, 1972; Crawhall and Banfler, 1972). It is proposed, therefore, that normal individuals have the two isozymes and only one is present in patients with Fabry's disease. Furthermore, it is proposed that the basic isozyme can be converted to the acidic form by combination with sialic acid residues, and that the defect in this disease is due to a lack of a specific sialyltransferase. On the basis of the studies of generalized gangliosidosis and Fabry's disease, it has recently been suggested that all of the lipidoses are possible lysosomal diseases representing a failure of interconversion of isozymes normally present in lysosomes (Douglas and Sawitsky, 1972).

XI. Comparison of Lipid Metabolism in Normal and Tumor Cells in Culture

A. Introduction

One of the most interesting applications of the study of lipid metabolism in cultured cells has been the comparison of normal and tumor cells in culture. This subject has been recently reviewed by Howard and Howard (1974). Cells in culture are often divided into two categories. When a piece of tissue from almost any fetal or adult organ is explanted, the usual observation is that cells of fibroblast-like morphology migrate out from the explant. This is referred to as a primary culture. If these cells are then serially subcultivated, a diploid cell line is formed. These have been found to retain a number of traits common to cells *in vivo*. They have a stable euploid karyotype; they cannot be cultivated indefinitely, that is, they have a definite and limited life span. Moreover, they have certain characteristic growth properties such as low saturation density, minimal ability to form colonies on soft agar, and high requirement for serum growth factors (Hay and Strehler, 1967; Hayflick and Moorhead, 1961; Swim and Parker, 1957; Tijo and Puck, 1958). Through a phenomenon referred to as transformation, a diploid cell line can be converted to an established, or mixoploid cell line. This can be induced by irradiation (Borek and Sachs, 1966) or carcinogens (Berwald and Sachs, 1963), but most often through the action of an oncogenic virus (Stoker and McPherson, 1961; Temin and Rubin, 1958). The main feature of transformed cells that distinguishes them from the nontransformed cells is their insensitivity to the controls that regulate cell multiplication.

They have an indefinite potential for proliferation, are heteroploid in chromosome development, and are morphologically pleiomorphic. They attain a higher cell density at confluency, and have a minimum requirement for serum growth promoting factors. They have a high plating efficiency and can form colonies on feeder layers in soft agar. Although the relationship has never been clearly defined, since established cell lines can arise directly when explants of tumors are cultured *in vitro*, and, since they can often form tumors when transplanted into a compatible host, it is generally considered that transformation *in vitro* is analogous to the malignant process *in vivo*. Thus, the comparison of normal and transformed tumor cell lines affords a system for the comparative biochemistry of the tumor process.

B. Lipid Composition of Normal and Transformed Cells

The first direct comparison of a diploid fibroblast line with its transformed derivative was performed by Howard and Kritchevsky (1969a) using the human fibroblasts WI-38 and a line derived from it by transformation with the oncogenic virus SV40. It was found that the total lipid content in the two cells was similar. There was, however, a decrease in the amount of phospholipid in the transformed cells. The distribution of neutral and phospholipid subclasses were similar between the two cells. Quigley *et al.* (1971) have performed similar studies of lipids of chick embryo fibroblasts before and after transformation with Rous sarcoma virus. They report no differences in cholesterol/phospholipid molar ratios or in the distribution of the phospholipid subclasses of the two cell types. Chao *et al.* (1972) have recently reported studies comparing hamster embryo fibroblasts with their transformed lines derived spontaneously or through the action of polyoma virus. Both transformed derivatives were found to have similar cholesterol content and phospholipid distribution, as compared with the normal cultures. However, a somewhat decreased phospholipid content in the transformed cells was also observed. The data obtained from the three comparative studies are presented in Table V.

Comparisons have also been made of the fatty acid composition of normal and transformed cells. Howard and Kritchevsky (1969a) found the same fatty acids present in the glycerolipids of WI-38 fibroblasts and their transformed derivatives, but there was a significant decrease in the amount of arachidonic acid present in both neutral and phospholipids of the transformed cells. Yau and Weber (1972) have also observed a decrease in arachidonic acid and an increase in oleic acid in chick embryo fibroblasts after transformation by Rous sarcoma virus. One

Table V

Comparison of Lipids in Normal and Transformed Cell Cultures

Cell	Human[a]		Chick[b]		Hamster[c]		
	WI-38	SV40-transformed	Chick embryo fibroblasts	RSV-transformed	Hamster embryo fibroblasts	Spontaneously transformed	Polyoma-transformed
Total lipid (mg/100 mg dry weight)	21	18					
Neutral lipid (mg/100 mg dry weight)	6.0	7.4					
cholesterol ester[d]	5.0	4.0					
triglyceride[d]	27	25					
free fatty acid[d]	21	26					
cholesterol[d]	35	35			7.6[e]	5.3[e]	6.4[e]
Phospholipid (mg/100 mg dry weight)	15	11			23.8[e]	17.4[e]	19.1[e]
phosphatidyl ethanolamine[f]	12	13	31	33–36	23	26	16
phosphatidyl inositol[f]	13	10	12	12–13	2.6	5.3	2.7
phosphatidyl serine[f]	12	4.2	12	12–13	14	12	17
phosphatidyl choline[f]	57	57	46	42	46	40	42
sphingomyelin[f]	7.4	13	10	8–9	15	17	23
lysolecithin[f]	2.9	2.0					

[a] Data of Howard and Kritchevsky (1969a).
[b] Data of Quigley *et al.* (1971).
[c] Data of Chao *et al.* (1972).
[d] % Total neutral lipid.
[e] μmoles per gram.
[f] % Total phospholipid.

possible explanation for the decreased arachidonate content is that the transformed cells are unable to biosynthesize arachidonic acid from serum linoleate by elongation and desaturation. WI-38 cells have been observed to be capable of desaturating exogenous linoleic acid, whereas their transformed derivatives are not capable of performing this desaturation process (Dunbar and Bailey, 1973). Thus, these cells would not be able to convert exogenous linoleic acid to arachidonic acid. Takaoka and Katsuta (1971) found that a number of established cell lines adapted to serum-free medium lacked desaturating ability. However, some transformed and tumor lines have been shown to be able to biosynthesize polyunsaturates (Dunbar and Bailey, 1973). Therefore, it is most likely that loss of the ability to desaturate is not a property of tumor cells, but simply a phenomenon that occurs as a result of prolonged passage in culture, as suggested by Harary *et al.* (1967).

C. Lipid Biosynthesis in Normal and Tumor Cells

When the lipids of cultured normal and tumor cells are compared, the source of lipid in these two cell types seems to be similar, that is, when cells are grown in serum-supplemented medium they obtain their lipids from the exogenous supply, usually serum free fatty acids. This has been demonstrated both for established cell lines (Bailey, 1967; Geyer, 1967) and for diploid fibroblasts (Howard and Kritchevsky, 1969b). These observations indicate that both diploid and heteroploid lines are able to synthesize the full complement of glycerides and phospholipids. On the other hand, both diploid (Jacobs *et al.*, 1973; Rothblat *et al.*, 1971) and transformed lines (Bailey, 1967; Evans *et al.*, 1965) have been cultured in lipid-free medium. Thus, both cell types are able to synthesize sufficient amounts of long chain fatty acids and cholesterol to satisfy growth and metabolic needs.

There have been very few direct comparisons of lipid metabolism between diploid or untransformed and transformed or established cell lines. When the phospholipid metabolism of chick embryo fibroblasts and their Rous sarcoma virus-transformed derivatives were compared (Quigley *et al.*, 1971) there were no differences in ^{32}P incorporation in phospholipid subclasses between the two cell types. These workers also report that the turnover of individual phospholipid subclasses was similar in the normal and transformed cells.

Since there is an obvious lack of, or release from control of, cell division in neoplastic cells, it is logical to pose the question of whether tumor cells have alterations in other areas of regulation of cell metabolism. Since Siperstein and Fagan (1966) proposed that there was a lack of a feedback inhibition of cholesterol synthesis in tumors due to a defect in the regulation of the enzyme β-hydroxy-β-methylglutaryl (HMG) CoA reductase, attention has been focused on the regulation of cholesterol biosynthesis in normal and tumor cell cultures. It has been demonstrated that a number of transformed cell lines possess an efficient mechanism for the control of cholesterol biosynthesis, that is, when exogenous lipid is supplied, cholesterol biosynthesis from both acetate and glucose is inhibited (Section V). When the regulation of cholesterol biosynthesis was directly compared in the diploid cell line WI-38 and its transformed derivative, however, a difference was observed between the two cell types (Howard and Kritchevsky, 1969a). This difference was thoroughly examined by Rothblat *et al.* (1971) who cultured both cell lines in medium supplemented with delipidized serum protein. Under these conditions, both cell lines synthesized cholesterol at approximately the same rate, and intracellular cholesterol levels were similar in both cell types. As increased levels of unesterified cholesterol were added to the medium, both cell lines showed a decrease in *de novo* sterol biosynthesis, with the diploid line exhibiting a greater reduction than that observed in the transformed cells. The explanation for this observed difference in the regulation of sterol metabolism between the two cell types awaits further study. One possibility is that the cells differ in the regulation of the enzyme HMG-CoA reductase since this seems to be the main point of control of cholesterol biosynthesis (Section V). Another possibility is that they differ in the occurrence of an additional regulatory point beyond mevalonic acid (Howard *et al.*, 1973). A direct comparison of the WI-38 cell and its transformed derivative, however, indicates there was only a 2-fold difference in mevalonic acid incorporation between the two cells (Butler and Bailey, 1973); this difference is not large enough to account for the difference in magnitude of feedback inhibition shown by Rothblat *et al.* (1971).

Another possible difference in the regulation of sterol biosynthesis between normal and tumor cells in culture has been proposed by Avigan *et al.* (1970). These workers found that stimulation of cholesterol biosynthesis from both acetate-^{14}C and $^{3}H_2O$ in lipid-free medium required the presence of solvent extracted serum protein; under these conditions, sterol biosynthesis in human fibroblasts was increased 166-fold as opposed to 3-to 25-fold for the established cell lines. This would imply a very basic difference in the regulatory mechanism between the normal fibroblasts and the established cell lines in culture. However, a thorough investigation of the control of cholesterol biosynthesis in cell cultures requires comparative studies of cholesterol uptake and excretion in the normal and transformed cells.

D. Studies of Membranes and Glycolipids

It has been suggested that tumor cells may contain modified surface membranes that are responsible for their altered growth behavior (Pardee, 1964), and a number of experimental observations demonstrating changes in surface properties of tumor cells in culture support this hypothesis (Kraemer, 1972). There seems to be no difference in lipid composition between membranes of normal and transformed cell cultures. Perdue *et al.* (1971a,b) have established that viral transformation, which results in a cell greatly altered in shape, cell association and adhesion can be accomplished without any necessary changes in the lipid composition of cell membrane. Cunningham (1972), however, has found alterations in phospholipid turnover between normal and transformed cells in culture. He has described several characteristic changes in phospholipid turnover that occur upon stimulation of cell division in 3T3 cells (Section VI). These changes were not observed in the polyoma-transformed 3T3 cells. He concluded that these changes in phospholipid turnover were related to a serum mediated control of cell density that is lost after transformation.

The most interesting studies on membrane lipids in normal and transformed cells concerns the comparison of glycolipid metabolism in the two cell types. Interest in glycosphingolipids was stimulated by Rapport *et al.* (1959) who found an accumulation of these compounds in tumors *in vivo*. A series of papers by Hakomori and co-workers (Hakomori, 1970; Kijimoto and Hakomori, 1971; Hakomori *et al.*, 1971) and Robbins and co-workers (Robbins and Macpherson, 1971; Sakijama *et al.*, 1972) studied glycolipids of cells of hamster and chick origin and their transformed derivatives. These cells have monosialyllactosylceramide (G_{M3}) as the predominant glycolipid and the results indicated that the nonmalignant, nontransformed cells consistently contained glycolipids of longer carbohydrate chain length than did the various transformed derivatives. Moreover, these changes could be related to density-dependent changes in glycolipid content in these cells (Hakomori, 1970); that is, as the cell density of the contact inhibited cells increases, there is an increase in the more complex neutral glycolipids, especially ceramide trihexoside (CTH). There is a reduction in these glycolipids in transformed cells and no cell density-dependent effects are observed.

Similar decreases in the concentration of more complex gangliosides have been observed in mouse cells and their transformed derivatives (Fishman *et al.*, 1973b; Brady *et al.*, 1973). Although these cells are able to biosynthesize gangliosides, Brady and Mora (1970) reported strikingly decreased amounts of gangliosides with longer carbohydrate chains (G_{M1} and G_{D1a}) in cells transformed by DNA tumor viruses. These alterations have been linked to deficiency of a key glucosyl transferase in the transformed cells (*N*-acetylgalactosaminyl transferase) (Cumar *et al.*, 1970; Fishman *et al.*, 1972). Ganglioside changes in mouse cells appear not to be dependent on cell density (Fishman *et al.*, 1973a; Yogeeswaran *et al.*, 1972) and appear to be more closely associated with viral transformation.

Studies similar to the glycolipid studies have also been reported for glycoproteins (Kraemer, 1972; Warren *et al.*, 1973) and they again fall into the general pattern of decreased complexity of carbohydrate side chains as a result of defective glycosylation in the transformed cells. These studies provide one of the best documented correlations of a chemical change associated with the altered surface properties induced by transformation, and thus constitute a powerful tool for use in the exploration of the mechanisms behind these changes and their relation to the malignant process.

XII. Summary and Conclusions

In summarizing the field of lipid metabolism in cultured cells, definite patterns are emerging in some areas of investigation, while in others, there are problems requiring further study. Moreover, new systems and methodology have arisen that should lead to the expansion of certain fields in the near future. The following is an attempt to list some of these emerging patterns and cautiously predict some of the future directions that studies in lipid metabolism might take. Studies on the incorporation of lipids into cells have centered on fatty acids and cholesterol (Sections III and V). In both cases, these compounds seem to enter by a physical adsorptive process, and the rate of entry is governed by the ratio of lipid to protein in the extracellular environment. This points to the importance of lipoprotein carriers in cell lipid uptake and raises questions concerning the relationship of lipoprotein configuration to the mechanisms of the uptake process. The kinetics of triglyceride and phospholipid entry into cells remain to be studied. However, it has become evident that both of these compounds are probably able to enter into cells intact and play a significant role as a source of intracellular lipid (Sections IV and VI). The study of the entry of these compounds into the cells should be even more closely linked to the role of the lipoprotein carrier in this process.

The intracellular content of each individual lipid class is the resultant of transport of exogenous lipid and *de novo* synthesis. This has been demonstrated in the case of cellular sterol content where cell biosynthesis is directly coordinated with sterol flux into and out of the cell (Section V). In the case of glycerolipids, when free fatty acids are present in the external medium in sufficient concentration they can serve as the source of almost all of the fatty acids in cell glycerolipids. If extracellular free fatty acids are depleted, triglycerides and probably phospholipids can act as sources of intracellular lipids, but, since their rate of entry is slow, *de novo* biosynthesis often occurs simultaneously. An interesting question arises whether the cells are able to adequately exclude lipid when it is present in excess in the medium. Since the phospholipid content of cells under a wide variety of conditions usually remains relatively constant, and since there is a rapid turnover of these compounds, it appears that the cell is able to adequately regulate its phospholipid content within a given range (Section VI). This is probably not true in the case of neutral lipids. A massive bloating of triglyceride droplets can occur in cells when there is a large excess of exogenous fatty acids. Although this triglyceride can be utilized for metabolic functions, it can accumulate to the point where it results in damage to the cells. This is probably also true in the case of cholesterol. Under conditions of a large excess of serum cholesterol, inclusions of free sterol and sterol ester accumulate within some cells. This overaccumulation of lipids that occurs within cells is probably relevant to certain disease states *in vivo.*

The cell culture system is particularly useful for studying lipid metabolism and its regulation. This system allows the study of lipid metabolism in the absence of the complex hormonal and physiological influences superimposed *in vivo,* and it permits observation of the inhibition and stimulation of lipid biosynthesis in response to changes in exogenous lipid supply. The regulatory enzymes that have been studied in cultured cells are listed in Table VI. Further studies are required in this field, particularly with regard to the enzymes that regulate glyceride assembly and phospholipid turnover. Studies in cell cultures should also contribute to the elucidation of the nature of effectors of enzyme activity. The recent description of a sterol carrier protein invites speculation that carrier proteins or modified forms of intracellular lipids are the actual compounds that induce or stimulate enzyme activity.

Attention has recently been focused on the investigation of cell membrane composition and metabolism in cultured cells (Section VI). There have been a number of isolated studies on phospholipid dynamics. These studies have revealed a general pattern of increased phospholipid turnover in response to cell perturbation or stimulation of cell division. In many instances, a generalized stimulation of phospholipid turnover occurs, and studies of isolated subclasses do not always fall into a con-

Table VI

REGULATORY ENZYMES OF LIPID METABOLISM STUDIED IN CELL CULTURES

Enzyme	Effector in the medium	Cell type	Reference
HMG-CoA reductase	Cholesterol, serum lipoproteins	HTC	Watson (1972)
Acetyl-CoA carboxylase	Serum lipid	Skin fibroblasts	Jacobs *et al.* (1973)
Acetyl-CoA synthetase	Serum lipid	L cells	Howard and Bailey (1973)
Phosphorylcholine glyceride transferase	Phytohemagglutinin	Lymphocytes	Nelson and Scribney (1972)

sistent pattern. The most striking observation in a number of cases, however, has centered around the metabolism of phosphoinositol and the formation of a cyclic inositol phosphate. Cell culture systems should be very useful in the elucidation of the functional significance of phosphoinositide turnover and its relationship to cell metabolism. The other interesting area of surface studies has concerned glycolipid metabolism and this has been reviewed in detail elsewhere (Fishman *et al.*, 1973b; Hakomori, 1974). These studies have uncovered a complex pattern of alterations in the chain lengths of ceramide hexosides and gangliosides. Alterations in these compounds and the enzymes that synthesize them are often associated with population density-induced inhibition of cell division, and they also may be related to the oncogenic transformation that occurs *in vitro*.

Several future areas of emphasis seem possible for the field of lipid metabolism in cultured cells. One of these areas concerns the study of lipids in differentiated cells, which are now becoming available (Section IX). Using these cells, comparisons can be made of the mechanisms of uptake and lipid biosynthesis in differentiated cell types, and lipid metabolism can be studied in relation to organ-specific functions. The availability of differentiated cells from vascular tissues should also yield a more useful model for the *in vitro* study of atherosclerosis. There is an increasing potential for the clinical application of the study of lipids in cell cultures. Studies on lipidoses have reached a rather advanced state (Section XI), and it should be possible to initiate similar studies on alterations in lipid metabolism occurring in diabetes, obesity, and hyperlipoproteinemia. Finally, new tools should become available for the investigation of basic questions of lipid metabolism and uptake. One is the development of specific inhibitors of the individual steps of lipid metabolism or uptake. The methodology developed for the study of cell genetics may provide another tool for the study of lipid metabolism in cell culture systems. Specifically, this would include techniques for cell fusion, as begun in studies of cholesterol metabolism, as well as the ability to select for mutants in various aspects of lipid metabolism. These new tools, in conjunction with other advances in methodology, should enable even more rapid future progress in this field.

References

Agranoff, B. W., and Hajra, A. K. (1971). *Proc. Nat. Acad. Sci. U. S.* **68**, 411.

Albutt, E. C. (1966). *J. Med. Lab. Technol.* **23**, 61.

Anderson, R. E., Cummings, R. B., and Snyder, W. F. (1969). *Biochim. Biophys. Acta* **176**, 491.

Avigan, J., Williams, C. D., and Blass, J. B. (1970). *Biochim. Biophys. Acta* **218**, 381.

Avigan, J., Bhathena, S. J., Williams, C. D., and Schriener, M. E. (1972). *Biochim. Biophys. Acta* **270**, 279.

Bailey, J. M. (1967). *In* "Lipid Metabolism in Tissue Culture Cells" (G. H. Rothblat and D. Kritchevsky, eds.), Wistar Symp. Monogr. No. 6, p. 85. Wistar Inst. Press, Philadelphia, Pennsylvania.

Bailey, J. M., and Dunbar, L. M. (1971). *Cancer Res.* **31**, 91.

Bailey, J. M., and Dunbar, L. M. (1973). *Exp. Mol. Pathol.* **18**, 142.

Bailey, J. M., Gey, G. O., and Gey, M. K. (1959). *Proc. Soc. Exp. Biol. Med.* **100**, 686.

Bailey, J. M., Howard, B. V., and Tillman, S. F. (1973). *J. Biol. Chem.* **248**, 1240.

Bailey, P. J., and Keller, D. (1971). *Atherosclerosis* **13**, 333.

Barley, F. W., Sato, G. H., and Abeles, R. H. (1972). *J. Biol. Chem.* **247**, 4270.

Bergeron, J. J. M. (1971). *Biochem. J.* **123**, 385.

Bergeron, J. J. M., Warmsley, A. M. H., and Pasternak, C. A. (1970). *Biochem. J.* **119**, 489.

Berwald, Y., and Sachs, L. (1963). *Nature (London)* **200**, 1182.

Birch, J. R., and Pirt, S. J. (1971). *J. Cell Sci.* **8**, 693.

Blough, H. A., and Tiffany, J. M. (1973). *Advan. Lipid Res.* **11**, 267.

Borek, C., and Sachs, L. (1966). *Nature (London)* **210**, 276.

Borek, C., Higashino, S., and Lowenstein, W. R. (1969). *J. Membrane Biol.* **1**, 274.

Bossmann, H. B., and Winston, R. A. (1970). *J. Cell Biol.* **45**, 23.

Brady, R. O. (1972). *Semin. Hematol.* **9**, 273.

Brady, R. O., and Mora, P. T. (1970). *Biochim. Biophys. Acta* **218**, 308.

Brady, R. O., Kanfer, J., and Shapiro, D. (1965). *Biochem. Biophys. Res. Commun.* **18**, 221.

Brady, R. O., Fishman, P. H., and Mora, P. T. (1973). *Fed. Proc., Fed. Amer. Soc. Exp. Biol.* **32**, 102.

Bremer, J., and Greenberg, D. M. (1960). *Biochim. Biophys. Acta* **37**, 173.

Burns, C. H., and Rothblat, G. H. (1969). *Biochim. Biophys. Acta* **176**, 616.

Butler, J. D., and Bailey, J. M. (1973). Personal communication.

Capuzzi, D. M., Rothman, V., and Margolis, S. (1971). *Biochem. Biophys. Res. Commun.* **45**, 421.

Chao, F., Eng, L. F., and Griffin, A. (1972). *Biochim. Biophys. Acta* **260**, 197.

Chen, R., and Dzoga, K. (1973). *Fed. Proc., Fed. Amer. Soc. Exp. Biol.* **32**, 856. (Abstr.)

Crawhall, J. C., and Banfler, M. (1972). *Science* **177**, 527.

Croce, C. M., Sawicki, W., Kritchevsky, D., and Koprowski, H. (1971). *Exp. Cell Res.* **67**, 427.

Croce, C. M., Kieba, I., Koprowski, H., Molino, M., and Rothblat, G. H. (1974). *Proc. Nat. Acad. Sci. U. S.* **71**, 110.

Culling, C. A., Reid, P. E., Trueman, L. S., and Dunn, W. L. (1973). *Proc. Soc. Exp. Biol. Med.* **142**, 434.

Cumar, F. A., Brady, R. O., and Kolodny, E. H. (1970). *Proc. Nat. Acad. Sci. U. S.* **67**, 757.

Cunningham, D. D. (1972). *J. Biol. Chem.* **247**, 2464.

Dawson, G., Kemp, S. F., Stoolmiller, A. C., Dorfmann, A., and Kennedy, J. P., Jr. (1971). *Biochem. Biophys. Res. Commun.* **44**, 687.

Dell'Orco, R. T., and Melnykovych, G. (1970). *Exp. Cell Res.* **60**, 257.

de Luca, C. (1966). *Exp. Cell Res.* **43**, 39.
Dils, R., Forsyth, I., and Strong, C. R. (1972). *J. Physiol.* (*London*) **222**, 94P.
Diringer, H., and Koch, M. A. (1973). *Biochem. Biophys. Res. Commun.* **51**, 967.
Diringer, H., Marggraff, W. D., Koch, M. A., and Anderer, F. A. (1972). *Biochem. Biophys. Res. Commun.* **47**, 1345.
Dirksen, T. R., Marinetti, G. V., and Peck, W. A. (1970). *Biochim. Biophys. Acta* **202**, 67.
Donisch, V., and Rossiter, R. J. (1965). *Cancer Res.* **25**, 1463.
Douglas, S. D., and Sawitsky, A. (1972). *Semin. Hematol.* **9**, 451.
Dunbar, L. M. (1972). PhD. Thesis, George Washington Univ., Washington, D. C.
Dunbar, L. M., and Bailey, J. M. (1973). Personal communication.
Eisinger, M. (1973). *In* "Tissue Culture, Methods and Applications" (P. F. Kruse and M. K. Patterson, eds.), p. 65. Academic Press, New York.
Elsbach, P. (1965). *Biochim. Biophys. Acta* **98**, 420.
Elsbach, P., Goldman, J., and Patriarca, P. (1972). *Biochim. Biophys. Acta* **280**, 33.
Epstein, C. J., Brady, R. O., Schneider, E. L., Bradley, R. M., and Shapiro, D. (1971). *Amer. J. Hum. Genet.* **23**, 533.
Evans, V. J., Bryant, J. C., Kerr, H. S., and Schilling, E. L. (1965). *Exp. Cell Res.* **36**, 439.
Fishman, P. H., McFarland, V. W., Mora, P. T., and Brady, R. O. (1972). *Biochem. Biophys. Res. Commun.* **48**, 48.
Fishman, P. H., Bassin, R., and McFarland, V. W. (1973a). *Fed. Proc., Fed. Amer. Soc. Exp. Biol.* **32**, 1348. (Abstr.)
Fishman, P. H., Brady, R. O., and Mora, P. T. (1973b). *In* "Tumor Lipids, Biochemistry and Metabolism" (R. Wood, ed.), p. 250. Amer. Oil Chem. Soc. Press, Champaign, Illinois.
Gallagher, W. R., Weinstein, D. B., and Blough, H. A. (1973). *Biochem. Biophys. Res. Commun.* **52**, 1252.
Gerschenson, L. E., Mead, J. F., Harary, I., and Haggerty, D. F. (1967). *Biochim. Biophys. Acta* **131**, 42.
Geyer, R. P. (1967). *In* "Lipid Metabolism in Tissue Culture Cells" (G. H. Rothblat and D. Kritchevsky, eds.), Wistar Symp. Monogr. No. 6, p. 33. Wistar Inst. Press, Philadelphia, Pennsylvania.
Geyer, R. P., and Neimark, J. M. (1959). *Amer. J. Clin. Nutr.* **7**, 86.
Goshima, K. (1971). *Exp. Cell Res.* **67**, 352.
Gottfried, E. L. (1967). *J. Lipid Res.* **8**, 321.
Gottfried, E. L. (1971). *J. Lipid Res.* **12**, 531.
Griffiths, J. B. (1972). *J. Cell Sci.* **10**, 515.
Hajra, A. K. (1970). *Biochem. Biophys. Res. Commun.* **39**, 1037.
Hakomori, S. (1970). *Proc. Nat. Acad. Sci. U. S.* **67**, 1741.
Hakomori, S. (1974). *Progr. Biochem. Pharmacol.* (in press).
Hakomori, S., Saito, T., and Vogt, P. K. (1971). *Virology* **44**, 609.
Ham, R. G. (1963). *Science* **140**, 802.
Hanaoka, F., and Yamada, M. (1971). *Biochem. Biophys. Res. Commun.* **42**, 647.
Harary, I., Gerschenson, L. E., Haggerty, D. F., Desmond, W., and Mead, J. F. (1967). *In* "Lipid Metabolism in Tissue Culture Cells" (G. H. Rothblat and D. Kritchevsky, eds.), Wistar Symp. Monogr. No. 6, p. 17. Wistar Inst. Press, Philadelphia, Pennsylvania.

Hay, R. J., and Strehler, B. L. (1967). *Exp. Gerontol.* **2**, 123.
Hayflick, L., and Moorhead, P. S. (1961). *Exp. Cell Res.* **25**, 585.
Holmes, R., Helms, J., and Mercer, G. (1969). *J. Cell Biol.* **42**, 262.
Howard, B. V., and Bailey, J. M. (1972). *Cancer Res.* **32**, 1533.
Howard, B. V., and Bailey, J. M. (1973). *Fed. Proc., Fed. Amer. Soc. Exp. Biol.* **32**, 602. (Abstr.)
Howard, B. V., and Howard, W. J. (1974). *Progr. Biochem. Pharmacol.* (in press).
Howard, B. V., and Kritchevsky, D. (1969a). *Int. J. Cancer* **4**, 393.
Howard, B. V., and Kritchevsky, D. (1969b). *Biochim. Biophys. Acta* **187**, 293.
Howard, B. V., Butler, J. D., and Bailey, J. M. (1973). *In* "Tumor Lipids, Biochemistry and Metabolism" (R. Wood, ed.), p. 200. Amer. Oil Chem. Soc. Press, Champaign, Illinois.
Inano, H., Tamaoki, B., and Tsubura, Y. (1972). *Endocrinology* **90**, 307.
Ishii, D. N., and Corbascio, A. N. (1971). *Anesthesiology* **34**, 427.
Jacobs, R. A., Sly, W. J., and Majerus, P. W. (1973). *J. Biol. Chem.* **248**, 1268.
Johnson, A. R., and Davenport, J. B. (1971). "Biochemistry and Methodology of Lipids." Wiley (Interscience), New York.
Kijimoto, S., and Hakomori, S. (1971). *Biochem. Biophys. Res. Commun.* **44**, 557.
Kinsella, J. E. (1972). *Biochim. Biophys. Acta* **270**, 296.
Kirsten, E. S., and Watson, J. A. (1973). Unpublished data.
Klintworth, G. K., and Hijmans, J. C. (1970). *Amer. J. Pathol.* **58**, 403.
Kraemer, P. M. (1972). *In* "Growth, Nutrition and Metabolism of Cells in Culture" (G. H. Rothblat and V. J. Cristofalo, eds.), Vol. 1, p. 371. Academic Press, New York.
Kruse, P. F., and Patterson, M. K. (1973). "Tissue Culture, Methods and Applications." Academic Press, New York.
Kuhl, W. E., and Spector, A. A. (1970). *J. Lipid Res.* **11**, 458.
Laine, R., Kettumen, M. L., Ghamberg, C. G., Kaariainen, L., and Renkonen, O. (1972). *J. Virol.* **10**, 433.
Lapetina, E. G., and Mitchell, R. H. (1973). *FEBS (Fed. Eur. Biochem. Soc.), Lett.* **31**, 1.
Lasfargues, E. Y., Coutinho, W. R., Lasfargues, J. C., and Moore, D. H. (1973). *In Vitro* **8**, 494.
Lengle, E., and Geyer, R. P. (1972). *Biochim. Biophys. Acta* **260**, 608.
Lengle, E., and Geyer, R. P. (1973). *Biochim. Biophys. Acta* **296**, 411.
Long, V. J., and Yardley, H. J. (1970). *J. Invest. Dermatol.* **54**, 174.
Lucas, D. O., Shohet, S. B., and Merler, E. (1971). *J. Immunol.* **106**, 768.
Lynch, R. D., and Geyer, R. P. (1972). *Biochim. Biophys. Acta* **260**, 547.
Maca, R. D., and Connor, W. E. (1971). *Proc. Soc. Exp. Biol. Med.* **138**, 913.
MacKenzie, C. G., MacKenzie, J. B., and Reiss, O. K. (1967). *In* "Lipid Metabolism in Tissue Culture Cells" (G. H. Rothblat and D. Kritchevsky, eds.), Wistar Symp. Monogr. No. 6, p. 63. Wistar Inst. Press, Philadelphia, Pennsylvania.
MacKenzie, C. G., MacKenzie, J. B., and Wisneski, J. A. (1970). *J. Lipid Res.* **11**, 571.
Maragoudakis, M. E. (1971). *J. Biol. Chem.* **246**, 4046.
Marcus, D. M., and Cass, L. E. (1969). *Science* **164**, 533.
Mellman, W. J., and Cristofalo, V. J. (1972). *In* "Growth, Nutrition and Metabolism of Cells in Culture" (G. H. Rothblat and V. J. Cristofalo, eds.), Vol. 1, p. 327. Academic Press, New York.

Menkes, J. H. (1972). *Lipids* **7**, 135.
Mizuno, N. S., Hoops, C. E., and Sinha, A. A. (1971). *Nature (London)* **229**, 22.
Murata, K., and Furukashi, T. (1969). *Biochim. Biophys. Acta* **176**, 432.
Nelson, J. D., and Scribney, M. (1972). *Can. J. Biochem.* **50**, 25.
Newman, H. A. I., and Zilversmit, D. B. (1962). *J. Biol. Chem.* **237**, 2078.
Newman, H. A. I., McCandless, E. L., and Zilversmit, D. B. (1961). *J. Biol. Chem.* **236**, 1264.
Nicolosi, R. J., Santerri, R. F., and Smith, S. C. (1972). *Exp. Mol. Pathol.* **17**, 29.
Nitowski, H. M. (1972). *Semin. Hematol.* **9**, 403.
Norris, G., and Reporter, M. (1970). *Nature (London)* **225**, 1246.
O'Brien, J. S., Okada, J., Fillerup, D. V., Veath, M. L., Adornato, B., Brenner, P. H., and Lerdy, J. G. (1971). *Science* **172**, 61.
Pardee, A. B. (1964). *Nat. Cancer Inst. Monogr.* **14**, 7.
Pasternak, C. A. (1972). *J. Cell Biol.* **53**, 231.
Pasternak, C. A., and Bergeron, J. J. M. (1970). *Biochem. J.* **119**, 473.
Patriarca, P., Beckerdite, S., Petis, P., and Elsbach, P. (1972). *Biochim. Biophys. Acta* **280**, 45.
Pedersen, B. N., Gromek, A., and Daehnfeldt, J. L. (1972). *Proc. Soc. Exp. Biol. Med.* **141**, 506.
Perdue, J. F., Kletzien, R., and Miller, K. (1971a). *Biochim. Biophys. Acta* **249**, 419.
Perdue, J. F., Kletzien, R., Miller, K., Pridmore, G., and Wray, V. L. (1971b). *Biochim. Biophys. Acta* **249**, 435.
Perona, G. P., Baccichetti, C., and Tenconi, K. (1968). *Lancet* **ii**, 358.
Peterson, J. A., and Rubin, H. (1969). *Exp. Cell Res.* **58**, 365.
Peterson, J. A., and Rubin, H. (1970). *Exp. Cell Res.* **60**, 383.
Pinsky, L., Powell, E., and Callahan, J. (1970). *Nature (London)* **228**, 1093.
Pinsky, L., Finkelberg, R., Straisfeld, C., Zilahi, B., Kaufman, M., and Hall, G. (1972). *Biochem. Biophys. Res. Commun.* **46**, 364.
Plagemann, P. G. (1971). *J. Lipid Res.* **12**, 715.
Porter, M. T., Fluharty, A. C., Trammet, J., and Kihara, H. (1971). *Biochem. Biophys. Res. Commun.* **44**, 660.
Quigley, J. B., Rifkin, D. P., and Reich, E. (1971). *Virology* **46**, 106.
Raff, R. A. (1970). *J. Cell. Physiol.* **75**, 341.
Rapport, M. M., Graf, L., Skipsky, V. P., and Alonzo, N. F. (1959). *Cancer* **12**, 438.
Reed, F. (1968). *J. Clin. Invest.* **47**, 749.
Renkonen, O., Kaarainen, L., Simons, K., and Ghamberg, C. G. (1971). *Virology* **46**, 318.
Renkonen, O., Ghamberg, C. G., Simons, K., and Kaarainen, L. (1972). *Biochim. Biophys. Acta* **255**, 66.
Reporter, M., and Raveed, D. (1973). *Science* **181**, 863.
Resch, K., and Ferber, E. (1970). *Eur. J. Biochem.* **27**, 153.
Ritter, M. C., and Dempsey, M. E. (1973). *Proc. Nat. Acad. Sci. U. S.* **70**, 265.
Robbins, P. W., and McPherson, I. (1971). *Nature (London)* **229**, 569.
Rodbell, M., Jones, A. B., Chiappe de Cingolani, G. E., and Birnbaumer, L. (1968). *Recent Progr. Horm. Res.* **24**, 215.
Romeo, G., and Migeon, B. R. (1970). *Science* **170**, 180.
Rothblat, G. H. (1969). *Advan. Lipid Res.* **7**, 135.
Rothblat, G. H. (1972). *In* "Growth, Nutrition and Metabolism of Cells in Culture"

(G. H. Rothblat and V. J. Cristofalo, eds.), Vol. 1, p. 297. Academic Press, New York.
Rothblat, G. H. (1973). Personal communication.
Rothblat, G. H., and Buchko, M. K. (1971). *J. Lipid Res.* **12**, 647.
Rothblat, G. H., and Burns, C. H. (1971). *J. Lipid Res.* **12**, 653.
Rothblat, G. H., Buchko, M. K., and Kritchevsky, D. (1968). *Biochim. Biophys. Acta* **164**, 327.
Rothblat, G. H., Burns, C. H., Conner, R. L., and Landrey, J. R. (1970). *Science* **169**, 880.
Rothblat, G. H., Boyd, R., and Deal, C. (1971). *Exp. Cell Res.* **67**, 436.
Rytter, D. J., and Cornatzer, W. E. (1972). *Lipids* **7**, 142.
Sabine, J. R. (1973). *In* "Tumor Lipids, Biochemistry and Metabolism" (R. Wood, ed.), p. 21. Amer. Oil Chem. Soc. Press, Champaign, Illinois.
Sakijama, H., Gross, S. K., and Robbins, P. W. (1972). *Proc. Nat. Acad. Sci. U. S.* **69**, 872.
Sato, G. H., Augusti-Tocco, G., Posner, M., and Kelley, P. (1970). *Recent Progr. Horm. Res.* **26**, 539.
Schimmer, B. P. (1969). *J. Cell. Physiol.* **74**, 115.
Schimmer, B. P. (1972). *J. Biol. Chem.* **247**, 3134.
Schneeberger, E. E., Lynch, R. D., and Geyer, R. P. (1971). *Exp. Cell Res.* **69**, 193.
Shapiro, A. L., Siegel, M., Scharff, M. D., and Robbins, E. (1969). *Invest. Ophthalmol.* **8**, 393.
Sinclair, A. J. (1971). *Can. J. Biochem.* **49**, 700.
Siperstein, M. D., and Fagan, V. M. (1966). *J. Biol. Chem.* **241**, 602.
Sloan, H. R., Uhlendorf, B. W., Kanfer, H. N., Brady, R. O., and Fredrickson, D. S. (1967). *Biochem. Biophys. Res. Commun.* **34**, 582.
Smith, V. (1972). *Anat. Rec.* **172**, 597.
Snyder, R. A., and Snyder, H. (1974). *Progr. Biochem. Pharmacol.* (in press).
Snyder, R. A., Brady, R. O., and Kornbluth, P. L. (1970). *Neurology* **20**, 412.
Sokoloff, L., and Rothblat, G. H. (1972). *Biochim. Biophys. Acta* **280**, 172.
Sokoloff, L., and Rothblat, G. H. (1973). Unpublished data.
Spector, A. A. (1971). *Progr. Biochem. Pharmacol.* **6**, 130.
Spector, A. A. (1972). *In* "Growth, Nutrition and Metabolism of Cells in Culture" (G. H. Rothblat and V. J. Cristofalo, eds.), Vol. 1, p. 257. Academic Press, New York.
Spector, A. A., and Brenneman, D. E. (1973). *Fed. Proc., Fed. Amer. Soc. Exp. Biol.* **32**, 672. (Abstr.)
Spector, A. A., and Soboroff, J. M. (1971). *J. Lipid Res.* **72**, 545.
Spector, A. A., and Soboroff, J. M. (1972). *J. Lipid Res.* **13**, 790.
Steinberger, E., Steinberger, A., and Ficher, H. I. (1970). *Recent Progr. Horm. Res.* **26**, 547.
Stoker, M., and McPherson, I. (1961). *Virology* **14**, 359.
Story, M. T., and Melnykovych, G. (1973). *Exp. Cell Res.* **77**, 437.
Suss, R., Kinzel, V., and Kreibich, G. (1971). *Experientia* **27**, 46.
Svennerholm, L. (1963). *J. Neurochem.* **10**, 613.
Swim, H. E., and Parker, R. F. (1957). *Amer. J. Hyg.* **66**, 235.
Takaoka, T., and Katsuta, H. (1971). *Exp. Cell Res.* **67**, 295.
Temin, H. M., and Rubin, H. (1958). *Virology* **6**, 669.
Temin, H. M., Pierson, R. W., and Dulak, N. C. (1972). *In* "Growth, Nutrition

and Metabolism of Cells in Culture" (G. H. Rothblat and V. J. Cristofalo, eds.), Vol. 1, p. 50. Academic Press, New York.

Tijo, J. H., and Puck, T. T. (1958). *J. Exp. Med.* **108**, 259.

Uhlendorf, B. W., Holtz, A. L., Mock, M. B., and Fredrickson, D. S. (1966). *In* "Inborn Disorders of Sphingolipid Metabolism" (S. M. Aronson and B. W. Volk, eds.), p. 443. Pergamon, Oxford.

Warmsley, A. M., and Pasternak, C. A. (1970). *Biochem. J.* **119**, 493.

Warren, L., Glick, M. C., and Nass, M. K. (1966). *J. Cell. Physiol.* **68**, 269.

Warren, L., Fuhrer, J. P., and Buck, C. A. (1973). *Fed. Proc., Fed. Amer. Soc. Exp. Biol.* **32**, 80.

Watson, J. A. (1972). *Lipids* **7**, 146.

Watson, J. A. (1973). *In* "Tumor Lipids, Biochemistry and Metabolism" (R. Wood, ed.), p. 34. Amer. Oil Chem. Soc. Press, Champaign, Illinois.

Weinstein, D. B. (1968). *In* "Biological Properties of Mammalian Surface Membranes" (L. Manson, ed.), Wistar Symp. Monogr. No. 8, p. 17. Wistar Inst. Press, Philadelphia, Pennsylvania.

Weismann, U. N., Rossi, E. E., and Hershkowitz, N. N. (1971). *New Engl. J. Med.* **284**, 672.

Williams, C. D., and Avigan, J. (1972). *Biochim. Biophys. Acta* **260**, 413.

Wilton, D. C. (1971). *Biochem. J.* **125**, 1153.

Wood, R., Walton, M., Healey, K., and Cummings, R. B. (1970). *J. Biol. Chem.* **245**, 4276.

Wood, R., and Nadler, H. L. (1972). *Amer. J. Hum. Genet.* **24**, 250.

Yasumura, Y., Tashjian, A. H., and Sato, G. H. (1966). *Science* **154**, 1186.

Yau, T. M., and Weber, M. J. (1972). *Biochem. Biophys. Res. Commun.* **49**, 114.

Yesair, D. W., Thayer, P. S., and Kensler, C. J. (1971). *Ann. N. Y. Acad. Sci.* **172**, 655.

Yogeeswaran, G., Sheinen, R. S., Wherrett, J. R., and Murray, R. K. (1972). *J. Biol. Chem.* **247**, 5146.

Effect of Diet on Activity of Enzymes Involved in Fatty Acid and Cholesterol Synthesis[1]

DALE R. ROMSOS AND GILBERT A. LEVEILLE

Department of Food Science and Human Nutrition, Michigan State University, East Lansing, Michigan

I. Introduction

Research in the area of lipid metabolism has increased remarkably in the past three decades. The recognition that adipose tissue was not merely a repository for excess body fat, but rather a dynamic, metabolically active tissue has stimulated a great deal of research on the metabolism of this tissue and its regulation. The possible relationship of aberrations in lipid metabolism to cardiovascular disease and obesity has also generated a heightened interest in research aimed at delineating

[1] Studies conducted by the authors were aided by Grants HE 13245, HL-14677, AM-10774, and AM-15847 from the National Institutes of Health, U. S. Public Health Service, Washington, D. C.

the abnormalities involved. Dietary factors, because of their affect on lipid metabolism, have become implicated as etiologic factors in the development of cardiovascular disease and of obesity. Alterations in specific metabolic pathways are suspected to be accompanied by changes in enzyme activity levels. It is consequently logical that considerable research should have developed to uncover changes in enzyme activities possibly related to altered states of lipid metabolism.

The present review will attempt to summarize the progress that has been made in understanding the influence of diet on lipid metabolism and the activity of associated enzymes. This review is not intended to be an all-encompassing compilation of papers published in this field. Rather, we have attempted to critically select those papers which have, in our opinion, contributed to our present understanding of the influence of diet on the regulation of lipid metabolism and associated enzyme activities. We shall consider individually, those enzymes thought to play a regulatory role in the conversion of carbohydrate (glucose) to fatty acids and cholesterol and to discuss the influence of diet on the regulation of these enzyme activities. It is our hope that this chapter will serve to summarize the current "state of the art," but in addition, we hope it will stimulate thought, provoke interpretations differing from our own, and encourage further research to clarify those many areas which remain ambiguous.

II. Dietary Adaptation of Specific Enzymes Involved in Fatty Acid and Cholesterol Synthesis

A. Glucokinase and Hexokinase

Glucose phosphorylation is a key step in the intracellular metabolism of glucose. The liver cell membrane appears to be freely permeable to hexoses; thus, glucose phosphorylation is the first controlled step in hepatic glucose utilization (Walker, 1966). Rat liver contains four distinct glucose phosphorylating enzymes. Three of the four are low K_m hexokinases (Types I to III) and are present in liver as well as many other tissues (Katzen and Schimke, 1965). Glucokinase, the high K_m Type IV hexokinase, is found only in liver tissue (Katzen and Schimke, 1965) and is the predominant hexokinase isoenzyme in that tissue (Sharma *et al.*, 1963). It has been suggested that the ultimate control of hepatic glycolysis may rest with glucokinase (Greenbaum *et al.*, 1971).

Since the K_m of glucokinase for glucose is about 10 mM as compared with a reported value of 0.1 m*M* for the other hexokinases (Sharma *et al.*, 1963), blood glucose concentration is of prime importance in affecting glucose utilization by liver cells. Glucokinase is not sensitive to feedback inhibition by glucose 6-phosphate, as are the other hexokinases, allowing the liver to dispose of excess glucose (Sols, 1965).

Circulating blood glucose levels are about two times higher in the chicken than in the rat; however, the chicken does not contain a high K_m hexokinase similar to that in rat liver (Landers, 1971; Ureta *et al.*, 1972, 1973). Maximum hexokinase activity for the chicken liver enzyme was obtained with glucose concentrations between 5 and 10 m*M* (Landers, 1971). This glucose concentration is far below that required for maximum activity of the rat liver enzyme and suggests a different control mechanism for hepatic glucose phosphorylation in the chicken.

A number of studies have demonstrated that the major hexokinase in rat liver, glucokinase, is an adaptive enzyme while the low K_m hexokinases of rat liver are much less subject to dietary modification. Fasting or alloxan diabetes markedly depress glucokinase activity without affecting the other hepatic hexokinase activities (Sharma *et al.*, 1963; Sols, 1965; Sols *et al.*, 1964; Dipietro and Weinhouse, 1960). Refeeding a high-carbohydrate diet following a fast increases glucokinase activity (Perez *et al.*, 1964) and the increase is greatest when glucose, rather than fructose, galactose, or mannose, is refed (Sharma *et al.*, 1963). Under these conditions no change in the hepatic low K_m hexokinase activities (Sharma *et al.*, 1963; Sols *et al.*, 1964) was observed.

Feeding a high-carbohydrate diet to weanling rats increases glucokinase activity while weaning rats to a carbohydrate-free, high-fat, or a high-protein diet maintains glucokinase activity at the low level observed in nursing pups (Walker and Eaton, 1967). Seiler *et al.* (1971) observed that gerbils fed a high-carbohydrate or a 15% coconut oil diet exhibited high hepatic glucokinase activity and hyperlipemia, whereas gerbils fed a 15% safflower oil-containing diet had a significantly lowered glucokinase activity as well as decreased blood lipid levels. They postulated that glucokinase may play a role in the regulation of lipid synthesis in the gerbil. In their experiments, type as well as quantity of dietary fat, affected glucokinase activity.

Maintaining normal levels of glucokinase activity appears to depend on both dietary and hormonal factors. Dietary carbohydrate and insulin are critical factors. Glucokinase activity in mouse liver cells maintained in tissue culture was increased upon addition of insulin to the buffer and decreased when insulin was removed from the buffer (Nakamura and Kumegawa, 1973). An exogenous dose of insulin did not increase the low level glucokinase activity observed in rats fed a carbohydrate-free diet. Glucagon or epinephrine injection prevented the increase in glucokinase activity (Niemeyer *et al.*, 1966; Ureta *et al.*, 1970) expected when rats were fed carbohydrate. Dibutyryl cAMP was also effective in blocking an increase in glucokinase activity. The antagonistic effect of glucagon and epinephrine on insulin-stimulated increases in glucokinase activity may be exerted through the participation of cAMP. Clearly, additional studies are required to clarify the effect of these hormones on glucokinase activity.

Injection of biotin into rats which were biotin-deficient, mildly diabetic or starved resulted in a considerable increase in hepatic glucokinase activity (Dakshinamurti and Cheak-tan, 1968a,b). The increase in glucokinase activity was blocked by inhibitors of protein synthesis. Biotin injection also increased the activity of other key glycolytic enzymes, namely, phosphofructokinase and pyruvate kinase (Dakshinamurti *et al.*, 1970). The effect of biotin on liver glucokinase activity appeared to be mediated through insulin (Dakshinamurti *et al.*, 1970). Insulin administration to alloxan diabetic rats markedly increased liver glucokinase. An increase in hepatic glucokinase activity was also produced by biotin injection but the effect was less marked than that observed when insulin was given. Simultaneous administration of both biotin and insulin did not enhance the stimulation of glucokinase any further than observed with insulin alone. Dakshinamurti *et al.* (1970) have postulated that biotin affects synthesis of glucokinase through its effect on insulin synthesis or release. A daily biotin supplement has been reported to increase serum immunoreactive insulin levels in male rats but not in female rats (Berdanier and Marshall, 1971). Biotin supplementation did not affect blood glucose levels in this study. Clearly additional studies are required to clarify the effect of biotin on hepatic glucokinase activity.

In tissues other than the liver, the low K_m hexokinases are of critical importance for the functioning of mammalian cells as virtually all cellular processes using glucose require that it be phosphorylated in the C-6 position (Sols, 1968).

Rat adipose tissue hexokinase activity is adaptive *in vivo*. It has been observed to decrease with fasting (Chandler and Moore, 1964; Moore *et al.*, 1964; Katzen and Schimke, 1965) and return to normal upon refeeding (Chandler and Moore, 1964; Hansen *et al.*, 1967). Human adipose tissue hexokinase activity also decreases upon fasting (Galton and Wilson, 1971). Hexokinase activity is also depressed in adipose tissue of alloxan-diabetic rats (Hansen *et al.*, 1967; MacLean *et al.*, 1967), but not in adipose tissue from diabetic humans (Galton and Wilson, 1971). These differences might be attributed to the type of diabetes present.

When alloxan-diabetic rats (insulin-poor) are injected with insulin, hexokinase activity increases (Hansen *et al.*, 1967); however, when human adult-onset diabetics (insulin-rich) are injected with insulin, hexokinase activity is unchanged (Galton and Wilson, 1971).

Rat adipose tissue contains types I, II, and III hexokinases (Katzen, 1967). In adipose tissue from young rats, type-II predominates, whereas in tissue of older rats, type-I predominates. Type-III hexokinase is present in low amounts in adipose tissue of both young and old rats. Katzen (1967) has noted that type-II hexokinase is present in large amounts in highly insulin responsive tissues such as the fat pad of young rats, whereas type-I hexokinase predominates in tissues that are relatively insensitive to insulin such as fat pads from older rats. Type-II hexokinase appears to be the more adaptive of the three isoenzymes in adipose tissue. When rats were fasted for 48 hours, adipose tissue type-I hexokinase was unchanged while type-II activity was decreased by 70% (Borrebaek, 1970).

When fasted rats are refed and simultaneously given inhibitors of protein synthesis, puromycin or cycloheximide, the expected increase in adipose tissue hexokinase activity was prevented (Hansen *et al.*, 1967). Incubation of adipose tissue from fasted rats, in the presence of insulin and glucose, caused an increase in hexokinase activity (Hansen *et al.*, 1967). Incubation of the tissue with insulin alone was not effective in increasing hexokinase levels; however, in the presence of either glucose or pyruvate, insulin did increase enzyme activity (Hansen *et al.*, 1970; Pilkis, 1970). This increased activity was accompanied by the incorporation of histidine-^{14}C into type-II hexokinase protein, which was blocked by actinomycin D (Hansen *et al.*, 1970). Thus the adaptive increase in adipose tissue hexokinase activity appears to result from *de novo* enzyme synthesis.

A large percentage of hexokinase activity in many tissues is bound to mitochondria (Anderson *et al.*, 1971). It has been postulated that binding of hexokinase to mitochondria may stabilize the enzyme (Borrebaek and Spydevold, 1969). The percentage of adipose tissue hexokinase associated with mitochondria is increased in carbohydrate-fed rats as compared with fasting rats (Borrebaek, 1970) and it is also increased *in vitro,* when insulin is added to the buffer (Borrebaek and Spydevold, 1969). These changes in binding appear to be associated with the type-II isoenzyme (Borrebaek, 1967, 1970; Borrebaek and Spydevold, 1969). The physiological significance of this phenomenon in the control of hexokinase activity and carbohydrate metabolism remains to be elucidated.

B. Glucose 6-Phosphate Dehydrogenase and 6-Phosphogluconate Dehydrogenase

There is a very close correlation between pentose–phosphate pathway activity and the rate of fatty acid synthesis in rat adipose tissue (Kather *et al.*, 1972a). It has been estimated that the pentose–phosphate pathway generates about 60% of the reduced nicotinamide adenine dinucleotides required for fatty acid synthesis in rat adipose tissue (Flatt and Ball, 1964; Katz *et al.*, 1966; Kather *et al.*, 1972a). Of the two pentose pathway enzymes responsible for reduced nicotinamide nucleotide production, glucose 6-phosphate dehydrogenase catalyzes the first step in the pathway and is more responsive to dietary manipulation than is 6-phosphogluconate dehydrogenase.

It is now well-established that rat liver glucose 6-phosphate dehydrogenase activity responds to dietary manipulations. Upon refeeding a high carbohydrate diet to previously fasted rats, hepatic glucose 6-phosphate dehydrogenase activity increases to levels several fold higher than observed in livers of nonfasted controls (H. M. Tepperman and Tepperman, 1958, 1963; J. Tepperman and Tepperman, 1958; Johnson and Sassoon, 1967; Szepesi and Freedland, 1969a; Szepesi *et al.*, 1972; Sassoon *et al.*, 1973). Potter and Ono (1961) demonstrated that puromycin would prevent an increase in hepatic glucose 6-phosphate dehydrogenase activity in refed rats suggesting that the increase in activity during refeeding resulted from *de novo* enzyme synthesis. Further experiments revealed that while the "overshoot" in enzyme activity was also blocked by 8-azaguanine the return of hepatic glucose 6-phosphate dehydrogenase activity to pre-fasting levels was not prevented. It was postulated that the overshoot in enzyme activity requires synthesis of additional RNA whereas additional RNA synthesis was not required for the return of enzyme activity to normal levels.

A number of studies have been directed at identifying the dietary component responsible for the marked increase in hepatic glucose 6-phosphate dehydrogenase activity observed when fasted rats are refed. When protein-free or protein-deficient diets are fed to previously fasted rats, hepatic glucose 6-phosphate or glucose 6-phosphate plus 6-phosphogluconate dehydrogenase activity was not increased (De La Garza *et al.*, 1970; McDonald and Johnson, 1965; Niemeyer *et al.*, 1962; Perez *et al.*, 1964; Vaughan and Winders, 1964; Peraino, 1967). Also, when rats were switched from a high-protein, carbohydrate-free diet to a high-carbohydrate, protein-free diet, hepatic glucose 6-phosphate dehydrogenase activity decreased 5-fold (Szepesi and Freedland, 1968a). Conversely when rats were switched from a protein-free to the carbohydrate-free diet, enzyme activity increased 9-fold. Thus adequate dietary protein is required for the adaptive increase in rat hepatic glucose 6-phosphate dehydrogenase activity.

In the presence of adequate dietary protein, an increase in dietary carbohydrate intake stimulates glucose 6-phosphate dehydrogenase activity. A number of studies have been directed at elucidating the role of dietary carbohydrate and insulin secretion on glucose 6-phosphate dehydrogenase activity. Weber and Convery (1966) concluded that insulin brings about the pronounced rise in glucose 6-phosphate dehydrogenase activity, observed in refeeding a high-carbohydrate diet and that the dietary carbohydrate merely stimulated insulin secretion. Others have also shown a relationship between insulin and glucose 6-phosphate dehydrogenase activity. Daily insulin injection increased hepatic glucose 6-phosphate dehydrogenase activity in both short-term (5 days) and longer term (80 days) studies (Berdanier *et al.*, 1971b; Freedland *et al.*, 1966). When insulin was injected into fasted-refed rats, the increase in hepatic glucose 6-phosphate dehydrogenase activity was 40-fold in contrast to a 10-fold increase observed in animals refed without insulin injection (Weber and Convery, 1966). Insulin injection into rats fed glucose, fructose, or high-protein diets increased glucose 6-phosphate dehydrogenase activity about 2-fold in all cases (Berdanier *et al.*, 1971b; Freedland *et al.*, 1966). Changes in food intake concomitant with insulin injection were not reported (Weber and Convery, 1966; Freedland *et al.*, 1966) or were unchanged (Berdanier *et al.*, 1971b).

Sassoon *et al.* (1968) and Rudack *et al.* (1971a) have reported that hepatic glucose 6-phosphate dehydrogenase activity is directly related to dietary carbohydrate intake. It was postulated that insulin has no direct effect on hepatic glucose 6-phosphate dehydrogenase activity (Rudack *et al.*, 1971a). Large doses of insulin did increase enzyme activity but it also stimulated dietary carbohydrate intake. This points out the need to carefully monitor food intake in studies of this nature.

Examination of the effect of various dietary carbohydrate sources on glucose 6-phosphate dehydrogenase activity revealed that sucrose or fructose-containing diets stimulate hepatic enzyme activity to a greater extent than glucose-containing diets (Chang *et al.*, 1971; Chevalier *et al.*, 1972; Freedland *et al.*, 1966; Szepesi and Michaelis, 1972). This stimulation in enzyme activity results even though fructose is less effective than glucose in stimulating insulin release (Grodsky and Forsham, 1966). Furthermore, dietary fructose intake is similar to dietary glucose intake (Chevalier *et al.*, 1972).

It is apparent that neither dietary carbohydrate intake nor insulin secretion alone can totally account for the changes observed in glucose

6-phosphate dehydrogenase activity. In the absence of insulin, dietary carbohydrate did not stimulate an increase in hepatic glucose 6-phosphate dehydrogenase activity (Weber, 1972) and similarly in the absence of dietary carbohydrate, insulin injections did not increase enzyme activity (Sassoon *et al.*, 1968). Also, the response of hepatic and adipose tissue glucose 6-phosphate dehydrogenase activity may in certain situations, vary independently of each other. Chevalier *et al.* (1972) have shown that ingestion of sucrose markedly increased hepatic, but not adipose, tissue glucose 6-phosphate dehydrogenase activity to values above those observed when glucose was consumed. The effect of dietary carbohydrate on glucose 6-phosphate dehydrogenase activity in lipogenic tissues is complex and may be related to the effect of the diet on fatty acid synthesis in these tissues. Fructose consumption increased the rates of fatty acid synthesis in the liver and decreased rates of synthesis in adipose tissue of rats (Chevalier *et al.*, 1972; Romsos and Leveille, 1974).

In addition to the effects that dietary protein and carbohydrate have on glucose 6-phosphate dehydrogenase activity in the rat, dietary lipids also influence its activity. Feeding a high-fat diet to previously fasted rats suppressed recovery of hepatic glucose 6-phosphate dehydrogenase activity (Johnson and Sassoon, 1967; Niemeyer *et al.*, 1962). Glucose 6-phosphate dehydrogenase activity was also depressed in adipose tissue homogenates of rats and pigs fed high-fat diets (Wiley and Leveille, 1973; Allee *et al.*, 1971c).

Several reports suggest that the composition of the fatty acids consumed may directly influence the activity of glucose 6-phosphate dehydrogenase. Muto and Gibson (1970) studied the effects of adding methyl esters of various fatty acids to a fat-free diet. Administration of small quantities of polyunsaturated fatty acids decreased hepatic glucose 6-phosphate dehydrogenase activity, whereas saturated fatty acids were without effect. Similar results were obtained by Yugari and Matsuda (1967) and by Bartley and Abraham (1972). Century (1972) clearly demonstrated that, under the condition of his experiments, hepatic glucose 6-phosphate dehydrogenase activity responded to the fatty acid composition of the diet and not to the level of lipid ingested (Table I). Hepatic glucose 6-phosphate dehydrogenase activity was not changed when the level of fat in the diet was increased from 0.6% to 15%, provided the level of essential fatty acids remained constant. Conversely glucose 6-phosphate dehydrogenase activity was markedly decreased when the level of essential fatty acids in the diet was increased while maintaining the total lipid content constant.

The mechanism(s) whereby glucose 6-phosphate dehydrogenase

Table I

Effect of Dietary Fat on Hepatic Glucose 6-Phosphate Dehydrogenase Activity in the Rat[a]

% of Total diet		Glucose 6-dehydrogenase activity
Dietary fat	Essential fatty acids (ω6)	(μmoles/gm/min)
0.5	0.25	18
7.0	0.24	18
15.0	0.23	19
7.0	3.48	4
15.0	3.58	5
15.0	7.45	2

[a] From Century (1972). Rats were fed the experimental diets for 4 to 7 weeks. Dietary fats consisted of various combinations of corn oil and beef fat.

activity responds to changes in the composition of dietary long-chain fatty acids has not been elucidated. It is questionable whether saturated fatty acids are absorbed with the same efficiency as polyunsaturated fatty acids. It would appear that some of the effects of dietary fatty acid composition on glucose 6-phosphate dehydrogenase activity may be explained on the basis of differences in efficiency of absorption of the test lipids. Undoubtedly other factors are also involved. For example, the rate at which various fatty acids are activated and metabolized would affect the tissue concentration of long-chain acyl-CoA derivatives. Long-chain acyl-CoA derivatives affect fatty acid synthesis (Section II,H) and consequently, the need for reducing equivalents and metabolite flux through the pentose pathway. Essential fatty acids are precursors of prostaglandins. The effect of dietary fatty acids on prostaglandin metabolism and the subsequent effect of prostaglandins on lipid metabolism and glucose 6-phosphate dehydrogenase activity is another area that warrants further study.

Medium-chain triglycerides are less effective in depressing hepatic and adipose tissue glucose 6-phosphate plus 6-phosphogluconate dehydrogenase activity than is corn oil (Wiley and Leveille, 1973). Addition of cholesterol to the diet also depressed hepatic, but not adipose tissue, glucose 6-phosphate dehydrogenase activity (Tsai and Dyer, 1973).

Alterations in glucose 6-phosphate dehydrogenase activity closely parallel the demand for reduced nicotinamide adenine dinucleotides to support fatty acid synthesis. Changes in glucose 6-phosphate dehydrogenase activity may be secondary to changes in utilization of the reduced nicotinamide nucleotides caused by alterations in the rates of fatty acid synthesis (H. M. Tepperman and Tepperman, 1958, 1961; J. Tepperman and Tepperman, 1958; Leveille, 1966). That control of the glucose 6-phosphate dehydrogenase reaction is achieved by cofactor limitation and not substrate limitation is suggested by the fact that the cellular glucose 6-phosphate concentration exceeds the K_m of glucose 6-phosphate dehydrogenase for this substrate by a factor of more than three (Greenbaum *et al.*, 1971; Kather *et al.*, 1972b). Sassoon *et al.* (1973) have suggested that the inducer of rat liver glucose 6-phosphate dehydrogenase activity may be a metabolite of glycogen.

The observations of the effect of diet on glucose 6-phosphate dehydrogenase activity in the rat are consistent with the hypothesis that changes in the activity of this enzyme are in response to changes in the rate of fatty acid synthesis. For example, dietary fructose stimulates hepatic, but not adipose tissue, lipogenesis and glucose 6-phosphate dehydrogenase activity (Zakim *et al.*, 1967; Chevalier *et al.*, 1972; Romsos and Leveille, 1974). Substitution of dietary fat for dietary carbohydrate decreases hepatic lipogenesis (Hill *et al.*, 1958) as well as glucose 6-phosphate dehydrogenase activity (Niemeyer *et al.*, 1962). Unsaturated fatty acids are more effective than saturated fatty acids and corn oil is more effective than medium chain triglycerides in depressing fatty acid synthesis as well as glucose 6-phosphate dehydrogenase activity (Du and Kruger, 1972; Wiley and Leveille, 1973).

While it is evident that glucose 6-phosphate dehydrogenase activity responds to various dietary treatments, the mechanisms initiating this response are not clear. It has recently been postulated that cAMP may be involved in the regulation of glucose 6-phosphate dehydrogenase activity (Rudack *et al.*, 1971b). These authors concluded that an increase in the level of cAMP may repress synthesis of lipogenic enzymes as well as induce synthesis of several gluconeogenic enzymes. Intraperitoneal injection of either cAMP or glucagon prevented the increase in hepatic glucose 6-phosphate dehydrogenase activity usually observed after refeeding a high-carbohydrate diet. However, Beitner and Naor (1972c) were unable to inhibit rat adipose tissue NADP-glucose 6-phosphate dehydrogenase activity by addition of cAMP to the tissue preparation. It is not possible, at this time, to conclude whether the effect of cAMP on glucose 6-phosphate dehydrogenase was a direct effect or whether it was secondary to a decrease in fatty acid synthesis caused by cAMP involvement at another point (Tepperman and Tepperman, 1972).

To gain further insight into the effect of diet on pentose-pathway dehydrogenases several investigators have determined the rate of enzyme synthesis and degradation in rats fed various diets. Rat liver glucose 6-phosphate dehydrogenase synthesis and degradation rates have been estimated by following the time course of change in enzyme specific activity between different steady state levels of the enzyme (Rudack *et al.*, 1971a; Szepesi and Freedland, 1969b). Berlin and Schimke (1965) have demonstrated that it is possible to determine the half-life of an enzyme using this technique. It must be assumed that the enzyme activity is proportional to the amount of enzyme protein which appears to be a valid assumption for glucose 6-phosphate dehydrogenase (Gozukara *et al.*, 1972). Other assumptions of this method are discussed by Szepesi and Freedland (1969b).

The half-life of hepatic glucose 6-phosphate dehydrogenase was estimated to be 36–39 hours when rats were changed from a protein-free to a 90% casein diet (Szepesi and Freedland, 1969b). Administration of cortisol to these rats increased the total enzyme activity without altering the rate of enzyme degradation. Feeding 60% glucose or 60% fructose-containing diets to rats that had been fed a commercial diet or fasted previously, or injecting insulin into glucose fed rats resulted in a half-life for hepatic glucose 6-phosphate dehydrogenase of 15 hours (Rudack *et al.*, 1971a). This value is lower than that reported by Szepesi and Freedland (1969b). Under these conditions, the observed changes in enzyme activity were attributed to changes in rate of enzyme synthesis. However, when rats were switched from a 60% glucose diet to the commercial diet, the half-life for glucose 6-phosphate dehydrogenase was increased to 69 hours (Rudack *et al.*, 1971a).

Rudack *et al.* (1971c) have also used kinetic analysis to evaluate the effect of dietary carbohydrate and fat on synthesis and degradation of rat liver 6-phosphogluconate dehydrogenase. The results obtained are similar to those obtained for glucose 6-phosphate dehydrogenase (Rudack *et al.*, 1971a). Refeeding fasted rats with either a 60% glucose or a 60% fructose-containing diet, administration of insulin to glucose-fed animals or addition of fat to a high-carbohydrate diet resulted in a half-life of 13.5 hours for rat liver 6-phosphogluconate dehydrogenase. The rate of enzyme synthesis was changed to account for the new steady state levels of enzyme activity (Rudack *et al.*, 1971c). Szepesi and Freedland (1968b) estimated that the half-life of 6-phosphogluconate dehydrogenase in rat liver was between 1 and 2 days in rats fed high carbohydrate diets. For both glucose 6-phosphate and 6-phosphogluconate dehydrogenase estimates of half-life obtained by Rudack *et al.* (1971a,c) are considerably lower than those obtained by Szepesi and Freedland (1968b, 1969b). The experimental methods and diets appear to be similar. Resolution of these differences must await further investigation.

Schimke and Doyle (1970) suggest that diet-induced differences in steady-state enzyme levels appear to be mediated largely through altered rates of synthesis. The limited data available suggest that changes in pentose-pathway dehydrogenase activity are also mediated largely through altered rates of synthesis. Further studies are needed to compare kinetic analysis, isotope incorporation, and immunochemical methods of determining enzyme synthesis and degradation rates under various dietary regimens.

Many enzymes catalyzing reactions involved at biochemical branch points exist in multiple forms which may be involved in metabolic control (Stifel and Herman, 1972). Multiple forms of glucose 6-phosphate and 6-phosphogluconate dehydrogenases have been reported in rat liver and adipose tissue and in human liver (Beitner and Naor, 1972a,b; Holten, 1972; Hori and Yonezawa, 1972; Lahat *et al.*, 1972; Schmukler, 1970; Taketa and Watanabe, 1971; Watanabe and Taketa, 1971; Watanabe *et al.*, 1972). The physiological significance of these forms and the effect of diet upon them remains to be established.

The relative importance of the pentose-pathway dehydrogenases for the generation of reduced nicotinamide adenine dinucleotides in ruminant adipose tissue (Baldwin *et al.*, 1973; Ingle *et al.*, 1972a) and chick liver (Goodridge, 1968a,b; Madappally *et al.*, 1971) may be of less significance than these dehydrogenases are in tissues of the rat or pig (Flatt and Ball, 1964; Katz *et al.*, 1966; Kather *et al.*, 1972a; O'Hea and Leveille, 1968, 1969a,b). Ruminant adipose tissue and chick liver are active lipogenic organs in which other NADP-linked dehydrogenases, such as NADP-isocitrate dehydrogenase and NADP-malate dehydrogenase, appear to play a significant role in the generation of reducing equivalents for fatty acid synthesis (Baldwin *et al.*, 1973; Ingle *et al.*, 1972a,b; Goodridge, 1968a,b; Madappally *et al.*, 1971; Yeh *et al.*, 1970). In contrast to the rat, the pentose-pathway dehydrogenases in chick liver exhibit low activity and are not responsive to dietary manipulations (Goodridge, 1968a; Madappally *et al.*, 1971). The physiological significance of this observation is not readily apparent. In ruminants, where little glucose is absorbed from the digestive tract, the low activity of the pentose-pathway would be a mechanism for conserving glucose (Ingle *et al.*, 1972a).

C. Phosphofructokinase and Aldolase

It is generally thought that phosphofructokinase plays an important role in the regulation of glycolysis (Passonnneau and Lowry, 1964; Denton and Martin, 1970). Fasting or alloxan diabetes markedly decrease rat liver phosphofructokinase activity while refeeding a high-carbohydrate diet or insulin injection increase phosphofructokinase activity above that observed in normally fed animals (Weber *et al.*, 1966). Examination of rat adipose tissue phosphofructokinase revealed that neither alloxan diabetes nor fasting significantly depressed phosphofructokinase activity while refeeding a high-carbohydrate diet or adapting animals to one 2-hour meal per day did result in a small increase in enzyme activity (Pogson and Denton, 1967; Leveille, 1970). More recently, Orevi *et al.* (1972) improved the assay for the determination of adipose tissue phosphofructokinase activity and demonstrated that adipose tissue phosphofructokinase did respond to dietary manipulation. Fasting rats for 96 hours depressed adipose tissue phosphofructokinase activity by 50% and refeeding the animals for only 12 hours returned enzyme activity to values above the fed control (Table II). It is not clear at this time whether the changes in phosphofructokinase activity resulted from activation-deactivation of existing enzyme protein or whether the changes in enzyme activity observed were due to an alteration in the quantity of enzyme protein present.

Many small molecular weight effectors have been implicated in the regulation of substrate flux through the phosphofructokinase step. Partial purification of rat adipose tissue phosphofructokinase and subsequent assays indicated that ATP and citrate acted as inhibitors of the enzyme while ADP, AMP, cAMP, phosphate, and sulfate activated the enzyme (Denton and Randle, 1966). The enzyme was very sensitive to activation by cAMP.

The physiological significance of some of the small molecular weight effectors on phosphofructokinase activity *in vivo* is not entirely clear. Glucagon or insulin produced rapid changes in hepatic phosphofructokinase activity in the rat (Taunton *et al.*, 1972). Glucagon injection increased hepatic cAMP levels about 3-fold and depressed phosphofructokinase activity about 2-fold within 4 minutes after injection while

Table II

Effect of Fasting and Refeeding on the Activity of Glycolytic Enzymes in Adipose Tissue[a,b]

Treatment	Hexokinase	Phosphofructokinase	Aldolase
Fed *ad libitum*	64	61	37
Fasted			
24 hr	52	36	25
96 hr	39	32	18
Refed			
12 hr	41	105	31
48 hr	98	67	46

[a] From Orevi *et al.* (1972).

[b] Enzyme values expressed in nmoles per minute per milligram of protein.

insulin injection increased enzyme activity by 50% without affecting cAMP levels. Similar results were obtained for pyruvate kinase. The role of cAMP in the alteration of phosphofructokinase activity is not clear. The *in vivo* effects observed (Taunton *et al.*, 1972) are opposite to the *in vitro* effects of cAMP (Denton and Randle, 1966) on phosphofructokinase. However, the *in vivo* experiments were conducted with hepatic enzyme while the *in vitro* experiments were conducted with the adipose tissue enzyme.

The physiological significance of the role of adenine nucleotides in the regulation of phosphofructokinase activity has been questioned. Adenine nucleotide levels in rat adipose tissue were not changed by fasting or fasting-refeeding (Ballard, 1972). Furthermore, alloxan diabetes did not change the level of adenine nucleotides in rat adipose tissue compared with normally fed rats (Denton *et al.*, 1966). Addition of either insulin or adrenalin to rat adipose tissue incubations was also without affect on adenine nucleotide levels (Denton *et al.*, 1966). Denton *et al.* (1966) also observed that the concentration of ATP in rat adipose tissue was only about 50% of that observed in rat heart or diaphragm, while the concentration of ADP and AMP were higher than that observed in the other tissues. Consequently, the ATP/ADP + AMP ratio is markedly different in adipose tissue than that observed in the other tissues. Changes in hepatic adenine nucleotide levels with fasting, refeeding a high-fat or a high-carbohydrate diet, or with alloxan diabetes in the rat are also not consistent with the hypothesis that adenine nucleotides play a major role in the regulation of glycolysis via an effect on phosphofructokinase activity (Start and Newsholme, 1970; Greenbaum *et al.*, 1971).

The *in vitro* demonstration of citrate as an inhibitor of adipose tissue phosphofructokinase might be in conflict with the role of citrate as an activator of acetyl-CoA carboxylase (Denton and Randle, 1966; Lane *et al.*, 1971). If these effects of citrate were present *in vivo*, glucose conversion to fatty acids would be inhibited by citrate at one point and activated by citrate at another point. Citrate levels in adipose tissue from either fed or fasted-refed rats were similar (Ballard, 1972; Denton *et al.*, 1966[2]). Examination of citrate levels in the livers of fed, fasted, alloxan-diabetic rats, or in rats refed either a high-carbohydrate or a high-fat diet were not consistent with changes in glycolysis (Greenbaum *et al.*, 1971). Thus, *in vivo* whole tissue concentrations of adenine nucleotides and citrate do not appear to be consistent with the hypothesis (and *in vitro* demonstration) that they are major modifiers of phosphofructokinase activity in adipose tissue and liver of the rat. Of course, the effect of cell

[2] See also Ballard and Hanson (1969).

compartmentation and other modifiers of effective metabolite levels, such as the ATP·Mg relationship and metabolite binding (Passonneau and Lowry, 1964; Sols and Marco, 1970) cannot be disregarded.

Start and Newsholme (1970) have suggested that fructose 6-phosphate may act as a modulator for hepatic phosphofructokinase. Greenbaum *et al.* (1971) obtained a good correlation between fructose 6-phosphate levels and the rate of glycolysis in rat liver under various dietary regimens known to affect lipogenesis. Hepatic fructose 6-phosphate levels were decreased by about 50% in fasted rats or in rats refed a high fat diet; however, in alloxan-diabetic animals injected with insulin or in animals refed a high-carbohydrate diet, the fructose 6-phosphate levels were returned to normal. Similarly glucose 6-phosphate and fructose 6-phosphate levels in rat adipose tissue were decreased upon fasting and increased upon refeeding a high-carbohydrate diet (Ballard, 1972; Orevi *et al.*, 1972). Another important point was that an increase in hepatic fructose 6-phosphate level raised the K_i for citrate inhibition of hepatic phosphofructokinase allowing a sufficient concentration of extramitochondrial citrate for fatty acid synthesis without inhibiting phosphofructokinase.

Orevi *et al.* (1972) have suggested that aldolase may participate in the control of glycolysis in rat adipose tissue. Aldolase activity in rat adipose tissue was lower than that of hexokinase or phosphofructokinase and was also decreased upon fasting (Table II). Aldolase activity in rat liver, unlike adipose tissue, was higher than that of glucokinase or phosphofructokinase (Orevi *et al.*, 1972) and does not appear to be adaptive (Adelman *et al.*, 1966). In adipose tissue, aldolase activity may be of physiological significance in the control of glycolysis (Orevi *et al.*, 1972).

D. Pyruvate Kinase

As with glucokinase and phosphofructokinase, the regulatory role of hepatic pyruvate kinase is well-established (Weber *et al.*, 1967). Its activity is important in the regulation of the dynamic balance between gluconeogenesis and glycolysis in the liver. Fasting and alloxan diabetes decrease hepatic pyruvate kinase activity while refeeding, following a fast, or an insulin injection increase enzyme activity to levels above those observed in normally fed rats (Weber *et al.*, 1966; Orevi *et al.*, 1972). Rat liver pyruvate kinase activity is increased by feeding high-carbohydrate diets and decreased by feeding a high-protein diet (Freedland *et al.*, 1966). Further, fructose feeding increased enzyme activity to a greater extent than did glucose-containing diets (Szepesi and Freedland, 1968a,b).

In contrast to results obtained in the rat, hepatic pyruvate kinase activity in the chicken did not appear to be regulated by dietary changes or by physiological changes known to affect lipogenesis (Pearce, 1971a,b,c). Feeding either glucose, fructose or fat-containing diets did not alter hepatic pyruvate kinase activity in the chicken, but had marked effects on the rat enzyme (Pearce, 1971c). Hepatic pyruvate kinase as well as phosphofructokinase activities were also unchanged with the onset of egg-laying, a condition known to increase citrate cleavage enzyme and malic enzyme activities in the chicken (Pearce, 1971b).

Like the chicken liver enzyme, pyruvate kinase activity in rat adipose tissue responds only minimally to dietary manipulations. Rat adipose tissue pyruvate kinase activity was not decreased in fasted or alloxan-diabetic animals (Orevi *et al.*, 1972); however, refeeding a high-carbohydrate diet to previously fasted animals did increase adipose tissue pyruvate kinase activity (Pogson and Denton, 1967). Allowing rats only one 2-hour meal per day, a condition known to increase adipose tissue lipogenesis, increased adipose tissue pyruvate kinase activity only slightly (Chakrabarty and Leveille, 1968).

Pyruvate kinase from rat liver is affected by a number of small molecular weight modifiers including ATP as an inhibitor and fructose diphosphate as an activator (Weber *et al.*, 1967, 1968; Sols and Marco, 1970). Rat liver contains two distinct pyruvate kinase enzymes; the major type (Type L) is subject to allosteric feed-forward control by fructose diphosphate while the minor component (Type M) is not (Tanaka *et al.*, 1967a,b). The L-type pyruvate kinase is adaptive while the M-type is not (Middleton and Walker, 1972). Chicken liver pyruvate kinase is also markedly stimulated by fructose diphosphate (Leveille, 1969). Fructose diphosphate enhances enzyme activity by reducing the K_m for its substrate phosphoenol pyruvate. Recently it was demonstrated that the L-type pyruvate kinase in rat liver can exist in an oxidized or a reduced form (Van Berkel *et al.*, 1973). These forms have different kinetic properties and may be involved in the regulation of enzyme activity.

Taunton *et al.* (1972) have shown that insulin and glucagon produce rapid reciprocal changes in the activity of rat liver pyruvate kinase. This observation is similar to their observation of the effect of these hormones on phosphofructokinase. The changes in enzyme activity occurred within minutes after injection of the hormone, implying direct activation of the enzyme rather than enzyme synthesis (Taunton *et al.*, 1972). When hepatic pyruvate kinase was assayed in the presence of fructose diphosphate, a brief overnight fast did not affect total enzyme activity. However, when assayed in the absence of fructose diphosphate, the brief fast decreased enzyme activity possibly because of a decrease in fructose diphosphate in the liver of the starved rat (Bailey *et al.*, 1968).

Pyruvate kinase in rat adipose tissue exists in two interconvertible forms (Pogson, 1968a,b). One of the forms resembles the allosteric pyruvate kinase of rat liver in sensitivity to fructose diphosphate; the other form is insensitive to activation by fructose diphosphate (Pogson, 1968b). Fructose diphosphate affects the interconversion of the two forms. The K_a of fructose diphosphate of adipose tissue pyruvate kinase is higher than that of the liver enzyme; however, fructose diphosphate levels also appear to be higher in the adipose tissue than in rat liver (Pogson, 1968b). The ratio of glucose 6-phosphate to fructose diphosphate in rat liver is about 20:1 (Greenbaum *et al.*, 1971) while the ratio is less than 2:1 in adipose tissue from fed animals (Ballard, 1972). Adipose tissue lacks fructose diphosphatase (Weber *et al.*, 1966) which might account for part of the difference.

Pyruvate kinase activity from both rat liver and rat adipose tissue is strongly inhibited by alanine (Seubert and Schoner, 1971; Marco *et al.*, 1971). The role of alanine as a negative effector of hepatic pyruvate kinase under conditions of increased gluconeogenesis has been discussed (Seubert and Schoner, 1971); however, the physiological significance of alanine inhibition of the adipose tissue enzyme is less clear. Rat adipose tissue is capable of converting pyruvate to glycerol (Ballard *et al.*, 1967; Reshef *et al.*, 1967; Leveille, 1967b). If this pathway is operative in the intact animal there must be strict regulation of pyruvate kinase.

Greenbaum *et al.* (1971) have postulated that the effect of fructose diphosphate on pyruvate kinase might be analogous to the effect of fructose 6-phosphate on phosphofructokinase. Fructose diphosphate level doubles in the liver when fasted rats are refed a high-carbohydrate diet (Greenbaum *et al.*, 1971). The ATP/ADP·Pi ratio also increases, but the increase in fructose diphosphate increases the K_i for ATP allowing glycolysis to proceed in the presence of an increased ATP level. Fructose diphosphate levels also double in the adipose tissue when fasted rats are refed (Ballard, 1972).

E. Pyruvate Dehydrogenase

It has been suggested that the pyruvate dehydrogenase complex is a likely candidate for metabolic regulation since pyruvate occupies a central position in metabolism (Reed, 1969). Pyruvate dehydrogenase catalyzes the first and apparently irreversible step in pyruvate oxidation. Control of pyruvate dehydrogenase has been ascribed to feedback inhibition by acetyl-CoA and/or NADH (Reed, 1969). More recently interconversion of active and inactive forms of pyruvate dehydrogenase by a phosphorylation-dephosphorylation reaction sequence has been considered as a mechanism for the control of pyruvate oxidation (Linn *et al.*, 1969). The active form of the enzyme is dephosphorylated while the inactive form is phosphorylated. This regulation of mammalian pyruvate dehydrogenase resembles that of glycogen synthetase (Larner and Villar-Palasi, 1971).

Pyruvate dehydrogenase in the rat liver and adipose tissue occurs in the active and the inactive form and the ratio of the two changes with the dietary state of the animal (Coore *et al.*, 1971; Denton *et al.*, 1971; Jungas, 1971; Soling and Bernhard, 1971; Wieland *et al.*, 1972). In the fed rat, about one-sixth of the total hepatic pyruvate dehydrogenase is in the active form while the active form accounts for about two-thirds of the total pyruvate dehydrogenase in adipose tissue (Wieland *et al.*, 1972; Jungas, 1971). Injection of fructose into rats, significantly increased the active form of hepatic pyruvate dehydrogenase within a few minutes without affecting total pyruvate dehydrogenase activity (Soling and Bernhard, 1971). Concomitant with the rapid increase in the active form of the enzyme, hepatic levels of ATP were dramatically decreased. Fasting rats for 24 hours decreased the active component from 20% down to 10% of the total hepatic pyruvate dehydrogenase activity, while refeeding for 90 minutes with glucose, returned the active fraction to 21% of total enzyme activity (Wieland *et al.*, 1972; Patzelt *et al.*, 1973). Injection of insulin or nicotinic acid increased and injection of oleate decreased, the active portion of rat liver pyruvate dehydrogenase. In all these cases, the total pyruvate dehydrogenase activity in rat liver was unchanged (Wieland *et al.*, 1972). In these experiments, metabolic states associated with decreased plasma free fatty acids (feeding, insulin or nicotinic acid injection) resulted in an increase in the active form of pyruvate dehydrogenase, whereas a rise in plasma free fatty acids (fasting or oleate injection) was associated with a decrease in the active form (Wieland *et al.*, 1972).

Patzelt *et al.* (1973) perfused rat livers to examine the effect of various substrates on pyruvate dehydrogenase activity. Addition of fructose or pyruvate to the perfusion medium, increased the active form of the enzyme from 20% up to about 60–70% of total activity, while perfusion with glucose or lactate resulted in only slight increases in the active form of the enzyme. Perfusion of the liver with fatty acids reduced the active form of the enzyme. In all these cases, the total activity of pyruvate dehydrogenase remained unchanged. Incubation of isolated rat liver mitochondria with pyruvate also increased the active form of the enzyme (Portenhauser and Wieland, 1972). Palmitoyl carnitine counteracted the effect of pyruvate on pyruvate dehydrogenase. These studies suggest that hepatic pyruvate dehydrogenase interconversion is under metabolic control and that pyruvate and fatty acids exert antagonistic effects on the steady state of the active and inactive forms.

The role of insulin in glucose transport and the resulting increase in fatty acid synthesis in rat adipose tissue is well-established; however, insulin also stimulates fatty acid synthesis from pyruvate (Coore *et al.*, 1971; Jungas, 1971). It has now been demonstrated that insulin increases the active form of pyruvate dehydrogenase in adipose tissue incubations (Coore *et al.*, 1971; Denton *et al.*, 1971; Jungas, 1971; Taylor *et al.*, 1973; Jungas and Taylor, 1972; Sica and Cuatrecasas, 1973). Glucose, fructose, or pyruvate additions also activate adipose tissue pyruvate dehydrogenase (Taylor *et al.*, 1973; Martin *et al.*, 1972; Jungas and Taylor, 1972) while oleate, octanoate, or betahydroxybutyrate decreased pyruvate dehydrogenase activity (Taylor *et al.*, 1973). Addition of ATP to an incubation medium decreased the active form of adipose tissue pyruvate dehydrogenase (Coore *et al.*, 1971; Denton *et al.*, 1971; Jungas, 1971; Martin *et al.*, 1972) while depletion of adipose tissue ATP levels caused by the addition of oligomycin, dinitrophenol, or anaerobic incubation activated pyruvate dehydrogenase (Taylor *et al.*, 1973). It has been suggested that cAMP is involved in the regulation of adipose tissue pyruvate dehydrogenase; however, the experiments reported to date have been inconclusive (Coore *et al.*, 1971; Denton *et al.*, 1971; Jungas, 1971; Schimmel and Goodman, 1972; Sica and Cuatrecasas, 1973).

Sica and Cuatrecasas (1973) have shown that insulin increased the total activity, as well as the activity of the active form, of pyruvate dehydrogenase in homogenates of rat adipose tissue. Their data suggest that significant changes in synthesis and/or degradation of pyruvate dehydrogenase can occur within 60 minutes. Pyruvate dehydrogenase is a complex enzyme whose activity is subject to complicated metabolic and hormonal control.

F. Citrate Cleavage Enzyme

In the conversion of glucose to fatty acids in adipose tissue and liver, acetyl-CoA is formed in the cell mitochondria and must be transferred to the cell cytoplasm to be incorporated into fatty acids. Lowenstein (1968) has discussed several mechanisms whereby mitochondrial acetyl-CoA might be transferred to the cell cytoplasm. Direct diffusion of acetyl-CoA out of the mitochondria is too slow to meet the demands of rapid lipogenesis (Spencer and Lowenstein, 1962). The possibility of acetate transfer via acetyl carnitine as being of major significance in the transfer of acetyl units for lipogenesis (Greville, 1969) has also been rejected.

A third possibility is transfer of acetyl-CoA from the mitochondria to the cytoplasm as free acetate. This would involve the action of acetyl-CoA hydrolase within the mitochondria and the reactivation of acetate via acetyl-CoA synthetase extramitochondrially (Lowenstein, 1968). Acetyl-CoA synthetase is present in rat liver and adipose tissue (Barth *et al.*, 1971, 1972; Kornacker and Lowenstein, 1965b; Martin and Denton, 1970; Murthy and Steiner, 1972) and is located primarily in the cell cytoplasm (Barth *et al.*, 1971, 1972; Martin and Denton, 1970). Acetyl-CoA synthetase is located primarily within the cell mitochondria in chick liver; however, acetyl-CoA synthetase activity in the cell cytoplasm is still sufficient to accommodate the most rapid rates of acetate conversion to fatty acids observed in isolated chick hepatocytes (Goodridge, 1973d).

Rat liver cytoplasmic acetyl-CoA synthetase appears to be adaptive, increasing about 3-fold upon refeeding a high-carbohydrate diet following a fast (Barth *et al.*, 1972). The activity of hepatic acetyl-CoA synthetase also decreases in diabetic rats and increases when the diabetic animals are given insulin (Kornacker and Lowenstein, 1965b). Murthy and Steiner (1972) have demonstrated that addition of oleate to a supernatant incubation mixture from rat liver, inhibited acetate incorporation into fatty acids to a greater extent than it did that of acetyl-CoA incorporation into fatty acids. They concluded that long-chain fatty acids may affect acetyl-CoA synthetase as well as acetyl-CoA carboxylase activity. Rat adipose tissue acetyl-CoA synthetase showed a pattern similar to the liver enzyme except that the increase after fasting was greater (10-fold) for the adipose tissue enzyme than that observed in liver (3-fold) (Barth *et al.*, 1972).

The origin of cytoplasmic acetate in the rat is not clear. Both liver and adipose tissue mitochondria contain acetyl-CoA hydrolase activity; however, the activities are very low (Lowenstein, 1968; Martin and Denton, 1970). Other suggested sources of acetate include ethanol (Krebs and Perkins, 1970), pyruvate and fatty acids (Hepp *et al.*, 1966), amino acids (Murthy and Steiner, 1972), and cecal fermentation (Yang *et al.*, 1970). Acetate is present in rat blood (Hochheuser *et al.*, 1964; Murthy and Steiner, 1973) and liver (Murthy and Steiner, 1973). The physiological significance of cytoplasmic acetyl-CoA synthetase in lipogenesis in liver and adipose tissue of nonruminants is not clear at this time. Citrate cleavage enzyme activity (see following discussion) is up to 5-fold higher in rat liver and adipose tissue than the activity of acetyl-CoA synthetase observed under a number of conditions (Kornacker and Lowenstein, 1965b; Hanson and Ballard, 1967; Martin and Denton, 1970).

A fourth possibility for the transfer of acetyl-CoA from the mitochondria is as citrate or a near biochemical relative (Lowenstein, 1968).

Extramitochondrially, citrate may be cleaved by action of citrate cleavage enzyme to form acetyl-CoA and oxaloacetate. It is generally accepted that citrate cleavage enzyme is of major importance in supplying extramitochondrial acetyl-CoA for lipogenesis (Greville, 1969).

Alloxan diabetes, fasting or fat-feeding decreases citrate cleavage enzyme activity in rat liver and adipose tissue (Kornacker and Lowenstein, 1964, 1965a,b; Brown and McLean, 1965; Srere and Foster, 1967; Berdanier *et al.*, 1971a; Wiley and Leveille, 1973; Gibson *et al.*, 1972) while refeeding a high-carbohydrate diet to previously fasted rats, markedly stimulates citrate cleavage enzyme activity in both liver and adipose tissue (Kornacker and Ball, 1965; Kornacker and Lowenstein, 1965a; Gibson *et al.*, 1972). Alloxan diabetes also decreases citrate cleavage enzyme activity in pig adipose tissue (Romsos *et al.*, 1971). Fat-feeding or fasting also decreases citrate cleavage enzyme activity in chicken liver (Goodridge, 1968b; Pearce, 1968; Yeh *et al.*, 1970), and pig adipose tissue (Allee *et al.*, 1971a,b,c; O'Hea and Leveille, 1969b). Other evidence in support of a role for citrate cleavage enzyme in lipogenesis, including the observation that citrate is an excellent source of carbon for lipogenesis in the fed rat, but not in the fasted rat, is presented by Greville (1969).

Yeh and Leveille (1970, 1971) have suggested that the depression in hepatic fatty acid synthesis, observed when chicks were fasted or fed high-fat diets, might be related in part to a reduction of citrate cleavage enzyme activity caused by a limitation in the availability of free CoA. They postulated that the increased level of circulating fatty acids observed when chicks were fasted or fed a high-fat diet would compete with citrate cleavage enzyme for cytoplasmic CoA. Hepatic long-chain acyl-CoA derivatives were increased and free CoA levels decreased when chicks were fasted or fed a high-fat diet (Yeh and Leveille, 1971; Goodridge, 1973c). Thus, changes in total tissue CoA levels are consistent with the hypothesis that dietary manipulation of hepatic free CoA levels may be involved in the regulation of citrate cleavage enzyme activity. In isolated chick liver cells, the ratio of acetyl-CoA to free CoA is much greater (Goodridge, 1973d) than that observed in freeze-clamped liver tissue (Yeh and Leveille, 1971). The reason(s) for this difference is not readily apparent.

Gibson *et al.* (1972) determined the half-life values for citrate cleavage enzyme in rat liver. The half-life for hepatic citrate cleavage enzyme was 20 hours when the rats were fed normally and 12 hours when they were refed following a fast. Enzyme activity was 6-fold higher in the refed state than in the normal state. Corresponding with this increase in enzyme activity was an 11-fold increase in the rate of citrate cleavage enzyme synthesis. Thus, Gibson *et al.* (1972) concluded that changes in the synthetic rate were the major determinant of net enzyme formation.

While the citrate cleavage reaction appears to be of prime importance in lipogenesis for many species, it appears to be of much less importance for the ruminant. Only a limited quantity of dietary hexoses are absorbed by ruminant animals (Lindsay, 1970); over 50% of the digested energy presented to the ruminant is absorbed in the form of volatile fatty acids, namely, acetate, propionate, and butyrate (Annison and Armstrong, 1970). Glucose incorporation into fatty acids as well as citrate cleavage enzyme activity is very low in ruminant adipose tissue (Hanson and Ballard, 1967; Ingle *et al.*, 1972a,b; Young *et al.*, 1969), the predominant site of fatty acid synthesis in both the ovine and bovine (Ingle *et al.*, 1972a,b). Furthermore, citrate cleavage enzyme activity from bovine adipose tissue was not altered by an 8-day fast or a high soluble-carbohydrate diet while two other lipogenic enzymes (glucose 6-phosphate dehydrogenase and malic enzyme) were increased in tissues of animals fed the high-carbohydrate diet (Young *et al.*, 1969).

In agreement with the high rates of fatty acid synthesis from acetate in ruminant adipose tissue (Ballard *et al.*, 1969; Ingle *et al.*, 1972b), acetyl-CoA synthetase is present (Hanson and Ballard, 1967; Chakrabarty and Romans, 1972). Acetyl-CoA synthetase activity in bovine adipose tissue is higher than that observed in rat adipose tissue (Hanson and Ballard, 1967). Furthermore, since acetyl-CoA synthetase activity in bovine adipose tissue is about 2-fold higher than acetyl-CoA carboxylase activity, it should not be rate-limiting in the conversion of acetate to fatty acids. For ruminant animals, acetyl-CoA synthetase, rather than citrate cleavage enzyme, appears to be of prime importance in supplying cytoplasmic acetyl-CoA for lipogenesis. It should be noted that intravenous infusion of glucose did increase citrate cleavage enzyme activity in ovine adipose tissue about 50-fold, to reach an activity similar to that observed in rat adipose tissue (Ballard *et al.*, 1972). However, under normal physiological conditions acetate, rather than glucose, is probably the more important lipogenic substrate for ruminant animals.

G. Malic Enzyme

Under conditions of enhanced lipogenesis, it has been demonstrated that the pentose pathway can provide only about 60% of the reducing equivalents required for fatty acid synthesis in rat adipose tissue (Flatt and Ball, 1964; Katz *et al.*, 1966). Transhydrogenation of NADH to NADPH in the cell cytoplasm is another potential source of reducing equivalents for fatty acid synthesis. It is now established that the conversion of oxaloacetate, formed in the citrate cleavage reaction, to malate via malate dehydrogenase and conversion of malate to pyruvate via malic enzyme provides a pathway for the generation of extramitochondrial NADPH (Wise and Ball, 1964; Young *et al.*, 1964; Leveille and Hanson, 1966). Ballard and Hanson (1967) have proposed that the pyruvate generated via the malic enzyme reaction in rat adipose tissue may be converted back to oxaloacetate in the presence of an extramitochondrial pyruvate carboxylase, thus forming a cycle. Martin and Denton (1970) have questioned the existence of extramitochondrial pyruvate carboxylase in rat adipose tissue. However, the absence of extramitochondrial pyruvate carboxylase would not negate the importance of malic enzyme in generating NADPH. Pyruvate formed by the malic enzyme reaction could enter the mitochondria for further metabolism.

Following the suggestion that malic enzyme may be involved in supplying NADPH to support fatty acid synthesis, numerous reports have appeared demonstrating that malic enzyme activity parallels that of fatty acid synthesis. Fasting or fat-feeding decreased malic enzyme activity in rat and chick liver and in rat, pig, and bovine adipose tissue (Allee *et al.*, 1971a,c, 1972; Goodridge, 1968b; Leveille and Hanson, 1966; Fabry *et al.*, 1970; Leveille and Yeh, 1972; Martin *et al.*, 1973; O'Hea and Leveille, 1969b; Pande *et al.*, 1964; Szepesi *et al.*, 1971a,b; Wise and Ball, 1964; Yeh *et al.*, 1970; Young *et al.*, 1964, 1969; Gibson *et al.*, 1972). Malic enzyme activity was also decreased in adipose tissue extracts from alloxan-diabetic rats and pigs (Wise and Ball, 1964; Romsos *et al.*, 1971).

When rats or pigs were fasted and then refed a high-carbohydrate diet, malic enzyme activity increased to values higher than observed in *ad libitum* fed control animals (Szepesi *et al.*, 1971a,b; Martin *et al.*, 1973). However, not all animals respond alike. The malic enzyme response of obese pigs and mice to fasting and refeeding appears to be impaired. Malic enzyme activity in lean pigs, decreased to about 60% of control fed values after 7 days of fasting and then increased to 175% of control fed values, 14 days after refeeding was initiated (Martin *et al.*, 1973). Malic enzyme activity also decreased when obese pigs were fasted; however, the adaptive increase in malic enzyme activity following refeeding was much slower than that observed in adipose tissue extracts from lean pigs. Malic enzyme in liver and adipose tissue of obese mice, also failed to show characteristic responses to fasting and refeeding observed in normal mice (Anderson and Hollifield, 1966; Kaplan and Fried, 1973). It should be noted that the rates of fatty acid synthesis in obese mice also do not appear to be influenced as much by a fast, as is fatty acid synthesis in control mice (Bray and York, 1971). Thus, it is important to recognize that not all animals respond alike to dietary manipulations and to consider these differences in the design and interpretation of experiments.

As discussed in Section II,B an increase in glucose 6-phosphate dehydrogenase activity in liver when fasted rats are refed requires an adequate intake of protein. The response of rat and chick hepatic malic enzyme to protein-free diets (Leveille and Yeh, 1972; Vaughan and Winders, 1964; Taketa *et al.*, 1970) is in contrast to that observed for glucose 6-phosphate dehydrogenase in rat liver. Feeding a nitrogen-free diet to previously fasted rats, increased hepatic malic enzyme activity, but not glucose 6-phosphate dehydrogenase activity (Vaughan and Winders, 1964; Taketa *et al.*, 1970). Similarly, hepatic malic enzyme activity, but not glucose 6-phosphate or NADP-isocitrate dehydrogenase activity, increased when rats were switched from a diet containing 18% lactalbumin to one containing 0.5% lactalbumin (Frenkel *et al.*, 1972). Leveille and Yeh (1972) fed chicks on a 3-day cycle; a protein-adequate diet was fed for 2 days, followed by a protein-free diet for 1 day (Table III). This continued for 7 cycles and the chicks were killed on day 1, 2, and 3 of the 8th cycle. Hepatic malic enzyme activity and *in vitro* rates of fatty acid synthesis were highest after feeding chicks the protein-free diet for one day. Glucose 6-phosphate dehydrogenase activity was not assayed in the chick studies since it is not adaptive and does not appear to be as important as malic enzyme, in furnishing reducing equivalents for fatty acid synthesis in chick liver (Section II,B).

Changes in malic enzyme activity are highly correlated with changes in the rate of fatty acid synthesis. It has now been demonstrated that changes in malic enzyme activity in chick and rat liver are due to changes in enzyme content rather than activation or inhibition of pre-

Table III

EFFECT OF A PROTEIN-FREE DIET ON MALIC ENZYME ACTIVITY AND FATTY ACID SYNTHESIS IN CHICK LIVER[a]

Day of cycle[b]	Malic enzyme[c]	Fatty acid synthesis[d]
1	169 ± 18	114 ± 20
2	94 ± 18	60 ± 18
3	271 ± 22	436 ± 56

[a] From Leveille and Yeh (1972).

[b] Chicks were fed on a 3-day cycle; a protein-adequate diet was fed for 2 days, followed by a protein-free diet on the 3rd day. Chicks were killed on day 1, 2, and 3 of the 8th cycle.

[c] nmoles substrate utilized per minute per milligram protein at 25°.

[d] nmoles glucose-U-^{14}C incorporated into fatty acids per 100 mg of liver slices per 2 hours.

formed enzyme (Silpananta and Goodridge, 1971; Isohashi *et al.*, 1971; Gibson *et al.*, 1972). Silpananta and Goodridge (1971) used immunological techniques to investigate the synthesis and degradation of malic enzyme in chicken liver. When neonatal chicks were fed a commercial diet for 11 days, there was a 63-fold increase in total enzyme activity and a 54-fold increase in the rate of enzyme synthesis, suggesting that the increase in enzyme activity resulted primarily from an increase in enzyme synthesis rather than a change in rate of enzyme degradation. Gibson *et al.* (1972) reached a similar conclusion when they examined malic enzyme in rat liver. The rate of malic enzyme degradation (half-life) in 8- to 11-day-old fed chicks was 55 hours (Silpananta and Goodridge, 1971). The half-life of the enzyme in fasted neonatal chicks was much longer (350 hours) while the half-life was decreased to 28 hours in the liver from 10-day-old fasted chicks. Silpananta and Goodridge (1971) point out the difficulty in estimating enzyme degradation in fasted chicks. While the half-life of malic enzyme was decreased when 8- to 11-day-old chicks were starved, there was also an increased rate of breakdown of all liver proteins. The reason(s) for the extremely long half-life of malic enzyme in livers of the fasted neonatal chicks is unknown.

Malic enzyme is confined almost exclusively to the extramitochondrial compartment in rat liver and adipose tissue (Brdiczka and Pette, 1971). This is not true for all tissues; 70% of the malic enzyme activity in heart tissue is located in mitochondria (Brdiczka and Pette, 1971). Saito and Tomita (1973) have recently shown that the extramitochondrial compartment of rat liver contains two immunologically distinct forms of malic enzyme. They identified these as the A (adipose tissue) and the H (heart) types. The A-type malic enzyme found in rat liver responded to fasting and refeeding while the H-type malic enzyme did not. Chick liver may contain isoenzymes of malic enzyme (Silpananta and Goodridge, 1971). The physiological significance of these isoenzymes has not been established.

H. Acetyl-CoA Carboxylase

Acetyl-CoA carboxylase catalyzes the first committed step in fatty acid biosynthesis, the carboxylation of acetyl-CoA to form malonyl-CoA. This enzyme appears to play a key role in the regulation of fatty acid synthesis in animal tissues (Vagelos, 1964; Lane *et al.*, 1971; Numa *et al.*, 1970). It is well-known that the activity of acetyl-CoA carboxylase is decreased in livers from alloxan-diabetic and fasted rats and elevated upon refeeding fasted animals a fat-free, high-carbohydrate diet (Numa *et al.*, 1970). In addition to changes in the tissue concentration of acetyl-CoA carboxylase, metabolic effectors also modify the catalytic efficiency of acetyl-CoA carboxylase (Lane *et al.*, 1971). The role of citrate in the activation of acetyl-CoA carboxylase and the inhibition of enzyme activity by long-chain acyl-CoA derivatives have been reviewed (Gibson *et al.*, 1966; Lane *et al.*, 1971; Numa *et al.*, 1965, 1970; Volpe and Vagelos, 1973).

The importance of long-chain acyl-CoA derivatives in functioning as feedback inhibitors of acetyl-CoA carboxylase was suggested years ago. Korchak and Masoro (1962) observed that after a 24-hour fast, hepatic acetyl-CoA carboxylase activity as measured *in vitro*, fell by only 50%, whereas fatty acid synthesis in liver slices was depressed by 99%. Similar results were also obtained when rats were fed diets containing fat (Bortz *et al.*, 1963). Bortz and Lynen (1963a) postulated that a negative feedback mechanism might be operative at the acetyl CoA carboxylase step to control, at least in part, the rate and extent of fatty acid synthesis in liver. They pointed out that the decreased capacity of liver to synthesize fatty acids, noted in diabetes, fasting, fat-feeding, and epinephrine injection was associated with an increased flux of fat to the liver.

Experiments by Bortz and Lynen (1963a) demonstrated that the addition of long-chain acyl-CoA derivatives to a purified preparation of rat liver acetyl-CoA carboxylase inhibited enzyme activity. The inhibition appeared to be competitive with acetyl-CoA for the active site. In a subsequent report, Bortz and Lynen (1963b) demonstrated a 4-fold accumulation of long-chain acyl-CoA derivatives in livers of rats fasted for 24 hours. Long-chain acyl-CoA derivatives were examined in livers of rats made diabetic with alloxan, fasted for 48 hours, or fed fat; in all cases, long-chain acyl-CoA derivatives were elevated about 2-fold when compared with rats fed a balanced diet (Tubbs and Garland, 1964). When the starved rats were refed sugar for 48 hours, levels of long-chain acyl-CoA derivatives in the liver returned to the pre-fasting level. Greenbaum *et al.* (1971) have reported similar data.

Incubation of rat epididymal adipose tissue with various combinations of insulin, adrenalin, and albumin indicated that fatty acid synthesis and the level of long-chain acyl-CoA were inversely correlated in some, but not all, experiments (Denton and Halperin, 1968). In more recent experiments, Halestrap and Denton (1973) observed a 2- to 4-fold increase in rat acetyl-CoA carboxylase activity when adipose tissue extracts were incubated in the presence of insulin. They postulated that the observed increase in acetyl-CoA carboxylase activity resulted from the reduction in long-chain acyl-CoA derivatives that occurred in the presence of insulin.

Further examination of the effect of long-chain acyl-CoA derivatives on enzyme activity revealed, that in addition to hepatic acetyl-CoA carboxylase (Bortz and Lynen, 1963a; Numa *et al.*, 1965), citrate synthetase (Srere, 1965; Tubbs and Garland, 1964; Wieland and Weiss, 1963), fatty acid synthetase (Dorsey and Porter, 1968), glucose 6-phosphate dehydrogenase (Eger-Neufeldt *et al.*, 1965; Taketa and Pogell, 1966) and glutamate, malate, glycerol-phosphate, isocitrate, and 6-phosphogluconate dehydrogenases (Taketa and Pogell, 1966) were all inhibited by long-chain acyl-CoA derivatives. A number of authors subsequently questioned the physiological significance of enzyme inhibition by long-chain acyl-CoA (Srere, 1965; Dorsey and Porter, 1968; Taketa and Pogell, 1966; Pande and Meade, 1968; Parvin and Dakshinamurti, 1970; Eger-Neufeldt *et al.*, 1965). These authors have suggested that long-chain acyl-CoA inhibits enzyme activity by virtue of its detergent nature. Dorsey and Porter (1968) have demonstrated that sodium lauryl sulfate (a strong detergent) inhibition of pigeon liver fatty acid synthetase is similar to that observed with palmitoyl-CoA.

The suggestion that palmitoyl-CoA inhibits fatty acid synthesis by acting as an inhibitor of acetyl-CoA carboxylase activity (Bortz and Lynen, 1963a) is very appealing, especially in light of the inverse relationship observed between liver long-chain CoA compounds and *de novo* fatty acid synthesis. Goodridge (1972) reexamined the effect of palmitoyl-CoA on enzyme inhibition. He postulated that palmitoyl-CoA may function as a nonspecific detergent, as previously suggested, at concentrations at or above the critical micellar concentration, but palmitoyl-CoA may exert specific effects at lower concentrations. To test this hypothesis, Goodridge (1972) used a high concentration of albumin in the *in vitro* system to ensure that the free concentration of palmitoyl-CoA was very low and not affected by addition of the test protein. Addition of albumin to a chick liver cytosol incubation stimulated fatty acid synthesis from citrate 10-fold (Goodridge, 1972) (Table IV). Addition of palmitoyl-CoA to the albumin-containing mixture depressed fatty acid

Table IV

EFFECT OF ALBUMIN AND PALMITOYL-CoA ON FATTY ACID SYNTHESIS FROM CITRATE-^{14}C IN CHICK LIVER CYTOSOL[a]

Addition to buffer	Relative rate of fatty acid synthesis
None	100
Albumin	1050
Palmitoyl-CoA + albumin	613

[a] From Goodridge (1972).

synthesis by about 50%. Further experiments to determine if enzymes were specifically inhibited indicated that fatty acid synthetase, NADP-isocitrate dehydrogenase, malic enzyme, citrate cleavage enzyme, glutamate dehydrogenase, and pyruvate kinase activities were not affected by palmitoyl-CoA addition (Table V). Palmitoyl-CoA did specifically inhibit acetyl-CoA carboxylase activity.

Goodridge (1972) next examined the reversibility of palmitoyl-CoA inhibition of acetyl-CoA carboxylase. The enzyme inhibition was reversed by addition of more albumin, of citrate, or of (+)-palmitoylcarnitine to the reaction cuvette. This reversal of inhibition tends to rule out a detergent action of palmitoyl-CoA. Addition of free fatty acids to the reaction cuvette did not inhibit acetyl-CoA carboxylase activity. Stearoyl-CoA appeared to be a more potent inhibitor of acetyl-CoA carboxylase than palmitoyl-CoA (Goodridge, 1973d). The intracellular concentration of stearate, but not palmitate, oleate, or linoleate, was correlated with fatty acid synthesis in chick liver (Goodridge, 1973c). Goodridge (1972) pointed out that only a small portion of the tissue fatty acyl-CoA needs to be free to affect acetyl-CoA carboxylase activity, and that the concentration of free fatty acyl-CoA might change markedly with a much smaller change in total fatty acyl-CoA, depending on concentration and/or affinity of the intracellular proteins that bind fatty acyl-CoA. Inhibition of acetyl-CoA carboxylase by fatty acyl-CoA is competitive with citrate; consequently, fatty acyl-CoA and extramitochondrial citrate may play important roles in the regulation of fatty acid synthesis (Goodridge, 1972).

While the role of citrate in the activation of acetyl-CoA carboxylase *in vitro* is well-documented (Lane *et al.*, 1971), attempts to correlate

Table V
EFFECT OF PALMITOYL-COA AND FREE FATTY ACIDS ON ENZYME ACTIVITY IN CHICK LIVER[a]

Enzyme	Addition to assay	
	Palmitoyl-CoA	Free fatty acid
Acetyl-CoA carboxylase	44[b]	115[b]
Fatty acid synthetase	97	104
NADP-isocitrate dehydrogenase	106	102
Malic enzyme	102	97
Citrate cleavage enzyme	112	111
Glutamate dehydrogenase	103	—
Pyruvate kinase	113	—

[a] From Goodridge (1972).
[b] Relative enzyme activity; experimental rate divided by the control rate × 100.

changes in tissue levels of citrate with rates of fatty acid synthesis have been largely unsuccessful (Ballard, 1972; Denton and Halperin, 1968; Goodridge, 1973c; Guynn *et al.*, 1972; Gregolin *et al.*, 1968; Ryder *et al.*, 1967; Spencer and Lowenstein, 1967). Utilizing perfused rat liver or isolated chick hepatocytes (Brunengraber *et al.*, 1973; Goodridge, 1973d), it was demonstrated that the citrate content of the tissue or isolated liver cell was positively correlated with the rate of fatty acid synthesis, presumably via the ability of citrate to activate acetyl-CoA carboxylase. Unfortunately, it is not yet possible to determine the intracellular distribution of citrate. Greenbaum *et al.* (1971) have shown that, based on the calculated distribution of citrate, it is possible to have marked shifts in citrate concentration within cellular compartments with only a minimal shift in total tissue citrate level.

Long-chain fatty acyl-CoA derivatives may, in addition to their direct affect on acetyl-CoA carboxylase, inhibit citrate transport from the mitochondria to the cytoplasm (Goodridge, 1973d; Halperin and Robinson, 1972; Halperin *et al.*, 1972) as well as reduce the availability of free CoA for the citrate cleavage reaction (Yeh and Leveille, 1970, 1971). Goodridge (1973d) postulated that the direct effects of long-chain acyl-CoA derivatives and citrate on acetyl-CoA carboxylase, as well as the effect of acyl-CoA derivatives on citrate transport, would allow small changes in these metabolites to be amplified to produce large changes in the rate of fatty acid synthesis.

Cyclic-AMP inhibited fatty acid synthesis in liver slices from rats (Allred and Roehrig, 1972; Tepperman and Tepperman, 1972; Bricker and Levey, 1972b) and chicks (Allred and Roehrig, 1972; Goodridge, 1973a). The mechanism whereby cAMP inhibits fatty acid synthesis has not been established; however, the effect of cAMP on lipolysis and subsequently on long-chain acyl-CoA derivatives offers a hypothesis whereby cAMP may affect acetyl-CoA carboxylase, via long-chain acyl-CoA derivatives (Goodridge, 1973a; Tepperman and Tepperman, 1972). Alternative mechanisms have also been proposed (Tepperman and Tepperman, 1972). Cyclic-AMP depressed the activity of acetyl-CoA carboxylase in rat liver slices and may have a direct effect on the enzyme (Allred and Roehrig, 1973). Carlson and Kim (1973) have recently suggested that rat liver acetyl-CoA carboxylase exists in an active dephosphorylated form and an inactive phosphorylated form.

The effects of metabolites on acetyl-CoA carboxylase activity are rapid and allow for the short-term regulation of the enzyme; however, the tissue concentration of acetyl-CoA carboxylase also responds to dietary manipulation. Changes in the tissue concentration would aid in the longer term regulation of acetyl-CoA carboxylase activity.

Majerus and Kilburn (1969) and Nakanishi and Numa (1970) have examined the role of enzyme synthesis and degradation in the regulation of acetyl-CoA carboxylase levels in rat liver. In these studies, either chicken liver acetyl-CoA carboxylase (Majerus and Kilburn, 1969) or rat liver acetyl-CoA carboxylase (Nakanishi and Numa, 1970) was purified and subsequently used to immunize rabbits. Antibodies to chicken liver acetyl-CoA carboxylase were shown to cross-react with the rat liver enzyme (Majerus and Kilburn, 1969). The antibodies were then used to determine the amount of acetyl-CoA carboxylase present in rat liver. It was demonstrated that the changes in acetyl-CoA carboxylase activity, as measured *in vitro*, represented changes in the quantity of enzyme protein rather than activation or inhibition of preformed enzyme. Consequently, the changes in acetyl-CoA carboxylase seen after feeding various diets for several days, probably resulted from changes in the quantity of acetyl-CoA carboxylase. This conclusion is subject to the reservation that a form of acetyl-CoA carboxylase which is both inactive and immunologically unreactive is not present.

To determine whether changes in acetyl-CoA carboxylase level result from changes in rates of enzyme synthesis and/or degradation, leucine-^{3}H was employed (Majerus and Kilburn, 1969; Nakanishi and Numa, 1970; see Schimke and Doyle, 1970, for a critique of methodology). Enzyme synthesis was estimated by measuring the extent of leucine-^{3}H incorporation into protein precipitated by anti-acetyl-CoA carboxylase following leucine-^{3}H injection into the rat. The loss of radioactivity from the enzyme prelabeled with leucine-^{3}H was used as a measure of the rate of enzyme degradation. Rats were fasted, fed fat-free or fat-containing diets or injected with alloxan and the changes in liver acetyl-CoA carboxylase activity followed (Majerus and Kilburn, 1969; Nakanishi and Numa, 1970). Acetyl-CoA carboxylase activity responded as expected. Feeding a fat-free diet to previously fasted rats, increased acetyl-CoA carboxylase specific activity 6- to 8-fold. Concomitantly, leucine-^{3}H incorporation into acetyl-CoA carboxylase was 4-fold greater in the fed rats than in the fasted animals. Nakanishi and Numa (1970) accounted for the fact that labeling of total soluble protein was reflected in acetyl-CoA carboxylase labeling by expressing label in enzyme as a ratio to that in total soluble protein. Under these conditions, the 7- to 8-fold increase in acetyl-CoA carboxylase synthesis rate resulting from feeding a fat-free diet to previously fasted rats accounted for virtually all the increase in hepatic enzyme activity (6- to 8-fold) (Majerus and Kilburn, 1969; Nakanishi and Numa, 1970). Acetyl-CoA carboxylase specific activity, as well as the relative rate of synthesis in livers of diabetic rats, was similar to that observed in livers from 48-hour fasted rats (Nakanishi and Numa, 1970).

Majerus and Kilburn (1969) calculated the rate of acetyl-CoA carboxylase degradation in rat liver and observed that the loss of isotope, expressed as half-life ($t_{1/2}$), was 48 and 50 hours in rats fed a fat-free or a normal rat chow diet, respectively. In close agreement, Nakanishi and Numa (1970) observed that the $t_{1/2}$ of acetyl-CoA carboxylase in liver was 55, 59, and 59 hours in rats fed a fat-free and chow diet and in alloxan-diabetic rats, respectively. While acetyl-CoA carboxylase activity changes markedly under these conditions, enzyme degradation was virtually unchanged. Thus, under these conditions, changes in acetyl-CoA carboxylase activity can be ascribed to changes in the rate of enzyme synthesis.

It was more difficult to estimate the rate of acetyl-CoA carboxylase degradation in fasted rats since steady state conditions were not reached (Nakanishi and Numa, 1970) or were approached only near the end of the experiment (Majerus and Kilburn, 1969). Values obtained for the $t_{1/2}$ of fasted rats were 18–31 hours. Thus, it appears that the decrease in enzyme specific activity resulting from fasting may be due to both a diminished enzyme synthesis and to an increased rate of enzyme degradation.

Jansen *et al.* (1967) and Lamdin *et al.* (1969) have shown that genetically obese hyperglycemic mice (C57BL/6J-ob) have a marked increase in hepatic lipogenesis with less of an increase in extrahepatic lipogenesis when compared with non-obese mice. Nakanishi and Numa (1971) investigated the synthesis and degradation of hepatic acetyl-CoA carboxylase in these obese mice using techniques similar to those previously described for rat liver (Nakanishi and Numa, 1970). They found that the enzyme protein from the liver of obese mice was indistinguishable from that obtained from non-obese mice and that the total enzyme activity was about 10-fold higher in the livers of the obese animals. This increased enzyme activity resulted from a 7.7-fold increase in enzyme synthesis and a 1.7-fold lower rate of enzyme degradation in livers from obese as compared to non-obese mice. The half-life of the enzyme was 115 and 67 hours in the obese and non-obese mouse livers, respectively. In agreement with the effect of dietary fat and of alloxan treatment of rats (Majerus and Kilburn, 1969; Nakanishi and Numa, 1970), the increase in acetyl-CoA carboxylase activity in obese mouse liver results primarily from an increased rate of enzyme synthesis and to a lesser extent from changes in the rate of degradation. Nakanishi and Numa (1970) have postulated that changes in hepatic acetyl-CoA carboxylase activity in a steady state, i.e., feeding fat-free or fat-containing diets, in alloxan-diabetic rats or in obese and non-obese mice, result from changes in enzyme synthesis with enzyme degradation remaining relatively constant. However, enzyme degradation may play an important role in rats that are not in a steady state, i.e., fasting.

In the rat, adipose tissue is quantitatively a more important site for *de novo* fatty acid synthesis than is the liver (Leveille, 1967a). The relationship between synthesis and degradation of adipose tissue acetyl-CoA carboxylase to changes in enzyme activity in adipose tissue remains to be established. That results of synthesis and degradation obtained in one tissue cannot be indiscriminately extrapolated to another tissue is pointed out by Fritz *et al.* (1969). They observed that there were markedly different rates of degradation for lactate dehydrogenase in liver, heart, and skeletal muscle.

Acetyl-CoA carboxylase is a biotin-containing enzyme (Lynen, 1967; Wakil *et al.*, 1958). Oxman and Ball (1961) demonstrated that CO_2 production from glucose was decreased in adipose tissue from biotin-deficient rats signifying a lowered rate of fatty acid synthesis. The impairment did not appear to occur in the conversion of glucose to pyruvate, but rather in the conversion of pyruvate to fatty acids, a sequence requiring the biotin-containing enzyme acetyl-CoA carboxylase. Donaldson (1964) also observed that biotin deficiency inhibited *in vivo* lipogenesis in the carcass, but not in the liver of biotin-deficient chickens. Examination of acetyl-CoA carboxylase activity in liver and adipose tissue revealed a decreased activity in biotin-deficient rats compared with normal animals (Dakshinamurti and Desjardins, 1968, 1969). The decrease in enzyme activity was more marked in adipose tissue than in liver. Jacobs *et al.* (1970) obtained similar results.

When biotin was injected into biotin-deficient rats, acetyl-CoA carboxylase activity rapidly increased in both liver and adipose tissue (Jacobs *et al.*, 1970; Desjardins and Dakshinamurti, 1971). Biotin-^3H was recovered in adipose tissue acetyl-CoA carboxylase (Jacobs *et al.*, 1970) and the increase in enzyme activity was not prevented by prior cycloheximide injection (Desjardins and Dakshinamurti, 1971). These results suggested that the apoenzyme was present in the adipose tissue of the biotin-deficient rat and that biotin injection was associated with conversion of apoenzyme to acetyl-CoA holocarboxylase. Conversion of the apoenzyme to acetyl-CoA holocarboxylase, in the supernatant fraction of adipose tissue from deficient rats has been demonstrated by addition of biotin to the incubation medium (Jacobs *et al.*, 1970; Desjardins and Dakshinamurti, 1971). Both Jacobs *et al.* (1970) and Desjardins and Dakshinamurti (1971), have noted that the liver enzyme does not appear as sensitive to biotin deficiency and less of the liver enzyme is in the apoenzyme form than was observed for the adipose tissue enzyme in biotin-deficient rats. The differential effect of biotin deficiency on acetyl-CoA carboxylase from these two tissues remains unexplained.

I. Fatty Acid Synthetase

Fatty acid synthetase catalyzes the conversion of acetyl-CoA and malonyl-CoA, in the presence of reduced-nicotinamide adenine dinucleotide phosphate to palmitic acid. The activity of fatty acid synthetase in rat liver extracts is markedly reduced by fasting, alloxan diabetes, or fat-feeding. Conversely, fatty acid synthetase activity is markedly increased by refeeding a fat-free diet following a fast or by administration of insulin to alloxan-diabetic rats (Burton *et al.*, 1969; Craig *et al.*, 1972b; Lakshmanan *et al.*, 1972; Tweto and Larrabee, 1972). Similarly, conversion of glucose to fatty acids and fatty acid synthetase activity are both elevated in liver from genetically obese mice (Chang *et al.*, 1967) and adipose tissue from meal-fed rats (Chakrabarty and Leveille, 1969).

Lakshmanan *et al.* (1972) investigated the effect of insulin and glucagon on rat liver fatty acid synthetase. Fatty acid synthetase activity was not increased in fasted alloxan-diabetic rats refed a high carbohydrate diet unless the animals were simultaneously given insulin. Glucagon injections inhibited the increase in fatty acid synthetase activity normally observed when fasted rats were refed a high-carbohydrate diet. Since the rats injected with either insulin or glucagon consumed about the same quantity of food as control noninjected animals, Lakshmanan *et al.* (1972) postulated that the activity of rat liver fatty acid synthetase was under the control of the relative concentrations of insulin and glucagon.

Early reports indicated that acetyl-CoA carboxylase was probably the rate-limiting enzyme in the fatty acid synthesis pathway since its activity was much lower than that observed for fatty acid synthetase. However, Chang *et al.* (1967) have suggested that the low activity of acetyl-CoA carboxylase could be explained on the basis of suboptimal assay conditions. Several investigators have subsequently shown that the activities of acetyl-CoA carboxylase and fatty acid synthetase were very similar in rat, mouse, chick liver, and in rat adipose tissue (Chang *et al.*, 1967; Craig *et al.*, 1972a; Liou and Donaldson, 1973; Chakrabarty and Leveille, 1969). Consequently, it has been suggested that acetyl-CoA carboxylase may not be the rate-limiting enzyme in fatty acid synthesis under all dietary conditions (Guynn *et al.*, 1972; Porter *et al.*, 1971).

Guynn *et al.* (1972) developed a procedure for the direct measure-

Table VI
FATTY ACID SYNTHESIS AND MALONYL-CoA LEVELS IN RAT LIVER[a]

Dietary condition[b]	Fatty acid synthesis[c]	Malonyl-CoA (μmoles/gm liver)
Fed *ad libitum*	0.32 ± 0.04	0.013 ± 0.001
Fasted-refed	0.19 ± 0.01	0.012 ± 0.001
Meal-fed	0.45 ± 0.02	0.025 ± 0.002

[a] From Guynn *et al.* (1972).

[b] Fasted-refed rats were fasted for 45 hours and refed chow for 3 hours. Meal-fed rats were allowed one 3-hour meal per day and were killed 3 hours after the beginning of the third meal.

[c] *In vivo* incorporation of tritium (from ^3H_2O) into fatty acids, expressed as C_2 units per minute per gm liver.

ment of malonyl-CoA levels in rat liver. Malonyl-CoA levels were not directly related to fatty acid synthesis (Table VI). The rate of hepatic fatty acid synthesis was 70% higher in *ad libitum* fed than in fasted-refed rats; however, malonyl-CoA levels were similar in the 2 groups of animals. Rats trained to consume their food within a 3-hour period each day, exhibited a 2-fold increase in hepatic malonyl-CoA levels, but only a 40% increase in the rate of fatty acid synthesis compared to *ad libitum* fed animals. These observations suggested to Guynn *et al.* (1972) that the rate of fatty acid synthesis in rats fed a high carbohydrate diet may be limited by the ability of the liver to utilize malonyl-CoA, i.e., by the activity of fatty acid synthetase.

To gain a better understanding of factors involved in the control of fatty acid synthetase, several investigators have recently examined the synthesis and degradation rates of fatty acid synthetase. The quantity of fatty acid synthetase protein in pigeon liver (Butterworth *et al.*, 1966) and in rat liver (Burton *et al.*, 1969; Volpe *et al.*, 1973) appears to correspond with enzyme activity. Burton *et al.* (1969) have shown that the rise in fatty acid synthetase activity, following the feeding of a fat-free diet to previously fasted rats, was a result of adaptive enzyme synthesis. Livers from fasted rats had only a very small amount of fatty acid synthetase protein while refeeding brought about a 30- to 50-fold increase in the absolute amount of enzyme. Hicks *et al.* (1965) had previously shown that the rise in hepatic fatty acid synthetase activity upon refeeding was prevented by inhibitors of protein synthesis.

In a recent report from Porter's laboratory, Craig *et al.* (1972b) prepared antibodies to rat liver fatty acid synthetase and studied the effects of fasting and refeeding a fat-free diet on synthesis and degradation of the enzyme. Leucine-^{14}C pulse-labeling and subsequent isolation of hepatic fatty acid synthetase indicated that the relative rate of enzyme synthesis, in rats refed the fat-free diet, was 78-fold greater than in fasted animals and 14-fold higher than observed in animals fed a commercial fat-containing diet. The observed rates of hepatic enzyme degradation were 69, 69, and 42–53 hours in rats fed the commercial and fat-free diets and in animals fasted 48 hours, respectively. Similarly, Tweto *et al.* (1971), Tweto and Larrabee (1972) and Volpe *et al.* (1973) observed that the half-life of rat liver fatty acid synthetase was about 70 hours in the fed state and 20 hours in the fasted state. Feeding a protein-free diet mimicked the effect of fasting on hepatic fatty acid synthetase levels (Tweto and Larrabee, 1972).

In agreement with results obtained for acetyl-CoA carboxylase (Majerus and Kilburn, 1969; Nakanishi and Numa, 1970) and malic enzyme (Silpananta and Goodridge, 1971), the rate of fatty acid synthetase degradation increased in fasted animals. It is difficult to obtain an estimate of enzyme degradation in fasting animals. As Craig *et al.* (1972b) point out, even if the synthesis of fatty acid synthetase were decreased to zero, the rate of degradation must have been faster than the value observed, to account for the marked decrease in enzyme activity during the first 48 hours of the fast. They measured the enzyme degradation after a 48-hour fast when enzyme activity was near a steady state.

It appears that under steady state conditions, hepatic fatty acid synthetase levels are regulated primarily by the rate of enzyme synthesis rather than rate of degradation (Craig *et al.*, 1972b; Volpe *et al.*, 1973). The rate of fatty acid synthetase degradation may play a role in controlling enzyme level during transitional periods from one steady state level to another such as in fasting.

J. β-Hydroxy-β-methylglutaryl-CoA Reductase

β-Hydroxy-β-methylglutaryl-CoA reductase (HMG-CoA reductase) is regarded as the rate-limiting enzyme in the hepatic conversion of acetate to cholesterol (Bucher *et al.*, 1959, 1960; Linn, 1967; Siperstein and Fagan, 1966; Siperstein, 1970). Both cholesterol synthesis from acetate and hepatic HMG-CoA reductase activity are depressed by cholesterol feeding and by starvation (Linn, 1967; Siperstein and Fagan, 1966; White and Rudney, 1970; Shapiro and Rodwell, 1971; Craig *et al.*, 1972a), and undergo marked diurnal fluctuations (Kandutsch and Saucier, 1969; Hamprecht *et al.*, 1969; Higgins *et al.*, 1971; Hickman *et al.*, 1972; Huber and Hamprecht, 1972; Huber *et al.*, 1973a; Shapiro and Rodwell, 1971, 1972; Slakey *et al.*, 1972; Dugan *et al.*, 1972; Back *et al.*, 1969). After 10 hours of cholesterol feeding, acetate incorporation into cholesterol and HMG-CoA reductase activity were both reduced by 80% (Shapiro and Rodwell, 1971).

A number of investigators have examined the rhythmic pattern of HMG-CoA in an attempt to further our understanding of cholesterol synthesis and its control. It has been shown that the cyclic pattern of HMG-CoA reductase is related to the feeding pattern and not the light pattern (Dugan *et al.*, 1972). When rats were fed *ad libitum*, the increase in hepatic HMG-CoA reductase activity was associated with the dark period; however, when rats were forced to eat while the room was illuminated, the peak enzyme activity occurred shortly after the 2 hour meal and during the light period (Table VII). While the diurnal rhythm is associated with the feeding period, the rhythmicity persists even when the animals are fasted (Hamprecht *et al.*, 1969; Hickman *et al.*, 1972; Dugan *et al.*, 1972). It has been suggested that a hormonal mechanism may be involved in the diurnal pattern (Hamprecht *et al.*, 1969). In one study, adrenalectomy abolished the diurnal variation in hepatic HMG-CoA reductase (Hickman *et al.*, 1972); however, in another study adrenalectomy was without affect (Huber *et al.*, 1972). Bilateral superior cervical ganglionectomy of rats or subjecting rats to constant light or constant darkness also failed to abolish the diurnal rhythm of hepatic HMG-CoA reductase (Huber *et al.*, 1973a).

Inhibitors of protein synthesis, puromycin and cycloheximide, block the diurnal variation of mouse and rat liver HMG-CoA reductase (Kandutsch and Saucier, 1969; Shapiro and Rodwell, 1969, 1971) suggesting that the diurnal rhythm involved protein synthesis. Higgins *et al.* (1971) following the incorporation of leucine-^{3}H into HMG-CoA reductase, observed that leucine-^{3}H was incorporated into HMG-CoA reductase dur-

Table VII
DIURNAL VARIATION OF HEPATIC HMG-CoA REDUCTASE IN *Ad Libitum* FED AND MEAL-FED RATS[a]

	Meal pattern[c]	
Hours[b]	*Ad libitum*	Meal-fed
4	100[d]	15
12	23	200
16	77	204
20	138	42

[a] From Dugan *et al.* (1972).
[b] Lights were on from 0700 to 1730.
[c] Meal-fed animals were allowed to eat from 0830 to 1030.
[d] Relative values.

ing the rising portion of the cycle but was not incorporated during the falling phase. It has been suggested that alterations in HMG-CoA reductase activity can be accounted for primarily by changes in the rate of enzyme synthesis with little or no change in rate of enzyme degradation (Higgins *et al.*, 1971; Edwards and Gould, 1972; Dugan *et al.*, 1972). Using cycloheximide to block HMG-CoA reductase synthesis, Edwards and Gould (1972) estimated that the half-life of the enzyme was approximately 4.2 hours. Using kinetic analysis, the half-life of HMG-CoA reductase was estimated to be about 2 hours (Dugan *et al.*, 1972; Hamprecht *et al.*, 1969). The short half-life of this enzyme is consistent with its marked diurnal variation.

A number of dietary factors are capable of altering hepatic cholesterol synthesis. However, data on the effect of diet, other than feeding diets containing cholesterol or fasting, on specific enzymes involved in cholesterol synthesis are limited. Craig *et al.* (1972a) have examined the effect of fasting, feeding fat-free diets and cholesterol-containing diets on hepatic HMG-CoA reductase activity in the rat (Table VIII). Addition of fat to the diet increased hepatic HMG-CoA reductase activity and cholesterol synthesis in the rat (Craig *et al.*, 1972a; Goldfarb and Pilot, 1972). Goldfarb and Pilot (1972) noted a progressive increase in hepatic HMG-CoA reductase activity as the level of corn oil in the diet was increased from 0 to 5 to 20%. The rats were trained to consume their food during an 8-hour period each day. When the diet containing 20% corn oil was fed, the level of HMG-CoA reductase started to increase before the 8-hour meal was offered. The authors speculated that this increase may have reflected an adaptation whereby bile acids were being synthesized in preparation for intake of diets containing lipid. An increased rate of bile acid synthesis would increase the demand for the cholesterol synthesis and HMG-CoA reductase activity.

Many dietary factors known to increase the rate of hepatic cholesterol synthesis, such as an increased level of dietary fat or protein and an

Table VIII

Effect of Dietary Regimen on Enzymes in Rat Liver[a]

Nutritional state	HMG-CoA reductase	Fatty acid synthetase	Acetyl-CoA carboxylase
Fed 4% fat diet	100[b]	100	100
Fasted	3	15	29
Fed fat-free diet	43	460	330
Fed 4% fat + 2% cholesterol diet	21	79	97

[a] From Craig *et al.* (1972a).
[b] Relative values.

increased polyunsaturated:saturated fatty acid ratio are also known to increase bile acid excretion (Yeh and Leveille, 1973; McGovern and Quackenbush, 1973). Whether the effect of these dietary factors on cholesterol synthesis is primary or a secondary response to their effect on bile acid synthesis remains to be established. Since the response of HMG-CoA reductase activity to cholestyramine (a bile acid sequestering agent) is not identical to the response of the enzyme to high fat diets, Goldfarb and Pilot (1972) have suggested that several mechanisms are probably involved in the stimulation of HMG-CoA reductase activity.

HMG-CoA reductase activity in livers of neonatal rats remain near adult levels during the first week after birth, but then reductase activity decreases and remains low until weaning at which time the activity increases to the adult level (McNamara *et al.*, 1972). Cycloheximide failed to block the increase in HMG-CoA reductase activity that occurred at weaning. In subsequent experiments, an inhibitor of HMG-CoA reductase was observed in the supernatant fraction of liver homogenates from suckling rats. An inhibitor of reductase activity was also found in raw milk. The nature of the inhibitor, apparently not cholesterol, and its role in the regulation of cholesterol synthesis is unknown at this time.

That β-hydroxy-β-methylglutaric acid (HMG) may be involved in the regulation of cholesterol synthesis has been demonstrated by Beg and Lupien (1972). Addition of HMG, but not cholesterol, to rat liver slice incubations blocked cholesterol synthesis from acetate. Further experiments indicated that the site of HMG inhibition was at the step mediated by HMG-CoA reductase; however, its mode of action is unknown. Whether HMG affects HMG-CoA reductase synthesis or degradation, inhibits enzyme activity or has another mode of action remains to be established.

Insulin injection stimulates rat liver HMG-CoA reductase activity (Lakshmanan *et al.*, 1973; Huber *et al.*, 1973b). A subcutaneous injection of insulin increased hepatic HMG-CoA reductase activity 2- to 7-fold within 2–3 hours after the injection (Lakshmanan *et al.*, 1973). The response was present in normal and diabetic rats as well as in animals that did not have access to food. This effect of insulin on hepatic HMG-CoA reductase was completely blocked by simultaneous glucagon administration. Huber *et al.* (1973b) observed that glucagon had a biphasic effect on HMG-CoA reductase. They postulated that the initial increase in HMG-CoA reductase activity, resulting from the injection of glucagon might have resulted from the insulintropic effect of glucagon. Addition of cAMP to an *in vitro* system containing rat liver slices markedly depressed cholesterol synthesis from acetate (Bricker and Levey, 1972a,b). The reduction in acetate conversion into cholesterol, as well as into fatty acids, in the presence of cAMP occurred without a concomitant decrease in acetate oxidation. The point at which cAMP affects acetate conversion into cholesterol remains to be established; however, the *in vivo* experiments of Lakshmanan *et al.* (1973) suggest that cAMP might affect HMG-CoA reductase activity.

In an attempt to determine whether HMG-CoA reductase is the rate-limiting enzyme in cholesterol synthesis, a number of situations have been examined. The variation in HMG-CoA reductase is sufficient to account for the variation observed in the conversion of acetate to cholesterol (Slakey *et al.*, 1972) and the changes in enzyme activity and rate of cholesterol synthesis are closely associated (Dugan *et al.*, 1972). However, Dugan *et al.* (1972) were able to dissociate enzyme activity and rate of synthesis. When rats, accustomed to a single 2-hour meal, were fasted on the day they were killed, hepatic HMG-CoA reductase activity still increased at meal time but cholesterol synthesis from acetate remained depressed. Slakey *et al.* (1972) also found that cholesterol synthesis from mevalonate was altered when rats were fed a fat-free diet suggesting a secondary control point beyond HMG-CoA reductase. Similar results have been reported by Shah (1973). Dugan *et al.* (1972) have also postulated that there may be another rate-limiting enzyme acting before HMG-CoA reductase, possibly HMG-CoA synthetase (White and Rudney, 1970). Sugiyama *et al.* (1972) have isolated two isoenzymes of HMG-CoA synthetase from cytoplasm of chicken liver. Cholesterol feeding markedly depressed the cytoplasmic HMG-CoA synthetase activity. Effects on the specific isoenzymes are unknown.

III. Overview

Following the recognition that adipose tissue was a dynamic, metabolically active tissue, the relative role of liver and adipose tissue to total *de novo* fatty acid synthesis was investigated. It is now apparent that the relative importance of these tissues varies with the species. Based on present knowledge, adipose tissue appears to be the major organ contributing to *de novo* fatty acid synthesis in the nonlactating pig and ruminant while the liver is more important in birds and presumably man. In rats and mice, both organs contribute significantly to *de novo* fatty acid synthesis. These observations are important to our further understanding of control mechanisms involved in the regulation of fatty acid synthesis. For example, hepatocytes are freely permeable to glucose while a major control point in glucose metabolism in adipose tissue is at the level of glucose entry into the adipocyte. Information is accumulating which indicates that the ratios of various metabolites in adipose tissue, such as the adenine nucleotide ratio or the glucose 6-phosphate to fructose 6-phosphate ratio, may differ from those observed in the liver of the same animal. In species, such as the rat, where both liver and adipose tissue contribute to *de novo* fatty acid synthesis, dietary manipulations generally affect both tissues in a similar fashion; however, there are exceptions. For example, rats fed fructose exhibit higher lipogenic enzyme activities in liver and lower activities in adipose tissue than rats fed glucose. These observations serve to emphasize the importance of considering enzyme activity and the control of metabolism in relation to the whole animal.

Changes in the activities of many of the enzymes discussed in Section II, closely paralleled changes in rates of fatty acid synthesis. However, it is important to note that the activities of many of these enzymes respond to rather than cause changes in fatty acid synthesis. The increase in fatty acid synthesis observed when rats were converted from nibblers to meal-eaters was not dependent upon an increased activity of glucose 6-phosphate dehydrogenase or 6-phosphogluconate dehydrogenase (Leveille, 1966). The increase in adipose tissue fatty acid synthesis preceded an increase in enzyme activity by about 2 days. Rats fasted for 48 hours and then refed a high-carbohydrate protein-free diet for 24-hours exhibited a 70-fold increase in hepatic glucose conversion to fatty acids without a concomitant change in glucose 6-phosphate dehydrogenase activity (Taketa *et al.*, 1970).

Malic enzyme activity also appears to respond to changes in fatty acid synthesis rather than control the rate of lipogenesis (Allee *et al.*, 1972; Leveille, 1966; Romsos *et al.*, 1971; Yeh and Leveille, 1970; Yeh *et al.*, 1970). When alloxan-diabetic pigs were given insulin injections, the rate of fatty acid synthesis in adipose tissue slices increased more than 4-fold within 24 hours while malic enzyme activity was not significantly increased during that time (Romsos *et al.*, 1971). Malic enzyme activity did increase later. *In vivo* and *in vitro* rates of hepatic fatty acid synthesis were depressed 5- to 10-fold within one hour after chicks were force fed corn oil (Yeh *et al.*, 1970). During this time malic enzyme activity was unchanged.

Foster and Srere (1968) tested the hypothesis that citrate cleavage enzyme regulated the rate of fatty acid synthesis in rat liver. When fasted rats were refed, the *in vitro* rate of hepatic fatty acid synthesis from citrate increased about 40-fold while citrate cleavage enzyme activity remained unchanged. When rats were injected with alloxan, fatty acid synthesis decreased 5-fold within 3 hours with little or no change in citrate cleavage enzyme activity. Similar experiments have demonstrated that changes in fatty acid synthesis precede changes in citrate cleavage enzyme activity in chick liver (Goodridge, 1968b; Yeh and Leveille, 1970; Yeh *et al.*, 1970) and in pig adipose tissue (Allee *et al.*, 1972; O'Hea and Leveille, 1969b; Romsos *et al.*, 1971). Unlike the results reported for the rat, chick, and pig, citrate cleavage enzyme activity closely paralleled changes in hepatic fatty acid synthesis in mice (Smith and Abraham 1970). However, since pyruvate and acetate were equally effective as precursors for fatty acid synthesis, Smith and Abraham (1970) concluded that citrate cleavage enzyme activity was always maintained at a level that would not limit fatty acid synthesis.

The observation of Korchak and Masoro (1962) that hepatic acetyl-CoA carboxylase activity fell only 50%, whereas fatty acid synthesis was depressed by 99% after a 24-hour fast suggested that changes in acetyl-CoA carboxylase resulted from a depression in lipogenesis rather than caused it. Similarly, when mice were weaned or when glucose was injected into neonatal chicks, changes in fatty acid synthesis preceded changes in acetyl-CoA carboxylase activity (Smith and Abraham, 1970; Goodridge, 1973b). Nishikori *et al.* (1973) studied the time course of changes in hepatic acetyl-CoA carboxylase activity, citrate, long-chain acyl-CoA derivatives, and the rate of fatty acid synthesis in liver slices of rats refed a fat-free, high-carbohydrate diet following a fast. Long-chain acyl-CoA levels decreased and citrate levels increased within 4 hours after feeding. The rate of fatty acid synthesis from acetate also increased during this period; however, the activity of acetyl-CoA carboxylase remained unchanged until 8 hours after the initiation of feeding.

Few studies have dealt with the time course of changes in fatty acid synthesis and fatty acid synthetase activity. Goodridge (1973b) incubated 18-day-old chick embryos in an atmosphere of 100% oxygen for 24 hours and increased hepatic fatty acid synthetase activity 2-fold without a concomitant increase in fatty acid synthesis. When mice were weaned, changes in fatty acid synthetase activity occurred more rapidly than changes in citrate cleavage or acetyl-CoA carboxylase activity, and closely paralleled changes in the capacity of liver slices to synthesize fatty acids (Smith and Abraham, 1970). This close correlation does not necessarily imply that fatty acid synthetase is controlling fatty acid synthesis. Guynn *et al.* (1972) have suggested that the quantity of hepatic fatty acid synthetase might regulate the rate of fatty acid synthesis in rats fed high-carbohydrate diets.

Unlike enzymes involved in fatty acid synthesis, a change in HMG-CoA reductase activity appears to precede changes in hepatic acetate conversion to cholesterol (Dugan *et al.*, 1972). This suggests that there might be a rate-limiting step prior to mevalonate formation. When rats trained to consume one 2-hour meal per day were fasted for one day, HMG-CoA reductase still exhibited a diurnal variation; however, acetate conversion to cholesterol remained low and unchanged (Dugan *et al.*, 1972). Thus it is possible to dissociate HMG-CoA reductase activity and cholesterol synthesis in rat liver.

In acute experiments, it is possible to have marked fluctuations in metabolic flux without affecting enzyme activity, as measured *in vitro*. Allosteric control of enzyme activity probably plays a major role in the rapid regulation of metabolic flux. Nonetheless, measurements of enzyme activity still contribute to our understanding of metabolism. Adaptive changes in enzyme content do reflect sustained changes in metabolic flux and such adaptations are likely involved in the longer term regulation of metabolism.

Information available on the enzymes discussed in Section II, suggest that changes in the rate of enzyme synthesis and to a lesser extent in enzyme degradation are involved in the alteration of enzyme content. An increase in enzyme activity is usually associated with a marked increase in the rate of enzyme synthesis with a lesser change in the rate of enzyme degradation. The rate of enzyme synthesis is markedly decreased as enzyme activity is reduced, and the rate of enzyme degradation may be increased under these conditions. Mechanism(s) whereby diet, hormones, metabolic flux, and metabolite stabilization of the enzyme interact to produce these changes in enzyme content awaits further study.

References

Adelman, R. C., Spolter, P. D., and Weinhouse, S. (1966). *J. Biol. Chem.* **241**, 5467.
Allee, G. L., Baker, D. H., and Leveille, G. A. (1971a). *J. Nutr.* **101**, 1415.
Allee, G. L., Baker, D. H., and Leveille, G. A. (1971b). *J. Anim. Sci.* **33**, 1248.
Allee, G. L., O'Hea, E. K., Leveille, G. A., and Baker, D. H. (1971c). *J. Nutr.* **101**, 869.
Allee, G. L., Romsos, D. R., Leveille, G. A., and Baker, D. H. (1972). *J. Nutr.* **102**, 1115.
Allred, J. B., and Roehrig, K. L. (1972). *Biochem. Biophys. Res. Commun.* **46**, 1135.
Allred, J. B., and Roehrig, K. L. (1973). *J. Biol. Chem.* **248**, 4131.
Anderson, J., and Hollifield, G. (1966). *Metab., Clin. Exp.* **15**, 1092.
Anderson, J. W., Herman, R. H., Tyrrell, J. B., and Cohn, R. M. (1971). *Amer. J. Clin. Nutr.* **24**, 642.
Annison, E. F., and Armstrong, D. G. (1970). *In* "Physiology of Digestion and Metabolism in the Ruminant" (A. T. Phillipson, ed.), p. 442. Oriel Press, Newcastle upon Tyne, England.
Back, P., Hamprecht, B., and Lynen, F. (1969). *Arch. Biochem. Biophys.* **133**, 11.
Bailey, E., Stirpe, F., and Taylor, C. B. (1968). *Biochem. J.* **108**, 427.
Baldwin, R. L., Reichl, J. R., Louis, S., Smith, N. E., Yang, Y. T., and Osborne, E. (1973). *J. Dairy Sci.* **56**, 340.

Ballard, F. J. (1972). *Biochim. Biophys. Acta* **273,** 110.
Ballard, F. J., and Hanson, R. W. (1967). *J. Lipid Res.* **8,** 73.
Ballard, F. J., and Hanson, R. W. (1969). *Biochem. J.* **112,** 195.
Ballard, F. J., Hanson, R. W., and Leveille, G. A. (1967). *J. Biol. Chem.* **242,** 2746.
Ballard, F. J., Hanson, R. W., and Kronfeld, D. S. (1969). *Fed. Proc., Fed. Amer. Soc. Exp. Biol.* **28,** 218.
Ballard, F. J., Filsell, O. H., and Jarrett, I. G. (1972). *Biochem. J.* **126,** 193.
Barth, C., Sladek, M., and Decker, K. (1971). *Biochim. Biophys. Acta* **248,** 24.
Barth, C., Sladek, M., and Decker, K. (1972). *Biochim. Biophys. Acta* **260,** 1.
Bartley, J. C., and Abraham, S. (1972). *Biochim. Biophys. Acta* **280,** 258.
Beg, Z. H., and Lupien, P. J. (1972). *Biochim. Biophys. Acta* **260,** 439.
Beitner, R., and Naor, Z. (1972a). *Biochim. Biophys. Acta* **268,** 761.
Beitner, R., and Naor, Z. (1972b). *Biochim. Biophys. Acta* **276,** 572.
Beitner, R., and Naor, Z. (1972c). *Biochim. Biophys. Acta* **286,** 437.
Berdanier, C. D., and Marshall, M. W. (1971). *Nutr. Rep. Int.* **3,** 383.
Berdanier, C. D., Szepesi, B., Moser, P., and Diachenko, S. (1971a). *Proc. Soc. Exp. Biol. Med.* **137,** 668.
Berdanier, C. D., Szepesi, B., Diachenko, S., and Moser, P. (1971b). *Proc. Soc. Exp. Biol. Med.* **137,** 861.
Berlin, C. M., and Schimke, R. T. (1965). *Mol. Pharmacol.* **1,** 149.
Borrebaek, B. (1967). *Biochim. Biophys. Acta* **141,** 221.
Borrebaek, B. (1970). *Biochem. Med.* **3,** 485.
Borrebaek, B., and Spydevold, O. (1969). *Diabetologia* **5,** 42.
Bortz, W. M., and Lynen, F. (1963a). *Biochem. Z.* **337,** 505.
Bortz, W. M., and Lynen, F. (1963b). *Biochem. Z.* **339,** 77.
Bortz, W. M., Abraham, S., and Chaikoff, I. L. (1963). *J. Biol. Chem.* **238,** 1266.
Bray, G. A., and York, D. A. (1971). *Physiol. Rev.* **51,** 598.
Brdiczka, D., and Pette, D. (1971). *Eur. J. Biochem.* **19,** 546.
Bricker, L. A., and Levey, G. S. (1972a). *Biochem. Biophys. Res. Commun.* **48,** 362.
Bricker, L. A., and Levey, G. S. (1972b). *J. Biol. Chem.* **247,** 4914.
Brown, J., and McLean, P. (1965). *Nature (London)* **207,** 407.
Brunengraber, J., Boutry, M., and Lowenstein, J. M. (1973). *J. Biol. Chem.* **248,** 2656.
Bucher, N. R. L., McGarrahan, K., Gould, E., and Loud, A. V. (1959). *J. Biol. Chem.* **234,** 262.
Bucher, N. R. L., Overath, P., and Lynen, F. (1960). *Biochim. Biophys. Acta* **20,** 491.
Burton, D. N., Collins, J. M., Kennan, A. L., and Porter, J. W. (1969). *J. Biol. Chem.* **244,** 4510.
Butterworth, P. D. W., Guchwait, R. B., Baum, H., Olsen, E. B., Margolis, S. A., and Porter, J. W. (1966). *Arch. Biochem. Biophys.* **116,** 453.
Carlson, C. A., and Kim, K. (1973). *J. Biol. Chem.* **248,** 378.
Century, B. (1972). *J. Nutr.* **102,** 1067.
Chakrabarty, K., and Leveille, G. A. (1968). *J. Nutr.* **96,** 76.
Chakrabarty, K., and Leveille, G. A. (1969). *Proc. Soc. Exp. Biol. Med.* **136,** 1051.
Chakrabarty, K., and Romans, J. R. (1972). *Comp. Biochem. Physiol.* **41B,** 603.
Chandler, A. M., and Moore, R. O. (1964). *Arch. Biochem. Biophys.* **108,** 183.
Chang, H. C., Seidman, I., Teebor, G., and Lane, M. D. (1967). *Biochem. Biophys. Res. Commun.* **28,** 682.

Chang, M. L. W., Lee, J. A., Schuster, E. M., and Trout, D. L. (1971). *J. Nutr.* **101**, 323.
Chevalier, M. M., Wiley, J. H., and Leveille, G. A. (1972). *J. Nutr.* **102**, 337.
Coore, H. G., Denton, R. M., Martin, B. R., and Randle, P. J. (1971). *Biochem. J.* **125**, 115.
Craig, M. C., Dugan, R. E., Muesing, R. A., Slakey, L. L., and Porter, J. W. (1972a). *Arch. Biochem. Biophys.* **151**, 128.
Craig, M. C., Nepokroeff, C. M., Lakshmanan, M. R., and Porter, J. W. (1972b). *Arch. Biochem. Biophys.* **152**, 619.
Dakshinamurti, K., and Cheah-tan, C. (1968a). *Can. J. Biochem.* **46**, 75.
Dakshinamurti, K., and Cheah-tan, C. (1968b). *Arch. Biochem. Biophys.* **127**, 17.
Dakshinamurti, K., and Desjardins, P. R. (1968). *Can. J. Biochem.* **46**, 1261.
Dakshinamurti, K., and Desjardins, P. R. (1969). *Biochim. Biophys. Acta* **176**, 221.
Dakshinamurti, K., Tarrago-Litvak, L., and Hong, H. C. (1970). *Can. J. Biochem.* **48**, 493.
De La Garza, S. A., Tepperman, H. M., and Tepperman, J. (1970). *J. Nutr.* **100**, 1027.
Denton, R. M., and Halperin, M. L. (1968). *Biochem. J.* **110**, 27.
Denton, R. M., and Martin, B. R. (1970). *In* "Adipose Tissue: Regulation and Metabolic Functions" (B. Jeanrenaud and D. Hepp, eds.), p. 143. Academic Press, New York.
Denton, R. M., and Randle, P. J. (1966). *Biochem. J.* **100**, 420.
Denton, R. M., Yorke, R. E., and Randle, P. J. (1966). *Biochem. J.* **100**, 407.
Denton, R. M., Coore, H. G., Martin, B. R., and Randle, P. J. (1971). *Nature (London)* **231**, 115.
Desjardins, P. R., and Dakshinamurti, K. (1971). *Arch. Biochem. Biophys.* **142**, 292.
Dipietro, D. L., and Weinhouse, S. (1960). *J. Biol. Chem.* **235**, 2542.
Donaldson, W. E. (1964). *Proc. Soc. Exp. Biol. Med.* **116**, 662.
Dorsey, J. A., and Porter, J. W. (1968). *J. Biol. Chem.* **243**, 3512.
Du, J. T., and Kruger, F. A. (1972). *J. Nutr.* **102**, 1033.
Dugan, R. E., Slakey, L. L., Briedis, A. V., and Porter, J. W. (1972). *Arch. Biochem. Biophys.* **152**, 21.
Edwards, P. A., and Gould, R. G. (1972). *J. Biol. Chem.* **247**, 1520.
Eger-Neufeldt, I., Teinzer, A., Weiss, H., and Weiland, O. (1965). *Biochem. Biophys. Res. Commun.* **19**, 43.
Fabry, P., Kleinfeld, R., Tepperman, H., and Tepperman, J. (1970). *Proc. Soc. Exp. Biol. Med.* **137**, 577.
Flatt, J. P., and Ball, E. G. (1964). *J. Biol. Chem.* **239**, 675.
Foster, D. W., and Srere, P. A. (1968). *J. Biol. Chem.* **243**, 1926.
Freedland, R. A., Cunliffe, T. L., and Zinkl, J. G. (1966). *J. Biol. Chem.* **241**, 5448.
Frenkel, R., Stark, M. J., and Stafford, J. (1972). *Biochem. Biophys. Res. Commun.* **49**, 1684.
Fritz, P. J., Vessell, E. S., White, E. L., and Pruitt, K. M. (1969). *Proc. Nat. Acad. Sci. U. S.* **62**, 558.
Galton, D. J., and Wilson, J. P. D. (1971). *Clin. Sci.* **41**, 545.
Gibson, D. M., Hicks, S. E., and Allmann, D. W. (1966). *Advan. Enzyme Regul.* **4**, 239.
Gibson, D. M., Lyons, R. T., Scott, D. F., and Muto, Y. (1972). *Advan. Enzyme Regul.* **10**, 187.

Goldfarb, S., and Pitot, H. C. (1972). *J. Lipid Res.* **13**, 797.
Goodridge, A. G. (1968a). *Biochem. J.* **108**, 663.
Goodridge, A. G. (1968b). *Biochem. J.* **108**, 667.
Goodridge, A. G. (1972). *J. Biol. Chem.* **247**, 6946.
Goodridge, A. G. (1973a). *J. Biol. Chem.* **248**, 1924.
Goodridge, A. G. (1973b). *J. Biol. Chem.* **248**, 1932.
Goodridge, A. G. (1973c). *J. Biol. Chem.* **248**, 1939.
Goodridge, A. G. (1973d). *J. Biol. Chem.* **248**, 4318.
Gozukara, E. M., Frolich, M., and Holten, D. (1972). *Biochim. Biophys. Acta* **286**, 155.
Greenbaum, A. L., Gumaa, K. A., and McLean, P. (1971). *Arch. Biochem. Biophys.* **143**, 617.
Gregolin, C., Ryder, E., and Lane, M. D. (1968). *J. Biol. Chem.* **243**, 4227.
Greville, G. D. (1969). *In* "Citric Acid Cycle-Control and Compartmentation" (J. M. Lowenstein, ed.), p. 1. Dekker, New York.
Grodsky, G. M., and Forsham, P. H. (1966). *Annu. Rev. Physiol.* **28**, 347.
Guynn, R. W., Veloso, D., and Veech, R. L. (1972). *J. Biol. Chem.* **247**, 7325.
Halestrap, A. P., and Denton, R. M. (1973). *Biochem. J.* **132**, 509.
Halperin, M. L., and Robinson, B. H. (1972). *In* "Insulin Action" (I. B. Fritz, ed.), p. 345. Academic Press, New York.
Halperin, M. L., Robinson, B. H., and Fritz, I. B. (1972). *Proc. Nat. Acad. Sci. U. S.* **69**, 1003.
Hamprecht, B., Nussler, C., and Lynen, F. (1969). *FEBS* (*Fed. Eur. Biochem. Soc.*), *Lett.* **4**, 117.
Hansen, R. J., Pilkis, S. J., and Krahl, M. E. (1967). *Endocrinology* **81**, 1397.
Hansen, R. J., Pilkis, S. J., and Krahl, M. E. (1970). *Endocrinology* **86**, 57.
Hanson, R. W., and Ballard, F. J. (1967). *Biochem. J.* **105**, 529.
Hepp, D., Prusse, E., Weiss, H., and Wieland, O. (1966). *Advan. Enzyme Regul.* **4**, 89.
Hickman, P. E., Horton, B. J., and Sabine, J. R. (1972). *J. Lipid Res.* **13**, 17.
Hicks, S. E., Allman, D. W., and Gibson, D. M. (1965). *Biochim. Biophys. Acta* **106**, 441.
Higgins, M., Kawachi, R., and Rudney, H. (1971). *Biochem. Biophys. Res. Commun.* **45**, 138.
Hill, R., Linazasoro, J. M., Chevallier, F., and Chaikoff, I. L. (1958). *J. Biol. Chem.* **233**, 305.
Hochheuser, W., Weiss, H., and Wieland, O. (1964). *Z. Klin. Chem.* **2**, 175.
Holten, D. (1972). *Biochim. Biophys. Acta* **268**, 4.
Hori, S. H., and Yonezawa, S. (1972). *J. Histochem. Cytochem.* **20**, 804.
Huber, J., and Hamprecht, B. (1972). *Hoppe-Seyler's Z. Physiol. Chem.* **353**, 307.
Huber, J., Hamprecht, B., Muller, O., and Guder, W. (1972). *Hoppe-Seyler's Z. Physiol. Chem.* **353**, 313.
Huber, J., Latzin, S., Langguth, O., Brauser, B., Gabel, V. P., and Hamprecht, B. (1973a). *FEBS* (*Fed. Eur. Biochem. Soc.*), *Lett.* **31**, 261.
Huber, J., Guder, W., Latzin, S., and Hamprecht, B. (1973b). *Hoppe-Seyler's Z. Physiol. Chem.* **353**, 313.
Ingle, D. L., Bauman, D. E., and Garrigus, U. S. (1972a). *J. Nutr.* **102**, 609.
Ingle, D. L., Bauman, D. E., and Garrigus, U. S. (1972b). *J. Nutr.* **102**, 617.
Isohashi, F., Shibayama, K., Maruyama, E., Aoki, U., and Wada, F. (1971). *Biochim. Biophys. Acta* **250**, 14.

Jacobs, R., Kilburn, E., and Majerus, P. W. (1970). *J. Biol. Chem.* **245,** 6462.
Jansen, G. R., Zanetti, M. E., and Hutchinson, C. F. (1967). *Biochem. J.* **102,** 870.
Johnson, B. C., and Sassoon, H. F. (1967). *Advan. Enzyme Regul.* **5,** 93.
Jungas, R. L. (1971). *Metab. Clin. Exp.* **20,** 43.
Jungas, R. L., and Taylor, S. I. (1972). *In* "Insulin Action" (I. B. Fritz, ed.), p. 369. Academic Press, New York.
Kandutsch, A. A., and Saucier, S. E. (1969). *J. Biol. Chem.* **244,** 2299.
Kaplan, M. L., and Fried, G. A. (1973). *Arch. Biochem. Biophys.* **158,** 711.
Kather, H., Rivera, M., and Brand, K. (1972a). *Biochem. J.* **128,** 1089.
Kather, H., Rivera, M., and Brand, K. (1972b). *Biochem. J.* **128,** 1097.
Katz, J., Landau, B. R., and Bartsch, G. E. (1966). *J. Biol. Chem.* **241,** 727.
Katzen, H. M. (1967). *Advan. Enzyme Regul.* **5,** 335.
Katzen, H. M., and Schimke, R. T. (1965). *Proc. Nat. Acad. Sci. U. S.* **54,** 1218.
Korchak, H. M., and Masoro, E. J. (1962). *Biochim. Biophys. Acta* **58,** 354.
Kornacker, M. S., and Ball, E. G. (1965). *Proc. Nat. Acad. Sci. U. S.* **54,** 899.
Kornacker, M. S., and Lowenstein, J. M. (1964). *Biochim. Biophys. Acta* **84,** 490.
Kornacker, M. S., and Lowenstein, J. M. (1965a). *Biochem. J.* **94,** 209.
Kornacker, M. S., and Lowenstein, J. M. (1965b). *Biochem. J.* **95,** 832.
Krebs, H. A., and Perkins, J. R. (1970). *Biochem. J.* **118,** 635.
Lahat, N., Beitner, R., and Pinsky, A. (1972). *Nature (London)* **237,** 50.
Lakshmanan, M. R., Nepokroeff, C. M., and Porter, J. W. (1972). *Proc. Nat. Acad. Sci. U. S.* **69,** 3516.
Lakshmanan, M. R., Nepokroeff, C. M., Ness, G. C., Dugan, R. E., and Porter, J. W. (1973). *Biochem. Biophys. Res. Commun.* **50,** 704.
Lamdin, E., Shreeve, W. W., Slavinski, R. H., and Oji, N. (1969). *Biochemistry* **8,** 3325.
Landers, R. E. (1971). Ph.D. Thesis, Univ. of Illinois, Urbana-Champaign.
Lane, M. D., Moss, J., Ryder, E., and Stoll, E. (1971). *Advan. Enzyme Regul.* **9,** 237.
Larner, J., and Villar-Palasi, C. (1971). *Curr. Top. Cell. Regul.* **3,** 195.
Leveille, G. A. (1966). *J. Nutr.* **90,** 449.
Leveille, G. A. (1967a). *J. Nutr.* **91** 267.
Leveille, G. A. (1967b). *Can. J. Physiol. Pharmacol.* **45,** 201.
Leveille, G. A. (1969). *Comp. Biochem. Physiol.* **28,** 733.
Leveille, G. A. (1970). *Fed. Proc.* **29,** 1294.
Leveille, G. A., and Hanson, R. W. (1966). *J. Lipid Res.* **7,** 46.
Leveille, G. A., and Yeh, Y. Y. (1972). *J. Nutr.* **102,** 733.
Lindsay, D. B. (1970). *In* "Physiology of Digestion and Metabolism in the Ruminant" (A. T. Phillipson, ed.), p. 438. Oriel Press, Newcastle upon Tyne, England.
Linn, T. C. (1967). *J. Biol. Chem.* **242,** 990.
Linn, T. C., Pettit, F. H., and Reed, L. J. (1969). *Proc. Nat. Acad. Sci. U. S.* **62,** 234.
Liou, G. I., and Donaldson, W. E. (1973). *Can. J. Biochem.* **51,** 1029.
Lowenstein, J. M. (1968). *In* "Metabolic Roles of Citrate" (T. W. Goodwin, ed.), Biochemical Society Symposia No. 27, p. 61. Academic Press, New York.
Lynen, F. (1967). *Biochem. J.* **102,** 381.
McDonald, B. E., and Johnson, B. C. (1965). *J. Nutr.* **87,** 161.
McGovern, R. F., and Quackenbush, F. W. (1973). *Lipids* **8,** 473.
MacLean, P., Brown, J., Walters, E., and Greenslade, K. (1967). *Biochem. J.* **105,** 1301.

McNamara, D. J., Quackenbush, F. W., and Rodwell, V. W. (1972). *J. Biol. Chem.* **247**, 5805.
Madappally, M. M., Paquet, R. J., Mehlman, M. A., and Tobin, R. B. (1971). *J. Nutr.* **101**, 755.
Majerus, P. W., and Kilburn, E. (1969). *J. Biol. Chem.* **244**, 6254.
Marco, R., Carbonell, J., and Llorente, R. (1971). *Biochem. Biophys. Res. Commun.* **43**, 126.
Martin, B. R., and Denton, R. M. (1970). *Biochem. J.* **117**, 861.
Martin, B. R., Denton, R. M., Pask, H. T., and Randle, P. J. (1972). *Biochem. J.* **129**, 763.
Martin, R. J., Gobble, J. L., Hartsock, T. H., Graves, H. B., and Ziegler, J. H. (1973). *Proc. Soc. Exp. Biol. Med.* **143**, 198.
Middleton, M. C., and Walker, D. G. (1972). *Biochem. J.* **127**, 721.
Moore, R. O., Chandler, A. M., and Tellenhorst, N. (1964). *Biochem. Biophys. Res. Commun.* **17**, 527.
Murthy, V. K., and Steiner, G. (1972). *Metab. Clin. Exp.* **21**, 213.
Murthy, V. K., and Steiner, G. (1973). *Metab. Clin. Exp.* **22**, 81.
Muto, Y., and Gibson, D. M. (1970). *Biochem. Biophys. Res. Commun.* **38**, 1.
Nakamura, T., and Kumegawa, M. (1973). *Biochem. Biophys. Res. Commun.* **51**, 474.
Nakanishi, S., and Numa, S. (1970). *Eur. J. Biochem.* **16**, 161.
Nakanishi, S., and Numa, S. (1971). *Proc. Nat. Acad. Sci. U. S.* **68**, 2288.
Niemeyer, H., Clark-Turri, L., Garces, E., and Vergara, F. E. (1962). *Arch. Biochem. Biophys.* **98**, 77.
Niemeyer, H., Perez, N., and Rabajille, E. (1966). *J. Biol. Chem.* **241**, 4055.
Nishikori, K., Iritani, N., and Numa, S. (1973). *FEBS (Fed. Eur. Biochem. Soc.), Lett.* **32**, 19.
Numa, S., Bortz, W. M., and Lynen, F. (1965). *Advan. Enzyme Regul.* **3**, 407.
Numa, S., Nakanishi, S., Hashimoto, T., Iritani, N., and Okozaki, T. (1970). *Vitam. Horm. (New York)* **28**, 213.
O'Hea, E. K., and Leveille, G. A. (1968). *Comp. Biochem. Physiol.* **26**, 1081.
O'Hea, E. K., and Leveille, G. A. (1969a). *J. Nutr.* **99**, 338.
O'Hea, E. K., and Leveille, G. A. (1969b). *J. Nutr.* **99**, 345.
Orevi, M., Gorin, E., and Shafrir, E. (1972). *Eur. J. Biochem.* **30**, 418.
Oxman, M. N., and Ball, E. G. (1961). *Arch. Biochem. Biophys.* **95**, 99.
Pande, S. V., and Mead, J. F. (1968). *J. Biol. Chem.* **243**, 6180.
Pande, S. V., Khan, R. P., and Venkitasubramanion, T. A. (1964). *Biochim. Biophys. Acta* **84**, 239.
Parvin, R., and Dakshinamurti, K. (1970). *J. Biol. Chem.* **245**, 5773.
Passonneau, J. V., and Lowry, O. H. (1964). *Advan. Enzyme Regul.* **2**, 265.
Patzelt, C., Loffler, G., and Wieland, O. H. (1973). *Eur. J. Biochem.* **33**, 117.
Pearce, J. (1968). *Biochem. J.* **109**, 702.
Pearce, J. (1971a). *Comp. Biochem. Physiol.* **40B**, 215.
Pearce, J. (1971b). *Biochem. J.* **123**, 717.
Pearce, J. (1971c). *Int. J. Biochem.* **2**, 271.
Peraino, C. (1967). *J. Biol. Chem.* **242**, 3860.
Perez, N., Clark-Turri, L., Rabajille, E., and Niemeyer, H. (1964). *J. Biol. Chem.* **239**, 2420.
Pilkis, S. J. (1970). *Biochim. Biophys. Acta* **215**, 461.

Pogson, C. I. (1968a). *Biochem. Biophys. Res. Commun.* **30**, 297.
Pogson, C. I. (1968b). *Biochem. J.* **110**, 67.
Pogson, C. I., and Denton, R. M. (1967). *Nature (London)* **216**, 156.
Porter, J. W., Kumar, S., and Dugan, R. E. (1971). *Progr. Biochem. Pharmacol.* **6**, 1.
Porterhauser, R., and Wieland, O. (1972). *Eur. J. Biochem.* **31**, 308.
Potter, V. P., and Ono, T. (1961). *Cold Spring Harbor Symp. Quant. Biol.* **26**, 355.
Reed, L. J. (1969). *Curr. Top. Cell. Regul.* **1**, 233.
Reshef, L., Niv, J., and Shapiro, B. (1967). *J. Lipid Res.* **8**, 688.
Romsos, D. R., and Leveille, G. A. (1974). *Biochim. Biophys. Acta* (in press).
Romsos, D. R., Leveille, G. A., and Allee, G. L. (1971). *Comp. Biochem. Physiol.* **40A**, 569.
Rudack, D., Chisholm, E. M., and Holten, D. (1971a). *J. Biol. Chem.* **246**, 1249.
Rudack, D., Davie, B., and Holten, D. (1971b). *J. Biol. Chem.* **246**, 7823.
Rudack, D., Gozukara, E. M., Chisholm, E. M., and Holten, D. (1971c). *Biochim. Biophys. Acta* **252**, 305.
Ryder, E., Gregolin, C., Chang, H. C., and Lane, M. D. (1967). *Proc. Nat. Acad. Sci. U. S.* **57**, 1455.
Saito, T., and Tomita, K. (1973). *J. Biochem. (Tokyo)* **73**, 803.
Sassoon, H. F., Watson, J., and Johnson, B. C. (1968). *J. Nutr.* **94**, 52.
Sassoon, H. F., Dror, Y., Watson, J. J., and Johnson, B. C. (1973). *J. Nutr.* **103**, 321.
Schimke, R. T., and Doyle, D. (1970). *Annu. Rev. Biochem.* **39**, 929.
Schimmel, R. J., and Goodman, H. M. (1972). *Biochim. Biophys. Acta* **260**, 153.
Schmukler, M. (1970). *Biochim. Biophys. Acta* **214**, 309.
Seiler, M. W., Hamilton, M. A., Lauris, V., Herrera, M. G., and Hegsted, D. M. (1971). *Amer. J. Physiol.* **221**, 548.
Seubert, W., and Schoner, W. (1971). *Curr. Top. Cell. Regul.* **3**, 237.
Shah, S. N. (1973). *Lipids* **8**, 284.
Shapiro, D. J., and Rodwell, V. W. (1969). *Biochem. Biophys. Res. Commun.* **37**, 867.
Shapiro, D. J., and Rodwell, V. W. (1971). *J. Biol. Chem.* **246**, 3210.
Shapiro, D. J., and Rodwell, V. W. (1972). *Biochemistry* **11**, 1042.
Sharma, C., Manjeshwar, R., and Weinhouse, S. (1963). *J. Biol. Chem.* **238**, 3840.
Sica, V., and Cuatrecasas, P. (1973). *Biochemistry* **12**, 2282.
Silpananta, P., and Goodridge, A. G. (1971). *J. Biol. Chem.* **246**, 5754.
Siperstein, M. D. (1970). *Curr. Top. Cell. Regul.* **2**, 65.
Siperstein, M. D., and Fagan, V. M. (1966). *J. Biol. Chem.* **241**, 602.
Slakey, L. L., Craig, M. C., Beytia, E., Briedis, A., Feldbruegge, D. H., Dugan, R. E., Qureshi, A. A., Subbarayan, C., and Porter, J. W. (1972). *J. Biol. Chem.* **247**, 3014.
Smith, S., and Abraham, S. (1970). *Arch. Biochem. Biophys.* **136**, 112.
Soling, H. D., and Bernhard, G. (1971). *FEBS (Fed. Eur. Biochem. Soc.), Lett.* **13**, 201.
Sols, A. (1965). *In* "The Nature and Treatment of Diabetes" (E. S. Leibel and G. A. Wrenshall, eds.), p. 118. Excerpta Med. Found., New York.
Sols, A. (1968). *In* "Carbohydrate Metabolism and Its Disorders" (F. Dickens, P. J. Randle, and W. J. Whelan, eds.), p. 53. Academic Press, New York.
Sols, A., and Marco, R. (1970). *Curr. Top. Cell. Regul.* **2**, 227.
Sols, A., Salas, M., and Vinuela, E. (1964). *Advan. Enzyme Regul.* **2**, 177.
Spencer, A. F., and Lowenstein, J. M. (1962). *J. Biol. Chem.* **237**, 3640.

Spencer, A. F., and Lowenstein, J. M. (1967). *Biochem. J.* **103**, 342.
Srere, P. A. (1965). *Biochim. Biophys. Acta* **106**, 445.
Srere, P. A., and Foster, D. W. (1967). *Biochem. Biophys. Res. Commun.* **26**, 556.
Start, C., and Newsholme, E. A. (1970). *FEBS (Fed. Eur. Biochem. Soc.), Lett.* **6**, 171.
Stifel, F. B., and Herman, R. H. (1972). *Amer. J. Clin. Nutr.* **25**, 606.
Sugiyama, T., Clinkenbeard, K., Moss, J., and Lane, M. D. (1972). *Biochem. Biophys. Res. Commun.* **48**, 255.
Szepesi, B., and Freedland, R. A. (1968a). *J. Nutr.* **94**, 37.
Szepesi, B., and Freedland, R. A. (1968b). *Can. J. Biochem.* **46**, 1459.
Szepesi, B., and Freedland, R. A. (1969a). *J. Nutr.* **99**, 499.
Szepesi, B., and Freedland, R. A. (1969b). *Arch. Biochem. Biophys.* **133**, 60.
Szepesi, B., and Michaelis, O. E. (1972). *Life Sci.* **11**, 113.
Szepesi, B., Berdanier, C. D., and Egawa, M. (1971a). *J. Nutr.* **101**, 863.
Szepesi, B., Berdanier, C. D., Diachenko, S. K., and Moser, P. B. (1971b). *J. Nutr.* **101**, 1147.
Szepesi, B., Vegors, R., and DeMouy, J. M. (1972). *Nutr. Rep. Int.* **5**, 281.
Taketa, K., and Pogell, B. M. (1966). *J. Biol. Chem.* **241**, 720.
Taketa, K., and Watanabe, A. (1971). *Biochim. Biophys. Acta* **235**, 19.
Taketa, K., Kaneshige, Y., Tanaka, A., and Kosaka, K. (1970). *Biochem. Med.* **4**, 531.
Tanaka, T., Harano, Y., Sue, F., and Morimura, H. (1967a). *J. Biochem. (Tokyo)* **62**, 71.
Tanaka, T., Sue, F., and Morimura, H. (1967b). *Biochem. Biophys. Res. Commun.* **29**, 444.
Taunton, O. D., Stifel, F. B., Greene, H. L., and Herman, R. H. (1972). *Biochem. Biophys. Res. Commun.* **48**, 1663.
Taylor, S. I., Mukherjee, C., and Jungas, R. L. (1973). *J. Biol. Chem.* **248**, 73.
Tepperman, H. M., and Tepperman, J. (1958). *Diabetes* **7**, 478.
Tepperman, H. M., and Tepperman, J. (1961). *Amer. J. Physiol.* **200**, 1069.
Tepperman, H. M., and Tepperman, J. (1963). *Advan. Enzyme Regul.* **1**, 121.
Tepperman, H. M., and Tepperman, J. (1972). *In* "Insulin Action" (I. B. Fritz, ed.), p. 543. Academic Press, New York.
Tepperman, J., and Tepperman, H. M. (1958). *Amer. J. Physiol.* **193**, 55.
Tsai, A. C., and Dyer, I. A. (1973). *J. Nutr.* **103**, 93.
Tubbs, P. K., and Garland, P. B. (1964). *Biochem. J.* **93**, 550.
Tweto, J., and Larrabee, A. R. (1972). *J. Biol. Chem.* **247**, 4900.
Tweto, J., Liberati, M., and Larrabee, A. R. (1971). *J. Biol. Chem.* **246**, 2468.
Ureta, T., Radojkovic, J., and Niemeyer, H. (1970). *J. Biol. Chem.* **245**, 4819.
Ureta, T., Radojkovic, J., Slebe, J. C., and Reichberg, S. (1972). *Int. J. Biochem.* **3**, 103.
Ureta, T., Reichberg, S. B., Radojkovic, J., and Slebe, J. C. (1973). *Comp. Biochem. Physiol.* **45B**, 445.
Vagelos, P. R. (1964). *Annu. Rev. Biochem.* **33**, 139.
Van Berkel, J. C., Koster, J. F., and Hulsmann, W. C. (1973). *Biochim. Biophys. Acta* **293**, 118.
Vaughan, D. A., and Winders, R. L. (1964). *Amer. J. Physiol.* **206**, 1081.
Volpe, J. J., and Vagelos, P. R. (1973). *Annu. Rev. Biochem.* **42**, 21.
Volpe, J. J., Lyles, T. O., Roncari, D. A. K., and Vagelos, P. R. (1973). *J. Biol. Chem.* **248**, 2502.

Wakil, S. J., Titchener, E. B., and Gibson, D. M. (1958). *Biochem. Biophys. Acta* **29**, 225.
Walker, D. G. (1966). *In* "Essays in Biochemistry" (P. N. Campbell and G. D. Greville, ed.), Vol. 2, p. 33. Academic Press, New York.
Walker, D. G., and Eaton, S. W. (1967). *Biochem. J.* **105**, 771.
Watanabe, A., and Taketa, K. (1971). *Enzyme* **12**, 694.
Watanabe, A., Taketa, K., and Kosaka, K. (1972). *Enzyme* **13**, 203.
Weber, G. (1972). *Isr. J. Med. Sci.* **8**, 325.
Weber, G., and Convery, H. J. H. (1966). *Life Sci.* **5**, 1139.
Weber, G., Singhal, R. L., Stamm, N. B., Lea, M. A., and Fisher, E. A. (1966). *Advan. Enzyme Regul.* **4**, 59.
Weber, G., Lea, M. A., Convery, H. J. H., and Stamm, N. B. (1967). *Advan. Enzyme Regul.* **5**, 257.
Weber, G., Lea, M. A., and Stamm, N. B. (1968). *Advan. Enzyme Regul.* **6**, 101.
White, L. W., and Rudney, H. (1970). *Biochemistry* **9**, 2725.
Wieland, O., and Weiss, H. (1963). *Biochem. Biophys. Res. Commun.* **13**, 26.
Wieland, O. H., Palzelt, C., and Löffler, G. (1972). *Eur. J. Biochem.* **26**, 426.
Wiley, J. H., and Leveille, G. A. (1973). *J. Nutr.* **103**, 829.
Wise, E. M., and Ball, E. G. (1964). *Proc. Nat. Acad. Sci. U. S.* **52**, 1255.
Yang, M. G., Manoharan, K., and Mickelsen, O. (1970) *J. Nutr.* **100**, 545.
Yeh, S. C., and Leveille, G. A. (1973). *J. Nutr.* **103**, 407.
Yeh, Y. Y., and Leveille, G. A. (1970). *J. Nutr.* **100**, 1389.
Yeh, Y. Y., and Leveille, G. A. (1971). *J. Nutr.* **101**, 911.
Yeh, Y. Y., Leveille, G. A., and Wiley, J. H. (1970). *J. Nutr.* **100**, 917.
Young, J. W., Shrago, E., and Lardy, H. A. (1964). *Biochemistry* **3**, 1687.
Young, J. W., Thorp, S. L., and DeLumen, H. Z. (1969). *Biochem. J.* **114**, 83.
Yugari, Y., and Matsuda, T. (1967). *J. Biochem.* (*Tokyo*) **61**, 541.
Zakim, D., Pardini, R. S., Herman, R. H., and Sauberlich, H. E. (1967). *Biochim. Biophys. Acta* **242**, 251.

Role of Phospholipids in Transport and Enzymic Reactions

BEATRIX FOURCANS

Department of Chemistry, Indiana University, Bloomington, Indiana

AND

MAHENDRA KUMAR JAIN[1]

Department of Chemistry, Indiana University, Bloomington, Indiana and Department of Chemistry and Health Sciences, University of Delaware, Newark, Delaware

[1] Present address: Department of Chemistry and Health Sciences, University of Delaware, Newark, Delaware 19711.

Man knows more than he understands

Adler

I. Introduction

A large number of cellular components are localized in/on membranes. For example, many "particulate" enzymes are membrane bound and their particulate nature reflects their association with the lipid matrix of biomembranes including the plasma membrane as well as those of mitochondria, endoplasmic reticulum, and other subcellular organelles. Existence of membrane-bound enzymes has been recognized for many years, but until recently, most could not be solubilized, and therefore, were considered unsuitable for purification and detailed study.

Fleischer and co-workers (1962) were probably the first to clearly demonstrate that lipids were required in a nonsubstrate role in certain enzymic reactions. They found that extraction of lipids from active particulate preparations resulted in a marked decrease in activity of several enzymes of mitochondrial electron transport system. The activity could be restored by addition of crude mitochondrial lipids or other highly unsaturated phospholipids. These findings emphasize the dual possibilities of dissociating membrane-bound enzymes into component proteins and phospholipids and restoring biological activity by combining the purified components to achieve reconstitution of a functionally intact part of the original membrane.

Dissociation and reconstitution of membrane-bound catalytic proteins permit the study of a novel parameter in biological catalysis—the role of lipids. The significance of this type of experimental approach is several fold: it permits study of the role of lipids in catalysis by proteins in an almost all-or-none fashion; it provides an understanding of the regulatory role of lipids as a system property that is evident only at a higher level of organization; it provides a model for lipid-protein interactions.

These and related experiments suggest that in addition to the well-known propensity of phospholipids to form bilayers, many of them have a direct influence on specific membrane components that are involved in catalytic and/or transport functions. Indeed, lipid-protein interactions appear to modulate the catalytic activity of proteins by influencing or determining their tertiary and quaternary structures. This could result in modification of their recognition and/or catalytic sites. Phospholipids provide a relatively nonpolar environment in which some reactions may proceed more efficiently, as the nonpolar environment may assist in binding and orientation of ligands (substrates, inhibitors, regulators) and influence the activity of water at the active site. It is also possible that interactions with phospholipids may confer on the proteins an amphipathic character (spatial separation of polar and apolar regions), required for their incorporation into biomembranes in active site forms. Localization of catalytic proteins on membranes may also affect the rate and equilibria of processes catalyzed and mediated by these sites (for a theoretical analysis, see Selegny *et al.*, 1971a,b). Thus the apolar chains of phospholipids determine not only the barrier characteristics, but also certain specific properties extrinsic to the lipid bilayer (Jain, 1972). Moreover, functionally active lipid-protein complexes may provide model systems for the study of those factors that underlie membrane phenomenon at the molecular level.

The purpose of this review is to summarize those aspects of our understanding of lipid-protein interactions that are important for the interpretation of both the general organization of membranes and their several biochemical functions. Specifically, we have examined the available data on the interaction of phospholipids with functional (both catalytic and transport) proteins with special reference to the phenomena outlined in the previous paragraphs. To the best of our knowledge, lipid-protein interactions, with emphasis on consequences for functional proteins have not been reviewed in detail to date (see however, Triggle, 1970; Rothfield and Romeo, 1971). The broader aspects of lipid-protein interactions as factors governing certain characteristics of bilayers (Jain, 1972), the role of nonpolar interactions in the organization of tertiary structures of proteins (Tanford, 1968; Stryer, 1968), catalysis in micelles (Cordes and Gitler, 1973), "membrane-associated proteins" as structural components (Fleischer *et al.*, 1971), general properties of membrane proteins (Rothfield and Finkelstein, 1968; Guidotti, 1972), dissociation and reconstitution of biomembranes (Razin, 1972), the effect of hydrolytic enzymes on membrane functions (Jain, 1973), lipid biosynthesis in bacterial membranes (Cronan and Vagelos, 1972; Lennarz, 1972), and general aspects of membrane biosynthesis (Siekevitz, 1972) have been reviewed elsewhere.

II. Criteria for Establishing and Determining the Role of Lipids in Biological Processes

Considerable circumstantial evidence has accumulated during the last decade suggesting a vital role for lipids in certain biological functions. This evidence is usually based on the correlation of specific genetic mutation or variation of gross phospholipid pattern with specific functions or components. Some of the specific examples are given below. Certain phospholipids tend to accumulate in certain membranes either due to selective destruction or to specific interaction with other membrane components. Thus, for example, there appears to be a positive correlation between high concentrations of SM[2] in plasma membranes and their cholesterol levels (Patton, 1970; Patton *et al.*, 1973). Preferential binding of SM membrane proteins of the sheep red cell is reflected in their high SM content as compared to red cell membranes of other species (Kramer *et al.*, 1972). Changes in lipid composition with age, and physiological and pathological states seem to suggest a correlation between membrane composition, biochemical and transport functions (Walker and Yurkowsky, 1967; Phillips *et al.*, 1969; Ellingson *et al.*, 1970; Rouser *et al.*, 1971; Patterson *et al.*, 1972; Pfeifer and McCay, 1972; Grinna and Barber, 1972; Baumann *et al.*, 1970; Zakim *et al.*, 1973; Holden *et al.*, 1973), and protein biosynthesis (Moore and Umbreit, 1965; also see below). Also, increased turnover of PI occurs within a few minutes following certain extracellular stimuli (Michell and Lapetina, 1972). Consistent with this, are observations suggesting enhancement of antigen-antibody induced histamine release by PS, but not by other lipids (Gothman *et al.*, 1971).

Considerable evidence exists suggesting a correlation between lipid composition and growth conditions. Thus, animals reared on fat-deficient diets show modification of the Golgi apparatus structure (Chapman *et al.*, 1973) and altered kinetic behavior of several regulatory enzymes (Carlson *et al.*, 1973; Goldemberg *et al.*, 1972, 1973, and references therein). Lipid class composition is known to be profoundly altered by changes in growth phases (Starka and Moravova, 1970; Nunn and Tropp, 1972; Thiele *et al.*, 1972; Cronan and Vagelos, 1972; Ingram and Fisher, 1973), growth conditions (Hunt, 1970; Bell *et al.*, 1972; Kanemasa *et al.*, 1972; Linnane *et al.*, 1972; Marcus and Kaneshiro, 1972), and cell population density in various lower organisms (Diringer and Koch, 1973). Significant differences between normal and Rous sarcoma virus-transformed cells have been observed with respect to glycolipid content (Hakomori *et al.*, 1971) and acyl group composition (reduced arachidonate content) of phospholipids (Yau and Weber, 1972). Moreover, it has been sug-

---

[2] Abbreviations used: ADP, adenosinediphosphate; AMP, adenosine monophosphate; ATP, adenosinetriphosphate; ATPase, adenosinetriphosphatase; BLM, black lipid membrane or bimolecular lipid membrane; CL, cardiolipin; c.m.c., critical micelle concentration; CTAB, cetyltrimethylammonium bromide; DOC, deoxycholate; DCCD, dicyclohexylcarbodiimide; 2,4-DNP, dinitrophenol; E_{act}, activation energy; EIM, excitation inducing material; ETC, electron transport chain; FA, fatty acid; MPL, mitochondrial phospholipids; ONPG, *o*-nitrophenylgalactoside; ORD, optical rotatory dispersion; PA, phosphatidic acid; PC, phosphatidylcholine; P_i, inorganic phosphate; PE, phosphatidylethanolamine; PI, phosphatidyl inositol; PL, phospholipid; PMS, phenazinemethosulfate; PP_i, inorganic pyrophosphate; PS, phosphatidylserine; SDS, sodium dodecylsulfate; SM, sphingomyelin; SMP, submitochondrial particles; T_c, transition temperature; TG, triglyceride; TPP, thiamine pyrophosphate.

gested that the incorporation of branched chain fatty acids into the viral envelope can alter the configuration of envelope protein and therefore, by implication, the viral genotype (Blough and Tiffany, 1969). The endotoxins of gram-negative bacteria appear to have their activity completely dependent on the covalently bound "lipid A" (Galanos *et al.*, 1972, and references therein). The toxic effects of unconjugated bilirubin on cellular respiration, oxidative phosphorylation, electron transport, and permeability and morphology of mitochondria appears to be due to its binding to lipids (Mustafa and King, 1970).

All these correlations do not necessarily prove involvement of lipid-protein interactions in these various processes. Nevertheless, in view of the variety of biological effects exhibited by lipids, the experimental approaches to evaluate the interactions of lipids and protein are quite varied. There is extensive evidence suggesting that, although some proteins can be removed from membranes by hydrophilic reagents, a significant proportion of total proteins is held hydrophobically and can be removed only by agents that disrupt hydrophobic interactions. It is not difficult to resolve the apparent contradiction between the large amount of protein held hydrophobically in membranes and the relatively small amount of lipid apparently involved in direct interaction with it. Many protein molecules are about 100-fold larger than a typical lipid molecule and many of these project outside the lipid bilayer (cf. Branton, 1969; Blaurock, 1972). Thus, provided that their tertiary structure is compact, proteins need immobilize only a fraction of their weight of lipid. This leads to a picture of a major class of membrane lipids and proteins distributed (and may not necessarily be "floating") randomly as single molecules or oligomers in a lamellar configuration. Although this picture is undoubtedly oversimplified, it has the merit of consistency and provides a theme for further discussion. However, this is not to suggest that lipids only provide a "molecular cement" (cf. Ball and Cooper, 1949; Edwards and Ball, 1954; Day and Levy, 1969; Triggle, 1969) for the construction of the biomembranes. Indeed, profound alterations in biological functions accompanying changes in phospholipid pattern (as mentioned earlier), suggest a rather strong structural and functional role of lipids that must find expression in events occurring at the molecular level.

Explicit characterization of lipid–protein interactions at the molecular level has not yet been possible. A variety of observations summarized in this review provide strong circumstantial evidence for participation of lipids in transport and catalytic processes at the molecular level (Table I). The methods that have been generally used for the study of lipid protein interactions are summarized as follows.

(a) Perturbation of functional lipoproteins by a variety of agents that

Table I

LIPID-ACTIVATED ENZYMES

Enzyme (Reference)	Source	Delipidation by	Reactivation by
NADH-cytochrome c/NADH-ubiquionone reductase (Machinist and Singer, 1965)	Beef heart mitochondria		Asolecithin > lecithin > mitochondrial lipid > cardiolipin
Jones and Wakil (1967); Jones *et al.* (1969)	Hen liver microsomes	Acetone	PL + native TG + FA PC LPC
NADH-cytochrome b_5 reductase (Rogers and Strittmatter, 1973)	Rabbit liver microsomes	DOC	Total microsomal lipid
Succinate-cytochrome c reductase (Yu *et al.*, 1973; see also Hall and Crane, 1971)	Beef heart mitochondria	Cholate	CoQ_6 + PE + cardiolipin
Monoamine oxidase (Oreland and Olivecrona, 1971; Olivecrona and Oreland, 1971)	Pig liver mitochondria	Methyl-ethyl ketone	Acidic phospholipids facilitate binding of protein to the membrane
D-β-Hydroxybutyrate dehydrogenase (Gotterer, 1967)	Liver mitochondria	(At pH 10)	NAD + thiols + PC. Other phospholipids are ineffective.
Deoxycorticosterone 11-β-hydroxylase (Williamson and O'Donnell, 1969)	Beef adrenal mitochondria	Acetone	Total mitochondrial lipids
GTP-dependent acyl-CoA synthetase (Galzigua *et al.*, 1967, 1969)	Liver mitochondria	Acetone	PC but not PE
Cytochrome oxidase (Awasthi *et al.*, 1970b; Chung *et al.*, 1970a,b; Lemberg, 1969)	Beef heart mitochondria	Detergent and organic solvent	Cardiolipin; crude MPL
Succinate oxidase (Brierley *et al.*, 1962)	Beef heart mitochondria	Acetone	Phospholipids
Succinate dehydrogenase (Cerletti *et al.*, 1967, 1969)	Beef heart mitochondria	Phospholipase A and C	Phospholipids
$NADPH'_2NAD$ oxidoreductase (Pesch and Peterson, 1965)	Rat heart mitochondria	Organic solvents; Phospholipase A	Crude lipid extract

S-fraction containing citric acid cycle enzymes (Bachmann *et al.*, 1966)	Beef heart mitochondria	Phospholipase A	?
ATPase (Pitotti *et al.*, 1972)	Rat liver	Cholate	LPC, DPG, PI, PS > PE > PC
Hexokinase (Craven and Basford, 1972; Wilson, 1973)	Brain mitochondria	Phospholipase C; Organic solvents	Divalent ions regulate binding; solubilized form is active
Thiamine triphosphatase (Barchi and Braun, 1972)	Nuclear membrane from rat brain	DOC	?
ATP-synthetase (Steckhoven and Van Moerkerk, 1972)	Heart mitochondria	Sodium bromide	P_i-ATP exchange activity is stimulated by crude PL
Glucose-6-phosphohydrolase (Garland and Cori, 1972)	Liver microsomes	DOC	Monoenoic PC; SM and LPC are ineffective
Duttera *et al.* (1968)	Rat liver microsomes	PLC	LPC > PE $\simeq$ total lipids $\simeq$ asolecithin $\gg$ PC
5′-Nucleotidase (Widnell and Unkeless, 1968)	Mouse liver	DOC	SM. Highly purified, lipid-free preparation is active (Evans and Gurd, 1973)
Phosphorylcholine-cytidyl transferase (Fiscus and Schneider, 1966)	Rat liver microsomes	Acetone or butanol	Mixed lipids Degraded lipids $\simeq$ LPC $\gg$ PC
Stearyl-coenzyme A desaturase (Jones *et al.*, 1969; Shimakata *et al.*, 1972)	Hen liver microsomes	Acetone	Crude lipids $\simeq$ PL + TG + FA > PC
Hydroxylase enzyme system containing cytochrome P-450 (Coon *et al.*, 1971; Williamson and O'Donnell, 1969)	Liver microsomes	Organic solvents	Dioleoyl-co dilauroyl PC. PE is ineffective
Adenylcyclase stimulated by F^- and hormones (Levey, 1971a,b; Pohl *et al.*, 1971)	Liver plasma membrane	PLC, detergents	PS confers glucagon and histamine sensitivity; PI stimulates norepinephrine sensitivity

Table I (***Continued***)

Enzyme (Reference)	Source	Delipidation by	Reactivation by
Phosphatidic acid phosphatase (Coleman and Hubscher, 1963)	Pig kidney microsomes	Organic solvents	Extracted lipids
Amino acid transfer RNA ligases (Hradec and Duseck, 1969)		Organic solvents	Cholesteryl 14-methyl hexadecanoate
Acyl-CoA glycerol-3-phosphate acyltransferase (Abou-Issa and Cleland, 1969)	Rat liver microsomes	PLA	PC or total lipid + DTT
Na + K-ATPase (see text)	Plasma membrane	Detergent, phospholipases, organic solvents	Several types of lipids
Ca-ATPase (Martonoshi *et al.*, 1968)	Rabbit skeletal muscle	Phospholipase	LPC and PA
Ca-binding activity (Carvalho, 1972)	Rabbit skeletal muscle		
DDT-dehydrochlorinase (Dinamarca *et al.*, 1971)	Housefly	Organic solvent	
UDP-glucuronyltransferase (Graham and Wood, 1969; Attwood *et al.*, 1971; Vessey and Zakim, 1972)	Guinea pig liver microsomes	PLA or PLC	Crude phospholipids
Phosphoacetyl-muramyl-pentapeptide translocase (Umbreit and Strominger, 1972)	*Micrococcus luteus*	Triton X-100	C_{55}-isoprenyl phosphate + neutral lipid + a polar lipid
Phenylalanine hydrolase (Fisher and Kaufman, 1973)	Rat liver		Lysolecithin
Glycoprotein: glycosyltransferase (Kirschbaum and Bosman, 1973)	Rat kidney	Triton X-100	Lysolecithin (+folic acid)
Prothrombinase (Hanahan *et al.*, 1969)	Blood plasma	?	PS + PE or PS + PC or PI or lipid from platelets
Lipoprotein lipase (Chung *et al.*, 1973)	Rat epididymal pad	Organic solvents	PC > PE > PS
RNA-polymerase A (Lezius and Mueller-Lornson, 1972)	Mouse myeloma	Several steps	PC or PE; transcription of double-stranded but not

	cells		single-stranded DNA is inhibited by CL.
N-Acetylglucosaminyltransferase (Labow *et al.*, 1973)	Rabbit liver microsomes	Phospholipase C	?
Steroid-glucuronyltransferase (Labow *et al.*, 1973)	Rabbit liver microsomes	Snake venom	Crude phospholipids
Lipase (Kariya and Kaplan, 1973)	Rat liver lysosomes	Detergents	CL $\simeq$ PS $\simeq$ PA $\gg$ detergents
Cyclic nucleotide-phosphodiesterase (Bublitz, 1973)	Rat brain	—	PI $\simeq$ LPC $>$ PE $\simeq$ PS $>$ SM $\simeq$ PC
N-Demethylation of (+) benzphetamine (Eling and DiAugustine, 1971)	Rat liver microsomes	Phospholipase C and D	?
Enzymes of glycolipid biosynthesis (Lennarz and Talamo, 1966)	*Micrococcus lysodeikticus*	$CHCl_3$/MeOH	Anionic surfactant
NADH-dehydrogenase (Nachbar and Salton, 1970)	*M. lysodeikticus*	Butanol	Crude lipid extract
Formate dehydrogenases (Ruiz-Herrera *et al.*, 1972)	*E. coli*	Brij-36T	Solubilized form is active
Dihydroorotate dehydrogenase (Karibian, 1973)	*E. coli* K12	Detergent and phospholipase A_2	PE $\gtrsim$ PG $\gg$ detergents
Infectivity of Semliki Forest virus (Friedman and Pastan, 1969)	—	Phospholipase C	—
C_{55}-Isoprenoid alcohol phosphokinase (Sandermann and Strominger, 1971; Sandermann, 1973)	*Staphylococcus aureus*	Butanol	PC, PG, CL, and fatty acid esters of sorbitan
Phospholipase A (Scandella and Kornberg, 1971)	*E. coli*	Organic solvent	Lipid-free enzyme aggregates
Cyclopropane fatty acid synthetase (Chung and Law, 1964)	*Clostridium butyricum*	Cationic and neutral detergents	Anionic surfactants stimulate activity
Lipoprotein lipase (Saiki *et al.*, 1969)	*Mucor gavanicus* IAM 6108	Organic solvents	PI, PC, PE, PS
UDP-galactose: lipopolysaccharide-α,3-galactosyltransferase (Endo and Rothfield, 1969)	*Salmonella typhymurium*	Ethanol	PE containing higher proportions of unsaturated or cyclopropane fatty acids

Table I (*Continued*)

Enzyme (Reference)	Source	Delipidation by	Reactivation by
Malate dehydrogenase (Tobari, 1964)	*Mycobacterium arium*	Detergent	Crude lipids, cardiolipin, Protein to lipid ratio 40 (w/w)
Pyruvate oxidase (Cunningham and Hager, 1971a,b)	*E. coli*	Crystallized enzyme	LPE (allosteric effector)
Enzyme II of phosphotransferase system (Kundig and Rosenman, 1971)	*E. coli*	Butanol + urea	PG
	E. coli	PLD	PG

enter the membrane phase offers a sensitive, though yet unexploited, method for studying lipid-protein interactions. Quite a few amphipathic agents, including organic solvents, *n*-alkanols, and several drugs, are known to interact with membranes and modify intermolecular packing in lamellar lipid bilayers (Seeman, 1972; Jain and Cordes, 1973a,b; Jain *et al.*, 1973b). A correlation of concentration of these agents which elicits equal response to their partition coefficient (generally against *n*-octanol) provides an approximate measure of the hydrophobicity of the environment in which the agent is localized while exerting its effect on the functional protein (Hansch and Dunn, 1972).

(b) Dissolution and dissociation of membranes by freezing-thawing, sonication, lyophilization, high-speed shaking with glass beads, ammonium sulfate fractionation, solubilization with organic solvents (Maddy, 1964; Curtis, 1971, and references therein), detergents (see as follows) such as lysolecithin (Denberg, 1973), and chaotropic agents such as urea and guanidine (Hatefi and Hanstein, 1969; Hatefi and Stampel, 1969; Hanstein *et al.*, 1971) under carefully controlled conditions are generally favored. These treatments lead to fragmentation of the membrane to varying extents. For example, mild treatment with detergents results in separation of the inner membrane of mitochondria into several phospholipid-containing fragments differing in composition. Though removal of phospholipids is often accompanied by separation of components, extraction of phospholipids does not necessarily solubilize membrane proteins.

Nonionic detergents are preferred for fragmentation of membranes. Of the various detergents, DOC has been extensively used for delipidation. DOC, although ionic, resembles nonionic detergents in its low denaturing effect on proteins (Ne'eman *et al.*, 1971). DOC is easily removed by gel filtration, dilution, or dialysis against aqueous methanol. This is a vital step in reconstitution studies. There are indications that DOC facilitates reconstitution by dispersing aggregated proteins. However, considerable caution is warranted in interpreting the results of reconstitution and reactivation experiments following disruption with detergents. For example, agents such as DOC (cf. Swanson and Stahl, 1966) and SDS (Scandella and Kornberg, 1971) may themselves, under certain experimental conditions, act as inhibitors, and reactivation of enzyme activity by added lipids may merely represent displacement of SDS or DOC by phospholipids. Nonionic detergents containing extended methylene chains (Swanson *et al.*, 1964) such as Triton X-100 (a highly branched decaoxyethylated ocytl phenol) or Brij 36T (decaoxyethylated lauryl ether) appear to be capable of solubilizing membrane components. The solubilized membrane components generally form small aggregates (Auborn *et al.*,

1971). Interestingly, a wide variety of proteins bind identical amounts of SDS on a weight to weight basis. Binding is independent of ionic strength and is primarily hydrophobic. The results suggest that only the monomeric form of the amphipath, not the micellar form, binds to proteins (Reynolds and Tanford, 1970).

(c) Dissociation and perturbation of the lipid-protein matrix by hydrolytic enzymes such as lipases and proteases have been reviewed elsewhere (Jain, 1973). Generally speaking, limited phospholipolysis neither breaks down the macroscopic structure of the membrane nor affects the thickness of the residual bilayer, even when the area of the bilayer is approximately halved. Most proteins appear to remain bound to the residual membrane, and their conformation as measured by ORD, is not significantly altered. A variety of enzyme activities however are lost; some of these can be restored by added phospholipid (see as follows). The loss of activity following treatment with phospholipases could be secondary, i.e., either due to products of hydrolysis, or to instability of delipidated proteins at room temperature (or higher) needed for the action of lipases. Studies in *Escherichia coli* show the heterogeneity of membranous enzymes with respect to their dependence upon the presence of intact membrane phospholipids (Mavis *et al.*, 1972).

(d) Restoration and/or reconstitution of functionally active lipoprotein fragments, vesicles, or membrane systems (for a review, see Razin, 1972) has been achieved in several cases. The lipid used for reconstitution may be present in one of the various lamellar forms including BLM, sonicated or unsonicated liposomes, detergent or solvent-dispersed lipid, or the lipid can be incorporated with the aid of proteins that catalyze exchange of lipids. A small amount of detergent added to delipidated proteins seems to promote reactivation presumably by destabilizing the added phospholipid micelle or lamellae. A large, but variable amount of lipid (usually more than 100-fold) on a molar basis is required for reactivation of most enzymes (Fig. 1) implying a nonstoichiometric interaction. Reconstitution of a complete enzyme system requires a specific order of addition of the components. Moreover, invariably there is a delay (up to several hours) in the activation of apoprotein following mixing with lipids. Sometimes a specificity for the nature of the activating lipid is observed with respect to (1) the phase characteristics of the lipid; (2) the nature of the polar groups; (3) the degree of unsaturation and branching.

In contrast to protein-protein interactions, the protein-lipid or lipid-lipid interactions are not so specific, nor are they strictly stoichiometric. The molecular mechanism of these associations includes both hydrophobic and electrostatic bonds between small lipid molecules, which may not require specific steric interrelation. The interaction between various

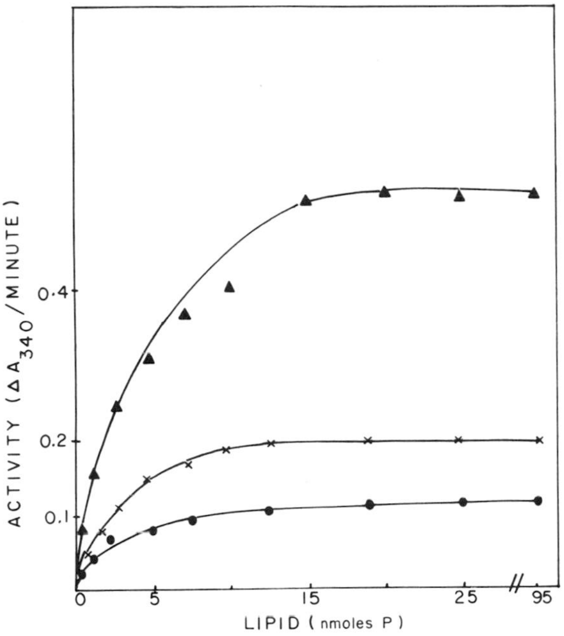

FIG. 1a. Activation of β-hydroxybutyrate dehydrogenase as a function of lipid added to the incubation medium containing thioglycerol, NAD, and Tris (pH 8.1). Mixed mitochondrial lipids were mixed with various concentrations of delipidated proteins: 12.7 μg (●—●); 25.4 μg (×—×); 50.8 μg (▲—▲) in a total volume of 0.1 ml. Incubation period 40 minutes at 29°. Reprinted with permission from G. S. Gotterer, *Biochemistry* 6, 2147 (1967). Copyright by the American Chemical Society.

membrane fragments also does not appear to be stoichiometric as between individual enzymes in multienzyme complexes.

Controlled, staged, and regulated treatment of different membranes with hydrolytic enzymes (Jain, 1973), delipidation by organic solvents (Fleischer *et al.*, 1967), "acid extraction" (Fleischer *et al.*, 1968), or detergent treatment (Ernster *et al.*, 1962; Pascaud *et al.*, 1970; Kagawa, 1972) have produced evidence of marked differential susceptibility of membranes to these agents. In some cases, a microscopically visible membrane structure remains after some proteins and lipids are removed. Generally speaking, these observations do not demonstrate either the existence of long-range order or the random distribution of the susceptible molecules in the membrane followed by a reordering of the remaining membrane components after the delipidation. However, with these techniques, it should be possible to dissociate membrane-bound functional lipoproteins into individual components and to restore their biological activity by recombining the purified components, thus achieving the reconstitution of a functional lipoprotein complex.

The applicability of these various experimental methods is probably best demonstrated by studies conducted by Racker and co-workers since early 1960. The experimental approaches toward resolution and reconstitution of a functional respiratory chain have utilized a variety of treatments of increasing severity to dissociate membranes, identify and characterize lipids, and structural and catalytic components (the "coupling factors"), and to reassociate and reconstitute a segment of the activity of ETC. As noted later, these studies have allowed significant insight into the understanding of the topography of the inner mitochondrial membrane components.

With the criteria just described, a variety of functional proteins and biomembrane functions have been shown to be lipid dependent (Table I). Some of the features of lipid-protein interaction elaborated by these studies may be summarized as follows.

(1) Most of the proteins activated by phospholipids are membrane-bound in their native state. However, not all membrane-bound enzymes are lipid activated.

(2) The functional lipoprotein complexes appear to be loosely defined stoichiometric entities on the basis of chemical composition, solubility characteristics, and their behavior in centrifuges, density gradients, and Sephadex columns. Several noncatalytic proteins also form loosely defined stoichiometric complexes with lipids (see Das *et al.*, 1965; Kuehn *et al.*, 1969; Lesslauer *et al.*, 1970; Giannoni *et al.*, 1971; Gitler and Montal, 1972b; Ivanetich *et al.*, 1973).

(3) Different concentrations of different lipids are required for maximal activation of the same apoenzyme. Furthermore, maximal activation observed with various lipids for the same apoenzyme is different. The affinity of the activating lipids for the apoenzyme may not necessarily be different.

(4) V_{max} for a completely reactivated enzyme differs with different activating lipids.

(5) Some lipid-activated enzymes show a hyperbolic dependence on the concentration of activating lipids, whereas others (especially those requiring intact bilayer for their function) show a sigmoidal dependence.

(6) The reactions catalyzed by various lipoproteins do not fall into any single category of enzyme reactions. Similarly, not all catalysts of any given class are necessarily lipid activated.

(7) The functional lipoprotein complexes are present in a variety of organelles, tissues, and organisms.

(8) The various lipid-activated enzymes present in the same membrane show heterogeneity with respect to their dependence upon the presence of specific phospholipid or upon the presence of intact phospholipid organization.

(9) Specificity for the activating lipid does not appear to be related to any given category of reactions, or the source or class of proteins. Often lipids activate only partial reactions in the overall process, and sometimes different lipids may activate different partial reactions in a series of reactions.

(10) In all the cases studied so far, the involvement of lipids in the modulation and regulation of protein functions appears to be through noncovalent interactions.

(11) The lipid-activated enzymes appear to have several subunits.

(12) Stabilization of enzymes by lipids appears to be a general mode of regulation of protein functions in membranes.

(13) Regulation of enzymic activity by lipids may be accomplished both by increasing or decreasing K_m; however, V_m is always increased in the presence of lipids.

(14) The apoenzymes are not necessarily devoid of catalytic activity.

(15) The interaction between various membrane fragments in biomembranes does not appear to be stoichiometric as observed between individual enzymes in multienzyme complexes.

(16) The activation energies for lipid-activated enzymes (20–40 kcal $mole^{-1}$) are generally higher than the corresponding values for water-soluble enzymes (10–20 kcal $mole^{-1}$).

III. Nonspecific Role of Lipids in Biological Processes

A. The Bilayer Matrix as a Determinant of Macroscopic Functions

The role of lipids as a structural matrix has been implicated in a variety of cellular processes. For all practical purposes, such a role arises from the bilayer form in which most (if not all) phospholipid molecules are present in biomembranes. The ratio of lipid to protein in biomembranes varies over a wide range, 4 in myelin to 0.3 in the inner mitochondrial membrane (Guidotti, 1972). However, in most membranes there is enough lipid to cover more than 70% of the surface area of the organelle or cell with a lipid bilayer. These and several related observations argue strongly for the presence of extended regions of a lipid bilayer in various biomembranes. Furthermore, not all membrane-bound proteins are localized in the lipid bilayer; a significant proportion may be localized in the interface region.

Localization of proteins onto/into membranes is facilitated by either electrostatic or hydrophobic interaction, or both. Thus for example, binding of monoamineoxidase (Olivecrona and Oreland, 1971; Oreland and Olivecrona, 1971) and hexokinase (Wilson, 1973) to membranes is mediated by ionic bonds with phospholipids, and the enzyme seems to be attached at the interface. In both of these cases, the lipid is required only for the binding of the proteins, and not for their catalytic activity. This type of binding may therefore lead to a situation where the presence or absence of a lipid factor may influence the intracellular distribution of an enzyme without affecting the enzyme activity.

Hydrophobic interactions have also been implicated in the binding of proteins to membranes. The C_{55}-isoprenoid alcohol phosphokinase is reactivated by lipids and detergents. The apoprotein is soluble in butanol and has a high content (58%) of nonpolar amino acids (Sandermann and Strominger, 1971). This extremely hydrophobic enzyme is located somewhere in the lipophilic interior of the bilayer—an environment suitable for "solubilization" and probably, orientation of this substrate, the C_{55}-isoprenoid alcohol. A combination of both electrostatic and hydrophobic interactions may be responsible for solubilization of cytochrome c in bilayers (Gitler and Montal, 1972a). It is noteworthy that association of cytochrome c with phospholipids does not alter the ORD spectrum of the protein (Lenaz *et al.*, 1969). Reversible structural changes in this protein and several others can, however, be induced by nonpolar substances (Wetlaufer and Lovrien, 1964), or following interaction with liposomes, as measured by changes in polypeptide conformation, the physical state of the fatty acid chains, or by monitoring the morphology and permeability of liposomes (Das *et al.*, 1965; Hammes and Schullery, 1970; Borovjagin and Moshkov, 1973; Blaurock, 1973; Mateu *et al.*, 1973; Kaminsky *et al.*, 1973; Ivanetich *et al.*, 1973; Morse and Deamer, 1973; Gordon *et al.*, 1969).

Structural and functional specialization in biomembranes are manifested in their chemical composition and organization such that the various components are integrated into a functional whole that transcends the sum properties of its parts. The system properties of biomembranes include among others, barrier characteristics, spatiotemporal anisotropy of interfacial processes, and integrative contribution of functional units (Jain, 1972). Thus, the dynamics of membrane-localized enzymes or multienzyme systems and the interaction among several such systems may be modulated not only by the activities and processes occurring in the membrane, but also by those in the surrounding medium. Thus for example, a simple lipid bilayer behaves as a passive barrier impermeable to most cellular metabolites and shows little transport specificity. However, in biomembranes, the molecules mediating the physicochemical processes are organized with fixed relationship to each other and to the surrounding media. Thus a series of enzymes that have an integrated function also have an apparent continuity of their morphology and function when localized on a lamellar matrix. The integration of catalytic and transport functions with the morphology of the lipid bilayer gives rise to "directionality" or anisotropy to the overall process with respect to the approach and release of substrates, products, and cofactors. Furthermore, since transport by definition is directional (vectorial), a coupling of a chemical reaction to transport (both membrane localized) would give rise to macroscopic anisotropy to the overall process, and to the possibility of "uphill" transport or to a modification of the free energy change involved in the overall process by compartmentalization of reactants and products. Some of these matters are developed as follows.

Several coupled processes, which involve a selective and specific modification of the barrier properties of the bilayer are known to occur in biomembranes. For example, the postsynaptic membrane allows passage of Na^+, K^+, and Cl^- ions following its interaction with acetylcholine and/or related drugs. This and several related substrate- or inducer-specific and permeant-selective transport systems have been reconstituted in BLM or liposomes (Table II). In these cases, the most important criterion for reconstitution of a functional bilayer is the barrier characteristic of the bilayer that is able to support the functional proteins. The properties of the matrix are modified by modifying the properties of the matrix-embedded proteins.

In some of the cases mentioned in Table II, the reconstitution appears to have been achieved by fusion of the membrane fragments (cf. Na + K-ATPase, Ca-ATPase, cytochrome oxidase, and the site III of ETC), while in others, an association of delipidated proteins has occurred spontaneously in the bilayer. Some of these systems show strong preference for a particular group of lipids that presumably reflects a requirement for a specific microviscosity and thickness of the hydrocarbon core (cf. Goodall, 1971, and unpublished observations).

A variety of agents induce the formation of multicomponent conduction pathways (channels) in BLM (Jain, 1972, for a review). During incorporation into BLM, these agents interact specifically with a certain component of the bilayer. Thus some of these channel-forming agents have an absolute requirement for a specific lipid, e.g., the polyene antibiotics are incorporated only into membranes containing 3-β-hydroxy-

Table II

Reconstituted Transport Systems Modified by Specific Ligands

System	Ligand(s)	Permeant/Effect	Reference
Acetylcholine receptor[a]	Acetylcholine	Na, K, Cl	DelCastillo *et al.* (1967); Parisi *et al.* (1972); Leuzinger and Schneider (1972); Jain *et al.* (1973b)
Antibody[a,b]	Complement	Na, K, Cl(?)	DelCastillo *et al.* (1966); Inoue *et al.* (1971); Kinsky (1972)
		Large molecules	Kataoka *et al.* (1973)
Na + K-ATPase[a]	ATP, Na, K, Mg	Na + K(?)	Jain *et al.* (1969, 1972)
ATPase (bacterial)[a]	ATP	Na, K	Redwood *et al.* (1969)
Na-Isomaltase-sucrase[a]	Sucrose	The products/ hydrolysis	Storelli *et al.* (1972)
Ca-ATPase[b]	ATP + Ca	Ca	Racker (1972)
Site I (NADH-ubiquinone reductase)[b]	NADH, ubiquinone, ascorbate + PMS	P_i-ATP exchange phosphorylation	Ragan and Racker (1973)

Site III (Cytochrome oxidase)[b] + cyt.c + PL + oligomycin sensitive ATPase	O_2, Cytochrome c	Proton gradient	Racker and Kandrach (1971); Hinckle *et al.* (1972); Kagawa and Racker (1971); Jasaitis *et al.* (1972)
K/or Na^+-selective ionophore[a]	+	Na^+ and/or K^+	Shamoo and Albers (1973); Goodall and Sachs (1972)
Glutamate and malate dehydrogenase[b]	Substrate	Inhibition of intrinsic activity	Dodd (1973)
Phytochrome[a]	Light	Ions	Roux and Yguerabide (1973)
Chlorophyll[a]	Light	Electronic(?)	Tien (1968)
Galactosyltransferase on monolayers	Lipopolysaccharide + phospholipid	Change in surface pressure	Romeo *et al.* (1970)
Glycoprotein from rbc[a]	Concanavalin A	Na, K	Tosteson *et al.* (1973)
Photosystem I and II[b]	Light − reductants	Photoreduction	Ji and Benson (1968); Benson *et al.* (1969); Shibuya *et al.* (1965); Huzishige *et al.* (1969)

[a] Reconstituted on BLM.
[b] Reconstituted on liposomes.

sterols. Other channel-forming agents such as EIM (an uncharacterized bacterial metabolite termed "excitation inducing material"), alamethicin, and gramicidin do not show an absolute requirement for specific lipids. However, experimental evidence suggests a certain degree of specificity of lipid-protein interaction that is reflected either in the kinetics of incorporating these agents or in the macroscopic behavior (conductance, in particular) of the modified bilayer. Thus, for example, the presence of equimolar amounts of cholesterol with phospholipids makes the kinetics of tyrocidine B incorporation bimolecular (Goodall, 1970). In the absence of cholesterol, the kinetics of channel formation appears to be third order. Macroscopic aspects of conductance change are probably best manifested in single-channel conductance measurements. The intrinsic conductance of BLM is so low, that under suitable conditions, it is possible to detect and characterize that conductance, characterizing or corresponding to a single channel formed by adsorption and association of channel-forming agents. At low concentrations of EIM in the medium, for example, the conductance of BLM increases as discrete and quantified jumps, which are multiples of a constant value dependent on the given composition of BLM. In many membrane systems, EIM channels have several conductance levels for each channel. Such channels may be opened or closed with either a single large jump (Ehrenstein *et al.*, 1970) or in several smaller steps having a sum equivalent to the large jump (Bean *et al.*, 1969; Bean, 1972). EIM channels in oxidized cholesterol BLM show only two conductance levels, whereas EIM, in BLM prepared from crude brain lipids or SM + tocopherol, show intermediate states as well. These results are best accounted for, in terms of an arrangement of a multimolecular complex of EIM and closely associated lipids, to develop open, closed, and intermediate states. Such lipid-specific regulation of conformation in membrane multicomponent systems, containing a large number of channels may account for several macroscopic characteristics of excitable membranes including EIM modified BLM (Mueller and Rudin, 1968) and probably nerve membranes (Jain *et al.*, 1970), as well.

The observations summarized in Table II suggest that reconstitution of a functional bilayer or incorporation of a variety of proteins into the bilayer matrix, leads to a reconstitution of macroscopic functions not exhibited by isolated or dissociated membrane fragments. This appears to be a general membrane phenomenon. In fact, the barrier role of membranes for maintaining proton gradients has been articulated in the chemiosmotic hypothesis for energy transduction during respiratory and photosynthetic electron transport.

For quite sometime now, a controversy has centered around the identification of the role of membranes in energy transduction in mitochondria, chloroplast, and bacterial protoplast membranes. The phenomenological expression of respiratory chain operation is the utilization of substrates and the consumption of oxygen leading to the formation of water and carbon dioxide with concomitant synthesis of ATP. Oxidative phosphorylation in intact mitochondria, SMP, and reconstituted phosphorylating particles requires a compartment limited by a membrane relatively impermeable to protons (Kagawa, 1972; Racker and Horstman, 1972). Respiratory control, phosphorylation, and proton translocation are all lost or inactivated in parallel fashion, in the presence of increasing amounts of cholate or uncoupling agents. The most convincing evidence for a structural requirement is the fact that certain functions are restored by reconstituting vesicles from isolated components (see as follows).

The presence of a proton pump and the formation of a potential across the inner mitochondrial membrane is of considerable interest in relation to the problem of respiratory control even if they should not represent the driving force for the generation of ATP. These various aspects of proton translocation across mitochondrial and chloroplast membranes have been articulated in the chemiosmotic hypothesis. The key features of this hypothesis are the protonmotive force (pH gradient) and the membrane potential that develop during respiration via loops of the electron transport chain. A detailed discussion of these aspects of energy transduction is beyond the scope of this review (however, see as follows). Several fundamental aspects of the rate processes have come to light through these studies and have given rise to a molecular basis for terms such as *coupling, asymmetry,* and *vectorial* characteristics in the context of chemical reactions associated with membranes.

B. The Bilayer Matrix as a Determinant of Microscopic Functions

Coupling of solute transport to exergonic chemical reactions is one of the least understood and most widely occurring biochemical phenomena (see Jain, 1972, Ch. 7). Many such processes involve formation or breakdown of high-energy phosphate bonds. Therefore, it is not surprising that membrane-bound ATPases are ubiquitous in nature. In higher organisms, the most comprehensively studied systems are the mitochondrial ATPases involved in oxidative phosphorylation, and the Na + K-ATPase and Ca-ATPase involved in transport of cations. ATPase, also active in the plasma membranes of bacteria is presumably involved in proton translocation or some such related process.

The bacterial membrane-bound ATPase is released when the membranes are washed in cation-free solutions (Abrams and Baron, 1968). A variety of cations are effective in preventing the release of the bound ATPase, including Mg^{++}, Mn^{++}, Ca^{++}, and spermidine. A stable ATPase membrane complex can be formed only in the presence of divalent cations and the membrane itself can accommodate only a limited number of ATPase sites. These results can be interpreted by assuming that the divalent ions act as ligands, mediating the binding of ATPase to specific binding sites in the membrane. However, cations could also induce a conformational change in the enzyme or in a specific component of the membrane, thereby permitting a direct interaction of ATPase with the membrane. As indicated in Table II, the purified ATPase from *Streptococcus fecalis* can be incorporated into BLM (Redwood *et al.*, 1969). The physiological significance of the observation that the incorporation of ATPase into BLM is accompanied by an increase in conductance is not clear however.

The mitochondrial ATPase exhibits several similarities to the bacterial membrane ATPase. In each case, the membrane-bound enzyme differs from the solubilized enzyme in several respects. Both are inactivated by *N,N'*-dicyclohexylcarbodiimide (DCCD) when the enzymes are membrane-bound (Harold *et al.*, 1969; Bulos and Racker, 1968). In contrast, the sensitivity to DCCD disappears when the enzymes are solubilized. Such observations indicate that the solubilization of these enzymes accompanies a change in the properties (accessibility to DCCD) of the protein. Such a change appears to be a fairly general characteristic of membrane enzymes. The membrane-bound mitochondrial ATPase is cold-stable and is completely inhibited by energy transfer inhibitors such as oligomycin, and by tributyltin, chlorpromazine, and rutamycin as well. The soluble ATPase (the coupling factor F_1 from mitochondria) is cold-labile and insensitive to energy transfer inhibitors. A factor F_0 (electron transfer vesicles) when added to F_1 restores the oligomycin sensitivity and cold stability (Kagawa and Racker, 1966; Knowles *et al.*, 1971). Further purification of F_0 yields a few coupling factors which are virtually devoid of cytochromes and phospholipids. The binding of F_1 to one of these coupling factors accompanies loss of ATPase activity that is completely restored following the addition of phospholipids. This reconstituted preparation is cold-stable, sensitive to energy transfer inhibitors, and is morphologically indistinguishable from SMP even though the ETC is missing. A similar reconstitution has also been achieved for ATPase from the chloroplast photosystem (Lien and Racker, 1971).

Racker and co-workers have recently reconstituted an ATP-P_i exchange system from four soluble proteins (coupling factors), two hydrophobic proteins, and phospholipids (cf. Table II). Following dialysis of a mixture of cholate-solubilized coupling factors, hydrophobic proteins, and phospholipids against 10% methanol in water, the ATP-P_i exchange reaction began to appear after 5 hours of dialysis, and reached its peak after 18 hours. However, ATPase activity is restored immediately after adding the phospholipids (Fig. 1b). The rapid removal of cholate by passage of the mixture through Sephadex yielded inactive preparations, suggesting that proper assembly is a slow process and requires vesicularization. PC and PE (1:4 for optimal activity) were both required for the reconstitution of the vesicles with high exchange activity due to site I (Ragan and Racker, 1973) and site III (Kagawa *et al.*, 1973a,b) of energy conservation. The presence of unsaturated fatty acyl groups (even those with unnatural side chains) in the phospholipid appears to be essential for the reconstitution of active vesicles. Phospholipids with fully saturated acyl groups were actually inhibitory. It appears that the assembly of vesicular structures in the presence of hydrophobic proteins is profoundly influenced by the composition of the phospholipids. It may also be noted that the phospholipid content of reconstituted vesicles (~3.5 μmoles/mg protein) is in large excess over that of SMP (0.7

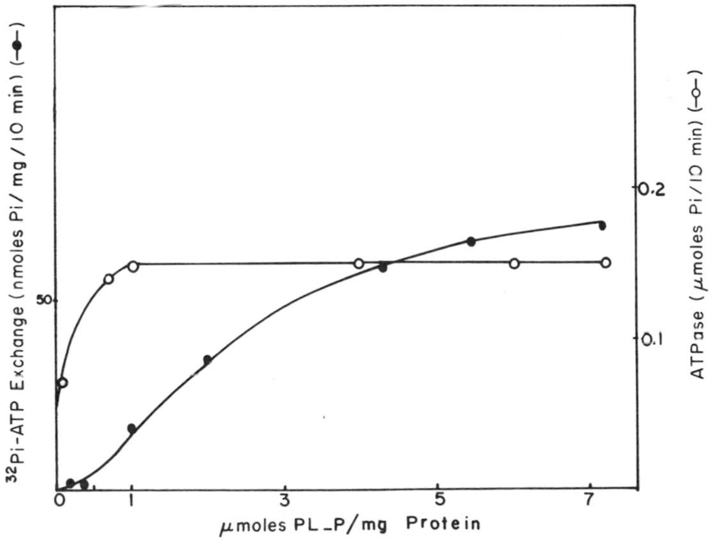

FIG. 1b. Effect of PL concentration on the restoration of $^{32}P_i$-ATP exchange and ATPase activity of 33P and 33-50P fraction derived from beef heart mitochondria. To the pallets of 33P (8.1 mg) or 33-50P (7.0 mg), 2 ml of 2% Na-cholate (pH 8.0) containing various amounts of 0 to 5% soybean lecithin were added. The mixture was homogenized with 0.5 ml of dialyzing solution and then dialyzed against 10% methanol. From Kagawa and Racker (1971).

μmole/mg protein). A slow assembly and large phospholipid content of the ATP-P_i exchanging and ATP-driven proton translocating particles is quite different from the phospholipid requirements of the oligomycin-sensitive ATPase and the electron transport chain, where simple addition of relatively small amounts of single phospholipids or even mild detergents results in an almost immediate (usually less than 10 minutes) activation of the lipid-depleted complexes. Furthermore, it seems that each segment of the respiratory chain has requirements that must be met by a proper ratio either of two phospholipids or by an appropriate mixture of several. This may explain the need for the rather complex phospholipid composition of the mitochondrial membrane that is not apparent from the investigation of an individual site of oxidative phosphorylation.

The reconstituted vesicles have a higher phospholipid content and lower proton permeability. The vescularization is essential for the restoration of both the uncoupler-sensitive ATP-P_i exchange and ATP-driven proton accumulation (Racker and Kandrach, 1971; Jasaitis *et al.*, 1972). These observations suggest the chemiosmotic hypothesis. These studies show that many aspects of energy coupling in mitochondria are present in cytochrome oxidase (or NADH-uniquinone reductase) and in coupling factors, when these components are properly incorporated into a phospholipid membrane and when polarity is created by having various substrates and cofactors isolated in suitable compartments. The orientation of the respiratory chain complex in the membrane is not critical as long as asymmetry can be achieved by providing reducing equivalents from one side of the membrane only, i.e., NADH from the outside for the first site and reduced cytochrome c from the inside for the third site.

The various studies leading to reconstitution of specific membrane function into a bilayer or liposomes (cf. Table II) seem to be based on the same general principles; however, specific conditions are different. The experimental variables are: temperature, pH, nature and fatty acid composition of the lipids, presence of trace amounts of detergents, rate of detergent removal and vesicle formation, asymmetry with respect to approach and release of substrate, products, and cofactors. Other considerations with regard to the stability of apoprotein and specific lipid requirements need also be considered. These aspects become apparent from the study of relatively simple enzyme systems that require lipid for optimal functioning. Some of these cases are described as follows.

Na + K-ATPase from the synaptosomal fraction of rat brain has been incorporated into BLM (Jain *et al.*, 1969, 1972). These studies suggest that incorporation of the enzyme into the bilayer reconstitutes a complete electrogenic cationic active transport system requiring specific lipids for its reconstitution. In fact, it has been reported that the Na + K-ATPase requires lipids for optimal activity (Schatzmann, 1962; Swanson *et al.*, 1964). Many types of lipids have been implicated: PC and PE (Tanaka and Strickland, 1965), PS (Ohnishi and Kawamura, 1964; Israel, 1969; Fenster and Copenhaver, 1967; Towle and Copenhaver, 1970), PS and PI (Wheeler and Whittem, 1970; Hegyvary and Post, 1969), inosithin (Hexum and Hokin, 1971), cholesterol (Noguchi and Freed, 1971; Jarnefelt, 1972), PG (Kimelberg and Papahadjopoulos, 1972), several neutral and acidic lipids (Bruni *et al.*, 1971; Palatini *et al.*, 1972), sulfatides (Karlsson *et al.*, 1971), and detergents including Triton X-100, DOC, and digitonin at low concentrations (Somogyi *et al.*, 1969; Ellory and Smith, 1969; Philippot and Authier, 1973). Among the synthetic surfactants various mono- and dialkyl (C_{10}–C_{14}) phosphates have been found to be effective in activating DOC-solubilized Na + K-ATPase (Tanaka *et al.*, 1971) as well as in reconstituting the Na-pump on the BLM (Jain *et al.*, 1969, 1972).

Such a broad diversity in the nature of activating lipids could reflect either the inherent specificity of the Na + K-ATPase from different sources or the method and extent of denaturation and delipidation. The diversity may also be a reflection of the consequences of impurities present in the added lipids, or may be due to some common property of the lipids in general. The possible activating effect of these lipids due to a chelating effect on inhibitory polyvalent ions can be ruled out (Specht and Robinson, 1973; Philippot and Authier, 1973; Forte *et al.*, 1973). Furthermore, a sigmoidal relationship seems to exist between the concentration of the added phospholipid and the degree of resultant activation. The phospholipid-induced activation is also paralleled by the amount of phospholipid bound to the protein (Palatini *et al.*, 1972). These reconstitution studies suggest that a large number of phospholipid molecules are required for activation of Na + K-ATPase activity. It may also be noted that the kinetic characteristics of both the membrane-bound and a highly purified Na + K-ATPase were found to be remarkably similar (Ratanabanangkoon *et al.*, 1973), but not identical.

The variability in the nature of phospholipid required for activation of Na + K-ATPase could also arise from the fact that delipidation achieved by various methods may only be partial and the enzyme may be partially inactivated. If the activating effect of specific phospholipids in partial reactions of the ATPase reaction cycle is different, one would expect a variability in the nature of the activating lipid. Although the nature of specific lipids, activating partial reactions of Na + K-ATPase is still subject to controversy, recent studies do show that these partial reactions may be catalyzed by different lipids.

Phospholipase digestion studies on a preparation of ATPase from *Electrophorus* have yielded significant information regarding participation of the various lipids in catalytic process (Goldman and Albers, 1973). The overall hydrolysis of ATP by Na + K-ATPase involves the following partial reactions:

$$E_1 + ATP \xrightarrow{Na^+} E_1\text{—}P + ADP \qquad (1)$$

$$E_1\text{—}P \xrightarrow{Mg^{++}} E_2 \sim P \qquad (2)$$

$$E_2 \sim P \xrightarrow{K^+} E_2 + P_i \qquad (3)$$

$$E_2 \xrightarrow{-Mg^{++}} E_1 \qquad (4)$$

Treatment with phospholipase A (*Naja naja*) removes all phosphatides with concomitant loss of enzyme activity and loss of the ability to form the phosphorylated intermediates. Treatment with phospholipase C (*Clostridium welchii*), which removes all PC, two-thirds of PE, and none of the PS, leads to only partial inactivation of ATPase activity; the steady-state level of the phosphoryl enzyme and the rate of Na-dependent nucleotide transphosphorylation are not affected. Also, phospholipase C treatment produces increased levels of E_2, and inhibition of ATPase and PNPase, by high concentration of Mg are more pronounced. The reduced turnover number of phospholipase C-treated ATPase is probably attributed to this same effect. The results suggest that PS is required for steps (1) and (3), and that PE acts as a modifier for steps (2) and (4) in the scheme previously given. These results are also consistent with the observation that the activity of phospholipase C-inactivated enzyme can be completely restored by PE. However, phospholipase A-inactivated enzyme activity is only partially restored by PS (see also Hegyvary and Post, 1969; Roelofsen *et al.*, 1971). This may imply that complete digestion with phospholipase A brings about irreversible changes in the ATPase.

Similar studies on rat brain (Stahl, 1973) and beef brain (Taniguchi and Tonomura, 1971) microsomal Na + K-ATPases, show that inactivation of various partial reactions can be effected by phospholipase digestion. However, significant differences are seen in these studies. Thus, for example, treatment of rat brain enzyme by phospholipase C (*C. welchii*) led to proportional loss of net Na + K-ATPase, K-PNPase, and Na-stimulated nucleotide exchange activities. These activities can be largely restored by PC, PS, SM, PI, PA, and PE. Some of the discrepancies in these studies could be attributed to incomplete removal of the products of hydrolysis of lipids and to differences in experimental design and conditions. However, it appears that activation of Na + K-ATPase by phospholipids is a largely nonspecific process. Acidic (anionic) lipids show a remarkable affinity for the enzyme complex and may play an important role in maintaining the active conformation or ion-binding ability (see as follows). Full activation of transport ATPase by phospholipids must be regarded as an effect in which the gross structure of a phospholipid aggregate cooperates (cf. Section III,A). Similar factors may be responsible for the activation of various partial reactions of mitochondrial ATP-synthetase by phospholipids (Steckhoven and Van Moerkerk, 1972).

The sarcoplasmic reticulum membrane of muscle is highly specialized in active transport of Ca^{++}, and this function is almost certainly due to a Ca-activated ATPase present in these membranes. Both the uphill transport of Ca^{++} and the Ca-ATPase are lipid-dependent, as both of these activities are inactivated by treatment with organic solvents and phospholipases (Martonoshi *et al.*, 1968, and references therein; MacLennan *et al.*, 1971). Generally, the decline in the Ca-ATPase and Ca^{++}-uptake activities is approximately the same and closely parallels the decline in membrane-lecithin content. Restoration of both functions can be achieved following the addition of phospholipids, but the structural requirements for the restoration of the two activities are somewhat different. Ca-ATPase activity is restored by phospholipids and various anionic and nonionic detergents, but not by cationic detergents. In contrast, restoration of Ca^{++}-transport activity has much more specific requirements for lecithin, lysolecithin, and phosphatidic acid; detergents are ineffective. The degree of unsaturation of phospholipids does not appear to be of any consequence for the reactivation of either process. This difference in activation of the two processes is consistent with the view that although both systems possess all the components necessary for ATPase and transport functions, the reconstituted vesicles in the presence of detergents are not sufficiently sealed to permit Ca^{++}-accumulation. Alternatively, it is possible that the binding of some yet unidentified component requires a specific lipid. Further studies suggest that a marked accumulation of phosphorylated enzyme intermediate occurs in phospholipase C-treated microsomes. This implies a phospholipid requirement for the decomposition of the phosphoprotein intermediate (Martonoshi *et al.*, 1971).

The observations presented so far suggest rather clearly that hydrolysis of ATP by various ATPases is dependent on phospholipids. Although there does not appear to be a requirement for a specific lipid, there is rather convincing evidence suggesting that some specific conformation in the reaction cycle does not take place in the absence of lipid. Such a conformation is presumably associated with the solute translocation.

In fact, the Ca-ATPase activity has been correlated to the fluidity of the membrane as determined by e.s.r. (Seelig and Hasselbach, 1971).

Several other enzyme systems, whose activation could be the result of a change in membrane environment or structure, or result from a change in catalytic site are discussed in subsequent sections of this review. However, yet another ATP-utilizing enzyme system, the adenylcyclase, is known to manifest its biological functions by modulating membrane properties. Adenylcyclase catalyzes the conversion of ATP to 3′,5′-cyclic AMP in the presence of divalent cations; this enzyme is also activated by fluoride ions. Many hormones also produce their effects by stimulating adenylcyclase (Robinson *et al.*, 1971); hormone-sensitive adenylcyclases are membrane-bound enzymes mostly present in the plasma membrane. Many tissues are highly specific in that they contain an adenylcyclase which is stimulated by only one or a few hormones. However, it appears that the active site of adenylcyclase itself is not the primary site of hormone action, but a secondary one whose behavior reflects change at the hormone-binding site. Treatment of the target cells with phospholipases (Tomasi *et al.*, 1970; Rethy *et al.*, 1971; Rodbell *et al.*, 1971) and solubilization in detergents (Levey, 1971a,b; Rethy *et al.*, 1971) destroys both the hormone- and fluoride-stimulated adenylcyclase activities. These observations suggest that the hormone specific site is a lipoprotein (see Jain, 1973, for a review). Hormone sensitivity can be partially restored by exposing the treated membranes to an aqueous suspension of membrane lipids (Levey, 1971a,b). Pure PS, PC, and PE are all capable of partially restoring hormone-stimulated activity of phospholipase A-treated enzyme complex. Of these, PS is the most effective for the recovery of glucagon and histamine-stimulated activity. Similarly, PI restores the norepinephrine activation of the solubilized adenylcyclase; however, this reconstituted preparation is unresponsive to glucagon, histamine, and thyroxine.

The ability of more than one kind of phospholipid to reverse the effect of phospholipase A-treatment indicates that part of the activating effect of lipids may be nonspecific, i.e., related only to maintaining a generally hydrophobic environment for those components of the adenylcyclase system that transmit the perturbation of hormone binding to the catalytic site of adenylcyclase. However, the differences in the effects of the various lipid fractions suggest that specific lipids may be required for proper orientation of the components for hormone recognition. Furthermore studies of the effects of PP_i, $MnCl_2$, certain drugs, digitonin, urea, and phospholipases suggest that at least on liver membranes, fluoride and glucagon modulate adenylcyclase activities by different processes (Pohl *et al.*, 1971). Observations mentioned in this section suggest that various ATP-utilizing enzymes manifest their biological functions by modulating membrane properties. For ATPases and adenylcyclases, the modulation of the solute translocation step or hormone recognition is dependent upon membrane lipid class. Furthermore, since most of the membrane-localized enzyme systems are significantly affected by ions (Na^+, K^+, Ca^{++}, Mg^{++}, F^-, and others), it would be interesting to know to what extent the lipids affect and/or regulate the binding and biological functions of these ions.

IV. Effect of Membrane Fluidity[3] and Lipid Phase Transitions on Functioning of Membrane-Bound Proteins

"Fluidity" of phospholipid chains is a predominant feature of bilayers; however, a precise knowledge of the structural and molecular basis of fluidity and of the rates of molecular motions involved is altogether lacking. For most practical purposes, fluidity of membrane lipids may be taken as a combination of physical and chemical disorder as determined by the mobility of chains, the lateral mobility of phospholipid molecules, and the extent of intermolecular interactions. The orientational ordering that characterizes a bilayer results in a macroscopic anisotropy. Any perturbation of such an anisotropic system will result in a response that is related to the perturbation by a material susceptibility, such as the dielectric permittivity when applying an electric field, the diamagnetic susceptibility for a magnetic field, elastic coefficient for a mechanical stress, and modification of intermolecular interactions by altered temperature or incorporation of various agents that may modify the interchain interactions. Under suitable conditions in anisotropic systems, the response to perturbations exhibits several characteristics: (a) a large number of molecules respond cooperatively such that the distance of correlated motion is large (up to several microns) compared to molecular dimensions; (b) the thermal energy, kT, is shared among all the molecules that are acting cooperatively, so that the thermal energy per molecular aggregate becomes comparable to the energies of interactions; (c) unlike isotropic systems, in anisotropic systems, their elasticity becomes comparable to their viscosity (cf. Frenkel, 1955).

The various features of anisotropic systems are manifested in certain

---

[3] Fluidity of a simple liquid is proportional to the fractional excess of its molal volume over the molal volume at which the molecules are so closely crowded as to prevent viscous flow while still retaining rotational freedom (Hildebrand, 1971). In the case of the lipid bilayer, fluidity would then be an approximate measure of void volume.

aspects of lipid-protein interactions in biomembranes. As discussed in the following section, the dependence of various enzymic and transport activities on the phase behavior of the bilayer (order-disorder transition of hydrocarbon chains) suggest that these various functions of biomembranes may be regulated by long-range interactions among the membrane lipids. Some of these aspects are examined as follows.

A. Temperature-Dependent Alteration of Membrane Fluidity

In a living cell, there is a definite requirement for fluidity of membrane matrix. Thus, most living membranes exist in a "liquid crystalline" state, attained in higher organisms by altered cholesterol content, whereas in lower organisms, the membrane fluidity is regulated by altered chemical randomness in fatty acid composition of phospholipids (unsaturation, chain-length, and branching). The physicochemical significance of this specific phase requirement for biological function is not yet established. However, a correlation has been found for variation of phospholipid pattern to passive permeability (Deuticke and Gruber, 1970) and several other membrane functions (see as follows). From these and other related observations, it appears that the biochemical functions (conformational change, lateral mobility, and lateral cooperativity) of membrane-bound proteins may be regulated by the physical state of the chains in the bilayer.

The fatty-acid composition of membrane lipids of unsaturated fatty acid auxotrophs of *E. coli* are dependent on the physicochemical properties of the supplement unsaturated fatty acids (Esfahani *et al.*, 1971b). The temperature characteristics of the transport of β-glucoside and β-galactosides (Fig. 2; see also Schairer and Overath, 1969; Wilson *et al.*, 1970; Overath *et al.*, 1970; Wilson and Fox, 1971), as well as the respiration and growth of *E. coli* (Overath *et al.*, 1970) indicates that the Arrhenius plots for all these various processes are biphasic, the slopes extrapolating to intersections at unique transition temperatures. Similar biphasic response has been observed for several other membrane functions (Table III).

The physiological consequences of unsaturated fatty acid deprivation in *E. coli* have been investigated (Hennings *et al.*, 1969; Glaser *et al.*, 1973). Removal of oleate from the mutant resulted in an inhibition of phospholipid, RNA and DNA synthesis, and in lysis of the cells growing in a rich medium. Protein synthesis declines later than the synthesis of other macromolecules. A specific inhibitor of unsaturated fatty acid synthesis, 3-decanonyl-*N*-acetyl-cysteamine, on gram-negative bacteria also exhibits similar effects (Kass, 1968; see also Robbins and Rotman,

1972). However, a functional β-galactoside transport system can be formed during the initial phase of starvation of unsaturated fatty acid auxotrophs (for a review, see Cronan and Vagelos, 1972). In these cells the transport protein is incorporated into a lipid phase that randomizes presumably by lateral diffusion of lipid molecules within the bilayer of the membrane (Overath *et al.*, 1971). It may be noted that on lowering the growth temperature of *E. coli* K12 from 37° to 17°, the cells resumed growth after a lag period of 40 minutes. During the lag period, the transition point in Arrhenius plots of the preinduced β-galactoside transport system were not changed while the saturated / unsaturated fatty acid ratio decreased gradually in PE, rapidly in PG, and slightly in cardiolipin (Kito *et al.*, 1973). These observations imply that the biphasic behavior of the transport system may be due to the lipid species that is not altered or renewed during the lag period. However, the observations suggesting that the synthesis of a physiologically functional transport system requires the simultaneous synthesis of membrane phospholipids (Wilson and Fox, 1971, and references therein), are in obvious contradiction with these conclusions. This difference appears to be due to a difference in growth temperature at which fatty acid incorporation is carried out after shifting the growth from one fatty acid to another (Tsukagoshi and Fox, 1973). Above the phase transition temperature (T_c), a mixing of the preformed and newly synthesized lipids occurs within the bilayer matrix. However, below T_c such lateral motion is either nonexistent or considerably slower. Furthermore, it has been suggested that below T_c, two different types of lipids may exist as separate "islands" (Linden *et al.*, 1973).

The transition temperatures for several of the membrane-associated functions in *E. coli* vary with the degree of unsaturation of the fatty acid supplement; they are highest for *trans*-monoenoic, intermediate with *cis*-monoenoic, and lowest for *cis*-polyenoic acids (Overath *et al.*, 1970, 1971). Similar transition temperatures were observed in studies of isolated phospholipids in monolayers at the air/water interface, suggesting that the transition temperatures observed in the membrane functions (transport of galactosides, in this case) reflected transition in the lipid portion of the membrane.

In most cases, the break in Arrhenius plots accompanies transition from low to high activation energies upon temperature decrease. It has been suggested that fluidization of the bilayer above T_c may be responsible for the reduction of E_{act}. This does not necessarily imply that the effect of phase transition is to modify the turnover rates of the permease or the enzyme. A biphasic Arrhenius plot could also arise from a change in the affinity of the substrate at nonsaturating concentrations. This ap-

Table III

PHASE TRANSITION CHARACTERISTICS OF VARIOUS MEMBRANE-BOUND ENZYMES

Enzyme/Function	Source	Transition temperature, °C (T_c)	Remarks[a] (Reference)
Na + K-ATPase	Rabbit kidney	20°	E_{act} 30 and 13–15 kcal (Charnock *et al.*, 1971)
	Reconstituted enzyme	30°	E_{act} 42 and 20 kcal for dipalmitoyl-PG activated enzyme (Kimelberg and Papahadjopoulos, 1972)
Succinic dehydrogenase	Mitochondria from various sources	6–20°	See text (Raison *et al.*, 1971a,b)
Glycerol-3-P and 1-acyl-glycerol-3-P acyltransferase	*E. coli* (FA auxotroph)	15° *cis-* 20° *trans-*	Monoenoic acids; no sharp transitions (Mavis and Vagelos, 1972)
Succinic-dichloroindophenol reductase	*E. coli* (FA auxotroph)	19° (oleate) 28° (elaidate)	Esfahani *et al.* (1971a,b, 1972)
Cyclopropane FA synthetase		21–23° (PE)	Chung and Law (1964)
Calicin E, induced changes	*E. coli*	Changes with growth temperature	Cramer *et al.* (1973)
β-Galactoside permease	*E. coli*	13° (oleate) 7° (linoleate)	E_{act} 30 and 15 kcal (Wilson *et al.*, 1970)

Proline transport	*E. coli*	26° (elaidate) 19° (oleate) 14° (linoleate)	E_{act} 30–35 and 15 kcal (Esfahani *et al.*, 1971a)
Resting potential	*Valonia*	15, 29.5°	Thorhaug (1971)
Ca-ATPase	*E. coli*	32°	T_c changes as a function of fatty acid supplement (Sineriz *et al.*, 1973)
ATPase	*Saccharomyces cerevisiae*	34–18°	T_c decreases as ergosterol content increases; E_{act} remains constant (Cobon and Haslem, 1973)
ATPase	Mycoplasma mycoids	20–30°	Cholesterol-dependent (Rottem *et al.*, 1973)
Succinate respiration	Rat liver mitochondria	20–25°	E_{act} is lower for uncoupled chain (Brinkmann and Packer, 1970)
β-Glucoside transport	*E. coli*	30–7° for various fatty acids	E_{act} 30 and 15 kcal (Wilson and Fox, 1971)
Protein synthesis	Rat liver microsome	22°	E_{act} 16 and 43 kcal (Towers *et al.*, 1972)
Denaturation of DNA in chromatin	Rat liver nucleus	75–80°	T_c is modified by degree of unsaturation of lipid (Goureau *et al.*, 1972)
Glucose-6-phosphatase and UDP-glucuronyltransferase	Guinea pig liver	19° for both	Eletr *et al.* (1973)
UDP-galactosyltransferase	*E. coli*	18–23°	Beacham and Silbert (1973)

[a] E_{act} is always higher at lower temperatures.

pears to be the case, at least for the biphasic response, for lactose permease in *E. coli* ML-308. As shown in Fig. 2, the sharp break in the Arrhenius plot for the transport of ONPG in *E. coli* is due to a temperature-dependent change in the apparent K_m; activation energy remains essentially insensitive to a change in temperature although a slow transition is observed above 25° in V_{max} (Sullivan *et al.*, 1974). These observations have significant bearing on the mechanism of translocation of ONPG by lactose permease. They imply that the turnover of the permease is not sharply affected by a change in temperature. A slow change in V_{max} for the transport is however consistent with the broad transitions observed by X-ray diffraction 15–20° above the breaks in the Arrhenius plots (Esfahani *et al.*, 1971c). The effect of change in fluidity, leading to a sharp transition in K_m (Fig. 2) is difficult to evaluate. However, such a change indicates that loading or unloading of the carrier or the binding

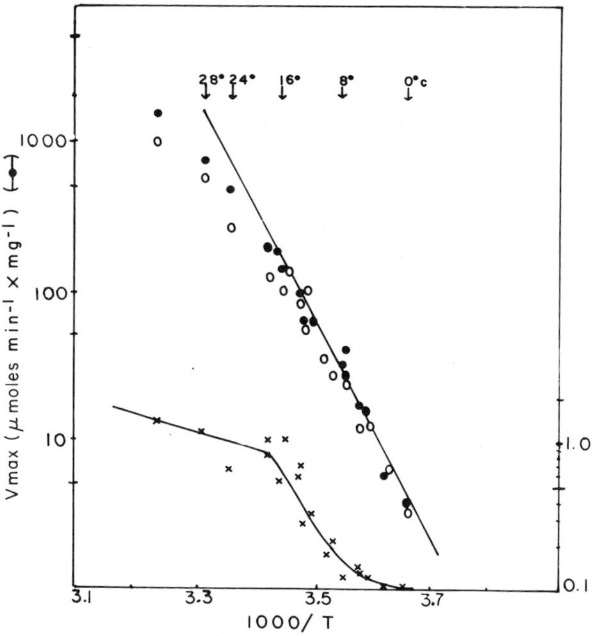

FIG. 2. Arrhenius plots for the net transport of ONPG by lactose permease in *E. coli* ML308. It may be noted that the biphasic response at 1.8 m*M* ONPG (○—○) is not observed at saturating concentrations of ONPG (●—●). The K_m values (×—×), however, show a sharp transition: mid-point at about 14–16°. These results show that a break in Arrhenius plot at a nonsaturating permeant concentration is due to a sharp change in the "affinity" of the permease (or binding protein) for the substrate rather than to a change in its turnover rate. From Sullivan *et al.* (1974).

of ONPG to permease is most sensitive to a change in temperature and is dependent upon the fluidity of the bilayer. The fact that transition in K_m occurs sharply and at about 10° below any change in V_{max} lends itself to speculation. These observations are however consistent with a hypothesis that changes in K_m and V_{max} reflect changes in two different regions of the bilayer. A slow change at a higher temperature leading to change in V_{max} is apparently due to fluidization of the terminal methylene region as observed by X-ray diffraction studies. However, this change is preceded by a relatively sharp change in the apolar region near the head group and/or a change in the head group region itself, a change that leads to an alteration in the apparent affinity of the permease for ONPG.

Biphasic Arrhenius plots have not been observed for all the membrane-bound enzymes in *E. coli.* The enzyme acyl-CoA: glycerol-3-phosphate acyltransferase has an apparent dependence on intact phospholipid, but does not reflect the phase characteristics of membrane lipids. Absence of phase transition in the activity of glycerol-3-phosphate acyltransferase and 1-acyl-glycerol 3-phosphate acyltransferase has been taken to imply a highly specific association of lipids with these enzymes (Sinensky, 1971; Mavis and Vagelos, 1972). It is postulated that the phase transitional characteristics of the bulk of the bilayer are distinct from that of the lipid associated with these proteins. Only the overall phase characteristics of the lipoprotein complex are affected by the physical properties of the lipid hydrocarbon chains. The higher slope of the plots for a membrane containing *trans*-monoenoic or predominantly saturated fatty acids suggests that the enzyme is a less effective catalyst when *cis*-monoenoic fatty acids are not available. These observations imply a microheterogeneity of membrane lipids with respect to the phase properties of the bulk of the bilayer. It is consistent with the observation that the temperature-activity profiles for various membrane functions in the same organism differ significantly (cf. Table III). An alternative interpretation of the difference in temperature-activity profiles is that different proteins may interact to different extents with neighboring lipid molecules. Thus even though the statistical distribution of lipids in the immediate vicinity of these proteins may be closely similar, their catalytic activities may vary differently as the phase characteristics of the bilayer change.

It is, however, not yet certain whether the phase change in the chains is transmitted directly to the catalytic site or whether it is transmitted indirectly through modulation of the polar region, as for example, the surface charge or water structure. It is also important to note that quite a few proteins show sharp breaks in Arrhenius plots due to thermally induced reversible changes in protein structure (Massey *et al.*, 1966; Talsky, 1971; see also Eletr and Inesi, 1972; McClard and Kolenbrander, 1973). Furthermore, in a system that involves the interaction of lipid aggregates and a water soluble enzyme system, the state of aggregation must be of considerable importance. In general, the c.m.c. of amphipathic molecules increases with temperature (Klevens, 1947; Brady and Huff, 1948) and therefore, it is possible that at the temperature, where the discontinuity is observed, the micelles may revert to monomolecular species.

Phase transition characteristics of lipid bilayers seem to modify activation energies for a variety of enzymes present in membranes of higher organisms (Table III). Na + ATPase, believed to be an integral part of the alkali cation transport system in higher animals, undergoes a change in activation energy near 20° (Gruener and Avi-Dor, 1966). Phase transition for Mg-ATPase is observed at 6°. Interestingly, the Na + K-ATPase activities of preparations from goldfish intestinal mucosa (Smith, 1967) and earthworm nerve cord (Lagerspetz *et al.*, 1973) show transitions that reflect the acclimatization temperature of these organisms. Similar changes have been noted for succinic dehydrogenase activity in goldfish (Hazel, 1972). The change in activation energy as noted earlier, appears to be a consequence of phase transition in the bilayer (cf., however, Low *et al.*, 1973). Therefore, transition temperatures reflect the different degrees of unsaturation of the fatty acyl chains of the membrane lipids associated with the ATPase. Reconstitution experiments are consistent with this hypothesis. DOC-treated Na + K-ATPase, activated by dipalmitoyl-PE, shows a phase transition at 30° (Kimelberg and Papahadjopoulos, 1972) but no such transition is observed in brain-PS activated (Priestland and Whittam, 1972), or partially delipidated-, or egg-PG-activated enzyme (Kimelberg and Papahadjopoulos, 1972). Activation energy of Mg-ATPase shows no such transition in the range studied. These observations on the relationship of bulk lipid phase transition to enzymic activity are consistent with the observations that the lipid composition of microsomes is qualitatively similar to that of residual lipids in DOC-treated preparations (Morgan *et al.*, 1963) even though the protein: lipid ratio is increased from 2.4 to 30 following DOC treatment. It is interesting to note that both native and reconstituted Ca-ATPase from sarcoplasmic reticulum do not show phase transition characteristics noted for Na + K-ATPase (The and Hasselbach, 1972).

Studies using calorimetic, X-ray diffraction, and spectroscopic methods suggest that a large variety of membrane functions are dependent on the phase properties of membrane lipids. In fact, various membrane-bound enzymes in mitochondria show anomalous Arrhenius plots (cf. Table III). Also, respiration in mitochondria from chill-sensitive plant tissue (tomato, cucumber fruit, sweet potato root), in contrast to the mitochondria from chill-resistant tissue (cauliflower buds, potato tubers, beet-root), is significantly reduced at temperatures below 10° (Lyons and Raison, 1970; Raison *et al.*, 1971a). These observations suggest that the immediate response of sensitive tissue below a critical temperature is consistent with the hypothesis that reduced temperatures affect some physical property of the mitochondrial membranes, e.g., the fluidity of the membrane lipids. For the effect of temperature adaptation on phospholipids of goldfish membranes see Anderson (1970).

Disruption of mitochondria from rat liver and sweet potato by sonication, hypotonic swelling, freezing and thawing does not alter the discontinuity in the Arrhenius plots exhibited by mitochondrial respiratory enzymes, including the succinate oxidase system, succinate dehydrogenase, and cytochrome c oxidase (Raison *et al.*, 1971a,b). Similarly, the activation energy of succinate oxidation by rat liver mitochondria, changes at a temperature of about 17° in *state* III as well as in the uncoupled state. The activation energy of the ADP-ATP and P_i-ATP exchange reactions and of the 2,4-DNP-induced ATPase also shows phase change (Kemp *et al.*, 1969). These observations suggest that an intact membrane structure is not required for the demonstration of transition temperatures. Disruption of mitochondrial membranes with detergents, however, brings about a change in the transition characteristics of all the enzyme systems with a loss of the discontinuity in the Arrhenius plot. Zeylemaker *et al.* (1971) have noted a break in the Arrhenius plot with both particulate and soluble succinate dehydrogenase of heart muscle, which they interpreted as indicating temperature-dependent conformational change in the enzyme. Moreover, the partitioning of a spin label in contracted mitochondria showed a break in the Arrhenius plot at about 24°, while no discontinuity was observed for expanded samples (Tinberg *et al.*, 1972). These results have been correlated to a change in particle density and aggregation in the outer membrane, results that imply an active involvement of lipid in the mitochondrial oscillatory state.

In intact mitochondria, all membrane-bound enzymes tested, except cytochrome c oxidase, have shown breaks in Arrhenius plots, while the soluble matrix enzymes (malic dehydrogenase and fumerase) do not have breaks or have different characteristics (Lenaz *et al.*, 1972a,b). However, the breaks in Arrhenius plots for these membrane-bound enzymes seem to occur at different temperatures. If these observations are correct, it may imply either a lipid specificity for these enzymes or a lack of correlation between membrane phase transition and enzyme activity. It may be pointed out, however, that considerable circumstantial evidence exists, suggesting that a conformational change in membrane proteins does affect the state of membrane lipids (Eletr and Inesi, 1972; Lanyi, 1973). In any case, the available evidence suggesting the role of membrane lipid phase transition in modulating the function of membrane proteins is at best circumstantial.

B. Drug-Induced Alteration of Membrane Fluidity

A variety of organic solvents and drugs may also modify interchain interactions and fluidity of the bilayer. Thus the conclusions arrived at for temperature-dependent phase transition studies should also be manifest in membranes modified with a variety of solvents and drugs that are partitioned into the bilayer. The effect of *n*-alkanols on a variety of biological functions associated with membranes is summarized in Table IV. These agents seem to have either an inhibitory or stimulatory effect on most functions; however, in some cases the concentration-dependent effect appears to be biphasic, that is, stimulatory at low concentrations and inhibitory at higher concentrations (Fig. 3). Thus, Na + K-ATPase, which requires lipid-protein interactions for its activity (see p. 172) is also stimulated or inhibited by various organic solvents including *n*-alkanols (Grisham and Barnett, 1972; Jain, unpublished observations; see also Fig. 3). Although the effect is biphasic at low temperatures, at higher temperatures only the inhibitory effect is observed.

The biphasic effect of *n*-alkanols on the various membrane processes (cf. Table IV and Fig. 3) appears to be due to a modification of lipid-lipid interactions (water permeability, altered susceptibility to phospholipases, decrease in the order parameter) or the protein-lipid interactions (activation of Na + K-ATPase and lactose permease activity). The most likely explanation for the biphasic response is that at lower temperatures, these alcohols increase the fluidity of chains and the interchain distance as one would induce in bilayers by increasing the temperature. However, at higher concentrations of alcohols or at higher temperatures, an increase in fluidity and the interchain distance would lead to a loss of optimal lipid-lipid or lipid-protein interaction.

In all the systems affected by a series of *n*-alkanols, a close correlation exists between the ability of the alcohols to modify intermolecular interactions and a certain specific function, e.g., ONPG uptake by lactose

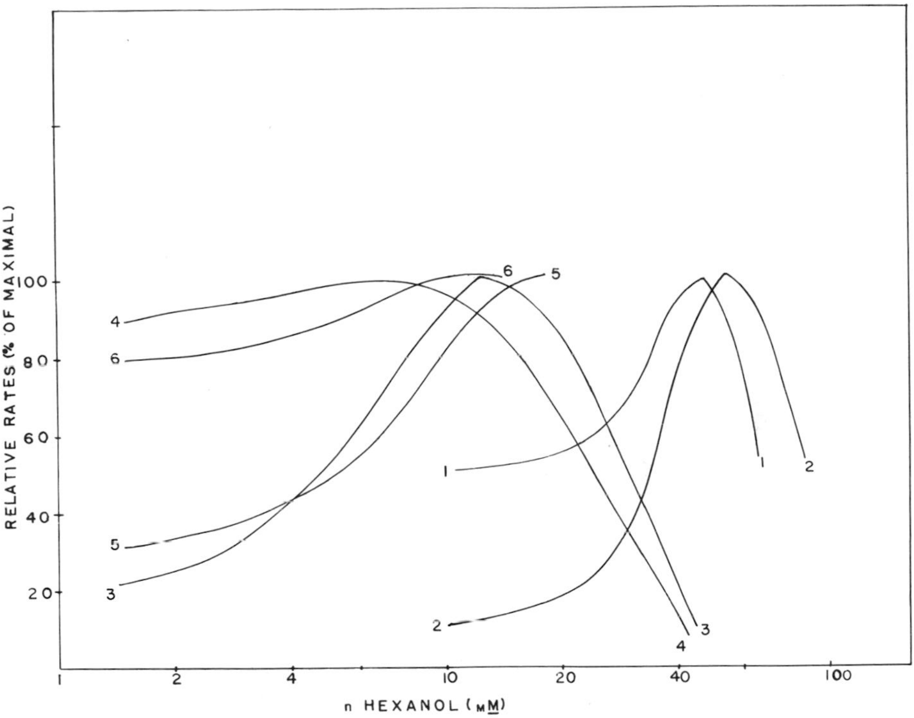

FIG. 3. Effect of *n*-hexanol on various membrane functions. (1) The rate of hypotonic swelling of unsonicated egg-PC liposomes at 25°. (2) Rate of hydrolysis of unsonicated egg-PC liposomes by phospholipase A (bee venom) at 37°. Similar profiles are observed for other phospholipases, too. (3) Na + K-ATPase activity of rabbit kidney microsomal preparation at 5°. (4) Same as (3) but at 37°. (5) The net rate of transport of ONPG by lactose permease in *E. coli* ML-308 at 0°. (6) Same as (5) but at 28°. Data for (1) from Jain *et al.* (1973a); (2) from Jain and Cordes (1973a); (3) and (4) from Jain (unpublished observations, 1971); (5) and (6) from Sullivan *et al.* (1974).

permease of *E. coli* (Fig. 4). The crucial factor in the effectiveness of the alcohols to modify lipid structure and various functions is the hydrophobicity of the alcohol. Up to a given chain length, the greater the hydrophobicity of the alcohol, the greater is its lipid solubility, and the more effective it is in increasing mobility of the bilayer. However, above a critical chain length, the alcohols have a lower efficacy (cf. Fig. 4). This could be due to anisotropy of alcohol localization into membranes between the chains where only an optimal chain length can be accommodated depending upon the length of the fatty acid residues and the position of double bonds. Alternatively, mobility changes induced

Table IV

ENZYMIC/TRANSPORT FUNCTIONS MODIFIED BY *n*-ALKANOLS[a]

Function	Tissue/Organism	*n*-Alkanols	Effect (Reference)
Water permeability	Liposomes	C_4–C_8	Increased (Jain *et al.*, 1973a)
Water permeability	Erythrocyte	C_4–C_6	Increased (Seeman *et al.*, 1971)
Urea-passive permeability	Frog-sartorius muscle	C_3–C_5	Increased (Horowitz and Fenichel, 1965)
Nonelectrolyte permeability	Erythrocyte	C_4	Increased (Hunter *et al.*, 1965)
Membrane expansion	Erythrocyte	C_1–C_8	Increased (Roth and Seeman, 1971)
Ca-binding	Erythrocyte	C_1–C_6	Increased (Seeman *et al.*, 1971)
Ca-binding	Sciatic nerve	C_3	Increased (Ehrenpreis, 1965)
Lipase activity	On insoluble substrate	C_3–C_{16}	Reduced rate of hydrolysis (Mattson *et al.*, 1970)
Phospholipase A and C	On lecithin as liposome	C_4–C_{12}	Biphasic (Jain and Cordes, 1973a,b)
Phospholipase D	On lecithin as liposome	C_4–C_8	Biphasic (Jain, unpublished data)
Cytochrome c-autooxidation		C_1–C_4	Biphasic (Kaminsky *et al.*, 1971)
Sugar transport	Erythrocyte	C_2, C_4	K_m increased, sugar exit inhibited (Krupka, 1971)
Sugar and choline transport	Erythrocyte	C_6	K_m increased (Clayton and Martin, 1971)
Amino acid transport	Rat intestine	C_2–C_4	Inhibited (Chang *et al.*, 1967)
Glucose and AA transport	Human intestine	C_2	Inhibited (Israel *et al.*, 1969a,b)
β-Galactoside permease	*E. coli* ML-308	C_4–C_{10}	Stimulated (Sullivan *et al.*, 1974)
Na + K-ATPase	Rabbit kidney	C_4–C_{10}	Biphasic at low temp. and only inhibitory at higher temp. (Jain, 1971 unpublished observations)
Na + K-ATPase	Rat brain	C_2, C_4	Inhibitory (Israel *et al.*, 1966; Grisham and Barnett, 1972)
Mg-ATPase and electron transport activity	Rat liver mitochondria *R. rubrum* chromatophore Spinach chloroplast	C_4–C_5	Moderately biphasic (Thore and Baltscheffsky, 1965)

Na-pump (open circuit potential)	Toad bladder	C_5–C_7	Biphasic (Wieser *et al.*, 1972 unpublished observations)
Adenylcyclase-glucagon sensitivity	Liver	C_1–C_4	Biphasic (Gorman and Bitensky, 1970)
-norepinephrine sensitivity	Liver	C_1–C_4	No response (Gorman and Bitensky, 1970)
K-permeability	Smooth muscle	C_2	Ca-activation is antagonized (Hurwitz *et al.*, 1962)
Electron transport	*Euglena* mitochondria	C_4–C_{12}	Biphasic (Togasaki *et al.*, 1971 unpublished observations)
		C_3–C_8	Inhibition (Lenaz, 1971)
Resting potential and action potential	Lobster axon	C_1–C_5	Reduced Na and K permeability (Houck, 1969)
	Frog nerve	C_1–C_8	Block action potential (Skou, 1958; Agin *et al.*, 1965)
	Squid axon	C_2–C_8	Reduced Na-conductance (Armstrong and Binstock, 1964; Moore *et al.*, 1964)
Contractility, miniature endplate potential and related phenomenon	Neuromuscular	C_1–C_3	Increased transmitter release and "input" resistance (Gage, 1965, and references therein; Okada, 1970)
Oxygen-uptake	Brain	C_2	Reduced (Larrabee *et al.*, 1952)
Motility	*Paramecium*	C_1–C_8	Immobilized (Rang, 1960)
Anaphylactic histamine release	Guinea pig	C_1–C_8	Inhibited (Rang, 1960)
Gut contractility	Guinea pig	C_1–C_8	Inhibited (Rang, 1960)
Brain oxygen consumption	Guinea pig	C_1–C_8	Inhibited (Rang, 1960)
Cell division	*Agmenellum quadruplicatum*	C_1–C_8	Stimulated (Ingram and Fisher, 1973)

[a] For examples involving gross organismic functions, see Hansch and Dunn (1972).

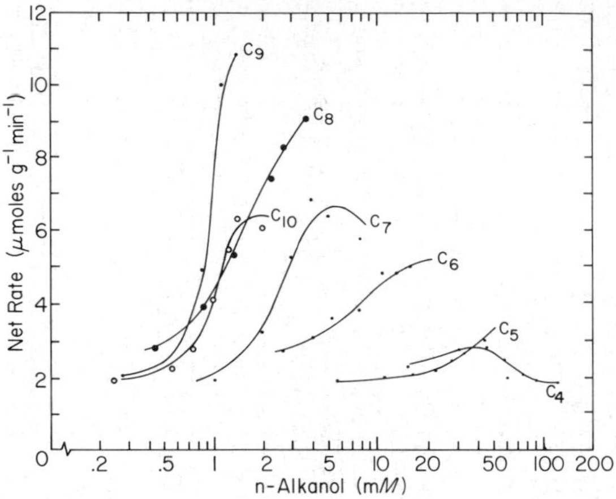

FIG. 4. Net rate of transport of ONPG by lactose permease in *E. coli* ML-308 at 0° in the presence of various *n*-alkanols (*n*-butanol through *n*-decanol). From Sullivan *et al.* (1974).

by lower alcohols may be much larger than those induced by higher alcohols at identical alcohol concentrations in the membrane. This is because, the longer the chain-length of the alkanol, the less perturbation it causes in the lipid chains between which it is intercalated. Longer chain alcohols provide enough hydrophobic overlap with the lipid chains to retain a stable bilayer even after disruption of interaction among acyl chains of phospholipid. Other possible explanations have not been completely ruled out yet.

These observations have strong bearing on the mode of action of a large variety of drugs collectively termed anesthetics and narcotics (Seeman, 1972). The strong affinity to membranes shown by these drugs is dependent upon their membrane/water partition coefficient. Moreover, the efficacy of these drugs is best correlated to their volume of occupation. An analogous dependence of molecular volume is noted in one of the theories of olfaction (Davies, 1969; Amoore *et al.*, 1969; Cherry *et al.*, 1970). Also many of the enzymes, localized in various membrane systems (Table I) and having an obligatory requirement for lipids, may show altered behavior following incorporation of small molecules in the membrane (cf. Chan, 1971).

There is practically no information on the conformational changes that various drugs induce in isolated membrane proteins. The anesthetic-induced expansion of membrane is generally about 10 times the anesthetic volume of occupation in the membrane (Seeman, 1972). The membrane events that could most readily account for this observation would be a change in orientation and/or packing of lipid molecules (Jain *et al.*, 1973a; Jain and Cordes, 1973a,b, and references therein), which may in turn, induce a change in conformation of membrane proteins. Activation or inhibition of various membrane functional proteins by various alcohols (Table IV) and related drugs could be accounted for by this hypothesis. In fact, studies on Na + K-ATPase and galactoside permease of *E. coli* provide definite evidence for a drug-induced modulation of functions or catalytic behavior of membrane-bound proteins (Sullivan *et al.*, 1974).

These observations collectively suggest that various membrane-bound enzymes may require a certain degree of fluidity for their conformational stability (Haest *et al.*, 1972) and optimal functioning. This is consistent with the hypothesis that the conformational transitions of proteins may be modified not only by the interdigitation of acyl chains with tertiary structure of the peptide, but also by the phase characteristics of the adjacent bilayer. This must be related to several yet uncharacterized aspects of biomembrane functions that may include stability, viscoelastic properties, synthesis, two-dimensional diffusion, and lateral cooperativity. The fluidity of chains may thus provide the required motional freedom, allowing enzymes within membranes to undergo conformational and translational mobility associated with their functions. Such aspects of bilayer fluidity are probably implied in the rotational freedom of rhodopsin in rods (Brown, 1972; Cone, 1972), in the aggregation of "particles and holes" in freeze-etch electron micrographs of *Tetrahymena* membranes below phase transition temperature (Speth and Wunderlich, 1973), in the control of cell growth (Inbar and Sachs, 1973), in membrane fusion (Howell *et al.*, 1972), in lateral diffusion of surface antigens in fused cells (Frye and Edidin, 1970), in antigen cap formation in cultured fibroblasts (Edidin and Weiss, 1972), and several other related processes (Weiss, 1973). Reaction of antibody to surface histocompatibility-2 antigens of cultured mouse fibroblasts causes aggregation of the cellular antigens into caps; these appear as areas of high antigen concentration localized away from cell processes. It has been suggested that after a stage of aggregation, the aggregates are swept into a stream of membrane flowing from the pseudopods of a cell, where new membrane components are continually added to the surface, back to some point at which they are internalized. Failure to form caps, under conditions that ought not affect membrane viscosity, is then a measure of the locomotory activity of cultured cells. Failure of cap formation may reflect the extent of contact inhibition of movement of a dense cell population and, hence, reflect some aspect of cell malignancy. Thus these various phenomena are related to the fluid state of the cell surface.

The aspects of lipid phase transitions may be related to ligand-induced conformational changes in membrane subunits or a rearrangement of membrane subunits. In different transition states, membrane subunits may have different physicochemical and biological activity. Such a possibility has been exploited to suggest models for membrane excitability (Changeux *et al.*, 1967). These and several other related models, however, are not consistent with the phenomenology of excitable membranes (Jain, 1972, p. 375). A highly speculative theory of all the possible membrane transition types and their regulation has been presented elsewhere (Kilkson, 1969). Experimentally, these various aspects of long-range lateral cooperativity have not been proved. However, the possibility of such membrane transition involvements, arising from conformational changes in proteolipid subunits, may be considered in phenomena related to energy transduction in photoreceptors and photosynthetic membranes where amplifications on the order of 10^4 to 10^6 are involved.

V. Specific Role of Lipids

The specific role of lipids in transport and catalytic activity is generally linked to the stabilization of active protein conformation. Lipids also seem to modify the cooperative behavior of multicomponent complexes. These aspects of lipid-protein interactions are best reflected in a modification of the kinetic properties of various catalytic proteins (Table V). Generally, delipidation leads to an increase of K_m, and a decrease in V_{max} and Hill coefficient. Exceptions are not uncommon. However, the information to substantiate such conclusions is rather limited and fragmentary. For such reasons, the discussion in the following section is at best phenomenological.

A. Specific Role of Nonspecific Lipids

Glucose-6-phosphatase and such enzymic activities as microsomal phosphatase, inorganic phosphate-glucose phosphotransferase, inorganic pyrophosphate-glycerolphosphotransferase, and nucleoside di- and triphosphatase have been shown to occur, attached to or as integral parts of, the structure of liver, kidney, and intestinal mucosal cell membranes. These enzymic activities are susceptible to large quantitative variation *in vivo*, in response to such stimuli as fasting and differing levels of insulin and adrenal corticosteroids (Fischer and Stetten, 1965).

Glucose-6-phosphatase (G-6-Pase) activity is inhibited by treatment of microsomes with organic solvents, DOC, Triton X-100, PC + LPC, all at concentrations above c.m.c. However, these same reagents at relatively low concentrations activate the enzymic activities up to 3-fold (Duttera *et al.*, 1968; Soodsma and Nordlie, 1969; Stetten *et al.*, 1969). Maximal activation of the solvent-extracted or phospholipase A-treated microsomal enzyme is however achieved by the addition of microsomal lipids or a crude preparation of asolectin (Fig. 5). Purified PC and SM are least effective in reactivating the enzyme, and PE is most effective. Although the exact biochemical role of phospholipids is not indicated from these studies, it is clear that phospholipid could induce changes in conformation of the native protein or apoprotein. Furthermore, detergent-induced activation of microsomal G-6-Pase activity has been interpreted to suggest that the native phospholipid environment acts to constrain maximal potential enzymic activity (Zakim, 1970). A similar role for *n*-alkanols has been suggested earlier (Section IV,B).

Complete reactivation of DOC-inactivated G-6-Pase activity has been

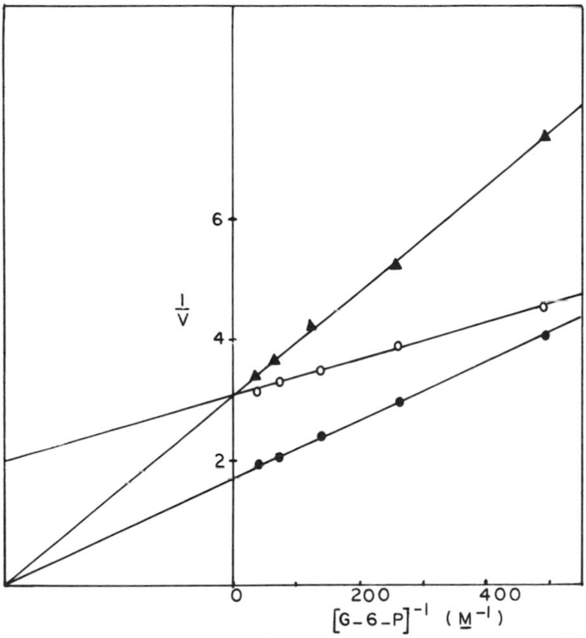

FIG. 5. The effect of phospholipase A treatment and phospholipid addition on Michaelis-Menten constants for the activity of glucose-6-phosphatase. Untreated microsomes (●—●); phospholipase A-treated microsomes alone (○—○); phospholipase-treated microsomes with soybean lecithin (3.8 mg/mg of microsomal protein) (▲—▲). Rate is given in micromoles of G-6-P hydrolyzed per minute per milligram of protein. From Zakim (1970).

Table V

EFFECTS OF LIPIDS ON KINETIC PARAMETERS OF VARIOUS ENZYMES

Enzymes	Hill coeffi-cient n	K_m (μmoles)	V_{max} (μmoles min^{-1} mg^{-1})	Reference
Pyruvate oxidase from *E. coli*		(pyruvate)		Cunningham and Hager (1971a,b)
Delipidated crystalline enzyme		28	10	
w/whole cell lipid	1.23	2.2	500	
w/PE	1.1	1.3	120	
w/PC	1.0	1.7	110	
w/lysoPC	3.0	2.2		
w/lysoPE	1.15	1.6	670	
w/PS	1.0	6.5	1250	
Lecithin, diolein, monoolein, and oleic acid all show almost identical activation: optimal chain length for activation appears to be C_{16} with one double bond.				
Glucose-6-phosphatase from bovine brain		(G-6-P)		Zakim (1970)
Native		2.6	0.112	
PLC-treated			0.062	
PLC-treated + asolectin			0.083	
Native		2.6	0.6	
PLA-treated		1.5	0.32	
PLA-treated + asolectin		2.6	0.32	
Succinate-cytochrome c reductase		(Succ) (PMS)	(Succ + PMS)	Yu *et al.* (1973)
Intact reductase		0.46 0.48	4600	
Delipidated		0.20 0.23	1900	
Delipidated + CoQ_6		0.21 0.20	1700	
Delipidated + cardiolipin		0.45 0.48	4400	
Delipidated + crude lipid extract		0.45 0.48	4500	
UDP-glucuronyltransferase (bovine liver)		K K′(UDPGA)		Vessey and Zakim (1971)
Intact enzyme		4000 2500	1.90	
PLA-treated/stable form		3900 2600	10.7	

PLA-treated/unstable form		6000	1650	13.3		
PLA-treated/deactivated form		4350	1190	4.55		
Triton-treated		2900	1050	8.80		
Na + K-ATPase from beef brain		(ATP)				Tanaka *et al.* (1971)
Native (control)		100		1.0		
Delipidated		100		0.1		
Delipidated + lecithin		100		1.2		
Delipidated + PS		100		1.0		
Delipidated + dialkylphosphate		100		0.9		
Na + K-ATPase from *Electrophorus*		(ATP)				Goldman and Albers (1973); see also Stahl (1973)
Native (control)						
Na-activation	2.04	18.1		1.96		
K-activation	1.54	0.57		1.68		
PLC-treated						
Na-activation	1.97	20.9		1.44		
K-activation	1.67	0.61		1.05		
Glucose-6-Phosphatase		(G-6-P)				Soodsma and Nordlie (1969)
Native		2.7		1.06		
+0.3% CTAB		0.5		0.67		
Inorganic pyrophosphatase		(PP_i)				Soodsma and Nordlie (1969)
Native		1.4		0.58		
+ 0.3% CTAB		0.43		0.71		
PP_i-Glucose phosphotransferase		(PP_i)	(Glucose)	(PP_i)	(Glucose)	Soodsma and Nordlie (1969)
Native		3.0	120	0.26	0.29	
0.3% CTAB		0.50	120	0.08	0.14	
				(approx.)	(approx.)	
D-β-Hydroxybutyrate dehydrogenase		NAD	β-OH-Butyrate	NAD	β-OH Butyrate	Gotterer (1967)
Mixed mitolipids for incubation						
75 *M*		22		1.0		
150 *M*		28	1700	1.5	1.0	
200 *M*			2000		1.5	
300 *M*		43	2600	3.0	2.5	

achieved by sonicated monoenoic-PC (Garland and Cori, 1972). Sonicated dipalmitoyl-PC was found to be ineffective, a condition which may be attributed to low fluidity of saturated hydrocarbon chains required for the insertion of the apoprotein into liposomes. Similarly, phospholipase C (from *C. welchii* and *Bacillus cereus*) treatment results in loss of 50–70% of the activity at 5° that can be completely restored by PC or PE + PS (1:1). However, incubation of phospholipase C-treated (at 5°) enzyme at 20° or 37° in the absence of substrate, results in complete and irreversible loss of activity (Cater *et al.*, 1970). Interestingly, marked difference in activation behavior is observed if delipidation is carried out using both phospholipases together (Cater and Hallinan, 1972). The G-6-Pase activity can then no longer be restored by the addition of PC. However, 80–100% of the activity is still restored by PE + PS (1:1). The results are interpreted to suggest that PC alone is unable to restore G-6-Pase activity. These findings, however, are in apparent contradiction to the observations of Garland and Cori described earlier. In general, results seem to suggest a rather selective role for "activating lipids" even though not all the lipids have an activating effect. It is quite possible that other lipids may activate the apoprotein if the physical state of the lipid is carefully controlled.

A variety of treatments that exert their primary effect on the lipid portion of the microsomal membrane also increase the activity of UDP-glucuronyltransferase with *p*-nitrophenol as the glucuronide acceptor (Vessey and Zakim, 1971). The fact that UDP-glucuroyltransferase retains activity after microsomes are treated with Triton X-100, exposed to pH 9.8, or sonicated, indicates that the enzyme activity does not depend on the specific phospholipid environment present in the native microsomes. As with G-6-Pase, not only is the native phospholipid environment unessential for full activity of UDP-glucuronyltransferase, it acts to constrain transferase activity. It was found that in those cases in which different treatments produced an enzyme with nearly identical V_{max}, there were differential effects on the binding of substrates to the enzyme. It could be deduced that the enzyme exists in several conformational forms characterized by different kinetic parameters. Since phospholipase A treatment alters the kinetic constants of the enzyme, the conformation of UDP-glucuronyltransferase must depend in part, on the nature of the microsomal lipid. These results lead to the conclusion that the stability of conformational isomers may vary with the lipid environment. These observations provide further evidence that regulation of the activities of microsomal enzymes by their lipid environment may be of general physiological importance.

Pyruvate oxidase is an enzyme involved in lipid biosynthesis. It binds both thiamine pyrophosphate (TPP) and FAD as prosthetic groups and catalyzes the oxidative decarboxylation of pyruvate to acetate and CO_2. Although this enzyme is found in the soluble fractions when cells are ruptured, it is membrane bound in the native state. It can also use ferricyanide and bromophenol-indophenol blue as electron acceptors even though in the native state, the electron transport chain acts as electron acceptor. As indicated in Table V, the activity of soluble pyruvate oxidase increases 15–20 fold by crude lipids extracted from *E. coli*, PL, mono- and diglycerides, and fatty acids when added in the presence of cofactors and substrates (Cunningham and Hager, 1971a,b). The kinetic features of crystalline and lipid-activated pyruvate oxidase as a function of substrate and cofactor concentration are shown in Fig. 6a,b. These studies suggest that the hydrophobic portion of these various lipids activates pyruvate oxidase, whereas the hydrophylic portion of the lipid molecule has no stimulatory effect. It is particularly interesting to note that diacyl phospholipid-activated enzyme shows Michaelis-Menten type saturation kinetics with respect to oxidation of pyruvate (Hill coefficient $n = 1$), whereas lysolecithin-activated enzyme has a coefficient of $n = 3$. The phosphatides also facilitate the binding of TPP. In the absence of lipids, TTP binding to the enzyme follows ordinary Michaelis-Menten type saturation kinetics (Fig. 6a). In the presence of phospholipids, TTP readily binds to the enzyme and shifts the K_m for TTP to a lower value (Fig. 6b). Relaxation-kinetics experiments indicate that the rate-limiting

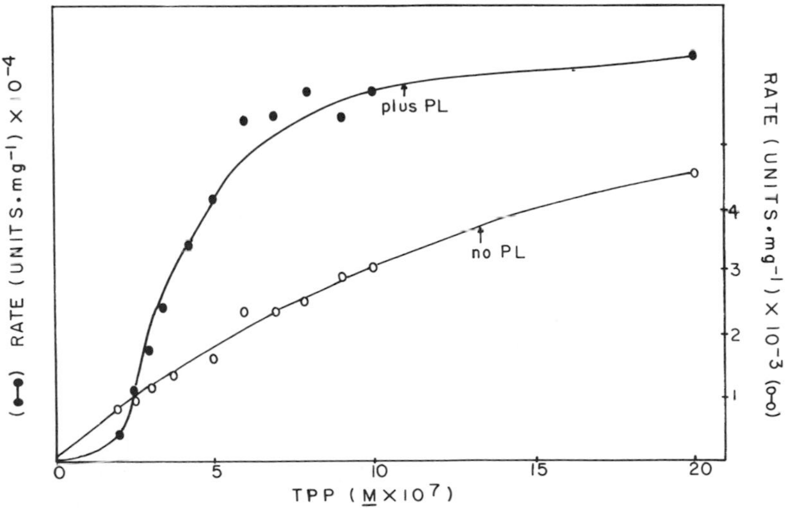

FIG. 6a. The plot of pyruvate oxidase activity as a function of TPP concentration in the presence (●—●) and absence (○—○) of phospholipid.

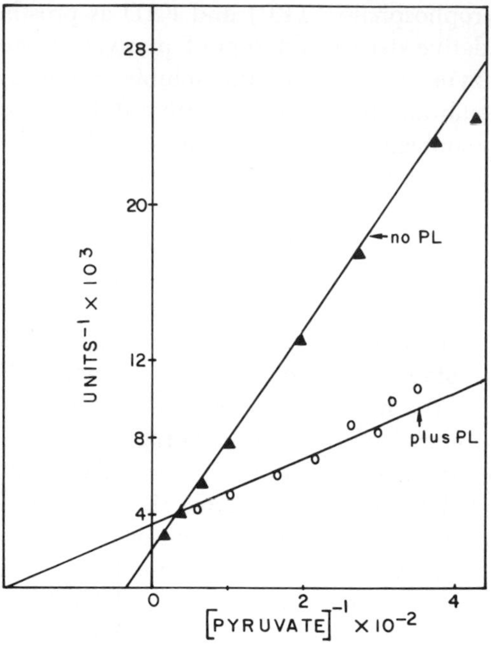

FIG. 6b. Double reciprocal plots of pyruvate oxidase activity as a function of TPP concentration in the presence (○—○) and absence (▲—▲) of phospholipids. The concentration of pyruvate oxidase was increased 30-fold for assays containing no phospholipid.

step, which is altered by the presence of phospholipids, occurs at or before the reduction of enzyme-bound flavin. In the presence of phospholipids the K_m values for pyruvate and TPP in the pyruvate oxidase reaction are altered, and the enzyme can be desensitized with respect to the activator as would be expected in an activating allosteric system (Fig. 6c). In this case, it seems that lipid-protein interaction may bring various active sites into a favorable tertiary conformation (allosteric effector). The incubation period required for complete activation of pyruvate oxidase suggests that the interaction between the flavoprotein and the phospholipid triggers a slow conformational change in the enzyme to the activated form. Phospholipid alone, in the absence of cofactor and substrate, is not sufficient to activate the enzyme. Incubation of the enzyme with phospholipid prior to the addition of substrate and cofactor results in a lower degree of activation. All these observations suggest a role of phospholipids in the catalytic oxidation of pyruvate and presumably in fatty acid biosynthesis.

One of the most widely recognized roles of lipids concerns enzyme

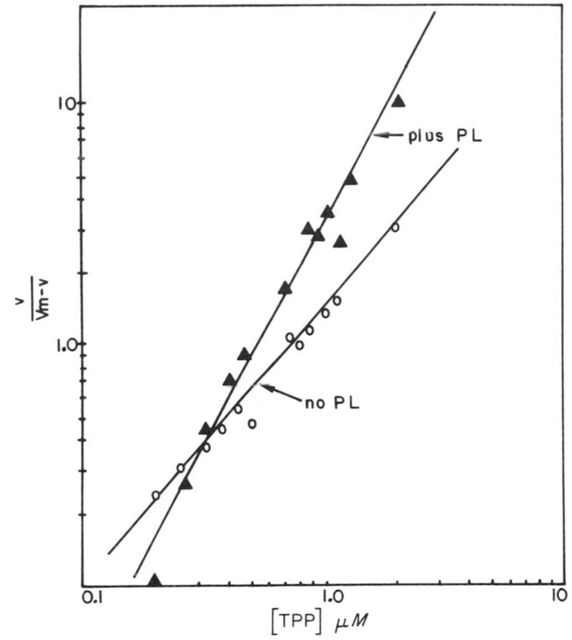

FIG. 6c. The Hill plot for TPP in the presence (▲—▲) and absence (○—○) of phospholipid. The values for rate were those used for plot (6a). Figures 6a,b, and c from Cunningham and Hager (1971b).

complexes responsible for electron transport. A full survey of this subject is beyond the scope of this review; however, we shall merely focus on those findings relevant to aspects of lipid-protein interactions. The inner mitochondrial membrane consists of a tight network of proteins and lipids. Treatment with phospholipase A and C leads to a loss of respiration and breakdown of the structural integrity of mitochondria (see Jolliot, 1972, for a review). The topography of the various electron transport components in the membrane is essential for their functional coordination (see Section III,A). Respiration and most of the functions of individual components of the electron transport chain are lost following solubilization of the membrane. However, under mild conditions four enzymic complexes can be separated (Hatefi *et al.*, 1962). Each of the complexes catalyzes the transfer of electrons along a limited segment of the chain. The four solubilized complexes reassociate to form membranous structures following the removal of the detergent (Tzagoloff *et al.*, 1967). Furthermore, the reassociation seems to follow a particular sequence. Incorporation within a single membrane of the complete set of complex is essential for reconstitution of full electron transport activity. Although beef-heart mitochondria contain nearly equimolar amounts of various electron carriers (heme a:b:c = 1:1:1.5; flavin, 1; CoQ, 8), the insoluble membranes reconstituted from the individual complexes show a continuous change in activity and density depending on the ratio in which the complexes were mixed.

Yamashita and Racker (1969) have succeeded in reconstituting ETC from partially purified individual components. The succinooxidase complex is thus reconstituted from succinate dehydrogenase, cytochrome b, c_1, and c, cytochrome oxidase, phospholipids, and CoQ_{10}. In the presence of phospholipids and CoQ_{10}, a particulate preparation of cytochrome b was mixed with succinate dehydrogenase, cytochrome c, cytochrome oxidase, and a partially purified preparation of cytochrome c_1. When this mixture was incubated (2–4 hours) at 30°, a complex which catalyzed the oxidation of succinate, was formed. The specific activity of succinate oxidation by the complex was considerably higher than that of the mitochondria and similar to that of phosphorylating SMP.

It is not surprising, therefore, that quite a few isolated enzymes of the electron transport chain have been studied for their interaction with lipids (see Table I). These studies show that lipid is essential for the optimal functioning of several individual enzymes of the electron transport chain. For example, CL, LPC, PE, and PI have all been claimed to be effective in restoring the activity of delipidated cytochrome oxidase preparation (see Lemberg, 1969, for a review). It appears that phospholipids provide a matrix in which the reactions between the hydrophobic oxidase and the hydrophilic cytochrome c are facilitated. It is, however, interesting to note that the active preparation of cytochrome oxidase may contain as little as 1% phospholipid (Morrison *et al.*, 1966), but more lipid and/or detergent is needed for maximal activation and membrane localization (Chung *et al.*, 1970b). Thus, removal of lipid by detergents, results in a decrease in both the apparent K_m for cytochrome c and apparent V_{max} when compared to control mitochondria (Table V). Following the addition of phospholipids, both K_m and V_{max} return to control value (Zahler and Fleischer, 1971). In acetone-delipidated mitochondria, although K_m returns to control values V_{max} could be restored, however, to only about half that of controls following the addition of lipids. The cause for this discrepancy is not yet certain.

The reactivation of succinooxidase activity in acetone-extracted mitochondria, and cholate-treated, succinate-cytochrome c reductase, requires the addition of CoQ_{10} and phospholipids only. These studies suggest that neither CoQ nor phospholipids alone can restore complete activity, but full restoration is obligated to both CoQ and PL. These findings (Brierley *et al.*, 1962) showed that PL are required for maximal activity in at least three parts of the electron transport chain: for electron transfer at the site of CoQ reduction and oxidation, and at the sites for the reduction and oxidation of cytochrome c. The results are compatible with the hypothesis that reactions involving CoQ and cytochrome c take place in a *lipid milieu.* The lipid may act either by reestablishing the active tertiary conformation of the enzyme protein or by providing an area for the attachment of a lipophilic reactant such as CoQ or lipid or cytochrome c.

It has been found that removal of ubiquinone from SMP leads to a decrease in activity of succinate dehydrogenase and a decrease in the K_m for succinate as well as for PMS (Rossi *et al.*, 1970; Yu *et al.*, 1973). Another related lipid-dependent enzyme complex is microsomal ETC, which catalyzes electron transfer, from NADH to cytochrome b_5 via the flavoprotein NADH cytochrome b_5 reductase. In this system, the reoxidation of reduced cytochrome b_5 reductase by cytochrome b_5 is a rate-limiting step. Removal of phospholipid markedly decreases the rate of cytochrome b_5 reduction, and reconstitution with liposomes completely restores the structural and functional characteristics of the NADH-cytochrome b_5 reductase electron transport pathway (Rogers and Strittmatter, 1973). Reconstitution with purified lipids has not been studied in this system; however, results suggest that interaction of phospholipids with both cytochrome b_5 and the reductase are essential for and, in fact, regulate the rate of electron transfer from NADH to cytochrome b_5 in microsomes. In all these and several other cases (succinate dehydrogenase, NADH-cytochrome c reductase, and several other cases cited in Table I), the role of lipid appears to provide proper milieu for the stabilization of active conformation of catalytic proteins.

These examples not only imply a nonspecific and rather undefined role of lipids in the ETC, some cases are known where a specific phospholipid is needed for the reactivation of specific enzymic activity. The specific role of these specific lipids is discussed in the following section.

B. Specific Roles of Specific Lipids

Among the various enzymes activated by specific lipids, D-β-hydroxy butyric dehydrogenase, which catalyzes the oxidation of β-hydroxybutyrate by NAD has been extensively studied (Sekuzu *et al.*, 1961, 1963; Jurtshuk *et al.*, 1961, 1963; Green and Fleischer, 1963; Gotterer, 1967; Nielsen and Fleischer, 1973; Nielsen *et al.*, 1973). Sekuzu *et al.* reported successful isolation of D-(−)-β-hydroxybutyric dehydrogenase by fractionation of mitochondrial particulates with cholate and ammonium sulfate, with subsequent release of a heat-stable factor. This factor was shown to be a phospholipid PC, and its requirement for reactivation of the enzyme was found to be both specific and absolute. Partially purified preparations of β-hydroxybutyric dehydrogenase must be preincubated in the presence of a thiol, NAD, and PC before maximal reactivation of the enzyme occurs in about 10 minutes. Maximum reactivation also requires unsaturated PC, as saturated PC can only partially reactivate the enzyme. Gotterer (1967) also demonstrated that the lipid requirement was specific for PC. Therefore, it seems that the composition and charge of the hydrophilic part of the lipid are important in determining the specificity. The time dependence of the activation process also appears to be due to the need for a deep interpenetration of PC into the enzyme. In the reconstituted enzyme, PC can not be regarded as a classic coenzyme, because the ratio of lecithin to protein in a complex with maximal activity is relatively high: 200 molecules of PC per catalytic site are required for maximal activation. However, PC ($\sim$30%) present in a mixed micelle with individually inactive PL, also maximally reactivates the enzyme at the same phospholipid-protein molar ratio. Kinetic analysis of membrane-bound and reconstituted β-hydroxy-butyrate dehydrogenases has provided an insight into how PC modulates the parameters of enzyme catalysis (cf. Gotterer, 1967; Nielsen and Fleischer, 1973; Nielsen *et al.*, 1973). The data suggest that the reaction proceeds by an *ordered bi bi* mechanism where NAD is the first substrate to add to the enzyme and NADH is the last product to leave. The mechanism is the same whether the enzyme is bound to the membrane or solubilized and reactivated by lipids. However, the apoenzyme reactivated by mitochondrial PL shows an increase in the K_m for the substrate (Table V). The magnitude of these increases is small, compared to the changes caused by substituting purified PC for crude MPL. Nevertheless, the 2-fold increase in the K_m values might reflect some alteration of the enzyme resulting from the isolation procedure or the influence of the membrane on the enzyme. The dissociation constants for NAD, measured with the MPL-activated enzyme, are virtually unchanged from the native dehydrogenase; however, they decrease 3- to 5-fold in PL-reactivated preparation. Thus the MPL-reactivated preparation resembles the native enzyme more closely.

When a suboptimal amount of MPL is used to reactivate the enzyme, only the V_{max} changes (see however, Gotterer, 1967) indicating that the enzyme is either fully active or fully inactive. This is consistent with the hypothesis that the reactivation is limited by the incorporation of apoprotein into the vesicle. Once incorporated, the vesicle provides a large excess of lipid to fully activate the enzyme molecule. The role of lipids in the functioning of β-hydroxybutyrate dehydrogenase is also consistent with the observed correlation of the competitive inhibition of β-hydroxybutyrate binding by a series of local anesthetics and their anesthetic potency (Gotterer, 1969). All these observations suggest a rather specific role of the choline moiety of PC in determining catalytic and binding functions of the enzyme.

Enzyme II of the phosphotransferase system also shows a specific phospholipid requirement for its activity (Roseman, 1969; Kundig and Roseman, 1971). The phosphotransferase system is thought to mediate the transport of many carbohydrates across bacterial cell membranes. The soluble part of this system consists of Enzyme I, which catalyzes the transfer of phosphate from PEP to a histidine-containing protein, HPr. The membrane-bound Enzyme II, catalyzes the transfer of phosphate from HPr to sugars. With the use of *n*-butanol-urea mixtures, Enzyme II is dissociated into two proteins + PG + Ca. For the reconstitution of Enzyme II activity, the four components have to be mixed in definite sequence. PG cannot be replaced by other phospholipids. Kaback and Milner (1970) have also demonstrated that PG is required for both the phosphorylation and uptake of α-methylglucoside mediated by the phosphotransferase of *E. coli* membrane vesicle. When membranes were treated with a crude phospholipase D preparation, the phosphorylation and uptake of α-methylglucoside were both completely inhibited. Under these conditions, approximately 50% of the membrane PG was hydrolyzed, whereas other PLs were much less degraded. It was also demonstrated that transport activity is spontaneously restored to normal within 15 minutes after removal of the phospholipase D. PG was specifically synthesized by the membrane preparation during that interval. The quantity of PG synthesized after the removal of phospholipase was extremely small. Therefore, it is quite possible that the redistribution of the remaining membrane PG could also account for reactivation even in the absence of lipid synthesis. The results are consistent with the hypothesis that PG is an integral part of the phosphotransferase system.

Selective extraction studies demonstrate a specific association of cytochrome oxidase and cardiolipin regardless of the method used for preparation of the oxidase. Enzyme activity and membrane formation capability is lost when the tightly-bound CL is removed. Results reported by Awasthi *et al.* (1970a,b) indicate that CL is bound to cytochrome oxidase by both ionic and nonpolar bonds, since CL can be completely removed only by treatment with ionic reagents together with detergents and organic solvents. They also indicate preferential association of specific lipids with enzymes involved in mitochondrial ETC. This leads to the conclusion that the presence of CL is necessary to maintain the enzyme in the proper configuration required for activity.

Brierley *et al.* (1962) have reported lipid activation of at least three separate regions of ETC involved in the oxidation of succinate (see also Lester and Fleischer, 1961). In these cases, the restoration of the activity is found to be proportional to the amount of phospholipid bound by the particles. All four of the phospholipids normally found in the mitochondria were equally active once bound to the particles, but showed differences in their ability to combine with the lipid-deficient mitochondria. CL, PE, and PI elicit the same response as total MPL; PC gives lower rates. However, under suitable binding conditions, PC also reactivates the enzyme maximally. These results suggest that the lipids may act specifically by reestablishing the native configuration of the apoproteins.

The enzyme 5′-nucleotidase of rat liver microsomes and plasma membranes may be obtained in a highly purified form as a lipoprotein containing essentially one phospholipid: SM (Widnell and Unkeless, 1968). These results indicated that SM might be specifically required for the activity. However, recently 5′-nucleotidase has been completely solubilized by *N*-dodecylsarcosinate, and the purified lipid-free protein retains its catalytic activity (Evans and Gurd, 1973).

The requirement for specific lipids has also been implicated in a variety of membrane functions including ion transport properties. The polar groups have been implicated as functionally important ion-exchange sites. Thus, for example, in the case of squid axon, these sites appear to be carboxyl groups. In fact, PS decarboxylase treatment of axon results in a decrease in spike height (Cook *et al.*, 1972), which could be associated with changes occurring in the PS molecules. Similarly an ion-sieving role of PS and PG has been implicated for Na + K-ATPase (Kimelberg and Papahadjopoulos, 1972). Besides the requirement for specific PL containing characteristic polar groups, there are several enzymes that show specificity toward lipids containing characteristic apolar chains. Some of the examples are discussed below.

The role of membranes and consequently, of lipids, in translation and transcription of genetic information has been implicated for quite sometime (Hallick *et al.*, 1969; Caliguiri and Tamm, 1969). One of the best characterized specific lipid-activated enzymes involved in this function is RNA-ligase. Extraction of rat liver amino acid-tRNA ligases with organic solvents results in a decreased combination of labeled amino acids with tRNA (Hradec and Duseck, 1968, 1969; Hradec, 1972; Bandopadhyay and Deutscher, 1973). The extracted lipid contains almost exclusively, the cholesterol esters of about 7–8 fatty acids and 14-methylhexadecanoic acid. Extraction of only a portion of the total lipid present in the enzyme preparation, results in complete inhibition of amino acid activation reaction without affecting the transfer activity of the enzyme.

Extraction of complete lipids results in complete loss of both activities. However, these two activities can be fully restored by the addition of CMN (cholesterol 14-methylhexadecanoate). Cholesteryl palmitate, cholesteryl margarate, and cholesteryl stearate were ineffective. The difference in the effectiveness of these esters may be due to their fluidity. It thus appears that CMN and related cholesteryl esters activate AA-tRNA ligase presumably by stabilization of the active configuration, facilitating the step of peptide chain elongation, or facilitating the binding of aminoacyl tRNA to ribosomes. The activating effect is obviously dependent on the configuration and chain-length of the fatty acid in the ester. Furthermore, the delay in the time course of AA-tRNA complex formation, found only in the presence of CMN added to the extracted enzymes, indicates that some time may be necessary for the recombination of the fatty acid with the enzyme before complete recovery of the activity. It is pertinent to note that there is some suggestive evidence that the association of polysomes with cell membranes is subject to regulation by steroid hormones (Cox and Mathias, 1969; Sunshine *et al.*, 1971).

The regulatory role of lipids has also been implicated in RNA synthesis. Lipids seem to regulate not only the stability, but also template specificity of RNA polymerase A from mouse myeloma cells. The purified polymerase is stimulated by neutral lipids such as PC and PE. However, the acid lipids, especially CL, inhibit the transcription of double stranded, but not single stranded DNA. Dimethylsulfoxide, both stabilizes and stimulates the enzymic activity and changes the template specificity in favor of single stranded DNA.

A specific requirement for PL has also been demonstrated in the case of lipoprotein-lipase by Chung *et al.* (1973). In the presence of a protein cofactor, marked variations of lipoprotein lipase activity were observed with different PL subclasses, as well as with different lecithin species. Among the PL studied, LPC appears to be most active. These results indicate that the hydrophobic acyl chains contribute significantly to the lipoprotein lipase activation, since increases in the length of the fatty acyl chains are accompanied by decreases in the enzyme activity.

The role of lipids has also been implicated in the functioning of rhodopsin. When the pigment is extracted with CTAB (Heller, 1968; Hall and Bacharach, 1970), virtually no lipid remains in the preparation, and the product, a glycoprotein, shows the characteristic spectral peak at 498 nm. At the same time, an increase in the reactivity of the SH group and inability of the visual pigment to be regenerated after bleaching was observed. Regenerability after bleaching and SH reactivity could be restored by addition of PE. The inability of rhodopsin to regenerate when its PL content was reduced below approximately 54 μmoles/μmole protein indicates that the phospholipid is an essential component of the functional pigment (Zorn and Futterman, 1970).

One of the best characterized lipid-activated enzyme systems is the galactosyl-transferase of *Salmonella typhimurium* studied by Romeo *et al.* (1970). Previous studies have shown that the purified transferase enzyme requires PL for activity (Endo and Rothfield, 1969). A low but measurable level of enzyme activity was seen in the absence of PL, and with increasing amounts of PE, there is a progressive increase in the initial rate of the reaction. A maximal reaction rate was seen when the ratio of PE to lipopolysaccharide was approximately 3:1 (w/w). This is consistent with the suggestion that the major role of phospholipid in the reaction is related to its interaction with the polysaccharide rather than to a direct action on the enzyme. The PL requirement is also satisfied by PG or CL, but not by PC. However, the purified enzyme is active only in the presence of PL containing unsaturated or cyclopropane fatty acids (Rothfield and Perlman, 1966). Full activity is thus restored with PE from *Azobacter agilis,* which contains approximately 60% unsaturated fatty acids, and by PE from *E. coli,* which contains a large proportion of cyclopropane fatty acids. Hydrogenated PE from *A. agilis* caused complete loss of activity, and no activity was seen with dipalmitoyl-, didecanoyl-, and dihexanoyl PE. The only kinetic evidence that the PL might also be stimulating the enzyme directly, is that the V_{max} of the reaction is significantly greater in the presence of PE, than in its absence. These studies suggest that PE plays two roles in activating UDP-galactose-lipopolysaccharide α-3-galactosyl transferase. First, it interacts with lipopolysaccharide to form a binary complex, whereby the binding sites on the polysaccharide are made accessible to the enzyme. Second, the activating lipid provides a second binding site for the enzyme. Didodecanoyl PE is apparently ineffective in this role as indicated by its failure to bind to the transferase enzyme in the absence of lipopolysaccharide. Stimulation of activity of the transferase system occurs only with phospholipids that are able to form complexes with both enzyme and lipopolysaccharide. The data are consistent with a speculative model in which the full catalytic activity of the enzyme requires specific binding both to the polysaccharide portion of lipopolysaccharide and to PE.

Malate dehydrogenase from *Mycobacterium avium* has a requirement for PL for activity (Tobari, 1964). However, it appears that CL could completely replace the bacterial PL, whereas Tween 80 and DOC are inactive. A striking feature of this PL reactivation is the minute amounts of PL required. For maximal activation, the ratio of CL to protein is 1:40 by weight. This suggests the formation of a specific PL:enzyme complex with a 1:1 mole proportion. Another interesting feature of this system is the ability of synthetic PL, without any unsaturated fatty acids, to restore the enzymic activity. Furthermore, the binding of lipid to the protein appears to be strong. Molar ratios of bound CL to cytochrome oxidase approaching 1:1 have been implicated in the stabilization of this enzyme (Awasthi *et al.*, 1971). The inactive CL:enzyme complex can be fully activated on addition of PL or detergents such as Emasol or Tween 80. Even a partial removal of tightly bound-CL results in some changes in the enzyme, so that it can not be fully activated on adding detergents; however, most phospholipids, CL in particular, activate the enzyme almost completely.

Of particular interest, with regard to the role of lipids in the catalytic activity of proteins, is the effect of several inhibitors on the lipid activated-enzyme or the apoenzyme. It has been shown that rutamycin and DCCD do not act on the coupling factor F_1 itself, but act indirectly, by preventing the activation of ATPase activity of these particles by phospholipids (Meissner and Fleischer, 1972). These and related observations suggest that lipids do not necessarily activate enzymes by interacting directly at the active site. Although experimental evidence is somewhat equivocal, the specificity of activation described in the previous examples strongly suggest that, due to its particular structure and charge, a given phospholipid activates an enzyme by stabilizing an active conformation. The process of lipid activation appears to be all or none, that is, the most prominent effect of lipid on the apoprotein is by altering its turnover rate, whereas the K_m remains relatively unchanged, although some significant exceptions are known. From the data available so far, it appears that lipids activate only partial reactions, and at least in the case of eel Na + K-ATPase, the various partial reactions are activated by different phospholipids. The substrate and inhibitor specificity, pH rate profiles, cofactor and/or metal ion requirements, kinetic behavior and reaction mechanism of lipid-activated enzyme remain essentially unchanged whether the enzyme is bound to the native membrane or is activated by purified lipids. The difference in maximal activation induced by various lipids generally appears to be due to differences in V_{max} of these reactivated systems rather than to a difference in their affinity for the substrate. These conclusions are consistent with the hypothesis that the lipid-activated enzymes assume a definite configuration, and the lipids may act by constraining the whole protein structure in an active conformation, thus leading to an enhancement of its stability.

VI. Partially Characterized Aspects of Lipid-Protein Interactions

Besides the role of lipids for conformation stabilization discussed so far, there are a variety of other possible modes through which lipids may modify functions of membrane-bound proteins. Some of these possible modes are discussed as follows. These modes arise because of the tripartite structure of lipid bilayers that give rise to three phases (hydrophobic, interfacial, and aqueous) of distinct polarity. The concentration of substrates and cofactors in these phases would be expected to have effect on the rate and equilibria of processes catalyzed by membrane-bound proteins. It should be pointed out, however, that these possibilities are based on highly circumstantial evidence; nevertheless they do offer plausible explanations for a variety of phenomena.

A. Lipids as Provider of Hydrophobic Environment

Lipids provide a nonaqueous environment and compartmentalize the essentially aqueous organism by various nonaqueous barriers. As indicated in previous sections, a variety of membrane-bound proteins lose their activity following delipidation. Thus the procedures for lipid extraction and solubilization of membrane proteins by organic solvents (Curtis, 1969, 1972; Maddy, 1964; Evans *et al.*, 1968; Lovrien, 1963; Lesslauer *et al.*, 1970; Lenaz, 1971; Lenaz *et al.*, 1970, 1972a; Helenius and Simons, 1971) suggest that the dominant modes of interaction between various membrane components are hydrophobic, characterized by a lack of covalent bonding, a large temperature coefficient, and a linear relationship with the hydrophobicity (chain length, etc.) of the lipid or the perturbing solvent. The hydrophobic interactions have been postulated to provide conformational stability to the protein molecules. However, there are various cases where the experimental data do not suggest any well-defined role of lipids except that the lipids may provide a *milieu* for the solubilization and orientation of the substrate or cofactor. The enzymes involved in lipid biosynthesis are probably the best examples in this category (Cronan and Vagelos, 1972); however, the biochemical details of this system are yet to be worked out. Similarly, the absorption spectrum of β-carotene in chloroplast lamellae shows a characteristic shift following lipid extraction (Ji and Benson, 1968). This is an indicator of a change in the environment in which this chromophore is localized.

One of the best characterized systems where the "hydrophobic solvent" role of lipid has been implicated, is the enzyme protoheme ferrolyase. This enzyme catalyzes the combination of Fe^{++} and protoporphyrin to form heme. The particulate preparation of this enzyme can be solubilized by detergents such as cholate and Tween. The residual activity of the delipidated protoheme ferrolyase is markedly enhanced following the addition of acidic and crude phospholipids (Sawada *et al.*, 1969). These authors suggested that the phosphate anion of the phospholipid might activate the enzymic reaction by attracting Fe^{++} to the active center. Since the rate of nonenzymic combination of Fe^{++} with porphyrins is found to be strongly solvent-dependent, it has been postulated that in the enzymic reaction, the hydrophobic part of the lipid molecule might also play the role of the favorable hydrophobic solvent.

Activation of various enzymes by nonspecific lipids has been implicated in the possible hydrophobic solvent role of lipids. Thus, for example, in acetone-extracted hen liver microsomes, the NADH-cytochrome reductase activity can be restored by a variety of lipids and detergents (Jones and Wakil, 1967). These authors have suggested that the activating effect of lipids may be due to the proper *milieu* provided by the lipid micelles for the orientation of the enzyme and probably its substrate, cytochrome c.

B. Regulation of Activity of Water by Lipids

Westhead and Malmstrom (1957) investigated the enolase reaction in a variety of mixed solvents. They found that the addition of organic solvent caused a marked inhibition of enolase activity. The inhibitory effect of various solvents was found to be independent of their dielectric constants, polarity, or chemical structure. However, the enolase activity (V_{max}) in all solvent systems was found to be related to the concentration of water in the mixture. Such observations suggest that the hydrophobic environment offered by a lipid bilayer may regulate the activities of various membrane-bound enzymes. However, so far no definite evidence in support of this hypothesis has appeared in the literature, although membrane-bound water has been implicated in several hypothetical models. For example, it has been postulated that the cell membrane contains a hydrogen-bonded framework of hydrate continuum that permeates the ordered lipoprotein structure (Fernández-Morán, 1962). Another model has proposed that changes in the configuration of the lipids may determine the water content of the membrane matrix (Kavanau, 1963). Similarly, Hechter (1965) has suggested that water may be an integrated structural component of biomembranes as are lipids and proteins. These assumptions find their origin in the physicochemical evidence suggesting the existence of "bound water" in macromolecules (Jacobson, 1955; Hechter *et al.*, 1960; Hearst and Vinograd, 1961; Singer, 1962). Since, hydrophobic attraction is in essence a water repulsion force, bound water is believed to manifest the existence of hydrophobic interactions (Kauzmann, 1959; Tanford, 1962; Nemethy and Scheraga, 1962). Thus, there are numerous possibilities for organization of water at biomembrane interfaces. There is indeed general agreement that water at biological interfaces has restricted freedom, and this may serve to regulate various hydrolytic reactions, as well as proton and electron transport. Furthermore, reactivities may be enhanced when the reactants are in an environment of highly ordered water molecules (Grant and Alburn, 1965, 1967).

Several attempts have been made to evaluate the role of water in reactions catalyzed by membrane-bound enzymes. The nonspecific inhibition of the respiratory chain has been observed with a variety of organic solvents (Tyler and Eastbrook, 1966). As much as 70% inhibition of the overall activity of substrate oxidation can be achieved without causing any significant alteration in the steady state reduction level of electron transfer components. These observations can be explained by postulating the effect of water on the modulation of tertiary structure of the electron transport chain components, such that the efficiency of their interaction is reduced. Alternatively, water may play a role in the transfer of reducing equivalents by participating in the protonation of an active group concomitant with the oxidation-reduction cycle. Yet another hypothesis recalls the suggestion made by Theorell (1943) and by Urry and Eyring (1963), that the hemoprotein-mediated electron transfer may occur through the resonating bonds of an imidazole ring. The replacement of water by either D_2O or organic solvents in the vicinity of the histidine groups (postulated to participate in the transfer of reducing equivalents) would be expected to influence the course of reactions. A somewhat similar hypothesis has been proposed to explain the inhibition of respiration by D_2O (Laser and Stater, 1960; see also Tyler and Eastbrook, 1966). D_2O inhibits at multiple sites in the respiratory chain. If the rate-limiting step in the segments of the respiratory chain involve proton gradient formation as a primary energy-conserving step, then the aforementioned observations could be rationalized. In addition, phosphorylation of ADP with P_i may be regulated by the activity of water in the membrane.

It is of interest that several studies have attributed the inhibition of enzymes by organic solvents to a reduction in water content (Westhead and Malmstrom, 1957). It has been shown that the inhibition of DPNH-oxidase activity of heart muscle by organic solvents is a linear function of the water content of the reaction mixture (Hatefi and Hanstein, 1969). The rate of oxidation is found to be independent of the concentration, tonicity, and chemical structure of the solvent.

Thus the experimental evidence implying the role of lipids in regulating the activity of water is at best meager. However, the implications of this possibility should not be underestimated.

C. Effect of Surface Charge Profile on Catalytic and Transport Functions

Besides regulating the binding of charged molecules at the interface, the surface charges of the bilayer contributed by lipids could also modify the double layer characteristics and, in so doing, modify the ion sieving characteristics of the bilayer not only for passive transport, but also for mediated transport (Hopfer *et al.*, 1970a,b; McLaughlin *et al.*, 1970). The surface charges of membrane-bound PA and PS have been implicated in the intercationic selectivity of the K^+-uptake process of the cation pump (Papahadjopoulos, 1971; Kimelberg and Papahadjopoulos, 1972).

The effect of surface charge in modifying the catalytic behavior of membrane-bound protein is probably best demonstrated in the case of the enzyme system responsible for the synthesis of cyclopropane fatty acids (Chung and Law, 1964). This enzyme system transfers the methyl group of S-adenosyl methionine to a *cis*-monoenoic fatty acid chain of PE to form a cyclopropane fatty acid chain. The enzyme is stimulated by anionic surfactants and is inhibited by cationic and neutral surfactants. The function of the charges on the activating lipid micelle is not known, but it appears that the interaction of the charges facilitates the catalytic reaction either by the proper orientation of the substrate and the active site of the enzyme, or by aiding the penetration of the enzyme into the micelle. Moreover, the addition of surfactant to the enzyme solution before the addition of substrates resulted in either no stimulation or an inhibition of the reaction. It thus appears that the inhibitory effect of SDS is due to denaturation of the enzyme; PE, one of the substrates, in some way protects the enzyme from this effect.

Of particular interest here is the observation that the state of PL dispersion is important for the action of the synthetase. The preferred method of PL dispersion is by dialysis rather than mechanical or sonic dispersion. These large aggregates of lipid have organized structures with concentric closed bilayers. Thus provision must be made for the transfer of a small group in the vicinity of a charge ($\text{—}\overset{|}{S^+}\text{—}CH_3$) from a hydrophilic donor to a hydrophobic acceptor isolated from the aqueous environment. It is then hardly surprising that the structure of the PL substrate is important. Formation of a reactive enzyme substrate complex must involve specific interactions of the enzyme surface with the PL surfaces. This interaction must depend, in part at least, on the complementariness of charges between the enzyme and phospholipid surfaces.

The applicability of this idea for cyclopropane FA-synthetase arises from the observation that the enzymic reaction velocity is sensitive to surface charge on the phospholipid aggregate. A similar concept has been advocated by Bangham (1963) for the reaction of phospholipases with phospholipids containing various lipids. An interpretation of rate activation of phospholipolysis by various agents may, however, be much more complicated than that implied in the complementariness of surface charge profile (see Jain, 1973; Jain and Cordes, 1973a,b). It appears that the primary factor determining the rate of PL hydrolysis by phospholipases in a bilayer is intermolecular separation between PL. The effect of surface charge may be secondary. For example, cationic sites on the bilayer surface could compete for the Ca^{++}-binding sites in the phospholipases thereby inhibiting its approach or orientation at the bilayer.

D. Covalently Bound Lipids

Biochemical functions of covalently bound lipids are not yet well characterized. It has been implied for quite some time now, that the cell membrane provides active sites for macromolecular synthesis (Hendler, 1968; Glick and Warren, 1969; Osborn, 1971) and probably for the amino-acid carrier mechanism (Tria and Barnabei, 1969). These suggestions are based on the observation that amino acids are rapidly incorporated into a lipid fraction as esters of phosphatidylglycerol. Aminoacyl-*t*RNA can serve as a primary donor of AA residues in this reaction. However, this reaction is not believed to serve in the synthesis of protein.

Recent studies indicate that the polysomes bound to the cell membrane constitute a qualitatively distinct pool and are not freely interchangeable with those free in the cytoplasm of eucaryotic cells. Membrane-bound polysomes appear to be engaged primarily in the synthesis of some membrane proteins and of the proteins exported from the cell; free ribosomes appear to synthesize proteins of the cell sap.

The cell envelope of gram-negative bacteria consists of a peptidoglycan layer (2–3 nm thick), sandwiched between the cytoplasmic membrane and an outer membraneous structure containing protein, PL, and lipopolysaccharides (LPS). LPS constitutes about 2–4% of the dry weight of bacteria or 20–30% of the dry weight of their cell walls (Braun and Rehm, 1969; Braun and Sieglin, 1970). In *E. coli* and closely related bacteria, about 10^5 lipoprotein molecules are covalently bound to the polysaccharide-peptide macromolecules. The total giant macromolecule is linked at every 10th–12th diaminopimelate residues of murein by the C-terminal lysine. The N-terminal end is probably blocked by a covalently bound lipid via glycerylcysteine (Hantke and Braun, 1973). The

LPS have been implicated as the antigenic components of the bacterial cell wall. It is responsible for the O-antigenic activity and presumably contains receptor sites for many bacteriophages. The bacterial LPS is a complex molecule in which a heteropolysaccharide chain is covalently linked to "lipid A" through a basal "core" polysaccharide (Luderitz *et al.*, 1966). The O-specific chains differ widely in structure from species to species, but always appear to be composed of oligosaccharide repeating units. The functional role of lipids bound to polysaccharide is not yet known; however, lipids seem to play a structural role in addition to their function as biosynthetic coenzymes (Troy *et al.*, 1971).

Involvement of specific membrane lipids in macromolecular synthesis has been shown to occur in two distinct ways: lipids may either activate the membrane-bound enzymes (as discussed in previous sections) or may act as true coenzymes participating directly in group transfer reactions. The most widely studied reactions of this class are membrane-associated glycosylation reactions involved in the synthesis of cell wall. The carrier lipids involved in this process are C_{40}–C_{80} isoprenyl alcohols (see Osborn, 1971, for a review) which may serve to anchor the polysaccharide to the cell envelope during biosynthesis (Troy *et al.*, 1971).

A novel role of covalently bound lipid has been suggested in the visual process. Poincelot *et al.* (1969) have found that 11-*cis*-retinylidine chromophore in native rhodopsin is actually bound to PE by an aldimine (azamethine) linkage. During photoconversion of metarhodopsin I to metarhodopsin II, this linkage migrates to the amino group of lysine on opsin. These results are, however, in apparent contradiction with the observation that phospholipase C treatment reduces the PC content of rhodopsin far below a 1:1 molar ratio without any significant loss of rhodopsin (Borggreven *et al.*, 1971). Similarly, the molar ratio of PS in rhodopsin could be reduced to 0.1 without any loss of activity (Borggreven *et al.*, 1972). During these treatments, the absorption spectrum, molar absorbance at 500 nm, and proteolytic properties of the rhodopsin remain virtually unchanged.

From the information currently available, it appears that covalently bound lipids are not widely involved in biological functions. However, involvement of such bondings may be important for macromolecular synthesis and antigenic and related functions associated with the cell surface.

VII. Epilogue and Prospects

The involvement of lipids in various molecular processes mediated by proteins is a well-established phenomenon. In this review, we have examined the various aspects of this problem, and have discussed some of the molecular aspects of lipid-protein interaction. Several important features of this phenomenon along with those described on pp. 160 and 190 may be noted: many different enzymes or enzyme systems from different sources (organelles, tissues, organisms) exhibit partial or complete dependence upon lipids for their activity, and most of them are localized in membranes. The various studies reviewed herein suggest that the lipid environment determines or controls quite a few of the biochemical functions of membrane-bound enzymes. The proximity of lipids seems to serve several purposes: the bilayer may serve as a simple permeability barrier, may provide a nonaqueous medium for the reactions, may act as anchorage for proteins and polysaccharides, may act as conformation stabilizer for catalytic and transport proteins. Furthermore, if a series of steps are involved in a reaction cycle, only a few steps may be modulated by lipids.

The lipid-activated enzymes are generally insoluble in aqueous buffers. Thus the lipid-dependence is best demonstrated by dissociation and reconstitution experiments. The extraction of lipids by organic solvents, detergents, and phospholipases leads to a loss of biochemical activity implying lipid involvement. Thus, depending upon the severity of dispersal techniques used, one may expect to vary both the size and composition of the fragments of parent membranes containing a particular activity. Under carefully controlled conditions (such as low temperature during extraction with organic solvents of varying polarity and amphiphilic character, low concentration of nonionic detergents, and limited phospholipolysis by specific phospholipases), the formation of membrane fragments would involve fracture of a macroscopic membrane assembly along a plane of weak intermolecular interactions. Dissolution of adhering bilayer lipids by partial delipidation may lead to progressive modification of lipid-protein interactions; complete removal of lipid may or may not solubilize an "apoprotein" in the aqueous buffer. Generally speaking, the delipidated apoproteins are unstable and devoid of catalytic activity. However, under carefully defined conditions of salt, surfactant, buffer and hydrogen ion concentration, and temperature, quite a few apoproteins have been at least partially purified by conventional methods.

The native activity of the various partially or fully delipidated apoproteins can be restored successfully following the addition of specific or crude lipids in various forms. Usually a large molar excess (more than 100-fold) of lipids is needed for reactivation of the apoproteins. So far, little is known about the physical state of the lipid needed for reactivation; however, sonication, detergent dispersion, dispersion by mixed solvents, dispersion by dialysis, reconstitution on preformed bilayers or liposomes have been employed with varying degree of success for different systems.

Most of the reconstitution studies show that the lipid should be above the phase transition temperature. This aspect of bilayer fluidity is also important for the formation of bilayers and viable liposomes. In general, those factors that induce fluidization by chemical or physical randomness in the core region of the bilayer (unsaturation, branching, cyclization, shorter chain fatty acids, addition of various drugs, solvents, and detergents) are important for reactivation or reconstitution. This probably is due to a greater void volume in these fluidized bilayers.

The aspects of bilayer fluidity and bilayer phase transition are probably best reflected in the biphasic behavior in Arrhenius plots for several membrane-bound enzymes. Unfortunately, most of these studies have been performed at nonsaturating concentrations of the substrate (or cofactors and activators), and no attempt has been made to demonstrate whether the effect of change in temperature on rate, is due to a change in the affinity of the substrate or the turnover rate. Low concentrations of several agents also activate (by several fold) some of the membrane-bound enzymes especially below their phase transition temperatures. Activation, accompanying fluidization of the bilayer, is consistent with the hypothesis that the rigidity of the chains in the bilayer below phase transition temperature (the so-called gel state) constrains the membrane-bound proteins. Fluidization above the phase transition temperature (liquid crystalline state) or incorporation of various agents into the bilayer relieves the constraints induced by the hydrocarbon chains. These observations suggest that a modification of the long-range interlipid interactions in the bilayer modifies the protein functions. Physiological and pharmacological implications of this phenomenon are yet to be explored. Changes in the properties of the membrane by alteration of its general composition or molecular arrangement of specific components may be an important regulating influence on some membrane-bound enzymes. Changes in membrane phospholipid profile may thus serve a major regulatory function in *in vivo* metabolic control. Other possible roles of lipids arising from their bilayer organization may be to provide restoring and/or initiating forces for gross "membrane conformational changes" which may trigger a variety of biologically important processes (cf. Weiss, 1973).

Besides the requirements for "fluidity" of chains in the hydrophobic core, reconstitution studies have also shown requirements for specific phospholipid species. The requirement for specific phospholipids is rarely absolute. Generally, a variety of closely related lipid molecules can substitute for a specific lipid. However, on a mole basis, a large number of lipid molecules seem to be required for the activation of an apoprotein molecule. The only exception is malic dehydrogenase which requires only equimolar quantities of lipid for activation. These and related observations seem to rule out the possibility of lipid involvement as cofactors. Both the specific and nonspecific roles of the lipid seem to arise largely from their capacity to stabilize and regulate the active conformation of the protein. Thus lipids may modulate substrate-, inhibitor-, cofactor-, and effector-binding, allosteric behavior, turnover number, and activation energy. In some enzymes, the conformational changes induced by the lipid may confer characteristics other than biochemical activity, e.g., stability, sensitivity to certain inhibitors and activators, and the ability to interact with other membrane proteins. Furthermore, localization of functional proteins on a bilayer gives rise to the possibilities of anisotropic (vectorial) regulation of approach of reactants, release of products, and coupling of reactions with translocation steps. In addition, when an enzyme is embedded in a membrane, allosteric control by soluble molecules may be limited by their solubility in the membrane; however, these effectors may exert their effects through bilayèr regions. Metabolically regulated local removal or replacement of phospholipid head groups or fatty acid chains could also exert an allosteric control on a membrane-bound enzyme system.

How these various molecular processes are modulated by the interaction of a large number of lipid molecules with an apoprotein is not known. However, these modalities are not expected to be very different from those observed for allosteric proteins. Inactivation of many enzymes, caused by a loss or modification of lipids, may result in a specific deaggregation from other proteins or components, or may cause a folding of the enzyme into an inactive conformation. How far such a regulatory mechanism operates within *in vivo* systems is still open to discussion.

The various parameters characterizing lipid-activated enzymes appear to be sensitive indicators of several aspects of membrane ultrastructure. Thus, a change of about 100% in an enzymic parameter may represent a change of only a few percent of some general protein parameter, hardly detectable by the usual physical techniques. Also, the observations on specific lipid dependency of membrane-bound enzymes emphasize a possible microheterogeneity in the bilayer: some enzymes require certain head groups and may even require a certain fatty acid pattern. Both of these features are probably best reflected in a relatively high degree of unsaturation in more polar lipids. Other correlations of this type may be found in the future.

In short, the study of lipid-activated enzymes and other functional membrane proteins has reached a stage where some meaningful generalizations can be made. Further studies would certainly include: correlation of fatty acid and head group patterns with specific functions, metabolic, physiological and pathological states; study of the variation of kinetic parameters with the nature of activating lipids; correlation of functional changes with subtle structural changes; evaluation of the role of lipids in regulating the activity of water; role of lipid as solvent for hydrophobic substrates; development of phospholipid mutants; studies pertaining to metabolic control of membrane lipids and its effect on the functional state of various cellular membranes; modification of membrane protein functions caused by "lipid-soluble" drugs and agents; modification of lipid-protein interactions in pathological states; development and study of mutants blocked in the synthesis of specific phospholipid class. Moreover, the role of lipids in modulating and regulating several functions of the same protein cannot be ignored; it is quite possible that conflicting observations and claims may be due to such a multiplicity of roles.

ACKNOWLEDGMENTS

We wish to express our grateful appreciation to Professor E. H. Cordes for various suggestions, comments, and criticism. We have benefited significantly from comments and suggestions made by Drs. E. Williams, J. Gurd, F. Feldman, R. Apitz, and the graduate students in the Biophysics Department at the Instituto Venezolano de Investigaciones Cientificas, Caracas (Venezuela).

References

Abou-Issa, H. M., and Cleland, W. W. (1969). *Biochim. Biophys. Acta* **176**, 692.
Abrams, A., and Baron, C. (1968). *Biochemistry* **7**, 501.
Agin, D., Hersh, L., and Holtzman, D. (1965). *Proc. Nat. Acad. Sci. U. S.* **53**, 952.
Amoore, J. E., Palmeri, G., Wanke, E., and Blum, M. S. (1969). *Science* **165**, 1266.
Anderson, T. R. (1970). *Comp. Biochem. Physiol., B* **33**, 663.
Armstrong, C. M., and Binstock, L. (1964). *J. Gen. Physiol.* **48**, 265.
Attwood, D., Graham, A. B., and Wood, G. C. (1971). *Biochem. J.* **123**, 875.
Auborn, J. J., Eyring, E. M., and Choules, G. L. (1971). *Proc. Nat. Acad. Sci. U. S.* **68**, 1996.
Awasthi, Y. C., Chung, T. F., Keenan, T. W., and Crane, F. L. (1970a). *Biochem. Biophys. Res. Commun.* **39**, 822.
Awasthi, Y. C., Ruzicka, F. J., and Crane, F. L. (1970b). *Biochim. Biophys. Acta* **203**, 233.
Awasthi, Y. C., Chuang, T. F., Keenan, T. W., and Crane, F. L. (1971). *Biochim. Biophys. Acta* **226**, 42.
Bachmann, E., Allmann, D. W., and Green, D. E. (1966). *Arch. Biochem. Biophys.* **115**, 153.

Ball, E. G., and Cooper, O. (1949). *J. Biol. Chem.* **180**, 113.
Bandopadhyay, A. K., and Deutscher, M. P. (1973). *J. Mol. Biol.* **74**, 257.
Bangham, A. D. (1963). *Advan. Lipid Res.* **1**, 65.
Barchi, R. L., and Braun, P. E. (1972). *J. Biol. Chem.* **247**, 7668.
Baumann, N. A., Harpin, M. L., and Bourre, J. M. (1970). *Nature (London)* **227**, 960.
Beacham, I. R., and Silbert, D. F. (1973). *J. Biol. Chem.* **248**, 5310.
Bean, R. C. (1972). *J. Membrane Biol.* **7**, 15.
Bean, R. C., Sheperd, W. C., Chan, S., and Eichner, J. T. (1969). *J. Gen. Physiol.* **53**, 741.
Bell, R. M., Mavis, R. D., and Vagelos, P. R. (1972). *Biochim. Biophys. Acta* **270**, 504.
Benson, A. A., Ji, T. H., and Gee, R. W. (1969). *Biophys. J.* **9**, A-36.
Blaurock, A. E. (1972). *Nature (London)* **240**, 556.
Blaurock, A. E. (1973). *Biophys. J.* **13**, 290.
Blough, H. A., and Tiffany, J. M. (1969). *Proc. Nat. Acad. Sci. U. S.* **62**, 242.
Borggreven, J. M. P. M., Rotmans, J. P., Bonting, S. L., and Daeman, F. J. M. (1971). *Arch. Biochem. Biophys.* **145**, 290.
Borggreven, J. M. P. M., Daeman, F. J. M., and Bonting, S. L. (1972). *Arch. Biochem. Biophys.* **151**, 1.
Borovjagin, V. L., and Moshkov, D. A. (1973). *J. Membrane Biol.* **13**, 245.
Brady, A. P., and Huff, H. (1948). *J. Colloid Sci.* **3**, 511.
Branton, D. (1969). *Annu. Rev. Plant Physiol.* **20**, 209.
Braun, V., and Rehm, K. (1969). *Eur. J. Biochem.* **10**, 426.
Braun, V., and Sieglin, U. (1970). *Eur. J. Biochem.* **13**, 336.
Brierley, G. P., and Merola, A. J. (1962). *Biochim. Biophys. Acta* **64**, 205.
Brierley, G. P., Merola, A. J., and Fleischer, S. (1962). *Biochim. Biophys. Acta* **64**, 218.
Brinkmann, K., and Packer, L. (1970). *J. Bioenerg.* **1**, 523.
Brown, P. K. (1972). *Nature (London), New Biol.* **236**, 35.
Bruni, A., Contessa, A., and Palatini, P. (1971). *Advan. Exp. Med. Biol.* **14**, 195.
Bublitz, C. (1973). *Biochem. Biophys. Res. Commun.* **52**, 173.
Bulos, B., and Racker, E. (1968). *J. Biol. Chem.* **243**, 3891.
Caliguiri, L. A., and Tamm, I. (1969). *Science* **166**, 885.
Carlson, C. W., Baxter, R. C., Ulm, E. H., and Pogell, B. M. (1973). *J. Biol. Chem.* **248**, 5555.
Carvalho, A. P. (1972). *Eur. J. Biochem.* **27**, 491.
Cater, B. R., and Hallinan, T. (1972). *Biochem. J.* **130**, 7P.
Cater, B. R., Poulter, J., and Hallinan, T. (1970). *FEBS (Fed. Eur. Biochem. Soc.), Lett.* **10**, 346.
Cerletti, P., Giovenco, M. A., Giordana, M. G., Giovenco, S., and Strom, R. (1967). *Biochim. Biophys. Acta* **146**, 380.
Cerletti, P., Caifa, P., Giordano, M. G., and Giovenco, M. A. (1969). *Biochim. Biophys. Acta* **191**, 502.
Chan, S. H. (1971). *Fed. Proc., Fed. Amer. Soc. Exp. Biol.* **30**, 1246.
Chang, T., Lewis, J., and Glazko, A. J. (1967). *Biochim. Biophys. Acta* **135**, 1000.
Changeux, J. P., Thiery, J., Tung, Y., and Kittel, C. (1967). *Proc. Nat. Acad. Sci. U. S.* **57**, 335.
Chapman, M. J., Mills, G. L., and Tayor, C. E. (1973). *Biochem. J.* **131**, 177.
Charnock, J. S., Dotty, D. M., and Russell, J. C. (1971). *Arch. Biochem. Biophys.* **142**, 633.

Cherry, R. J., Good, G. H., and Chapman, D. (1970). *Biochim. Biophys. Acta* **211,** 409.
Chung, A. E., and Law, J. H. (1964). *Biochemistry* **3,** 967.
Chung, J., Scanu, A. M., and Reman, F. (1973). *Biochim. Biophys. Acta* **296,** 116.
Chung, T. F., Awasthi, Y. C., and Crane, F. L. (1970a). *Proc. Indiana Acad. Sci.* **79,** 110.
Chung, T. F., Sun, F. F., and Crane, F. L. (1970b). *J. Bioenerg.* **1,** 227.
Clayton, P., and Martin, K. (1971). *J. Physiol.* (*London*) **218,** 50P.
Cobon, G. S., and Haslam, J. M. (1973). *Biochem. Biophys. Res. Commun.* **52,** 320.
Coleman, R., and Hubscher, G. (1963). *Biochim. Biophys. Acta* **73,** 257.
Cone, R. A. (1972). *Nature* (*London*), *New Biol.* **236,** 39.
Cook, A. M., Low, E., and Ishijimi, M. (1972). *Nature* (*London*), *New Biol.* **239,** 150.
Coon, M. J., Autor, A. P., and Strobel, H. W. (1971). *Chem. Biol. Interactions* **3,** 248.
Cordes, E. H., and Gitler, C. (1973). *Progr. Bioorg. Chem.* **2,** 1.
Cox, R. F., and Mathias, A. P. (1969). *Biochem. J.* **115,** 777.
Cramer, W. A., Phillips, S. K., and Keenan, T. W. (1973). *Biochemistry* **12,** 1177.
Craven, P. A., and Basford, R. E. (1972). *Biochim. Biophys. Acta* **255,** 620.
Cronan, J. E., and Vagelos, P. (1972). *Biochim. Biophys. Acta* **265,** 25.
Cunningham, C. C., and Hager, L. P. (1971a). *J. Biol. Chem.* **246,** 1583.
Cunningham, C. C., and Hager, L. P. (1971b). *J. Biol. Chem.* **246,** 1575.
Curtis, P. J. (1969). *Biochim. Biophys. Acta* **183,** 239.
Curtis, P. J. (1971). *Biochem. J.* **122,** 41P.
Curtis, P. J. (1972). *Biochim. Biophys. Acta* **255,** 833.
Das, M. L., Haak, E. D., and Crane, F. L. (1965). *Biochemistry* **4,** 859.
Davies, J. T. (1969). *J. Coll. Interface Sci.* **29,** 296.
Day, C. E., and Levy, R. S. (1969). *J. Theor. Biol.* **22,** 541.
DelCastillo, J., Rodriguez, A., Romero, C. A., and Sanchez, V. (1966). *Science* **153,** 185.
DelCastillo, J., Rodriguez, A., and Romero, C. A. (1967). *Ann. N. Y. Acad. Sci.* **144,** 803.
Denburg, J. L. (1973). *Biochim. Biophys. Acta* **298,** 967.
Deuticke, B., and Gruber, W. (1970). *Biochim. Biophys. Acta* **211,** 369.
Dinamarca, M. L., Levenbook, L., and Valdes, E. (1971). *Arch. Biochem. Biophys.* **147,** 374.
Diringer, H., and Koch, M. A. (1973). *Biochem. Biophys. Res. Commun.* **51,** 967.
Dodd, G. H. (1973). *Eur. J. Biochem.* **33,** 418.
Duttera, S. M., Byrne, W. L., and Ganoza, M. C. (1968). *J. Biol. Chem.* **243,** 2216.
Edidin, M., and Weiss, A. (1972). *Proc. Nat. Acad. Sci. U. S.* **69,** 2456.
Edwards, S. W., and Ball, E. G. (1954). *J Biol. Chem.* **209,** 619.
Ehrenpreis, S. (1965). *J. Cell. Comp. Physiol.* **66,** 159.
Ehrenstein, G., Lecar, H., and Nossel, R. (1970). *J. Gen. Physiol.* **55,** 119.
Eletr, S., and Inesi, G. (1972). *Biochim. Biophys. Acta* **290,** 178.
Eletr, S., Zakim, D., and Vessey, D. A. (1973). *J. Mol. Biol.* **78,** 351.
Eling, T. E., and DiAugustine, R. P. (1971). *Biochem. J.* **123,** 539.
Ellingson, J. S., Hill, E. E., and Lands, W. E. M. (1970). *Biochim. Biophys. Acta* **196,** 176.
Ellory, J. C., and Smith, M. W. (1969). *Biochim. Biophys. Acta* **193,** 137.
Endo, A., and Rothfield, L. (1969). *Biochemistry* **8,** 3508.

Ernster, L., Siekevitz, P., and Palade, G. E. (1962). *J. Cell Biol.* **15**, 541.
Esfahani, M., Limbrick, A. R., Knutton, S., Oka, T., and Wakil, S. J. (1971a). *Proc. Nat. Acad. Sci. U. S.* **68**, 3180.
Esfahani, M., Ioneda, T., and Wakil, S. J. (1971b). *J. Biol. Chem.* **246**, 50.
Esfahani, M., Limbrick, A. R., Knutton, S., and Wakil, S. J. (1971c). *Fed. Proc., Fed. Amer. Soc. Exp. Biol.* **30**, 1120.
Esfahani, M., Crowfoot, P. D., and Wakil, S. J. (1972). *J. Biol. Chem.* **247**, 7251.
Estaugo, S. F., Laraga, V., Corrales, M. A., Duch, C., and Munoz, E. (1972). *Biochim. Biophys. Acta* **255**, 960.
Evans, R. J., Banderman, S. L., Heinlein, K., and Davidson, J. A. (1968). *Biochemistry* **7**, 3095.
Evans, W. H., and Gurd, J. W. (1973). *Biochem. J.* **133**, 189.
Fenster, L. J., and Copenhaver, J. H., Jr. (1967). *Biochim. Biophys. Acta* **137**, 406.
Fernández-Morán, H. (1962). *Circulation* **26**, 1039.
Fischer, C. J., and Stetten, M. R. (1965). *Biochim. Biophys. Acta* **121**, 102.
Fiscus, W. G., and Schneider, W. C. (1966). *J. Biol. Chem.* **241**, 3324.
Fisher, D. B., and Kaufman, S. (1973). *J. Biol. Chem.* **248**, 4345.
Fleischer, S., Brierley, G. P., Klouwen, H., Slautterback, D. B., with technical assistance of Carpenter, E., and Moran, T. (1962). *J. Biol. Chem.* **237**, 3264.
Fleischer, S., Fleischer, B., and Stoeckenius, W. (1967). *J. Cell Biol.* **32**, 193.
Fleischer, S., Zahler, W. L., and Ozawa, H. (1968). *Biochem. Biophys. Res. Commun.* **32**, 1031.
Fleischer, S., Zahler, W. L., and Ozawa, H. (1971). *Biomembranes* **2**, 105.
Forte, J. G., Forte, T. M., and Heinz, E. (1973). *Biochim. Biophys. Acta* **298**, 827.
Fox, C. (1969). *Proc. Nat. Acad. Sci. U. S.* **63**, 850.
Frenkel, J. (1955). "Kinetic Theory of Liquids." Dover, New York. (See esp. Chs. IV and V.)
Friedman, R. M., and Pastan, I. (1969). *J. Mol. Biol.* **40**, 107.
Frye, L. D., and Edidin, M. (1970). *J. Cell Sci.* **7**, 319.
Gage, P. W. (1965). *J. Pharmacol. Exp. Ther.* **150**, 236.
Galanos, C., Rietschel, E. T., Luderitz, O., Westphal, O., Kim, Y. B., and Watson, D. W. (1972). *Eur. J. Biochem.* **31**, 230.
Galzigua, L., Rossi, C. R., Sartorelli, L., and Gibson, D. M. (1967). *J. Biol. Chem.* **242**, 2111.
Galzigua, L., Sartorelli, L., Rossi, C. R., and Gibson, D. M. (1969). *Lipids* **4**, 459.
Garland, R. C., and Cori, C. F. (1972). *Biochemistry* **11**, 4712.
Giannoni, G., Padden, F. J., and Roe, R. J. (1971). *Biophys. J.* **11**, 1018.
Gitler, C., and Montal, M. (1972a). *Biochem. Biophys. Res. Commun.* **47**, 1486.
Gitler, C., and Montal, M. (1972b). *FEBS (Fed. Eur. Biochem. Soc.), Lett.* **28**, 329.
Glaser, M., Bayer, W. H., Bell, R. M., and Vagelos, P. R. (1973). *Proc. Nat. Acad. Sci. U. S.* **70**, 385.
Glick, M. C., and Warren, L. (1969). *Proc. Nat. Acad. Sci. U. S.* **63**, 563.
Goldemberg, A. L., Farias, R. N., and Trucco, R. E. (1972). *J. Biol. Chem.* **247**, 4299.
Goldemberg, A. L., Farias, R. N., and Trucco, R. E. (1973). *Biochim. Biophys. Acta* **291**, 489.
Goldman, S. S., and Albers, R. W. (1973). *J. Biol. Chem.* **248**, 867.
Goodall, M. C. (1970). *Biochim. Biophys. Acta* **203**, 28.
Goodall, M. C. (1971). *Arch. Biochem. Biophys.* **147**, 129.
Goodall, M. C., and Sachs, G. (1972). *Nature (London)* **237**, 252.

Gordon, A. S., Wallach, D. F. H., and Straus, J. H. (1969). *Biochim. Biophys. Acta* **183**, 405.
Gorman, R. E., and Bitensky, M. W. (1970). *Endocrinology* **87**, 1075.
Gothman, A., Adams, H. R., and Knoohuisen, M. (1971). *Science* **173**, 1034.
Gotterer, G. S. (1967). *Biochemistry* **6**, 2147.
Gotterer, G. S. (1969). *Biochemistry* **8**, 641.
Goureau, M. F., Cernohorsky, I., Chapman, D., and Raulin, J. (1972). *Physiol. Chem. Phys.* **4**, 399.
Graham, A. B., and Wood, G. C. (1969). *Biochem. Biophys. Res. Commun.* **37**, 567.
Grant, N. H., and Alburn, H. E. (1965). *Science* **150**, 1589.
Grant, N. H., and Alburn, H. E. (1967). *Arch. Biochem. Biophys.* **118**, 292.
Green, D. E., and Fleischer, S. (1963). *Biochim. Biophys. Acta* **70**, 554.
Grinna, L. S., and Barber, A. A. (1972). *Biochim. Biophys. Acta* **288**, 347.
Grisham, C. M., and Barnett, R. E. (1972). *Biochim. Biophys. Acta* **266**, 613.
Gruener, N., and Avi-Dor, Y. (1966). *Biochem. J.* **100**, 762.
Guidotti, G. (1972). *Annu. Rev. Biochem.* **41**, 731.
Haest, C. W. M., DeGier, J., Van Es, G. A., Verkleij, A. J., and Van Deenen, L. L. M. (1972). *Biochim. Biophys. Acta* **288**, 43.
Hakomori, S., Saito, T., and Vogt, P. K. (1971). *Virology* **44**, 609.
Hall, J. D., and Crane, F. L. (1971). *Biochim. Biophys. Acta* **241**, 682.
Hall, M. O., and Bacharach, A. D. E. (1970). *Nature (London)* **225**, 637.
Hallick, L., Boyce, R. P., and Echols, H. (1969). *Nature (London)* **223**, 1239.
Hammes, G. G., and Schullery, S. E. (1970). *Biochemistry* **9**, 2555.
Hanahan, D., Barton, P. G., and Cox, A. (1969). *In* "Human Blood Coagulation" (H. C. Hemker, E. A. Loeliger, and J. J. Veltkamp, eds.), p. 24. Springer-Verlag, Berlin and New York.
Hansch, C., and Dunn, N. J., Jr. (1972). *J. Pharm. Sci.* **61**, 1.
Hanstein, W. G., Davis, K. A., and Hatefi, Y. (1971). *Arch. Biochem. Biophys.* **147**, 534.
Hantke, K., and Braun, V. (1973). *Eur. J. Biochem.* **34**, 284.
Harold, F. M., Baarda, J. R., Baron, C., and Abrams, A. (1969). *J. Biol. Chem.* **244**, 2261.
Hatch, F. T., and Bruce, A. L. (1968). *Nature (London)* **218**, 1166.
Hatefi, Y., and Hanstein, W. G. (1969). *Proc. Nat. Acad. Sci. U. S.* **62**, 1129.
Hatefi, Y., and Stampel, K. E. (1969). *J. Biol. Chem.* **244**, 2350.
Hatefi, Y., Haavik, A. G., Fowler, L. R., and Griffiths, D. E. (1962). *J. Biol. Chem.* **237**, 2661.
Hazel, J. R. (1972). *Comp. Biochem. Physiol., B* **43**, 837, 863.
Hearst, J. E., and Vinograd, J. (1961). *Proc. Nat. Acad. Sci. U. S.* **47**, 825.
Hechter, O. (1965). *Fed. Proc., Fed. Amer. Soc. Exp. Biol.* **24**, 591.
Hechter, O., Wittstruck, T., McNiven, M., and Lester, G. (1960). *Proc. Nat. Acad. Sci. U. S.* **46**, 783.
Hegyvary, C., and Post, R. L. (1969). "The Molecular Basis of Membrane Function" (D. C. Tosteson, ed.), p. 519. Prentice-Hall, Englewood Cliffs, New Jersey.
Helenius, A., and Simons, K. (1971). *Biochemistry* **10**, 2542.
Heller, J. (1968). *Biochemistry* **7**, 1906.
Hendler, R. W. (1968). "Protein Biosynthesis and Membrane Biochemistry." Wiley, New York.
Hennings, U., Dennert, G., Rehm, K., and Deppe, G. (1969). *J. Bacteriol.* **98**, 784.

Hexum, T., and Hokin, L. E. (1971). *Fed. Proc., Fed. Amer. Soc. Exp. Biol.* **30**, 1169. (Abstr.)
Hildebrand, J. H. (1971). *Science* **174**, 490.
Hinckle, P. C., Kim, J. J., and Racker, E. (1972). *J. Biol. Chem.* **247**, 1338.
Holden, J. T., Utech, N. M., Hageman, G. D., and Kenyon, C. N. (1973). *Biochem. Biophys. Res. Commun.* **50**, 266.
Hopfer, U., Lehninger, A. L., and Lennarz, W. J. (1970a). *J. Membrane Biol.* **2**, 41.
Hopfer, U., Lehninger, A. L., and Lennarz, W. J. (1970b). *J. Membrane Biol.* **3**, 142.
Horowitz, S. B., and Fenichel, R. J. (1965). *Ann. N. Y. Acad. Sci.* **125**, 572.
Houck, D. J. (1969). *Amer. J. Physiol.* **216**, 364.
Howell, J. I., Ahkong, R. F., Cramp, F. C., Fisher, D., Tampion, W., and Lucy, J. A. (1972). *Biochem. J.* **130**, 44P.
Hradec, J. (1972). *Biochem. J.* **126**, 1225.
Hradec, J., and Duseck, Z. (1968). *Biochem. J.* **110**, 1.
Hradec, J., and Duseck, Z. (1969). *Biochem. J.* **115**, 873.
Hunt, A. L. (1970). *Proc. Aust. Biochem. Soc.* **3**, 63.
Hunter, F. R., George, J., and Ospina, B. (1965). *J. Cell. Comp. Physiol.* **65**, 299.
Hurwitz, L., Battle, F., and Weiss, G. B. (1962). *J. Gen. Physiol.* **46**, 315.
Huzishige, H. H., Usiyama, T., Kikuti, T., and Azi, T. (1969). *Plant Cell Physiol.* **10**, 441.
Inbar, M., and Sachs, L. (1973). *FEBS (Fed. Eur. Biochem. Soc.), Lett.* **32**, 124.
Ingram, L. O., and Fisher, W. D. (1973). *Biochem. Biophys. Res. Commun.* **50**, 200.
Inoue, K., Kataoka, T., and Kinsky, S. C. (1971). *Biochemistry* **10**, 2574.
Israel, Y. (1969). *In* "The Molecular Basis of Membrane Function" (D. Tosteson, ed.), p. 529. Prentice-Hall, Englewood Cliffs, New Jersey.
Israel, Y., Kalant, H., and Leblanc, A. E. (1966). *Biochem. J.* **100**, 27.
Israel, Y., Salazar, I., and Rosenman, E. (1969a). *J. Nutr.* **96**, 499.
Israel, Y., Valenzuela, J. E., Salazar, I., and Ugarte, G. (1969b). *J. Nutr.* **98**, 222.
Ivanetich, K. M., Henderson, J. J., and Kaminsky, L. S. (1973). *Biochemistry* **12**, 1822.
Jacobson, B. (1955). *J. Amer. Chem. Soc.* **77**, 2919.
Jain, M. K. (1972). "The Bimolecular Lipid Membrane: A System." Van Nostrand-Reinhold, New York.
Jain, M. K. (1973). *Curr. Top. Membranes Transp.* **4**, 175.
Jain, M. K., and Cordes, E. H. (1973a). *J. Membrane Biol.* **14**, 101.
Jain, M. K., and Cordes, E. H. (1973b). *J. Membrane Biol.* **14**, 119.
Jain, M. K., Strickholm, A., and Cordes, E. H. (1969). *Nature (London)* **222**, 871.
Jain, M. K., Marks, R. H. L., and Cordes, E. H. (1970). *Proc. Nat. Acad. Sci. U. S.* **67**, 799.
Jain, M. K., White, F. P., Williams, E., Strickholm, A., and Cordes, E. H. (1972). *J. Membrane Biol.* **8**, 363.
Jain, M. K., Toussaint, D. G., and Cordes, E. H. (1973a). *J. Membrane Biol.* **14**, 1.
Jain, M. K., Mehl, L. E., and Cordes, E. H. (1973b). *Biochem. Biophys. Res. Commun.* **51**, 192.
Jarnefelt, J. (1972). *Biochim. Biophys. Acta* **266**, 91.
Jasaitis, A. A., Nemecek, I. B., Severina, I. I., Skulachev, V. P., and Smirnova, S. M. (1972). *Biochim. Biophys. Acta* **275**, 485.
Ji, T. H., and Benson, A. A. (1968). *Biochim. Biophys. Acta* **150**, 686.
Jolliot, A. (1972). *Annee Biol.* **11**, 351.
Jones, P. D., and Wakil, S. J. (1967). *J. Biol. Chem.* **242**, 5267.

Jones, P. D., Holloway, P. W., Peluffo, R. O., and Wakil, S. J. (1969). *J. Biol. Chem.* **244**, 744.

Jurtshuk, P., Jr., Sekuzu, I., and Green, D. E. (1961). *Biochem. Biophys. Res. Commun.* **6**, 76.

Jurtshuk, P., Jr., Sekuzu, I., and Green, D. E. (1963). *J. Biol. Chem.* **238**, 3595.

Kaback, H., and Milner, L. S. (1970). *Proc. Nat. Acad. Sci. U. S.* **65**, 1008.

Kagawa, Y. (1972). *Biochim. Biophys. Acta* **265**, 297.

Kagawa, Y., and Racker, E. (1966). *J. Biol. Chem.* **241**, 2461, 2467.

Kagawa, Y., and Racker, E. (1971). *J. Biol. Chem.* **246**, 5477.

Kagawa, Y., Kandrach, A., and Racker, E. (1973a). *J. Biol. Chem.* **248**, 676.

Kagawa, Y., Johnson, L. W., and Racker, E. (1973b). *Biochem. Biophys. Res. Commun.* **50**, 245.

Kaminsky, L. S., Wright, R. L., and Davison, A. J. (1971). *Biochemistry* **10**, 458.

Kaminsky, L. S., Henderson, J. J., and Ivanetich, K. M. (1973). *Biochem. Biophys. Res. Commun.* **51**, 40.

Kanemasa, Y., Yoshioka, T., and Hayashi, H. (1972). *Biochim. Biophys. Acta* **280**, 444.

Karibian, D. (1973). *Biochim. Biophys. Acta* **302**, 205.

Kariya, M., and Kaplan, A. (1973). *J. Lipid Res.* **14**, 243.

Karlsson, K. A., Samuelsson, B. E., and Steen, G. C. (1971). *J. Membrane Biol.* **5**, 169.

Kass, L. R. (1968). *J. Biol. Chem.* **243**, 3223.

Kataoka, T., Williamson, J. R., and Kinsky, S. C. (1973). *Biochim. Biophys. Acta* **298**, 158.

Kauzmann, W. (1959). *Advan. Protein Chem.* **14**, 1.

Kavanau, J. L. (1963). *Nature (London)* **198**, 525.

Kemp, A., Groot, G. S. P., and Reitsma, H. J. (1969). *Biochim. Biophys. Acta* **180**, 28.

Kilkson, R. (1969). *In* "Symmetry and Function of Biological Systems at the Macromolecular Level: Nobel Symposia II" (A. Engstrom and S. Strandberg, eds.), p. 257. Almqvist & Wicksell, Stockholm.

Kimelberg, H. K., and Papahadjopoulos, D. (1972). *Biochim. Biophys. Acta* **282**, 277.

Kinsky, S. C. (1972). *Biochim. Biophys. Acta* **265**, 1.

Kirschbaum, B. B., and Bosmann, H. B. (1973). *FEBS (Fed. Eur. Biochem. Soc.) Lett.* **34**, 129.

Kito, M., Aibara, S., Kato, M., Ishinaga, M., and Hata, T. (1973). *Biochim. Biophys. Acta* **298**, 69.

Klevens, H. B. (1947). *J. Phys. Colloid Chem.* **51**, 1143.

Knowles, A. F., Guillory, R. J., and Racker, E. (1971). *J. Biol. Chem.* **246**, 2672.

Kramer, R., Schlatter, C., and Zahler, P. (1972). *Biochim. Biophys. Acta* **282**, 146.

Krupka, R. M. (1971). *Biochemistry* **10**, 1148.

Kuehn, G. D., McFadden, B. A., Johnson, R. A., Hill, J. M., and Shumway, L. K. (1969). *Proc. Nat. Acad. Sci. U. S.* **62**, 407.

Kuiper, P. J. C., Livne, A., and Meyerstir, N. (1971). *Biochim. Biophys. Acta* **248**, 300.

Kundig, W., and Roseman, S. (1971). *J. Biol. Chem.* **246**, 1407.

Labow, R. S., Williamson, D. G., and Layne, D. S. (1973). *Biochemistry* **12**, 1548.

Lagerspetz, K. Y. H., Kohonen, J., and Tirsi, R. (1973). *Comp. Biochem. Physiol., B* **44**, 823.

Lanyi, J. K. (1973). *Biochemistry* **12**, 1433.

Larrabee, M. G., Ramos, J. G., and Bulbring, E. (1952). *J. Cell. Comp. Physiol.* **40**, 461.
Laser, H., and Stater, E. C. (1960). *Nature (London)* **187**, 1115.
Lemberg, M. R. (1969). *Physiol. Rev.* **49**, 48.
Lenaz, G. (1971). *J. Bioenerg.* **2**, 119.
Lenaz, G., Sechi, A. M., Masotti, L., and Castelli, G. P. (1969). *Biochem. Biophys. Res. Commun.* **34**, 392.
Lenaz, G., Sechi, A. M., Parenti-Castelli, G., and Masotti, L. (1970). *Arch. Biochem. Biophys.* **141**, 79, 89.
Lenaz, G., Parenti-Castelli, G., Sechi, A. M., and Masotti, L. (1972a). *Arch. Biochem. Biophys.* **148**, 391.
Lenaz, G., Sechi, A. M., Parenti-Castelli, G., Landi, L., and Bertoli, E. (1972b). *Biochem. Biophys. Res. Commun.* **49**, 536.
Lennarz, W. J. (1972). *Accounts Chem. Res.* **5**, 361.
Lennarz, W. J., and Talamo, B. (1966). *J. Biol. Chem.* **241**, 2707.
Lesslauer, W., Wissler, F. C., and Parsons, D. (1970). *Biochim. Biophys. Acta* **203**, 199.
Lester, R. L., and Fleischer, S. (1961). *Biochim. Biophys. Acta* **47**, 358.
Leuzinger, W., and Schneider, M. (1972). *Experientia* **28**, 256.
Levey, G. S. (1971a). *J. Biol. Chem.* **246**, 7405.
Levey, G. S. (1971b). *Ann. N. Y. Acad. Sci.* **185**, 449.
Leziùs, A., and Mueller-Lornson, B. (1972). *Hoppe-Seyler's Z. Physiol. Chem.* **353**, 1872.
Lien, S., and Racker, E. (1971). *J. Biol. Chem.* **246**, 4298.
Linden, C. D., Wright, K. L., McConnel, H. M., and Fox, C. F. (1973). *Proc. Nat. Acad. Sci. U. S.* **70**, 2271.
Linnane, A. W., Haslam, J. M., and Forrester, I. T. (1972). *In* "Biochemistry and Biophysics of Mitochondrial Membranes" (G. F. Azzone, E. Carafoli, A. L. Lehninger, E. Qugliariello, and N. Siliprandi, eds.), p. 523. Academic Press, New York.
Lovrien, R. (1963). *J. Amer. Chem. Soc.* **85**, 3677.
Low, P. S., Bada, J. L., and Somero, G. N. (1973). *Proc. Nat. Acad. Sci. U. S.* **70**, 430.
Luderitz, O., Staub, A. M., and Westphal, O. (1966). *Bacteriol. Rev.* **30**, 192.
Lyons, J. M., and Raison, J. K. (1970). *Plant Physiol.* **45**, 386.
McClard, R. W., and Kolenbrander, H. M. (1973). *Can. J. Biochem.* **51**, 556.
Machinist, J. M., and Singer, T. P. (1965). *J. Biol. Chem.* **240**, 3182.
McLaughlin, S. G. A., Szabo, G., Eisenman, G., and Ciani, S. M. (1970). *Proc. Nat. Acad. Sci. U. S.* **67**, 1268.
MacLennan, D. H., Seeman, P., Iles, C. H., and Yip, C. (1971). *J. Biol. Chem.* **246**, 2702.
Maddy, A. H. (1964). *Biochem. Biophys. Acta* **88**, 448.
Marcus, L., and Kaneshiro, T. (1972). *Biochim. Biophys. Acta* **288**, 296.
Martonoshi, A., Donley, J., and Halpin, R. A. (1968). *J. Biol. Chem.* **243**, 61.
Martonoshi, A., Donley, J., Pucell, A., and Halpin, R. (1971). *Arch. Biochem. Biophys.* **144**, 529.
Massey, V., Curti, B., and Ganther, H. (1966). *J. Biol. Chem.* **241**, 2347.
Mateu, L., Luzzati, V., London, Y., Gould, R. M., Vosseberg, F. G. A., and Olive, J. (1973). *J. Mol. Biol.* **75**, 697.
Mattson, F. H., Volpenhein, R. A., and Benjamin, L. (1970). *J. Biol. Chem.* **245**, 5335.

Mavis, R. D., and Vagelos, P. R. (1972). *J. Biol. Chem.* **247**, 652.
Mavis, R. D., Bell, R. M., and Vagelos, P. R. (1972). *J. Biol. Chem.* **247**, 2835.
Meissner, G., and Fleischer, S. (1972). *Biochim. Biophys. Acta* **255**, 19.
Michell, R. H., and Lapetina, E. G. (1972). *Nature (London), New Biol.* **240**, 258.
Moore, J. W., Ulbricht, W., and Tanaka, M. (1964). *J. Gen. Physiol.* **48**, 279.
Moore, L. D., and Umbreit, W. W. (1965). *Biochim. Biophys. Acta* **103**, 466.
Morgan, T. E., Tinker, D. O., and Hanahan, D. J. (1963). *Arch. Biochem. Biophys.* **103**, 54.
Morrison, M., Bright, J., and Rouser, G. (1966). *Arch. Biochem. Biophys.* **114**, 50.
Morse, P. D., and Deamer, D. W. (1973). *Biochim. Biophys. Acta* **298**, 769.
Mueller, P., and Rudin, D. (1968). *J. Theor. Biol.* **18**, 222.
Mustafa, M. G., and King, T. E. (1970). *J. Biol. Chem.* **245**, 1084.
Nachbar, M. S., and Salton, M. R. J. (1970). *Biochim. Biophys. Acta* **223**, 309.
Ne'eman, Z., Kahane, I., and Razin, S. (1971). *Biochim. Biophys. Acta* **249**, 169.
Nemethy, G., and Scheraga, H. A. (1962). *J. Chem. Phys.* **36**, 3401.
Nielsen, N. C., and Fleischer, S. (1973). *J. Biol. Chem.* **248**, 2549.
Nielsen, N. C., Zahler, W. L., and Fleischer, S. (1973). *J. Biol. Chem.* **248**, 2556.
Noguchi, T., and Freed, S. (1971). *Nature (London), New Biol.* **230**, 148.
Nunn, W. D., and Tropp, B. E. (1972). *J. Bacteriol.* **109**, 162.
Ohnishi, T., and Kawamura, H. (1964). *J. Biochem. (Tokyo)* **56**, 377.
Okada, K. (1970). *Jap. J. Physiol.* **20**, 97.
Olivecrona, T., and Oreland, L. (1971). *Biochemistry* **10**, 332.
Oreland, L., and Olivecrona, T. (1971). *Arch. Biochem. Biophys.* **142**, 710.
Osborn, M. J. (1971). *In* "Structure and Function of Biological Membranes" (L. I. Rothfield, ed.), p. 343. Academic Press, New York.
Overath, P., Schairer, H. U., and Stoffel, W. (1970). *Proc. Nat. Acad. Sci. U. S.* **67**, 606.
Overath, P., Hill, E. E., and Lamnek-Hirsch, I. (1971). *Nature (London), New Biol.* **234**, 264.
Palatini, P., and Bruni, A. (1970). *Biochem. Biophys. Res. Commun.* **40**, 186.
Palatini, P., Dabbeni-Sala, F., and Bruni, A. (1972). *Biochim. Biophys. Acta* **288**, 413.
Papahadjopoulos, D. (1971). *Biochim. Biophys. Acta* **241**, 254.
Parisi, M., Reader, T. A., and DeRobertis, E. (1972). *J. Gen. Physiol.* **60**, 454.
Pascaud, H., Auliac, P. B., Ehrhart, J.-C., and Pascaud, M. (1970). *Biochim. Biophys. Acta* **219**, 339.
Patterson, D. S. P., Sweasey, D., and Harding, J. D. J. (1972). *J. Neurochem.* **19**, 2791.
Patton, S. (1970). *J. Theor. Biol.* **29**, 489.
Patton, S., McCarthy, R. D., Plantz, P. E., and Lee, R. F. (1973). *Nature (London), New Biol.* **241**, 241.
Pesch, L. A., and Peterson, J. (1965). *Biochim. Biophys. Acta* **96**, 390.
Pfeifer, P. M., and McCay, P. B. (1972). *J. Biol. Chem.* **247**, 6763.
Philippot, J., and Authier, M. H. (1973). *Biochim. Biophys. Acta* **298**, 887.
Phillips, G. B., Dodge, J. T., and Howe, C. (1969). *Lipids* **4**, 544.
Pitotti, A., Contessa, A. R., Dabbeni-Sala, F., and Bruni, A. (1972). *Biochim. Biophys. Acta* **274**, 528.
Pohl, S. L., Krans, H. M. J., Kozyreff, V., Birnbaumer, L., and Rodbell, M. (1971). *J. Biol. Chem.* **246**, 4447.
Poincelot, R. P., Millar, P. J., Kimbel, R. L., Jr., and Abrahamson, E. W. (1969). *Nature (London)* **221**, 256.

Priestland, R. N., and Whittam, R. (1972). *J. Physiol.* (*London*) **220**, 353.
Quastel, J. H. (1956). *In* "Enzymes: Units of Biological Structure and Function" (O. H. Gaebler, ed.), p. 523. Academic Press, New York.
Racker, E. (1972). *J. Biol. Chem.* **247**, 8198.
Racker, E., and Horstman, L. L. (1972). *In* "Energy Metabolism and the Regulation of Metabolic Process in Mitochondria" (M. A. Mehlman and R. W. Hanson, eds.), p. 1. Academic Press, New York.
Racker, E., and Kandrach, A. (1971). *J. Biol. Chem.* **246**, 7069.
Ragan, C. I., and Racker, E. (1973). *J. Biol. Chem.* **248**, 2563.
Raison, J. K., Lyons, J. M., and Thomson, W. W. (1971a). *Arch. Biochem. Biophys.* **142**, 83.
Raison, J. K., Lyons, J. M., Mehlhorn, R. J., and Keith, A. D. (1971b). *J. Biol. Chem.* **246**, 4036.
Rang, H. P. (1960). *Brit. J. Pharmacol.* **15**, 185.
Ratanabanangkoon, K., Dixon, J. F., and Hokin, L. E. (1973). *Arch. Biochem. Biophys.* **156**, 342.
Razin, S. (1972). *Biochim. Biophys. Acta* **265**, 241.
Redwood, W. R., Muldner, H., and Thompson, T. E. (1969). *Proc. Nat. Acad. Sci. U. S.* **64**, 989.
Rethy, A., Tomasi, V., and Trevisani, A. (1971). *Arch. Biochem. Biophys.* **147**, 36.
Reynolds, J. A., and Tanford, C. (1970). *Proc. Nat. Acad. Sci. U. S.* **66**, 1002.
Robbins, A. R., and Rotman, B. (1972). *Proc. Nat. Acad. Sci. U. S.* **69**, 2125.
Robinson, G. A., Butcher, R. W., and Sutherland, E. W. (1971). "Cyclic AMP." Academic Press, New York.
Rodbell, M., Krans, H. M. J., Pohl, S. L., and Birnbaumer, L. (1971). *J. Biol. Chem.* **246**, 1861.
Roelofsen, B., Zwaal, R. F. A., and Van Deenen, L. L. M. (1971). *Advan. Exp. Med. Biol.* **14**, 209.
Rogers, M. J., and Strittmatter, P. (1973). *J. Biol. Chem.* **248**, 800.
Romeo, D., Hinckley, A., and Rothfield, L. (1970). *J. Mol. Biol.* **53**, 491.
Roseman, S. (1969). *J. Gen. Physiol.* **51**, 1395.
Rossi, E., Norling, B., Persson, B., and Ernster, L. (1970). *Eur. J. Biochem.* **16**, 508.
Roth, S., and Seeman, P. (1972). *Biochim. Biophys. Acta* **255**, 207.
Rothfield, L., and Finkelstein, A. (1968). *Annu. Rev. Biochem.* **37**, 463.
Rothfield, L., and Perlman, M. (1966). *J. Biol. Chem.* **241**, 1386.
Rottem, S., Cirillo, V. P., DeKruyff, B., Shinitzky, M., and Razin, S. (1973). *Biochim. Biophys. Acta* **323**, 509.
Rouser, G., Yamamoto, A., and Kritchevsky, G. (1971). *Arch. Intern. Med.* **127**, 1105.
Roux, S. J., and Yguerabide, J. (1973). *Proc. Nat. Acad. Sci. U. S.* **70**, 762.
Ruiz-Herrera, J., Alvarez, A., and Figueroa, I. (1972). *Biochim. Biophys. Acta* **289**, 254.
Saiki, T., Suzuki, T., Takagi, Y., Narasaki, T., Tamura, G., and Arima, K. (1969). *Agr. Biol. Chem.* **33**, 1101.
Sandermann, H., and Strominger, J. L. (1971). *Proc. Nat. Acad. Sci. U. S.* **68**, 2441.
Sandermann, H., Jr. (1973). *FEBS* (*Fed. Eur. Biochem. Soc.*), *Lett.* **29**, 256.
Sauner, M.-T., and Levy, M. (1971). *Biochim. Biophys. Acta* **241**, 97.
Sawada, H., Takeshita, M., Sugita, Y., and Yoneyama, Y. (1969). *Biochim. Biophys. Acta* **178**, 145.

Scandella, C. J., and Kornberg, A. (1971). *Biochemistry* **10**, 4447.
Schairer, H. U., and Overath, P. (1969). *J. Mol. Biol.* **44**, 209.
Schatzmann, H. J. (1962). *Nature (London)* **196**, 677.
Schuberth, J., and Sundwall, A. (1967). *J. Neurochem.* **14**, 807.
Seelig, J., and Hasselbach, W. (1971). *Eur. J. Biochem.* **21**, 17.
Seeman, P. (1972). *Pharmacol. Rev.* **24**, 583.
Seeman, P., Chau, M., Goldberg, M., Sauks, T., and Sax, L. (1971). *Biochim. Biophys. Acta* **225**, 185.
Sekuzu, I., Jurtshuk, P., Jr., and Green, D. E. (1961). *Biochem. Biophys. Res. Commun.* **6**, 71.
Sekuzu, I., Jurtshuk, P., and Green, D. E. (1963). *J. Biol. Chem.* **238**, 975.
Selegny, E., Broun, G., and Thomas, D. (1971a). *Physiol. Veg.* **9**, 25.
Selegny, E., Kernevez, J.-P., and Broun, G. (1971b). *Physiol. Veg.* **9**, 51.
Shamoo, A. E., and Albers, R. W. (1973). *Proc. Nat. Acad. Sci. U. S.* **70**, 1191.
Shibuya, I., Honda, H., and Mauro, B. (1965). *Seikagaku* **37**, 561.
Shimakata, T., Mihara, K., and Sato, R. (1972). *J. Biochem. (Tokyo)* **72**, 1163.
Siekevitz, P. (1972). *Annu. Rev. Physiol.* **34**, 117.
Sinensky, M. (1971). *J. Bacteriol.* **106**, 444.
Sineriz, F., Farias, R. N., and Trucco, R. E. (1973). *FEBS (Fed. Eur. Biochem. Soc.), Lett.* **32**, 30.
Singer, S. (1962). *Advan. Protein Chem.* **17**, 1.
Skou, J. C. (1958). *Biochim. Biophys. Acta* **30**, 625.
Smith, M. W. (1967). *Biochem. J.* **105**, 65.
Somogyi, J., Budai, M., Nyiro, L., Kaluza, G. A., Nagel, W., and Willig, F. (1969). *Acta Biochim. Biophys.* **4**, 219.
Soodsma, J. F., and Nordlie, R. (1969). *Biochim. Biophys. Acta* **191**, 636.
Specht, S. C., and Robinson, J. D. (1973). *Arch. Biochem. Biophys.* **154**, 314.
Speth, V., and Wunderlich, F. (1973). *Biochim. Biophys. Acta* **291**, 621.
Stahl, W. L. (1973). *Arch. Biochem. Biophys.* **154**, 56.
Starka, J., and Moravova, J. (1970). *J. Gen. Microbiol.* **60**, 251.
Steckhoven, F. S., and Van Moerkerk, H. T. B. (1972). *Biochem. Biophys. Res. Commun.* **47**, 7.
Stetten, M. R., Malamed, S., and Federman, M. (1969). *Biochim. Biophys. Acta* **193**, 260.
Storelli, C., Vogeli, H., and Semenza, G. (1972). *FEBS (Fed. Eur. Biochem. Soc.), Lett.* **24**, 287.
Stryer, L. (1968). *Annu. Rev. Biochem.* **37**, 25.
Sullivan, K., Jain, M. K., and Koch, A. (1974). *Biochim. Biophys. Acta* (in press).
Sunshine, G. H., Williams, D. J., and Rabin, B. R. (1971). *Nature (London), New Biol.* **230**, 133.
Swanson, P. D., and Stahl, W. L. (1966). *Biochem. J.* **99**, 396.
Swanson, P. D., Bradford, H. F., and McIlwain, H. (1964). *Biochem. J.* **92**, 235.
Talsky, G. (1971). *Angew. Chem., Int. Ed. Engl.* **10**, 548.
Tanaka, R., and Strickland, K. P. (1965). *Arch. Biochem. Biophys.* **111**, 583.
Tanaka, R., Sakamoto, T., and Sakamoto, Y. (1971). *J. Membrane Biol.* **4**, 42.
Tanford, C. (1962). *J. Amer. Chem. Soc.* **84**, 4240.
Tanford, C. (1968). *Advan. Protein Chem.* **23**, 121.
Taniguchi, K., and Tonomura, Y. (1971). *J. Biochem. (Tokyo)* **69**, 543.
The, R., and Hasselbach, W. (1972). *Eur. J. Biochem.* **28**, 357.
Theorell, H. (1943). *Ark. Kemi, Mineral. Geol., Ser. A* **4**, 16.

Thiele, O. W., Dreysel, J., and Herman, D. (1972). *Eur. J. Biochem.* **29,** 224.
Thore, A., and Baltscheffsky, H. (1965). *Acta Chem. Scand.* **19,** 1591, 1600.
Thorhaug, A. (1971). *Biochim. Biophys. Acta* **225,** 151.
Tien, H. T. (1968). *Nature (London)* **219,** 272.
Tinberg, H. M., Packer, L., and Keith, A. D. (1972). *Biochim. Biophys. Acta* **283,** 193.
Tobari, J. (1964). *Biochem. Biophys. Res. Commun.* **15,** 50.
Tomasi, V., Koretz, S., Ray, T. K., Dunnick, J., and Marinetti, G. V. (1970). *Biochim. Biophys. Acta* **211,** 31.
Tosteson, M. T., Lau, F., and Tosteson, D. C. (1973). *Nature (London), New Biol.* **243,** 112.
Towers, N. R., Raison, J. K., Kellerman, G. M., and Linnane, A. W. (1972). *Biochim. Biophys. Acta* **287,** 301.
Towle, D. W., and Copenhaver, J. H. (1970). *Biochim. Biophys. Acta* **203,** 124.
Tria, E., and Barnabei, O. (1969). *In* "Structural and Functional Aspects of Lipoproteins in Living Systems" (E. Tria and A. M. Scanu, eds.), p. 144. Academic Press, New York.
Triggle, D. J. (1969). *J. Theor. Biol.* **25,** 499.
Triggle, D. J. (1970). *Recent Progr. Surface Sci.* **3,** 273.
Troy, F. A., Frerman, F. E., and Heath, E. C. (1971). *J. Biol. Chem.* **246,** 118.
Tsukagoshi, N., and Fox, C. F. (1973). *Biochemistry* **12,** 2822.
Tyler, D. D., and Eastbrook, R. W. (1966). *J. Biol. Chem.* **241,** 1672.
Tzagoloff, A. (1969). *J. Biol. Chem.* **244,** 5020.
Tzagoloff, A., MacLennan, D. H., McConnell, D. B., and Green, D. E. (1967). *J. Biol. Chem.* **242,** 2051.
Umbreit, J. N., and Strominger, J. L. (1972). *Proc. Nat. Acad. Sci. U. S.* **69,** 1972.
Urry, D. W., and Eyring, H. (1963). *Proc Nat. Acad. Sci. U. S.* **49,** 253.
Vessey, D. A., and Zakim, D. (1971). *J. Biol. Chem.* **246,** 4649.
Vessey, D. A., and Zakim, D. (1972). *Biochim. Biophys. Acta* **268,** 61.
Walker, B. L., and Yurkowsky, M. (1967). *Biochem. J.* **103,** 218.
Weiss, D. E. (1973). *Angew. Chem., Int. Ed. Engl.* **29,** 249.
Westhead, E. W., and Malmstrom, B. G. (1957). *J. Biol. Chem.* **228,** 605.
Wetlaufer, D.-B., and Lovrien, R. (1964). *J. Biol. Chem.* **239,** 596.
Wheeler, K. P., and Whittam, R. (1970). *J. Physiol. (London)* **207,** 303.
Widnell, G. C., and Unkeless, J. C. (1968). *Proc. Nat. Acad. Sci. U. S.* **64,** 1050.
Williamson, D. G., and O'Donnell, V. J. (1969). *Biochemistry* **8,** 1289.
Wilson, G., and Fox, C. F. (1971). *J. Mol. Biol.* **55,** 49.
Wilson, G., Rose, S. P., and Fox, C. F. (1970). *Biochem. Biophys. Res. Commun.* **38,** 617.
Wilson, J. E. (1973). *Arch. Biochem. Biophys.* **154,** 332.
Yamashita, S., and Racker, E. (1969). *J. Biol. Chem.* **244,** 1220.
Yau, T. M., and Weber, M. J. (1972). *Biochem. Biophys. Res. Commun.* **49,** 114.
Yu, L., Yu, C., and King, T. E. (1973). *Biochemistry* **12,** 540.
Zahler, W. L., and Fleischer, S. (1971). *J. Bioenerg.* **2,** 209.
Zakim, D. (1970). *J. Biol. Chem.* **245,** 4953.
Zakim, D., Goldenberg, J., and Vessey, D. A. (1973). *Biochim. Biophys. Acta* **297,** 497.
Zeylemaker, W. P., Jansen, H., Veegar, C., and Slater, E. C. (1971). *Biochim. Biophys. Acta* **242,** 14.
Zorn, M., and Futterman, S. (1970). *J. Biol. Chem.* **246,** 881.

The Composition and Possible Physiologic Role of the Thyroid Lipids[1]

LEON A. LIPSHAW[2] AND PIERO P. FOÀ

Department of Research, Sinai Hospital of Detroit, Detroit, Michigan

I. Introduction

The follicular epithelium and the colloid of the thyroid gland contain abundant material with affinity for lipid stains (Langendorf, 1889; Erdheim, 1903; Wegelin, 1910; Karwicka, 1911; Buscaino, 1914; Jaffé, 1927; Grafflin, 1939; Preto-Parvis *et al.*, 1954; Noseda, 1934). Lipids have been found also in the interalveolar tissue (Haeberli, 1916; Gossmann, 1927; Foà *et al.*, 1951) and have been extracted in large amounts from normal and abnormal thyroid tissue (Iscovesco, 1908, 1912, 1913; Ferguson, 1933; Foà *et al.*, 1951; Turner, 1960). The chemical nature and the possible physiologic role of these lipids have not been fully investigated: it has been suggested that they may act as iodide carriers (Vilkki, 1962; Posner and Ordonez, 1969, 1970), contribute to the pathogenesis of Hashimoto's disease (Helwig and Wilkinson, 1960, 1962) and of certain forms of goiter (Foà *et al.*, 1951), or serve as substrates and regulators of thyroid metabolism (Freinkel *et al.*, 1961, 1962; Freinkel and Saef,

[1] This work was aided by Grants No. AM06034 and No. RR05641 from the National Institute of Arthritis and Metabolic Diseases, USPHS.

[2] Dr. Lipshaw is Post-doctoral Trainee, NIH Diabetes Training Program No. AM05474. Part of this work was done in fulfillment of requirements for a Ph.D. degree in physiology at Wayne State University, Detroit, Michigan.

1961). Indeed, in normal thyroid slices, free fatty acids (FFA) are oxidized actively even in the presence of glucose, which becomes the preferred substrate only when thyroid slices are incubated in a medium containing thyroid stimulating hormone (TSH) (Freinkel *et al.*, 1962; Freinkel, 1964a,b). Under these conditions, glucose and FFA are utilized in part as a calorigenic source, in part for the synthesis of lipids, and in particular of phospholipids (Freinkel, 1964a; Freinkel and Scott, 1964; Scott *et al.*, 1968). The experiments described in this paper were designed to investigate the effects of treatment with TSH or with propylthiouracil (PTU) on the composition of thyroid lipids and on the incorporation of tracer amounts of radiocarbon into lipids of thyroid slices. Some observations on the content and on the radioactivity of cholesterol, an area of thyroid metabolism that had been almost totally neglected, led to the suggestion that cholesterol biosynthesis, functioning as an irreversible trap for acetyl-CoA, may serve as a key regulator of metabolic pathways.

II. Methods and Materials

A. Animals and Tissue Incubation

Forty-five albino rabbits of both sexes, weighing 2.8 to 4.1 kg, housed in individual cages with free access to food and water were divided into 4 groups of 10–12 animals each, as follows: group I, untreated controls; group II, treated with a single intravenous injection of TSH[3] (3.0 IU in 0.6 ml of saline) exactly 2 hours before sacrifice; group III, treated with 2 daily subcutaneous injections of TSH (1.0 IU at 9:00 A.M. and 2.0 IU at 5:00 P.M.) for 7 days; group IV, treated with PTU[4] (80 mg/100 ml of drinking water) for 67–74 days. At the end of the treatment the animals were fasted for 14 to 17 hours, weighed and after withdrawal of 10 ml of blood from the central artery of the ear, were killed by the intravenous injection of about 40 ml of air. Immediately after death, trachea, larynx, and attached thyroid were excised as rapidly as possible, avoiding unnecessary trauma to the blood vessels and were placed in ice cold Krebs–Ringer bicarbonate buffer (pH 7.4). The thyroid lobes were dissected, scrupulously trimmed of extraneous fat and connective tissue, weighed on a torsion balance, and cut into slices about 1.0 mm thick. Seventy to 90 mg of tissue were placed in 20 ml beakers with 5.5 ml of

[3] Thytropar, Armour Pharmaceutical Co., P. O. Box 511, Kankakee, Illinois 60901.

[4] Eli Lilly and Co., 307 E. McCarty Street, Indianapolis, Indiana 46206.

fresh Krebs–Ringer bicarbonate buffer containing 5 μCi of acetate-1-^{14}C (28 mCi/mM), with or without glucose (1.3 mg/ml) and were incubated for 3 hours in a Dubnoff metabolic incubator oscillating at the rate of 90 excursions per minute. The atmosphere was a mixture of 95% O_2 and 5% CO_2; the rate of gas flow was 9 l/minute; the incubation temperature was 37°C. At the end of incubation the thyroid slices were washed in several portions of ice cold saline, blotted lightly with filter paper, weighed again, and transferred to a cold Potter-Elvehjem glass homogenizer.

B. Extracton and Separation of Lipids

The incubated tissue was homogenized in 1.0 ml of water. A 0.1 ml aliquot of this homogenate was diluted to 1.0 ml with water and 0.1 ml of this suspension was used for the measurement of total protein by the method of Lowry *et al.* (1951); the remainder was treated according to the method of Folch *et al.* (1957) for lipid extraction. After evaporation of the solvent under a stream of nitrogen, the lipids were redissolved in 0.5 ml of a 2:1 chloroform–methanol mixture and a 30 μl aliquot of this solution was dried, weighed on an electrobalance[5] to the nearest microgram, and the concentration of total lipid in the tissue sample was calculated. Duplicate aliquots of the same solution, containing between 100 and 300 μg of lipid, were analyzed for phospholipid (PL), monoglyceride (MG), free fatty acids (FFA), free cholesterol (Δ^5), 1,2 and 1,3 diglyceride (DG), triglyceride (TG), and cholesterol ester (Δ^5E) by thin layer chromatography (TLC), using the double solvent system of Freeman and West (1966), followed by final development in hexane. The TLC plates (20 × 20 cm) were coated with a 350 μm layer of silica gel containing 13% calcium sulfate,[6] according to the method of Stahl (1965).

C. Measurement of Radioactivity

After chromatography, the TLC plates were sprayed lightly with a 0.01% solution of Rhodamine 6G in methanol, the lipid fractions were located and identified under ultraviolet light and scraped into 22 ml scintillation vials containing about 200 mg of thixotropic powder[7] and 15 ml of scintillation fluid (0.05% POPOP[7] and 0.3% PPO[7] in 15 ml toluene). A sample of silica gel was scraped and used as a blank. The radioactivity was measured in a Tri-Carb liquid scintillation system[7] with an

---

[5] Cahn Division, Ventron Instruments, 7500 Jefferson Street, Paramount, California 90723.

[6] Brinkman Instruments, 110 S. River Road, Des Plains, Illinois 60016.

[7] Packard Instrument Co., 2200 Warrenville Road, Downers Grove, Illinois 60515.

efficiency of 60% and was expressed as counts per minute per milligram of tissue protein.

D. ANALYTICAL PROCEDURES

TG, FFA, and Δ^5 were measured by densitometry (Blank *et al.*, 1964). For this purpose, the lipids were separated on TLC plates as described above, the plates were sprayed with 70% sulfuric acid saturated with potassium dichromate and baked in an oven for 2 hours at 220°C. Densitometric analysis of the charred lipid fractions (see Fig. 1) was carried out by automatic scanning at the rate of 2.5 cm/min, using a densitometer[8] with an attached TLC stage and a light collimating system 0.1 mm wide and 15 mm long. The areas under the curves, simultaneously integrated, were related to the log of the spot density. Standard curves were prepared from known quantities of standard lipid mixtures that had been chromatographed and charred. Serum FFA concentrations were measured using the method of Dole and Meinertz (1960). The fatty acid composition of the PL and TG fractions was determined by

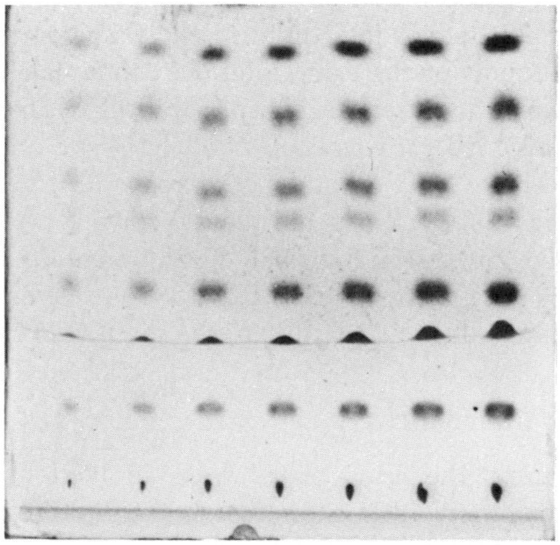

FIG. 1. Representative thin layer chromatogram of lipid standards separated on silica gel G. Abbreviations: PL = phospholipid; MG = monoglyceride; FFA = free fatty acid; Δ^5 = free cholesterol; 1,2 and 1,3 DG = diglyceride; TG = triglyceride; Δ^5E = cholesterol ester. Separation, identification, and densitometry are described in Section II.

[8] No. 530, Photovolt Corp., 1115 Broadway, New York, New York 10010.

gas-liquid chromatography (GLC), using the method of Morrison and Smith (1964). For this purpose, the fractions were treated with a 14% solution of boron trifluoride in methanol[9] and the resulting methyl esters were separated isothermally on a 6 ft × ⅛ in. U-shaped column, commercially packed with 6% diethyleneglycolsuccinate (DEGS) on a solid support of Diatoport S (80–100 mesh). The temperatures of the column, of the detector, and of the injection port were 180°C, 230°C, and 270°C, respectively. The instrument used was a model 400, F and M gas chromatograph[10] equipped with a flame ionization detector. The flow rate of the helium carrier gas was 25 ml/minute. The fatty acid peaks were identified by means of carbon-log plots (McNair and Bonelli, 1969) using an equal weight mixture of 18 fatty acid methyl esters and the retention time data of Hofstetter *et al.* (1965). The areas under each peak were measured with an automatic integrator.[11]

E. Histology

Samples of thyroid tissue were fixed in Bouin's solution, embedded in paraffin, cut (5 μm) and stained with Masson's trichrome and Harris' hematoxylin. Other samples were fixed in 10% formalin, frozen, cut (10 μm) and stained with oil red O and Harris' hematoxylin.

III. Results

Figure 2 shows that all three forms of treatment produced the expected nuclear enlargement and hypertrophy of the follicular cells and vacuolization of the colloid, indicating that thyroglobulin proteolysis and resorption had occurred. Prolonged treatment with TSH or with PTU also caused cellular hyperplasia and reduced the size of the follicular lumens. Figure 3 shows that most of the neutral lipid was in the adipocytes of the interstitial tissue. TSH injections did not modify the weight of the thyroid significantly, although after 7 days of treatment, there was a significant reduction in body weight. After treatment with PTU for 10 weeks, the weight of the thyroid was increased more than 3-fold (Table I and Fig. 4).

Table II shows that the average lipid content of the normal rabbit thyroid is similar to that of the ovary, several times greater than that of

---

[9] Analabs, Inc., P. O. Box 501, North Haven, Connecticut 06473.
[10] Hewlett-Packard Co., Route 41 and Starr Road, Avondale, Pennsylvania 19311.
[11] Disc Instrument Co., Santa Ana, California 92795.

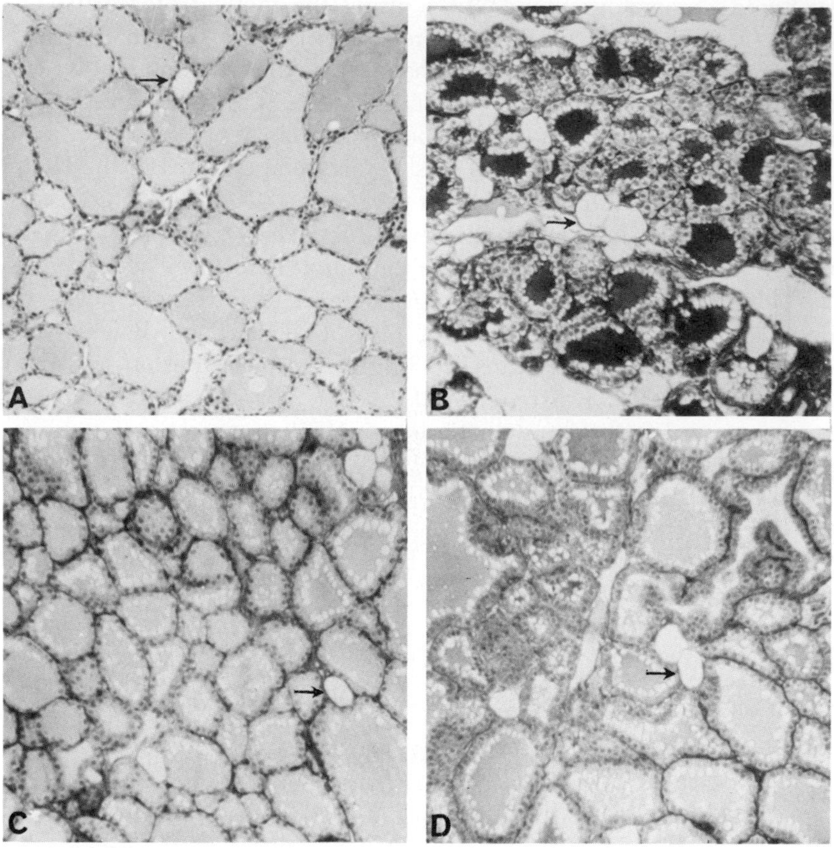

FIG. 2. Photomicrographs of rabbit thyroid. (A) Control; (B) Two hours after a single injection of TSH; (C) After 7 daily TSH injections; (D) After 10 weeks of oral PTU administration. Masson's trichrome and Harris' hematoxylin; × 150. Arrows point to interstitial adipocytes.

the kidney and of the liver, and about one-third as great as that of the adrenals. However, as shown in Fig. 5, most of the lipid of the adrenals and the ovaries is composed of free and esterified steroids, while the normal thyroid contains mostly TG (88.5%).

Two hours after a single injection of TSH, the concentrations of total lipid, TG, FFA, and Δ^5 in rabbit thyroid were significantly elevated, but after 7 daily injections of TSH, only the increase of FFA and Δ^5 persisted. After 10 weeks of treatment with PTU, total lipid and TG concentrations were markedly decreased, the level of Δ^5 was significantly increased, while that of FFA was unchanged (Table III). A representative thin-layer chromatogram of thyroid lipid is shown in Fig. 6.

Figure 7 shows that fasting caused the expected increase in the serum

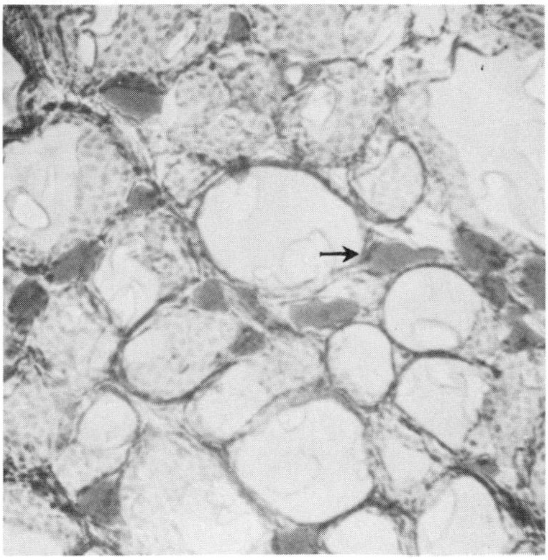

FIG. 3. Photomicrograph of a frozen section of normal rabbit thyroid. Oil red O and Harris' hematoxylin; × 150. The arrow points to typical globules of fat in the interstitial tissue (red in the original slide). Symbols as in Fig. 8.

concentration of FFA, that a greater increase (about 29% above fasting levels) occurred 2 hours after a single injection of TSH and a still greater one (about 42% above fasting levels) after 7 days of treatment with TSH. Rabbits treated with PTU had normal fasting serum FFA levels. Thus, the tissue level of FFA correlated well with that of the serum.

Slices of thyroid excised 2 hours after the rabbits had received a single injection of TSH incorporated an average of 1.8 times as much acetate radiocarbon into total lipid as thyroid slices obtained from control rabbits, even though there was no significant change in the activity of the

Table I

EFFECT OF TREATMENT ON BODY WEIGHT AND THYROID WEIGHT[a]

Treatment	No. of rabbits	Change in body weight (gm)	Thyroid weight (mg)
Controls	12	—	194 ± 10
Two hours after TSH	11	—	225 ± 19
After 7 days of TSH	11	−200 ($p < .001$)	192 ± 15
After 10 weeks of PTU	11	+173	663 ± 15 ($p < .001$)

[a] Ave. ± sem. statistical probability (p) calculated by comparison with control values.

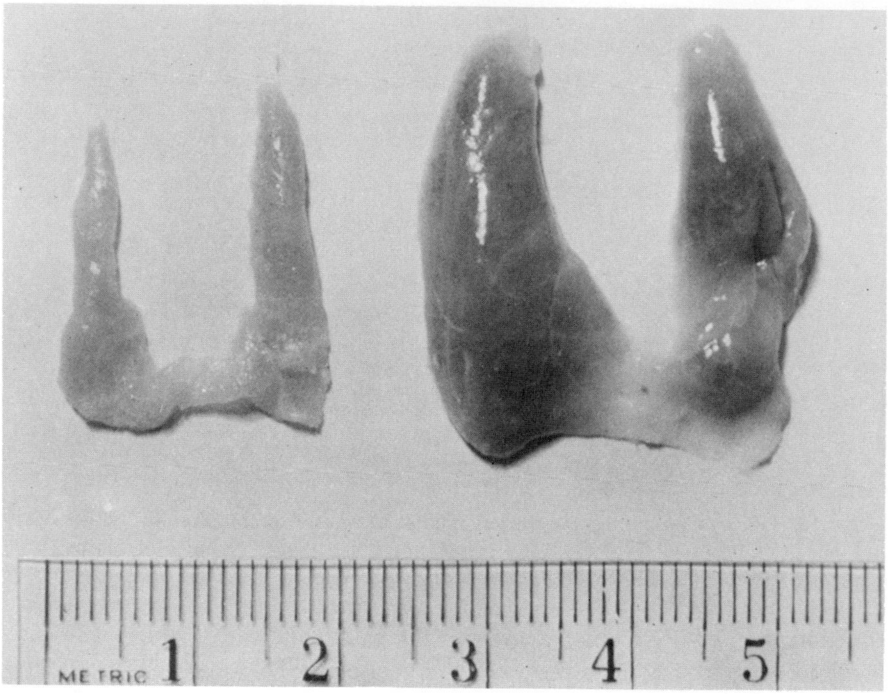

FIG. 4. Fresh rabbit thyroids. *Left*, Control. *Right*, after 10 weeks of oral PTU administration.

Table II

AVERAGE CONCENTRATION OF LIPID IN FIVE RABBIT ORGANS[a]

Organ	No. of samples	Total lipid (mg/gm wet wt)
Thyroid	12	114.3 (50.2–195.0)[b]
Liver	4	34.0 (24.1–45.6)
Kidney	4	22.2 (13.5–34.6)
Ovary	3	113.4 (106.3–121.8)
Adrenal	1	337.0

[a] The determinations were performed following incubation of tissue slices in 5.5 ml of Krebs–Ringer bicarbonate buffer (pH 7.4), containing glucose (1.3 mg/ml) and acetate-1-^{14}C (5.0 μCi) for 3 hours.

[b] Range of values in parentheses.

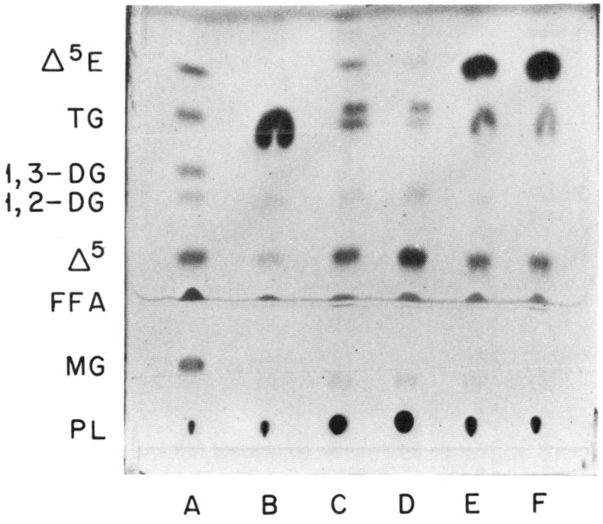

FIG. 5. Thin layer chromatogram showing the composition of lipid in five normal rabbit organs. A = lipid standards; B = thyroid; C = liver; D = kidney; E = ovary; F = adrenal. Each column represents 240 μg of total lipid. Abbreviations as in Fig. 1.

Table III

EFFECT OF TREATMENT UPON THYROID LIPIDS[a,b]

Treatment	Total lipid	Triglyceride	FFA	Free cholesterol
Controls	(11) 100 ± 14	(11) 89 ± 13	(10) 1.04 ± 0.16	(10) 0.80 ± 0.07
Two hours after TSH	(9) 162 ± 14 ($p < .01$)	(9) 143 ± 13 ($p < .025$)	(9) 5.58 ± 0.93 ($p < .001$)	(9) 1.55 ± 0.16 ($p < .001$)
After 7 days of TSH	(9) 112 ± 15	(9) 96 ± 14	(9) 2.96 ± 0.44 ($p < .001$)	(9) 1.65 ± 0.17 ($p < .001$)
After 10 weeks of PTU	(11) 48 ± 5 ($p < .005$)	(11) 37 ± 4 ($p < .005$)	(11) 1.20 ± 0.10	(11) 1.16 ± 0.09 ($p < .01$)

[a] In mg/100 mg of protein. Essentially the same relationships are obtained by calculating the values on the basis of tissue wet weight.

[b] Ave. ± sem. Number of determinations in parentheses. Statistical probability (p) calculated by comparison with control values.

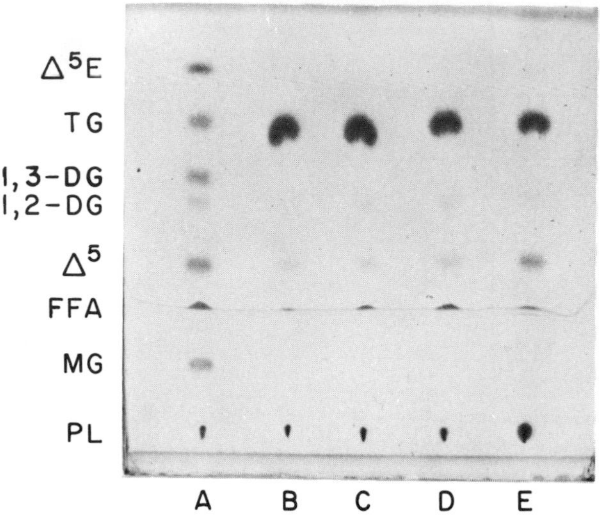

FIG. 6. Effect of treatment on the composition of lipids of rabbit thyroid. A. Lipid standards; B. Controls; C. Two hours after a single injection of TSH; D. After 7 daily TSH injections; E. After 10 weeks of oral PTU administration. Each column represents 120 μg of total lipid. Although comparatively abundant in the rabbit thyroid, Δ^5 represents only a small fraction of the total lipid because of the very high concentration of TG in this organ. Abbreviations as in Fig. 1.

TG, Δ^5, and Δ^5E fractions. Still larger quantities of label were incorporated by thyroid slices obtained after 7 days of treatment with TSH and after 10 weeks of treatment with PTU (3.7 and 3.9 times more than the amount incorporated by control slices, respectively, Figs. 8–11). Between 46 and 54% of the total ^{14}C incorporated into thyroid lipid was in the PL

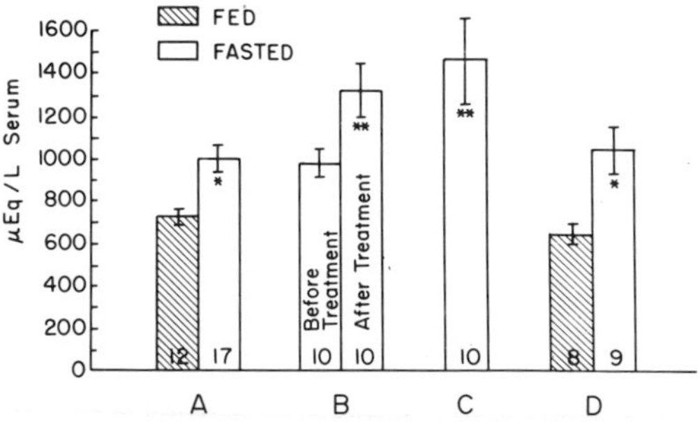

FIG. 7. Effect of treatment on the concentration of FFA in the serum of fed and fasted rabbits. A = controls; B = two hours after single injection of TSH; C = after 7 daily TSH injections; D = after 10 weeks of oral PTU administration. The number of observations is indicated on each bar. * $p < 0.05$ as compared to values found in fed animals. ** $p < 0.05$ as compared to values found in A or in the animals before treatment.

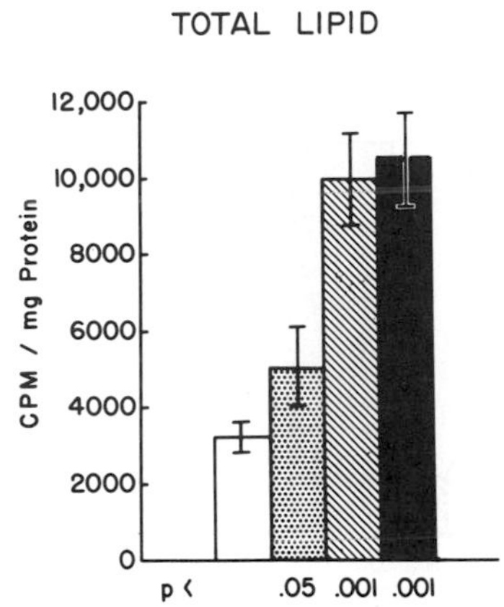

FIG. 8. Effect of treatment on the incorporation of acetate carbon into the total lipid rabbit thyroid. □ Controls (12); ▦ two hours after a single injection of TSH (11); ▧ after 7 daily TSH injections (9); ■ after 10 weeks of oral PTU administration.

(Fig. 12). Thus, regardless of the type of treatment, the radioactivity was about evenly divided between PL and neutral lipids. Two hours after a single injection of TSH, the amount of label incorporated into FFA was three times larger than the amount incorporated by the FFA of control glands. As a result of this effect, after TSH treatment, the FFA accounted for 12.3% of the total lipid radioactivity or significantly more than the 8.0% noted in control tissues (Fig. 13). The three forms of treatment also significantly stimulated the incorporation of ^{14}C in the MG and the DG fractions (Figs. 14 and 15). Figure 10 shows that the incorporation of ^{14}C into Δ^5 was unaffected by a single injection of TSH.

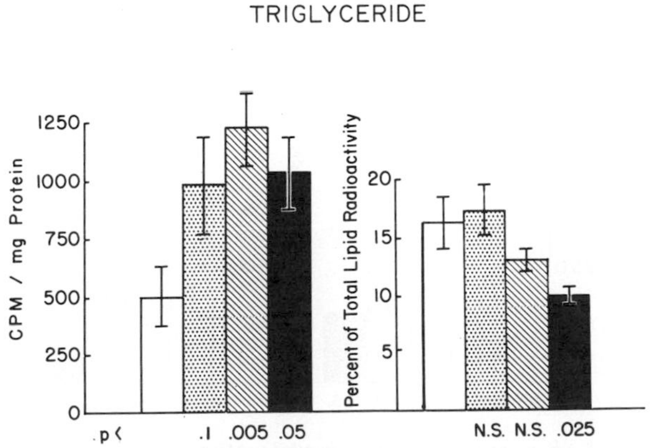

FIG. 9. Effect of treatment on the incorporation of acetate carbon into triglyceride. Symbols as in Fig. 8.

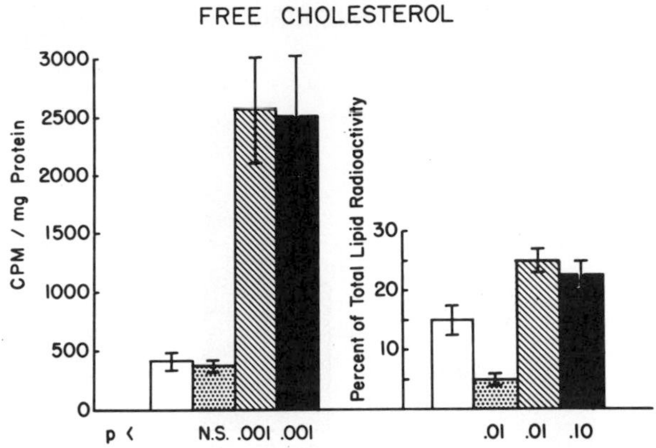

FIG. 10. Effect of treatment on the incorporation of acetate carbon into free cholesterol. Symbols as in Fig. 8.

Thus, in this case, compared to control tissues, Δ^5 accounted for a significantly smaller percentage of the total lipid ^{14}C activity. On the other hand, after prolonged treatment with TSH, the incorporation of ^{14}C into Δ^5 was increased 6.6 times above control levels, accounting for 24.1% of the total incorporated label. After prolonged treatment with PTU, the incorporation of label into Δ^5 had increased 6.4 times and accounted for 20.9% of the total. In fact, following both types of treatment, the relative increase in the ^{14}C activity of Δ^5 was greater than that of the PL, which increased only 3 to 4 times (Fig. 12). The ^{14}C activity of Δ^5E was also significantly increased by prolonged treatment with PTU. However, under no circumstances did the activity of Δ^5E represent more than 1.8% of the total ^{14}C incorporated into lipid (Fig. 11). Thus, the effects of

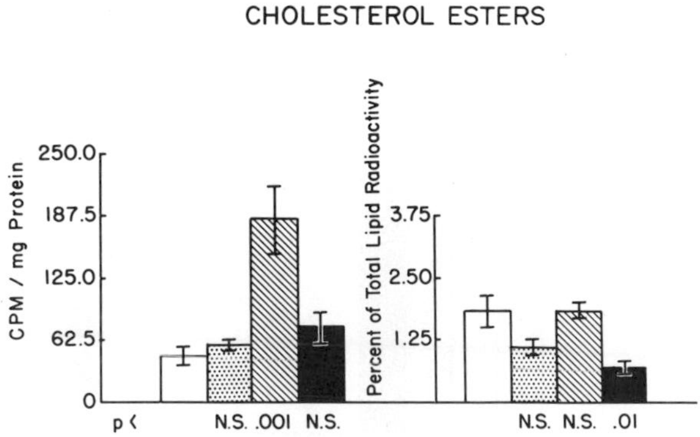

FIG. 11. Effect of treatment on the incorporation of acetate carbon into cholesterol ester. Symbols as in Fig. 8.

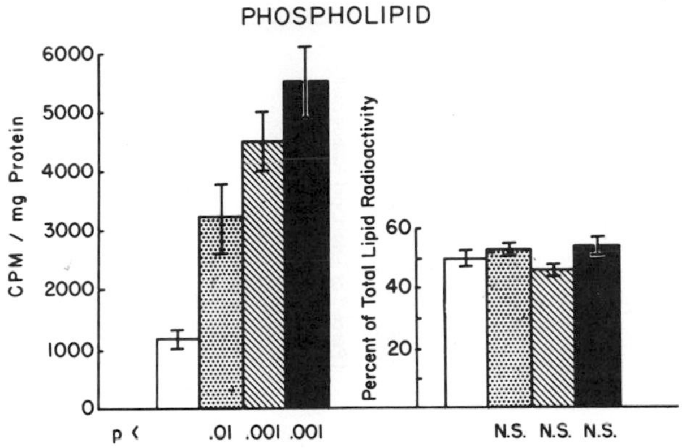

FIG. 12. Effect of treatment on the incorporation of acetate carbon into phospholipid. Symbols as in Fig. 8.

prolonged treatment with TSH on the incorporation of ^{14}C into the various lipid fractions by thyroid slices *in vitro* were very similar to those of prolonged treatment with PTU.

Table IV shows that the addition of glucose to the incubation medium stimulated the incorporation of ^{14}C into all the lipid fractions except the Δ^5 fraction of thyroids of treated rabbits. Indeed, in two out of three experiments, thyroid slices from rabbits treated with PTU and incubated with glucose, incorporated less ^{14}C into Δ^5 than paired slices incubated without glucose.

Table V shows that palmitic (16:0) and oleic (18:1) acids together represented 48% or more and linoleic (18:2) and stearic (18:0) acids together, another 18% or more of the fatty acids in PL and TG. Not more than 1.0% of the TG fatty acids were longer than 18 carbon atoms. PL

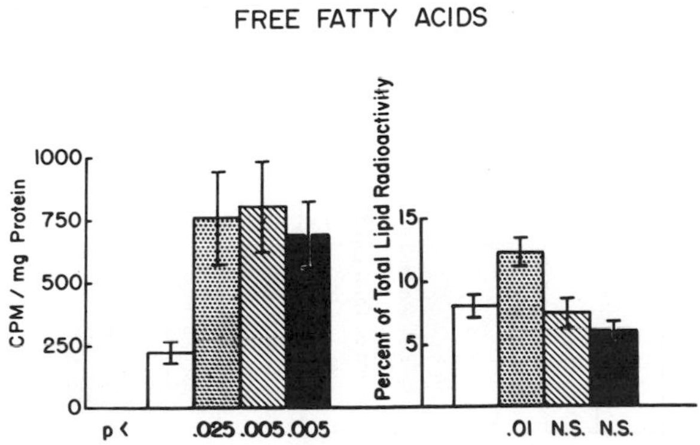

FIG. 13. Effect of treatment on the incorporation of acetate carbon into free fatty acid. Symbols as in Fig. 8.

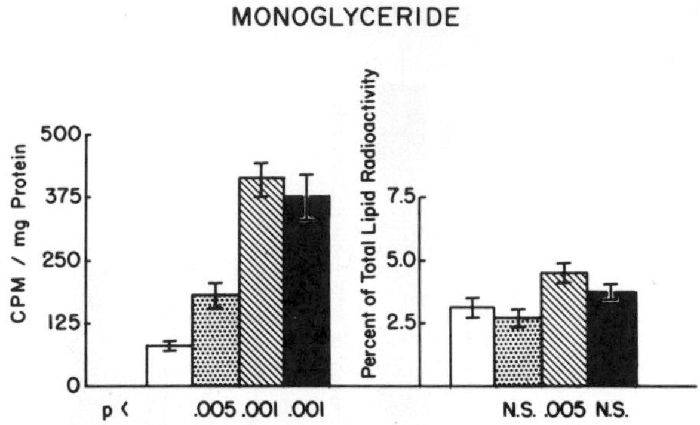

FIG. 14. Effect of treatment on the incorporation of acetate carbon into monoglyceride. Symbols as in Fig. 8.

contained the largest amount of fatty acids with 20 carbon atoms or more. Of these long chain fatty acids, arachidonic acid (20:4) was the most abundant and accounted for 4.9 to 13.1% of the total fatty acids but less than 0.5% of the fatty acids in TG. After a single injection of TSH or after treatment with TSH for 7 days the PL contained a significantly larger proportion of palmitic acid than the corresponding fractions from the thyroid of control rabbits and of rabbits treated with PTU. The type of treatment did not appear to influence the percentage of palmitic and oleic acid in the TG fractions.

Table VI shows that prolonged treatment with PTU resulted in a significant increase in the specific activity of thyroid TG, FFA, and Δ^5. Prolonged treatment with TSH had a similar effect, except that the increase in the specific activity of FFA did not reach the level of significance. On the other hand, 2 hours after a single injection of TSH, the

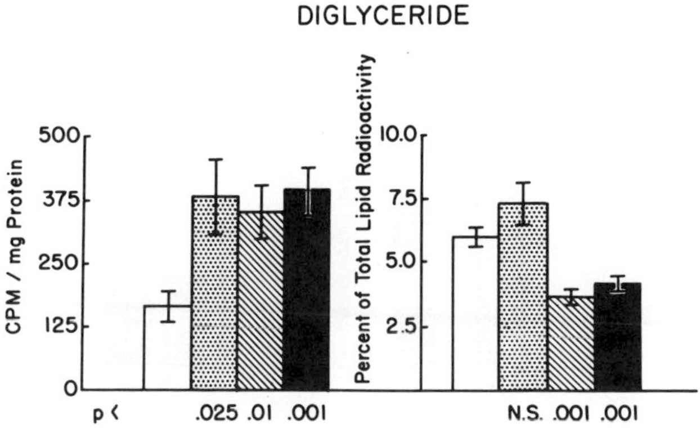

FIG. 15. Effect of treatment on the incorporation of acetate carbon into diglyceride. Symbols as in Fig. 8.

Table IV

EFFECT OF GLUCOSE UPON THE INCORPORATION OF ^{14}C INTO THYROID LIPIDS[a]

	Total lipid		Neutral lipid		Phospholipid		Free cholesterol	
	+	−	+	−	+	−	+	−
Controls	3725	1402	2012	587	1713	815	777	274
	3213	1475	1270	574	1943	901	141	101
	2728	351	1439	211	1289	140	482	114
Two hours after TSH	3943	1744	1898	852	2045	892	218	193
	1682	1465	781	753	901	712	83	142
	3171	2109	1305	855	1866	1254	233	120
After 10 weeks of PTU	17154	13688	10283	7156	6871	6532	5356	4465
	16085	9148	4501	5134	11584	4014	1033	1620
	9455	8680	4299	4146	5156	4534	1822	2148

[a] Cpm/mg protein of paired tissues incubated in Krebs–Ringer bicarbonate buffer with (+) and without (−) glucose (1.3 mg/ml). Three experiments of each type.

specific activity of TG and FFA did not change significantly while that of Δ^5 was significantly reduced.

IV. Discussion

The thyroid of the rabbit was found to be rich in TG, resembling in this respect, that of sheep (Scott and Beeston, 1966) and of man (Freinkel, 1964a,b). In the rabbit, most of the TG was in the adipocytes of the interstitial tissue, in close proximity to follicular cells. After incubation, thyroid slices excised from animals treated with a single injection of TSH contained more TG and more FFA than slices obtained from control animals, suggesting that TSH had stimulated the extraction of FFA from the blood. The FFA concentration in the serum of these animals was also significantly elevated. We believe that these changes in TG may have been facilitated by the lipolytic action of TSH upon adipose tissue, increasing the amount of available FFA.

There is substantial, even if indirect, evidence to support this hypothesis. Thus, TSH stimulates adipose tissue lipase (Rudman, 1965) and causes lipolysis (Freinkel, 1961; Rudman, 1965; Hart and McKenzie 1971), increasing the rate of FFA and glucose extraction by the thyroid (Goldsmith *et al.*, 1965). Adipose tissue lipolysis, induced by a variety of hormones, results in an accumulation of TG in liver and kidney (Grande and Prigge, 1970; De Oya *et al.*, 1971). TSH stimulates lipo-

Table V

Gas-Liquid Chromatographic Analysis of the Fatty Acids of Rabbit Thyroid Lipids[a]

	Phospholipid			
Fatty acid	Controls	Two hours after TSH	After 7 days of TSH	After 10 weeks of PTU
14:0	0.9 ± 0.24	1.3 ± 0.16	1.1 ± 0.07	0.5 ± 0.11
14:1	0.3 ± 0.15	0.6 ± 0.22	0.3 ± 0.13	0.2 ± 0.06
14:2	0.9 ± 0.10	0.4 ± 0.11	0.5 ± 0.07	1.7 ± 0.27
15:0	0.4 ± 0.12	0.9 ± 0.23	1.3 ± 0.57	0.3 ± 0.07
16:0	23.2 ± 2.93	31.4 ± 0.50[b]	33.3 ± 1.78[b]	22.6 ± 0.90
16:1	3.8 ± 0.70	4.9 ± 0.54	5.1 ± 1.23	3.2 ± 0.16
16:2	1.7 ± 0.47	1.2 ± 0.22	1.5 ± 0.15	1.8 ± 0.30
17:0	1.3 ± 0.57	2.4 ± 0.31	3.4 ± 0.66	0.8 ± 0.15
18:0	8.2 ± 1.18	11.0 ± 0.65	13.1 ± 0.46	8.6 ± 0.35
18:1	29.5 ± 2.09	19.9 ± 0.50[c]	24.8 ± 2.58	26.1 ± 0.74
18:2	13.4 ± 1.53	11.0 ± 0.99	8.2 ± 1.53	17.0 ± 0.82
18:3	0.5 ± 0.20	0.9 ± 0.43	0.3 ± 0.16	0.2 ± 0.08
20:0	0.4 ± 0.22	1.1 ± 0.37	0.4 ± 0.14	0.3 ± 0.13
20:2	1.0 ± 0.3	1.6 ± 0.44	0.7 ± 0.18	0.5 ± 0.06
20:3	Trace[d]	Trace	Trace	Trace
20:4	10.8 ± 1.03	10.6 ± 0.84	4.9 ± 0.82	13.1 ± 0.58
20:5	—	Trace	—	—
22:?	1.9 ± 0.69	—	—	1.9 ± 0.35
24:?	1.3 ± 0.47	—	0.7 ± 0.36	0.8 ± 0.30
Unknown	0.50	0.80	0.40	0.40
	Triglyceride			
Fatty acid	Controls	Two hours after TSH	After 7 days of TSH	After 10 weeks of PTU
14:0	4.3 ± 0.18	3.2 ± 0.22	4.3 ± 0.17	3.6 ± 0.17
14:1	0.9 ± 0.14	0.4 ± 0.07	0.4 ± 0.05	0.6 ± 0.06
14:2	Trace	—	Trace	0.1 ± 0.02
15:0	0.3 ± 0.03	0.4 ± 0.08	0.3 ± 0.07	0.4 ± 0.72
16:0	34.8 ± 2.02	33.6 ± 1.64	38.9 ± 0.84	27.9 ± 2.07
16:1	10.4 ± 0.75	7.3 ± 0.61	8.2 ± 0.66	9.2 ± 0.79
16:2	Trace	0.1 ± 0.04	0.2 ± 0.06	0.3 ± 0.13
17:0	0.6 ± 0.2	0.6 ± 0.12	0.8 ± 0.25	0.7 ± 0.18
18:0	7.3 ± 0.58	6.3 ± 0.94	5.1 ± 0.49	9.1 ± 0.67

Table V (*Continued*)

Fatty acid	Triglyceride: Controls	Two hours after TSH	After 7 days of TSH	After 10 weeks of PTU
18:1	27.0 ± 1.28	25.7 ± 0.88	23.5 ± 0.77	31.8 ± 1.25
18.2	11.4 ± 1.18	17.8 ± 1.25	14.4 ± 1.66	13.0 ± 1.26
18:3	2.2 ± 0.28	3.9 ± 0.48	2.7 ± 0.24	2.2 ± 0.87
20:0	—	—	—	—
20:2	—	0.3 ± 0.13	0.2 ± 0.03	0.3 ± 0.15
20:3	—	0.2 ± 0.10	—	—
20:4	—	—	—	0.4 ± 0.09
20:5	—	—	—	—
22:?	—	—	—	0.3 ± 0.10
24:?	—	—	—	—
Unknown	0.80	0.20	0.20	0.10

[a] Ave. ± sem. of six determinations in each group. Statistical probability (p) calculated by comparison with control values.

[b] $p < .05$. [c] $p < .01$.

[d] Average content represented less than 0.2% of the total fatty acids.

Table VI

EFFECT OF TREATMENT UPON THE SPECIFIC ACTIVITIES OF RABBIT THYROID NEUTRAL LIPIDS[a]

Treatment	Triglyceride	FFA	Free cholesterol
Controls	(11) 0.6 ± 0.09	(10) 21.2 ± 4.40	(11) 48.9 ± 11.19
Two hours after TSH	(9) 0.9 ± 0.28	(9) 19.5 ± 5.45	(9) 21.6 ± 4.80 ($p < .01$)
After 7 days of TSH	(11) 1.3 ± 0.25 ($p < .025$)	(11) 29.7 ± 4.26	(11) 134.7 ± 18.62 ($p < .001$)
After 10 weeks of PTU	(11) 2.6 ± 0.25 ($p < .001$)	(11) 59.2 ± 12.6 ($p < .025$)	(11) 194.7 ± 33.5 ($p < .005$)

[a] Cpm × 10^{-2}/mg lipid. Ave. ± sem. Number of determinations in parentheses. Statistical probability (p) calculated by comparison with control values.

genesis in thyroid slices when both FFA and glucose are provided Freinkel *et al.*, 1961) and finally, TG deposition in the thyroid may occur during starvation when the concentration of serum FFA is elevated (Freinkel, 1964a). The alternate hypothesis that the additional TG synthesized by the thyroid after a single injection of TSH was derived not from fatty acid, but from carbohydrate is unlikely because thyroid tissue contains only small quantities of glycogen (Merlevede *et al.*, 1963; Freinkel, 1964a; Ahn, 1971) and because exogenous glucose utilized by the thyroid for lipid synthesis is almost totally converted to glyceride–glycerol (Scott *et al.*, 1970) while in our experiments, most of the TG radioactivity was found in the fatty acid moiety.

After a single injection of TSH, the incorporation of ^{14}C into FFA had increased three-fold, representing the largest rise noted in any of the lipid fractions examined. Prolonged treatment with TSH or with PTU increased the level of FFA radioactivity to about the same extent as a single injection of TSH. Thus, an increase in the net biosynthesis of fatty acids appears to have been an early response to TSH and to have continued as long as the growth of the thyroid was stimulated either by TSH or by PTU. However, after prolonged treatment with TSH, while the level of FFA in the serum remained elevated and the radioactivity of the TG fraction continued to increase, the TG content of the thyroid returned toward control values. A combination of increased incorporation and decreased amount suggests that under these conditions, fatty acids were being utilized faster than they were being produced, perhaps because of the increased metabolic demand.

The increased incorporation of label into phospholipid suggests that fatty acids were also utilized for the synthesis of the cytostructural elements necessary for glandular growth. Another and possibly larger portion of fatty acids may have been degraded to acetyl-CoA, giving rise, eventually, to the increased amount of cholesterol found under these circumstances. A similar explanation could apply to the increased cholesterol synthesis observed following stimulation of thyroid growth with PTU, except that in this case, the major source of fatty acids probably was within the thyroid itself, as demonstrated by the decrease in the TG concentration of the thyroid and by the failure of the serum FFA concentration to increase.

As in most other mammalian tissues (Masoro, 1968), the predominant fatty acids in the rabbit thyroid were palmitic and oleic, followed by linoleic and stearic. The TG fraction contained only a small amount of fatty acids with more than 18 carbon atoms. The absence of long chain fatty acids is a characteristic of adipose tissue TG in most species, including man (Hirsch, 1962), and is additional evidence that the thyroid TG represents mostly storage fat. There were relatively more long chain fatty acids, mostly unsaturated, in the PL fraction. The most abundant of these was arachidonic acid. This difference in composition is consistent with the suggestion that TG and PL were derived from separate pools of DG precursors (Rhodes, 1964). An abundance of unsaturated fatty acids is characteristic of tissues actively engaged in metabolic processes (Rhodes, 1964), such as those stimulated to produce hormone or to grow.

Thyroid slices incubated in a medium containing glucose incorporated more acetate radiocarbon into lipid than paired thyroid slices incubated in the absence of glucose, regardless of whether the tissue was derived from control or from treated rabbits. This finding is consistent with previous observations (Freinkel and Scott, 1964; Scott *et al.*, 1966a) except that, according to these studies, the availability of glucose stimulated the synthesis of lipids in the resting thyroid, but had no net effect upon lipogenesis in the presence of TSH *in vitro*. It is possible that TSH given *in vivo*, may not have been bound to the membrane receptors as effectively as TSH added directly to the incubation medium (Pastan *et al.*, 1966). Another difference between our results and those of previous studies (Freinkel and Scott, 1964; Scott *et al.*, 1966b, 1968) is that in these experiments TSH preferentially stimulated the synthesis of 1,2 DG, indicating a selective effect on the synthesis of phospholipids, whereas, in our experiments, the synthesis of TG was stimulated as well, perhaps because of the constant supply of FFA available to the thyroid prior to its extirpation. Indeed, it has been demonstrated that when the incubation medium contained FFA as well as glucose, TSH also stimulated the synthesis of neutral lipids (Freinkel *et al.*, 1961; Freinkel, 1964a).

One dose of TSH did not alter the incorporation of ^{14}C into thyroid Δ^5, but significantly increased the Δ^5 content of the gland. Again, it is improbable that glucose may have been the source of this additional Δ^5, because the incorporation of ^{14}C into Δ^5 was not affected by the absence of glucose from the medium and because, when thyroid slices were incubated with TSH and with uniformly labeled glucose, only 2 to 8% of the total ^{14}C incorporated into lipid was found in Δ^5, Δ^5E, and FFA combined (Scott *et al.*, 1968). Rather, we believe that the increase in thyroid Δ^5, observed after an injection of TSH, may have been the result of an increased extraction of Δ^5 from the circulation by the hyperemic gland. On the other hand, the marked increase in the ^{14}C-activity of Δ^5, following prolonged treatment with TSH or with PTU, is best explained by an increased rate of Δ^5 synthesis from acetyl-CoA, derived from fatty acid oxidation. Since the synthesis of 1 mole of Δ^5 requires 18 moles of acetyl CoA, this reaction could prevent the accumulation of acetyl-CoA which otherwise would inhibit glucose metabolism (Lynen *et al.*, 1963;

Landau *et al.*, 1965; Masoro, 1965, 1968; Randle *et al.*, 1965; Tepperman and Tepperman, 1965; Weber *et al.*, 1966) and acetyl-CoA carboxylase activity and, hence, the synthesis of fatty acids (Masoro, 1965; Mayes and Felts, 1967). Perhaps here lies an explanation for the facts: "that the rates of fatty acid biosynthesis and cholesterol biosynthesis are negatively correlated and that the rates of fatty acid catabolism and cholesterol biosynthesis are positively correlated," interesting correlations that "do not provide much biochemical insight into the control mechanism [Masoro, 1968]." Another advantage of cholesterol biosynthesis would be the associated oxidation of NADPH to NADP, a necessary cofactor for the hexose monophosphate shunt (HMS) and for the HMS-dependent formation of iodotyrosine (Stanbury, 1957) and of ribose (Hall, 1963; Hall and Tubman, 1965). Additional NADP would continue to be derived from lipogenesis and from extra mitochondrial sources (Rous, 1971). Thus, the synthesis of cholesterol may play an important regulatory role in the metabolism of the thyroid and possibly of other tissues. Indeed, there is evidence that NADP generated from the synthesis of fatty acids is an important source of this cofactor (Leboeuf and Cahill, 1960; Flatt and Ball, 1966; Rous, 1971). In other tissues, such as the gonads and the adrenals, the increased availability of cholesterol and of NADPH would provide the substrate and the coenzyme necessary for the synthesis of steroid hormones (Dey *et al.*, 1972). These concepts are summarized in Fig. 16.

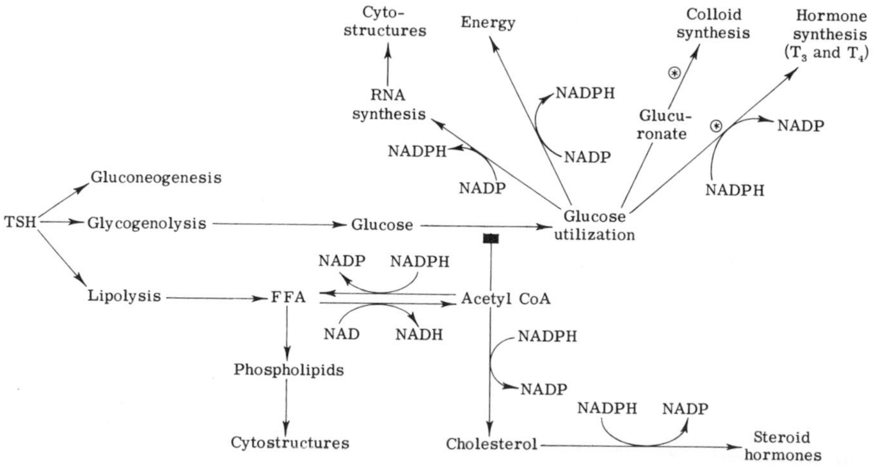

FIG. 16. By diverting acetyl-CoA to cholesterol, TSH would remove the inhibition to and provide the NADP necessary for glucose utilization. All reactions except those indicated by ⊛, may occur also in tissues other than the thyroid.

V. Summary

We have studied the lipids of the rabbit thyroid under normal conditions, 2 hours after an intravenous injection of thyroid stimulating hormone (TSH), after 7 days of daily subcutaneous injections of TSH, and after 10 weeks of treatment with propylthiouracil (PTU) given orally. The thyroids were excised, weighed, sliced, and incubated in Krebs–Ringer bicarbonate buffer with or without glucose and traces of acetate-1-^{14}C. Following incubation, the tissue lipids were extracted, fractionated, and analyzed by thin layer and gas-liquid chromatography. The radioactivity of the lipid fractions was measured by liquid scintillation. We also measured body weight and the concentration of free fatty acids (FFA) in the serum and determined by histologic techniques that treatment with TSH or PTU had caused the expected morphologic changes.

Most of the lipid was contained in the adipocytes of the thyroid interstitium, in close proximity to the follicular cells. Of the neutral lipid fractions, triglyceride (TG) was most abundant, followed by FFA, and cholesterol (Δ^5). The latter was almost entirely unesterified.

Two hours after an injection of TSH, the serum FFA concentration was increased and so was the TG and the FFA content of the thyroid. After 7 days of treatment with TSH, the serum FFA concentration increased and the thyroid contained still larger amounts of lipid, except that TG was reduced to normal levels. The serum FFA concentration of rabbits given PTU for 10 weeks was normal. These animals developed goiters that were rich in Δ^5, whereas TG was about half the normal concentration. In all thyroids, PL was the most active lipid fraction, accounting for about half of the total ^{14}C incorporation. One injection of TSH caused an increase in the radioactivity of all lipid fractions, except Δ^5. Seven days of TSH or 10 weeks of PTU treatment produced a further increase in PL radioactivity, but mostly affected the activity of Δ^5, which showed the largest proportionate increase. Incubation of thyroid slices in the absence of glucose, depressed the incorporation of ^{14}C into all lipid fractions, except the Δ^5 of stimulated thyroids.

An evaluation of our data in relation to those of other workers suggests the following interpretation: Two hours after an injection of TSH, the TG content of the thyroid increased because the TSH-induced lipolysis increased the amount of FFA available for esterification. During this initial phase of TSH stimulation there was a generalized increase in the turnover of all lipid moieties, except Δ^5, and fatty acid synthesis was accelerated. Glucose served as the primary oxidative substrate and provided glycerol for fatty acid esterification. Following prolonged TSH treatment, fatty acid synthesis was still elevated, but was overtaken by fatty acid catabolism. A significant fraction of the acetyl-CoA produced in this manner was converted to Δ^5, now produced in increased amounts. It is suggested that the synthesis of Δ^5, acting as an irreversible trap for acetyl-CoA, may serve to minimize the inhibitory effect that acetyl-CoA accumulation would have on glycolysis and on fatty acid biosynthesis and thus serve as a metabolic regulator in the thyroid and possibly, in other tissues.

References

Ahn, C.-S. (1971). *Endocrinology* **88**, 1341.

Blank, M. L., Schmit, J. A., and Privett, O. S. (1964). *J. Amer. Oil Chem. Soc.* **41**, 371.

Buscaino, V. M. (1914). *Riv. Istoch. Norm. Patol.* **1**, 171.

De Oya, M., Prigge, W. F., Swenson, D. E., and Grande, F. (1971). *Amer. J. Physiol.* **221**, 25.

Dey, S. K., Gupta, J. S., Ghosh, S., and Deb, C. (1972). *Acta Endocrinol.* (*Copenhagen*) **70**, 758.

Dole, V. P., and Meinertz, H. (1960). *J. Biol. Chem.* **235**, 259.

Erdheim, J. (1903). *Beitr. Pathol. Anat. Allg. Pathol.* **33**, 158.

Ferguson, J. A. (1933). *Arch. Pathol.* **15**, 244.

Flatt, J. P., and Ball, E. G. (1966). *J. Biol. Chem.* **241**, 2862.

Foà, C., Spallicci, M., and Giovanna, G. (1951). *Sci. Med. Ital.* **1**, 164.

Folch, J., Lees, M., and Stanley, G. H. S. (1957). *J. Biol. Chem.* **226**, 497.

Freeman, C. P., and West, D. (1966). *J. Lipid Res.* **7**, 324.

Freinkel, N. (1961). *J. Clin. Invest.* **40**, 476.

Freinkel, N. (1964a). *In* "Metabolism and Physiological Significance of Lipids" (R. M. C. Dawson and D. N. Rhodes, eds.), pp. 453–479. Wiley, New York.

Freinkel, N. (1964b). *In* "The Thyroid Gland" (R. Pitt-Rivers and W. R. Trotter, eds.), Ch. 7, Vol. 1. pp. 131–162, Butterworth, London.

Freinkel, N., and Saef, E. C. (1961). *Endocrine Soc. 43rd Meet., New York.*

Freinkel, N., and Scott, T. W. (1964). *Nature* (*London*) **204**, 1313.

Freinkel, N., Litojua, A. D., and Saef, E. C. (1961). *Nature* (*London*) **191**, 804.

Freinkel, N., Saef, E. C., Litonjua, A. D., and Arky, R. A. (1962). *Clin. Res.* **10**, 224.

Goldsmith, R. S., Ingbar, S. H., Bass, D. E., and Bigbee, H. (1965). *Curr. Top. Thyroid Res., Proc. Int. Thyroid Conf., 5th, Rome,* pp. 555–563.

Gossman, H. P. (1927). *Arch. Pathol. Anat. Physiol. Klin. Med.* **265**, 137.

Grafflin, A. L. (1939). *J. Morphol.* **65**, 207.

Grande, F., and Prigge, W. F. (1970). *Amer. J. Physiol.* **218**, 1406.

Haeberli, E. (1916). *Arch. Pathol. Anat. Physiol. Klin. Med.* **221**, 333.

Hall, R. (1963). *J. Biol. Chem.* **238**, 306.

Hall, R., and Tubman, J. (1965). *Curr. Top. Thyroid Res. Proc. Int. Thyroid Conf., 5th, Rome,* pp. 564–571.

Hart, I. R., and McKenzie, J. M. (1971). *Endocrinology* **88**, 26.

Hellwig, C. A., and Wilkinson, P. N. (1960). *Growth* **24**, 169.

Hellwig, C. A., and Wilkinson, P. N. (1962). *Growth* **26**, 297.
Hirsch, J. (1962). *Adipose Tissue Organ, Proc. Devel. Conf. Lipids, Carmel, Calif., 1961*, pp. 79–125.
Hofstetter, H. H., Sen, H., and Holman, R. L. (1965). *J. Amer. Oil Chem. Soc.* **42**, 537.
Iscovesco, H. (1908). *C. R. Soc. Biol.* **65**, 84, 106.
Iscovesco, H. (1912). *C. R. Soc. Biol.* **72**, 318.
Iscovesco, H. (1913). *C. R. Soc. Biol.* **75**, 361.
Jaffé, R. H. (1927). *Arch. Pathol.* **3**, 955.
Karwicka, M. D. (1911). *Beitr. Pathol. Anat. Allg. Pathol.* **33**, 158.
Landau, B. R., Katz, J., Bartsch, G. E., White, L. W., and Williams, R. H. (1965). *Ann. N. Y. Acad. Sci.* **131**, 43.
Langendorf, O. (1889). *Arch. Anat. Physiol., Physiol. Abt., Suppl.* B.D., 219.
Leboeuf, B., and Cahill, G. F. (1960). *Fed. Proc., Fed. Amer. Soc. Exp. Biol.* **19**, 226.
Lowry, O. H., Rosenbrough, N. J., Forr, A. L., and Randall, R. J. (1951). *J. Biol. Chem.* **193**, 265.
Lynen, F., Matsihashi, M., Nima, S., and Schweizer, T. (1963). *In* "The Control of Lipid Metabolism" (J. K. Grant, ed.), Biochemical Society Symposia, Vol. 24, pp. 43–55. Academic Press, New York.
McNair, H. M., and Bonelli, E. J. (1969). "Basic Gas Chromatography." Varian Aerograph Assoc. Consolidated Printers, Berkeley, California.
Masoro, E. J. (1965). *Ann. N. Y. Acad. Sci.* **131**, 199.
Masoro, E. J. (1968). "Physiological Chemistry of Lipids in Mammals," Ch. 11. Saunders, Philadelphia, Pennsylvania.
Mayes, P. A., and Felts, J. M. (1967). *Nature (London)* **215**, 716.
Merlevede, W., Weaver, G., and Landau, B. R. (1963). *J. Clin. Invest.* **42**, 1160.
Morrison, W. R., and Smith, L. M. (1964). *J. Lipid Res.* **5**, 600.
Noseda, I. (1934). *Zeit. Mikrosk.-Anat. Forsch.* **60**, 192.
Pastan, I., Roth, J., and Macchia, V. (1966). *Proc. Nat. Acad. Sci. U. S.* **56**, 1802.
Posner, I., and Ordonez, L. (1969). *Biochim. Biophys. Acta* **187**, 588.
Posner, I., and Ordonez, L. (1970). *Proc. Soc. Exp. Biol. Med.* **134**, 591.
Preto-Parvis, V., Roncoroni, G., and Ferrario-Agostini, A. (1954). *Riv. Istoch. Norm. Patol.* **1**, 171.
Randle, P. J., Garland, P. B., Newsholme, E. A., and Hales, C. N. (1965). *Ann. N. Y. Acad. Sci.* **131**, 324.
Rhodes, D. N. (1964). *In* "Metabolism and Physiological Significance of Lipids" (R. M. C. Dawson and D. N. Rhodes, eds.), pp. 621–624. Wiley, New York.
Rous, S. (1971). *Advan. Lipid Res.* **9**, 73.
Rudman, D. (1965). *Ann. N. Y. Acad. Sci.* **131**, 102.
Scott, T. W., and Beeston, J. W. B. (1966). *J. Lipid Res.* **7**, 455.
Scott, T. W., Jay, S. M., and Freinkel, N. (1966a). *Endocrinology* **79**, 591.
Scott, T. W., Good, B. F., and Ferguson, K. A. (1966b). *Endocrinology* **79**, 949.
Scott, T. W., Mills, S. C., and Freinkel, N. (1968). *Biochem. J.* **109**, 325.
Scott, T. W., Freinkel, N., Klein, J. H., and Nitzan, M. (1970). *Endocrinology* **87**, 854.
Stahl, E. (1965). "Thin Layer Chromatography," Ch. B. Academic Press, New York.
Stanbury, J. B. (1957). *J. Biol. Chem.* **228**, 801.
Tepperman, J., and Tepperman, H. M. (1965). *Ann. N. Y. Acad. Sci.* **131**, 404.

Turner, C. D. (1960). "General Endocrinology," 3rd Ed., p. 109. Saunders, Philadelphia, Pennsylvania.
Vilkki, P. (1962). *Arch. Biochem. Biophys.* **97**, 425.
Weber, G., Convey, H. J., Lea, M. A., and Stamm, N. B. (1966). *Science* **154**, 1357.
Wegelin, C. (1910). *Frankfurt. Z. Path.* **4**, 147.

Glycosyl Glycerides

P. S. SASTRY

Department of Biochemistry, Indian Institute of Science, Bangalore, India

I. Introduction

Since Thudichum's discovery of cerebroside, numerous lipids consisting of carbohydrate residues have been found in a variety of biological materials and these have generally come to be known as "glycolipids." Several structurally diverse lipids are included among the glycolipids and the "glycosyl glycerides" are a recent addition to this class of compounds. The glycosyl glycerides are structurally similar to phosphatides and are composed of carbohydrate residues glycosidically linked at the 3-position of *sn*-1,2-diglycerides. These lipids have also been described as monogalactosyl- and digalactosyl glycerol lipids (Carter *et al.*, 1961b), galactolipids (Benson *et al.*, 1958; Sastry and Kates, 1964b) or glycerogalactolipids (Rumsby, 1967), when the sugar moiety is galactose and more generally as glycosyl diglycerides (Vorbeck and Marinetti, 1965a) or glyceride glycolipids (Pieringer, 1968). As it is now known that a variety of carbohydrates constitute the sugar moieties of this class of lipids and as the diacyl-; and 1-alkyl, 2-acyl-analogs have been found, the term glycosyl glycerides (Carter *et al.*, 1965) would best describe this class of lipids.

Since their discovery a little over a decade ago, the glycosyl glycerides have been found to be widely distributed in plants, bacteria, and animal tissues. In the chloroplast and in certain bacteria, the glycosyl glycerides are quantitatively major lipid components. In animal tissues, the glycosyl glycerides seem to be confined to the nervous tissues, where they occur in significant amounts. Evidence has accumulated suggesting a fundamental role for these lipids in the photosynthetic apparatus and in myelin, though the precise function is far from clear. In this review, an account of the discovery, elucidation of structure, natural distribution, metabolism and functional role of the glycosyl glycerides is presented.

The plant sulfolipid, sulfoquinovosyl glyceride, discovered by Benson and co-workers (1959a), though included in the category of glycosyl glycerides, is not discussed here as the available information on this lipid has been reviewed (see Benson, 1963a; Kates, 1970).

II. Discovery and Elucidation of Structure

The first evidence for the occurrence of glycosyl glycerides was obtained in Carter's laboratory. Carter *et al.* (1956) isolated two lipocarbohydrate fractions from bleached wheat flour and on alkaline hydrolysis, each fraction yielded a mixture of galactosylglycerols. These were separated and identified by periodate oxidation and enzymatic cleavage as β-D-galactopyranosyl-1-glycerol and α-D-galactopyranosyl-$(1 \rightarrow 6)$-β-D-galactopyranosyl-1-glycerol. Earlier, a similar carbohydrate was shown to occur in several red algae (Colin and Gueguen, 1930) and in the marine algae *Irideae laminariodies* (Putman and Hassid, 1954), but this carbohydrate was shown to be α-D-galactopyranosyl-2-glycerol and it does not seem to occur as a glycosyl glyceride. Wickberg (1958a) found a glycoside in two other red algae, *Polysiphonia fastigata* and *Corillina officianalis*, and showed it to be α-D-galactopyranosyl-$(1 \rightarrow 6)$-β-D-galactopyranosyl-$(1 \rightarrow 1)$-glycerol, identical to one of the glycosides isolated from wheat flour. Due to substitution in the 1-position, the glycerol residue in the galactosyl glycerols is optically active. By comparison with chemically synthesized 1-glycerol-α- and β-galactosides in both D and L forms, Wickberg (1958a,b) established that the glycerol residue has the

D-configuration in the digalactosylglycerol isolated from red algae as well as from wheat flour. In the first report of Carter *et al.* (1956), neither the configuration of the glycerol moiety nor the number and nature of the fatty acid residues in the glycosyl glycerides of wheat flour were determined. Later, Mason and Johnston (1958) isolated a nearly pure digalactosyl glyceride from unbleached wheat flour, but here again the complete structure of the intact lipid was not deduced. From the experiments on photosynthesis of galactosyl glycerides in *Chlorella*, Benson *et al.* (1958) concluded that they existed as monoglycerides. Studies by Weenink (1959, 1961) on the lipids of forage grasses and red clover, similarly indicated that the galactosyl glycerides are derivatives of monoglycerides. The pure lipid components had not been separated in either of the above reports and the determination of the exact structure had to await the isolation of pure intact glycosyl glycerides. This was accomplished again by Carter *et al.* (1961a) and relatively pure monogalactosyl and digalactosyl glycerides were isolated from wheat flour. Subsequent studies on structure elucidation (Carter *et al.*, 1961b) have established the structures of the two galactosyl glycerides as 2,3-diacyl-1-β-D-galactopyranosyl-D-glycerol and 2,3-diacyl-1-(α-D-galactopyranosyl-(1 → 6)-β-D-galactopyranosyl)-D-glycerol and confirmed the D-configuration of glycerol in these glycolipids. By quite different techniques, Miyano and Benson (1962) arrived at the same D-configuration for the glycerol moiety of the galactosylglycerols of *Chlorella.*

In a number of studies, it was observed that galactosyl glycerides occur in high concentrations in *Chlorella* and that they are the major neutral lipids of the photosynthetic tissues (Benson *et al.*, 1958, 1959b; Wintermans, 1960). However, in contrast to earlier work, four glycolipids (designated as glycolipids a,b,c, and d) besides the plant sulfolipid, were identified by Kates (1959, 1960) in runner bean leaves by silicic acid paper chromatography. Deacylation and acid hydrolytic investigations showed the presence of glucose, galactose, and an unknown sugar, and it was inferred that runner bean leaf glycolipids have more complex structures than those deduced for the glycolipids of *Chlorella* (Kates, 1959). An essentially similar complexity was noted in the glycolipids of spinach leaves and chloroplasts by Zill and Harmon (1962). Subsequently, Sastry and Kates (1963, 1964a) isolated three pure glycolipid components from runner bean leaves by repeated silicic acid column chromatography and solvent fractionation. Two of these glycolipids were identified as monogalactosyl and digalactosyl diglycerides, while the third glycolipid was shown to be a glucocerebroside (Sastry and Kates, 1964a). Detailed structural analysis of the runner bean glycosyl glycerides has shown them to be 2,3-di-*O*-linolenoyl-1-*O*-β-D-galactopyranosyl-D-glycerol and 2,3-di-

O-linolenoyl-1-*O*-β-(6-*O*-α-D-galactopyranosyl-D-galactopyranosyl)-D-glycerol (Sastry and Kates, 1964b). The leaf lipids are thus identical to the wheat flour galactosyl diglycerides except for fatty acid composition. In the nomenclature of lipids recommended by the IUPAC-IUB Commission on Biochemical Nomenclature, the structures of monogalactosyl and digalactosyl diglycerides are 1,2-diacyl-3-*O*-β-D-galactopyranosyl-*sn*-glycerol and 1,2-diacyl-3-*O*-(α-D-galactopyranosyl-(1 → 6)-*O*-β-D-galactopyranosyl)-*sn*-glycerol, respectively (for chemical structures, see Fig. 1).

Since the discovery of monogalactosyl and digalactosyl diglycerides in plants, the occurrence of several structural analogs have been found in plants, animals, and particularly in bacteria; these are described in Section IV,A,B, and C.

III. Isolation and Analytical Methodology

A. Extraction

Glycosyl glycerides occur as membrane-bound lipid components in plant and animal tissues as well as in bacteria, presumably as lipoprotein complexes, and they are readily extracted along with phospholipids by procedures that ensure disruption of the lipid-protein bonds. This is best achieved by the use of polar organic solvents such as isopropanol, methanol, and ethanol and with mixtures of alcohols and chloroform. There are precautions that should be taken to obtain quantitative extraction of glycosyl glycerides, that is, to avoid enzymic degradation and loss due to autoxidation particularly in leaves where glycosyl glycerides occur in association with highly unsaturated fatty acids.

Various procedures that have been used for the extraction of total lipids from leaf or root tissue (Kates, 1970) are adequate to obtain glycosyl glycerides and these involve fragmentation of fresh tissue in a mortar under liquid nitrogen or Dry Ice and extraction of the powdered material with boiling isopropanol followed by chloroform in a Waring blender (Sastry and Kates, 1964a; Kates and Eberhardt, 1957). Blending fresh tissues with isopropanol at room temperature has also been used (Nichols, 1963, 1964; Galliard, 1968a). Extraction with boiling 95% ethanol followed by blending with chloroform-methanol mixtures (Weenink, 1964), extraction with methanol-chloroform (7:3) with gentle heating to 50°C (Roughan and Batt, 1968), or extraction with chloroform-methanol mixtures alone (O'Brien and Benson, 1964; Allen *et al.*, 1964) is effective with leaf tissues. Simple Soxhlet extraction with petroleum ether (30°–60°C) sufficed for the extraction of glycosyl glycerides from the seeds of *Briza spicata* (Smith and Wolff, 1966). A convenient procedure of extraction of lipids including glycosyl glycerides is that of Bligh and Dyer (1959); this method has been used with leaves (Helmsing, 1967a), cell fractions, and chloroplasts (Sastry and Kates, 1964c; Allen *et al.*, 1966a,b), algae (Sastry and Kates, 1965), and diatoms (Kates and Volcani, 1966).

Glycosyl glycerides of animal tissues are readily extracted with chloroform:methanol mixtures. The procedure of Folch *et al.* (1957) is most widely used for animal tissues (Norton and Brotz, 1963; Rumsby and Gray, 1965; Steim, 1967), and a slight modification of this procedure using lesser solvent to tissue ratio has been applied for the extraction of brain, brain fractions, and other tissues (Inouc *et al.*, 1971). Proteolipid-protein from total lipid extract of brain tissue is usually removed by repeated drying of the extract at 60° in the presence of water, but in our experience, washing with 0.1 *M* tripotassium citrate by the procedure of Webster and Folch (1961) is more convenient.

Moist or freeze-dried bacterial cells may be extracted by stirring with chloroform:methanol (2:1 v/v) at room temperature (Brundish *et al.*, 1965c; Reeves *et al.*, 1964). Complete extraction of bacterial lipids may also be achieved by heating the wet cells with methanol at 60–65° for 5 minutes with a solvent to cell material ratio of 10:1, followed by the addition of chloroform to give a final chloroform-methanol concentration of 2:1 (v/v) (Vorbeck and Marinetti, 1965a; Exterkate and Veerkamp, 1969).

Crude lipid extracts are usually purified by washing with water or salt solutions according to the Folch *et al.* (1957) method, but this might cause losses of more hydrophilic glycolipids into the aqueous phase (Shaw, 1970). Removal of nonlipid contaminants by filtration through Sephadex G-25 (Wells and Dittmer, 1963) may be more satisfactory.

B. Isolation Procedures

A variety of techniques have been used for the large-scale isolation of glycosyl glycerides from the total lipid extracts and these include precipitation with solvents, countercurrent distribution and column chromatography on silicic acid, Florisil, diethylaminoethyl cellulose, and a carbon-Celite preparation. None of the methods listed above when used alone is adequate to achieve the isolation of pure compounds, and a combination of several techniques is usually necessary.

Removal of phospholipids from the total lipid extracts by precipitation with cold acetone has been used as a step in the isolation of glycosyl diglycerides (Sastry and Kates, 1964b; Weenink, 1964; Rumsby and

Gray, 1965; Steim, 1967). This method does not effect a complete separation of these glycolipids from phospholipids in plant tissue extracts. While most of the monogalactosyl diglyceride is found in the acetone-soluble fraction, a significant amount of digalactosyl diglyceride with a more saturated fatty acid composition is usually precipitated with phospholipids (Sastry and Kates, 1964b; Weenink, 1964). Similar losses of monogalactosyl glyceride during acetone precipitation of phospholipids also occur with brain tissue (Rumsby and Rossiter, 1968).

Countercurrent distribution may be used with leaf and seed lipid extracts, as a preliminary step to obtaining a gross separation of the nonpolar lipids (chlorophyll, pigments, glycerides) from more polar, electrically neutral lipids (galactosyl glycerides, lecithin, phosphatidylethanolamine) and highly polar and acidic lipids (digalactosyl diglyceride, phosphatidyl glycerol, sulfolipid, phosphatidyl inositol) with solvent systems such as carbon tetrachloride-methanol-water 65:25:4 (Allen *et al.*, 1964, 1966a); or petroleum ether (b.p. 80–100°)-95% aqueous methanol (Nichols, 1964). Countercurrent distribution with hexane-90% methanol as the solvent system has been successfully used in the isolation of monogalactosyl and digalactosyl glycerides from seeds which have an abundance of these lipids (Smith and Wolff, 1966).

Column chromatography is by far the most useful technique in the separation of glycosyl glycerides from other lipids. The monoglycosyl glycerides may be eluted from silicic acid columns with acetone or 25–50% acetone (Vorbeck and Marinetti, 1965a; Rumsby and Rossiter, 1968) or 2–5% methanol in chloroform while the diglycosyl glycerides require 10% methanol in chloroform for elution (Sastry and Kates, 1964b; Brundish *et al.*, 1965c). Chromatography on diethylaminoethyl cellulose or Florisil (Rouser *et al.*, 1967) is quite effective and generally, repeated chromatography on the same or different adsorbent is necessary to obtain pure glycosyl glycerides. For example, use of Florisil, diethylaminoethyl cellulose, and silicic acid columns in succession has been employed for the isolation of galactosyl diglycerides from *Chlorella pyrenoidosa* and alfalfa (O'Brien and Benson, 1964), but the yields with this procedure are low. Better yields may be obtained by repeated chromatography on silicic acid or on carbon-Celite columns (Van der Veen *et al.*, 1967). A simple batch elution procedure with various solvent mixtures after adsorption on silica gel, a procedure that is rapid and yields glycosyl glycerides of reasonable purity has been described (DeStefanis and Ponte, 1969). It may be used when starting materials are abundant and quantitative isolation is not the objective. Chromatography on Sephadex LH-20 may also be used for the purification and isolation of these glycolipids (Helmsing, 1967b; Maxwell and Williams, 1968a,b). Phospholipid contaminants in trace amounts in the purified glycosyl glyceride fractions may be removed by passage through Amberlite MB-3 (Sastry and Kates, 1964b).

C. Analytical Methods

1. *Separation of Glycosyl Glycerides*

The analytical separation and small-scale isolation of the glycosyl glycerides from the total lipid extracts are best achieved by thin-layer chromatography on silica gel (Nichols, 1964; Nichols and James, 1964; Renkonen and Varo, 1967). This method is particularly useful in studies with plant tissues where these lipids are relatively abundant rather than with bacteria and animal tissues. Several solvent systems effect a good separation of the glycosyl glycerides from other lipids and phospholipids; these lipids may be visualized with iodine, sulfuric acid spray, or with the more specific periodate-Schiff reagent (Baddiley *et al.*, 1956) or diphenylamine spray (Wagner *et al.*, 1961). The most commonly used solvent systems are (1) chloroform-methanol-water (62:25:4) (Lepage, 1964), (2) chloroform-methanol-7 *N* NH_4OH (60:25:4) (Nichols, 1964), (3) chloroform-methanol-acetic acid-water (65:15:10:4) (Nichols, 1964), (4) diisobutyl ketone-acetic acid-water (40:25:3.7) (Nichols, 1963) or (80:50:10) (Lepage, 1964). In addition, acetone-acetic acid-water (100:2:1) (Gardner, 1968) and acetone-benzene-water (91:30:8) (Pohl *et al.*, 1970) give a good separation of glycosyl glycerides from all other lipids. In the acidic or basic chloroform-methanol solvent systems, the R_f of monogalactosyl diglyceride ranges from 0.77–0.88 and sometimes does not separate well from pigments. Better separation of monogalactosyl diglyceride may be obtained with diisobutyl ketone-acetic acid-water system where the R_f is about 0.51 (Lepage, 1964). The separation of digalactosyl diglyceride from phosphatidyl choline is also not adequate in unidimensional thin-layer chromatography with chloroform-methanol systems. However, Clayton *et al.* (1970) achieved excellent separation of monogalactosyl diglyceride, digalactosyl diglyceride, and 6-*O*-acyl monogalactosyl diglyceride from all other lipids in wheat flour by unidimensional chromatography on silica gel with chloroform-methanol-ammonia (30% w/v)-water (60:35:5:2.5) solvent. Complete separation of all the lipid components from plant tissues may also be obtained by two-dimensional chromatography with chloroform-methanol-7 *N* NH_4OH (65:30:4) in the first direction and chloroform-methanol-acetic acid-water (170:75:25:6) in the second direction (Nichols, 1964). Equally good separations may be obtained with chloroform-methanol-

Table I

PAPER AND GAS-LIQUID CHROMATOGRAPHIC DATA OF GLYCOSYLGLYCEROLS

Glycosylglycerol	Pyridine:ethyl acetate:water 4:10:10 (v/v) upper phase		Butanol: pyridine:water 6:4:3 (v/v)		Phenol: water 5:2 (w/w)	Butanol: propionic acid:water 151:75:110 (v/v)	Gas-liquid chromatography of trimethylsilyl derivatives on 150 cm 3% SE-52 column	
	R_{Glc}	R_{Gal}	R_f	$R_{Glc(1)}$	R_f	R_f	185° $T^1(1)$	255° T^2 (1)
O-α-D-Glcp-(1 → 1)-D-glycerol				1.00			1.0	
O-β-D-Glcp-(1 → 1)-D-glycerol				1.02			1.36	
O-α-D-Glcp-(1 → 1)-L-glycerol				1.00			1.00	
O-β-D-Glcp-(1 → 1)-L-glycerol				1.00			1.36	
O-α-D-Galp-(1 → 1)-D-glycerol				0.86			0.97	

O-β-D-Galp-(1 → 1)-D-glycerol		0.8 (4)		0.85	0.62 (2)	0.25 (2)	1.08	
					0.65 (3)	0.24 (3)		
O-α-D-Galp-(1 → 2)-α-D-Glcp-(1 → 1)-D-glycerol				0.43				1.00
O-β-D-Glcp-(1 → 2)-α-D-Glcp-(1 → 1)-D-glycerol				0.57				1.06
O-β-D-Glcp-(1 → 2)-β-D-Glcp-(1 → 1)-D-glycerol				0.65				0.93
O-β-D-Glcp-(1 → 3)-D-Glcp-(1 → 1)-D-glycerol				0.79				0.91
O-β-D-Glcp-(1 → 4)-β-D-Glcp-(1 → 1)-D-glycerol				0.43				1.10
O-β-D-Glcp-(1 → 6)-β-D-Glcp-(1 → 1)-D-glycerol				0.49				1.33
O-α-D-Glcp-(1 → 2)-α-D-Glcp-(1 → 1)-L-glycerol				0.52				1.07
O-α-D-Glcp-(1 → 2)-α-D-Glcp-(1 → 1)-D-glycerol	0.82 (5)		0.2 (5)	0.53				1.06
O-α-D-Galp-(1 → 6)-β-D-Galp-(1 → 1)-D-glycerol		0.2 (4)			0.46 (2)	0.13 (2)		
					0.50 (3)	0.10 (3)		
O-α-D-Galp-(1 → 6)-α-D-Galp-(1 → 6)-β-D-Galp-(1 → 1)-D-glycerol					0.38 (2)	0.04 (2, 3)		
					0.35 (3)			

KEY: T^1 = Elution time relative to that of α-D-Glcp-(1 → 1)-D-glycerol; T^2 = Elution time relative to that of α-D-Galp-(1 → 2)-α-D-Glcp-(1 → 1)-D-glycerol; R_{Glc} = Mobility relative to that of glucose; R_{Gal} = Mobility relative to that of galactose.

Numbers in parentheses are references: (1) Brundish and Baddiley (1968); (2) Ferrari and Benson (1961); (3) Galliard (1969); (4) Sastry and Kates (1964b); (5) Pierienger (1968).

water (65:25:4) in the first direction and diisobutyl ketone-acetic acid-water (80:50:10) in the second direction (Lepage, 1964). With hexane-ether-acetic acid (90:14:1) as the developing solvent, the glycosyl glycerides remain at the origin and triple development in this solvent may be used to separate labeled neutral lipid precursors (fatty acids, diglycerides) in incorporation studies. The glycosyl glycerides may then be fractionated by development with chloroform-methanol-acetic acid-water (170:25:25:6) in the second direction (Bajwa and Sastry, unpublished experiments).

Glycosyl glycerides may also be separated on silicic acid impregnated paper by the Marinetti procedure (see Kates, 1967), the method applied in earlier investigations on leaf glycolipids (Sastry and Kates, 1964b). A number of solvent systems for chromatography on silicic acid impregnated paper (Whatman SG 81) have been described that may be useful in the identification of glycosyl glycerides (Wenger *et al.*, 1970).

2. *Analysis of the Products of Hydrolysis*

a. Glycosylglycerols. For the elucidation of structure and also for quantitative determination, the glycosyl glycerides are usually subjected to hydrolytic procedures. On mild alkaline hydrolysis (Dawson, 1967), the glycosyl glycerides yield the corresponding glycosylglycerols that may be further hydrolyzed to the component sugars and glycerol with 2 *N* HCl for 4 hours at 100°C (Sastry and Kates, 1964b).

The glycerol glycosides and the sugar moieties may be identified by paper chromatography or by gas-liquid chromatography. The relative mobilities of some of the glycosides on paper chromatograms in different solvent systems are recorded in Table I. The glycerol glycosides may also be analyzed as their *O*-trimethylsilyl ether derivatives by gas-liquid chromatography, and a comparison of the elution times of several glycosides (Table I) shows that this technique may be applied in the identification of naturally occurring glycosyl glycerides. This technique distinguishes the positional isomers of diglycosylglycerols as well as anomers of glycosylglycerols, but not the diastereomers (Steim, 1967; Brundish and Baddiley, 1968).

b. Fatty Acids. The fatty acid composition of glycosyl glycerides may be determined by gas-liquid chromatography of the methyl esters obtained by methanolysis of the glycolipids (Kates, 1964b; James, 1960; Stein *et al.*, 1967).

3. *Separation of Molecular Species*

The molecular species of glycosyl glycerides may be separated by argentation thin-layer chromatography (Nichols and Moorhouse, 1969;

Eccleshall and Hawke, 1971) or by gas-liquid chromatography of the trimethylsilyl derivatives of hydrogenated intact lipids (Auling *et al.*, 1971).

4. *Quantitative Estimation*

The quantitative estimation of glycosyl glycerides is usually carried out by determining the sugar content either by the anthrone method (Morris, 1948) or by the phenol-sulfuric acid method (Dubois *et al.*, 1956). The estimation may be done on the intact lipids or on the glycosylglycerols obtained by deacylation. Determination of the sugar content of the intact glycolipids may also be done in the presence of silica gel (Roughan and Batt, 1968). Glycosylglycerols have been quantitatively estimated by gas-liquid chromatography of their *O*-trimethysilyl ether derivatives with maltose as an internal standard. The limit of assay accuracy for the gas-liquid chromatographic technique is about 5 nmoles/gm of wet weight tissue (Inoue *et al.*, 1971).

IV. Occurrence and Distribution

A. Plants

1. *Monogalactosyl and Digalactosyl Diglycerides*

a. Quantitative and Qualitative Distribution. Monogalactosyl and digalactosyl diglycerides, originally discovered in wheat flour by Carter *et al.* (1956), have since been found to be widely distributed in a variety of plant tissues. The total lipid content of plant tissues varies from about 10% in leaves to about 35–40% in the chloroplasts and unicellular algae on a dry weight basis and the glycosyl glycerides, including the sulfoquinovosyl diglyceride account up to 40% of the total lipids (Kates, 1970). Thus monogalactosyl- and digalactosyl glycerides are the major lipid components in photosynthetic tissues. Their chemical structures are given in Fig. 1. However, their relative quantitative distribution varies among the plant tissues and the available data are summarized in Table II. In higher plants, leaves contain monogalactosyl- and digalactosyl diglycerides in concentrations ranging from about 0.6 to 15 μmole/gm and 0.5 to 7 μmole/gm fresh weight, respectively. Their occurrence is not limited to the photosynthetic tissues only and these glycolipids have also been found in fruits, seeds, roots, and tubers in usually lesser amounts (Table II). Monogalactosyl- and digalactosyl diglycerides have been detected in the flowerbuds of the cotton plant, *Gossypium hirsutum* (Thompson and Hedin, 1965; Thompson *et al.*, 1968); in the cereal: bajra,

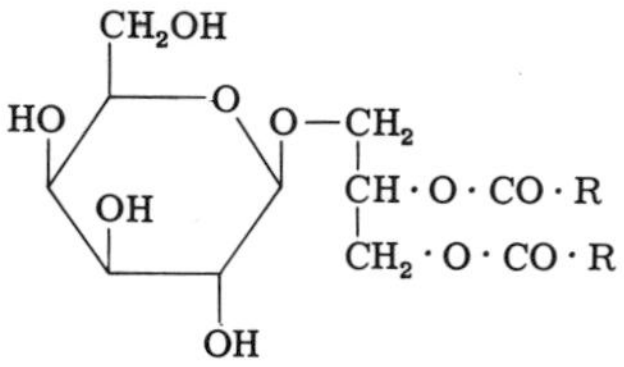

(a) Monogalactosyl diglyceride (1,2-diacyl-3-*O*-β-D-galactopyranosyl-*sn*-glycerol)

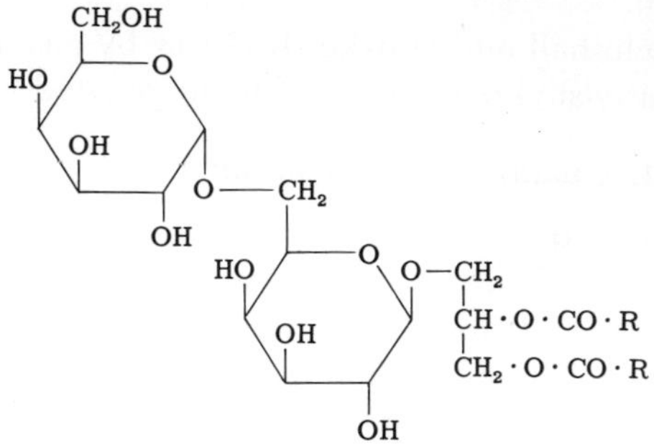

(b) Digalactosyl diglyceride [1,2-diacyl-3-*O*-(α-D-galactopyranosyl-(1 → 6)-*O*-β-D-galactopyranosyl)-*sn*-glycerol]

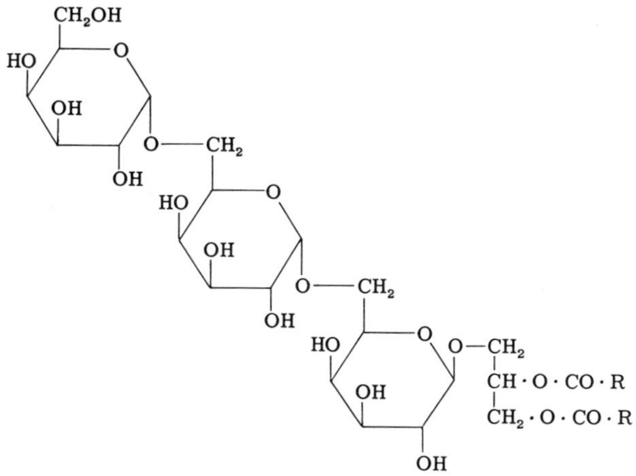

(c) Trigalactosyl diglyceride [1,2-diacyl-3-*O*-(α-D-galactopyranosyl-(1 → 6)-*O*-α-D-galactopyranosyl-(1 → 6)-*O*-β-D-galactopyranosyl)-*sn*-glycerol]

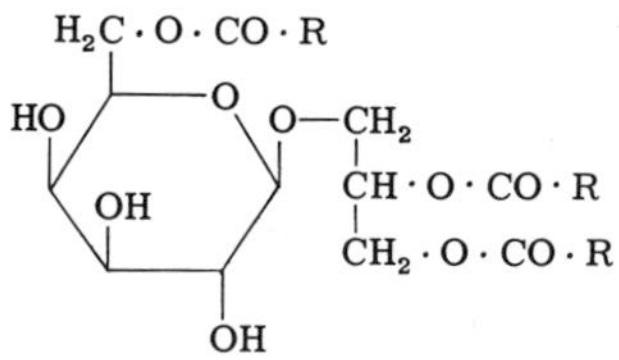

(d) 6-*O*-Acyl monogalactosyl diglyceride

FIG. 1. Structures of plant galactosyl glycerides.

Table II
Distribution of Monogalactosyl Diglyceride (MGD) and Digalactosyl Diglyceride (DGD) in Plant Tissues

Plant tissue	MGD µmoles/gm wet weight	MGD % total lipid	DGD µmoles/gm wet weight	DGD % total lipid	Molar ratio MGD:DGD	Ref.[c]
Leaves						
Runner bean (*Phaseolus multiflorus*)	2.02	16.6	0.4	4.0	5.1	(1)
Red clover (*Trifolium pratense*)	8.76		5.84		1.5	(2)
Soybean (*Glycine soja*)	7.12		4.84		1.47	(2)
Oriental cocklebur (*Xanthium*	3.64		2.74		1.33	(2, 3)
orientale)	6.10		5.90		1.03	
Perennial ryegrass (*Lolium*	6.76		4.12		1.64	(2, 3)
perenne)	5.10		3.95		1.29	
Blechnum fluviatile	5.60		2.30		2.44	(3)
Maidenhair tree (*Ginkgo biloba*)	4.70		2.80		1.68	(3)
Pinus radiata	2.80		1.96		1.43	(3)
Rose (*Rosa Cv*)	5.6		4.6		1.22	(3)
Rowan (*Sorbus aucuparia*)	10.2		7.16		1.42	(3)
White clover (*Trifolium repens*)	8.6		5.2		1.65	(3)
Lucerne (*Medicago sativa*)	8.6		5.2		1.65	(3)
Poplar (*Populus italica*)	4.95		3.8		1.3	(3)
Camellia japonica	3.10		3.10		1.0	(3)
Squash (*Cucurbita pepo*)	4.10		2.70		1.52	(3)
Tomato (*Solanum lycopersicum*)	5.08		2.46		2.06	(3)
Lettuce (*Lactuca sativa*)	0.68		0.68		1.0	(3)
Cocksfoot (*Dactylis glomerata*)	8.00		5.10		1.57	(3)
Paspalum dilatatum	6.00		3.60		1.67	(3)
Maize (*Zea mays*)	3.10		2.30		1.35	(3)
Pumpkin	6.4		4.2		1.52	(4)
Sugar beet (*Beta vulgaris*)	2.4		1.3		1.85	(5)
Elder (*Sambucus nigra*)	5.6		2.6		2.16	(5)
Alfalfa	5.95[a,b]	4.3	9.94[a,b]	8.6	0.6	(6)
Alfalfa (*Medicago sativa*)		11.7		8.0		(7)
Broad bean (*Vicia faba* L.)					1.42	(8)
Barley						
green	1.48		1.09		1.36	(9)
etiolated	0.66		0.49		1.35	(9)
Mango (*Mangifera indica*)	5.3		4.0		1.33	(10)
Poinciana regia	5.5		4.5		1.22	(10)
Bouganvillea spp.	7.9		4.25		1.86	(10)
Eucalyptus rostrata	14.6		4.25		3.44	(10)
Tecoma stans	8.3		4.8		1.73	(10)
Cauliflower (*Brassica oleracea*)	2.0		0.8		2.5	(10)
Radish (*Raphanus sativus*)	1.9		0.9		2.11	(10)
Xanthium leaf	2.8		1.9		1.47	(11)

Table II (*Continued*)

Plant tissue	MGD µmoles/gm wet weight	MGD % total lipid	DGD µmoles/gm wet weight	DGD % total lipid	Molar ratio MGD:DGD	Ref.[c]
Spinach leaf	2.7		1.5		1.8	(11)
Dryopteris filix—mas		15.0		11.0		(12)
Antirrhinum majus		25.5		20.0		(12)
Fruits						
Cucumber	0.03[a]	2.4	0.05[a]	4.7	0.6	(13)
Green pepper	0.12[a]	2.4	0.27[a]	6.6	0.44	(13)
Apple pulp						
preclimacteric	0.054	4.8	0.114	12.2	0.47	(14)
postclimacteric	0.015	1.3	0.052	5.3	0.29	(14)
Seeds						
Briza spicata	73.1[a]	29.0	102.1[a]	49.0	0.72	(15)
Roots and tubers						
Parsnip root (*Pastinaca sativa*)	0.17		0.34		0.5	(3)
Potato tuber (*Solanum tuberosum*)	0.092	5.7	0.185	14.2	0.5	(16)
Sweet potato tubers		13.6		6.3		(17)
Algae						
Anacystis nidulans	42.6[a,b]	30	12.8[a,b]	12	3.32	(18)
Chlorella pyrenoidosa	18.1[a,b]	4.2	25.6[a,b]	7.2	0.71	(6)
Mesotaenium caldariorum	10.0		5.5		1.82	(3)
Ulva lactuca	53[a,b]		66.2[a,b]		0.8	(19)
Enteromorpha intestinalis	51.7[a,b]		96.0[a,b]		0.54	(19)
Fucus vesiculosus		7.3		6.4		(12)
Batrachospermum moniliforme		11.6		11.7		(12)
Cyanidium caldarium	19.7[b]		20.2[b]		0.98	(20)
Cyanidium caldarium						
20°C	2.14[b]		1.89[b]		1.13	(21)
55°C	0.29[b]		0.48[b]		0.6	(21)
Mosses and liverworts						
Moss (mixture of *Furoria* and *Leptobryium pyriforme*)	2.68		1.5		1.78	(3)
Marchantia bertoroana	1.07		0.66		1.62	(3)

[a] Molecular weight of MGD and DGD was assumed to be 774 and 936, respectively.

[b] Micromoles per gram dry weight.

[c] Key to references: (1) Sastry and Kates (1964b); (2) Roughan and Batt (1968); (3) Roughan and Batt (1969); (4) Roughan (1970); (5) Wintermans (1960); (6) O'Brien and Benson (1964); (7) Van der Veen *et al.* (1967); (8) Maxwell and Williams (1968b); (9) Gardner (1968); (10) Bajwa and Sastry (unpublished data); (11) Wintermans (1963); (12) Radunz (1969); (13) Kinsella (1971); (14) Galliard (1968b); (15) Smith and Wolff (1966); (16) Galliard (1968a); (17) Walter *et al.* (1971); (18) Hirayama (1967); (19) Brush and Percival (1972); (20) Allen *et al.* (1970); (21) Kleinschmidt and McMahon (1970).

Pennisetum typhoideum (Pruthi and Bhatia, 1970), in buckwheat, *Fagopyrium sagitatum* (Obara and Miyata, 1969); in rape seeds, *Brassica napus* and *Crambe abyssinica* (McKillican, 1966; Appelqvist, 1972); in soybeans (Singh and Privett, 1970); in tomato and turnip roots (Willemot and Boll, 1967; Lepage, 1967); and in Narcissus bulbs (Nichols and James, 1964). The seed *Briza spicata* contains an unusually high amount of both mono- and digalactosyl diglycerides (Smith and Wolff, 1966). In lower plants, the occurrence of these two glycolipids has been shown in blue green algae: *Anacystis nidulans* and *Anabaena variabilis* (Levin *et al.*, 1964; Nichols *et al.*, 1965; Hirayama, 1967); euglenids (Rosenberg, 1963; Rosenberg and Gouaux, 1967); green algae: *Chlorella pyrenoidosa* (Ferrari and Benson, 1961; O'Brien and Benson, 1964), *Chlorella vulgaris* (Nichols, 1965a), *Ulva lactuca, Enteromorpha intestinalis, Cladophora rupestris, Urospora, Codium fragile, Monostroma gravellei, Mongeotia, Acetabularia crenulata* (Brush and Percival, 1972), and *Mesotaenium caldariorum* (Roughan and Batt, 1969); diatoms: *Navicula pelliculosa, Cylindrotheca fusiformis, Cyclotella cryptica, Nitzschia angularis, Nitzschia thermalis,* and *Phaeodactylum tricornutum* (Kates and Volcani, 1966, 1968); dinoflagellate: *Gonyaulax polyedra* (Patton *et al.*, 1966); brown alga: *Fucus vesiculosus;* red alga: *Batrachospermum moniliforme* (Radunz, 1969); in the acidophilic and thermophilic alga: *Cyanidium caldarium* (Allen *et al.*, 1970; Kleinschmidt and McMahon, 1970); in mosses and liverworts (Roughan and Batt, 1969).

In the photosynthetic tissues of higher plants, the molar concentration of monogalactosyl diglyceride is generally much higher than digalactosyl diglyceride. In contrast, the nonphotosynthetic tissues of plants and most unicellular algae show a preponderance of digalactosyl diglyceride.

b. Fatty Acid Composition. A large number of plant tissues have been analyzed for the fatty acid composition of their glycosyl glycerides and the data are presented in Tables III and IV. In general, plant lipids and particularly the lipids of photosynthetic tissues contain a high amount of polyunsaturated fatty acids. Since the glycosyl glycerides are the major lipid components of the chloroplast, they are usually found associated with fatty acids with a high degree of unsaturation. In the leaves of several species such as runner bean (Sastry and Kates, 1964b), alfalfa (O'Brien and Benson, 1964), pumpkin (Roughan, 1970), castor (Nichols *et al.*, 1967), and holly (Nichols, 1965b), the fatty acid component of the mono- and digalactosyl diglycerides is almost exclusively α-linolenic acid. However, in the glycosyl glycerides of leaves from a variety of angiosperm species, 7,10,13-hexadecatrienoic acid, a lower homolog of linolenic acid is found as the major fatty acid (Allen *et al.*, 1964; Jamieson and Reid, 1971b) while in *Euglena gracilis* and *Chlamydomonas rein-*

Table III

FATTY ACID COMPOSITION (%) OF MONOGALACTOSYL DIGLYCERIDE (MGD) AND DIGALACTOSYL DIGLYCERIDE (DGD) IN PHOTOSYNTHETIC TISSUES

		14:0 + 14:Un-sat.	16:0	16:1	16:2	16:3	18:0	18:1	18:2		18:3		18:4	20:4	20:5	Oth-ers	Ref.[i]
						$\Delta^{7,10,13}$			$\Delta^{5,9}$	$\Delta^{9,12}$	$\Delta^{5,9,12}$ or $\Delta^{6,9,12}$	$\Delta^{9,12,15}$	$\Delta^{5,9,12,15}$ or $\Delta^{6,9,12,15}$				
Leaves																	
Runner bean (*Phaseolus multiflorus*)	MGD		2	tr			tr	tr		2		96					(1)
	DGD		5	tr			1	tr		1		93					
Alfalfa	MGD	tr	3	tr			tr	tr		2		95					(2)
	DGD	tr	14	tr			3	tr		1		82				1	
Red clover (*Trifolium pratense*)	MGD	tr	17	tr			1	1		6		75					(3)
	DGD	tr	9	1			2	2		3		83					
Pumpkin (*Cucurbita pepo*)	MGD	tr	3	tr			tr	tr		tr		96					(4)
	DGD	tr	9	tr			tr	tr		tr		89					
Castor	MGD	2	6					tr		tr		91					(5)
	DGD		11							4		85					
Holly (*Ilex acquifolium*)	MGD		1				tr	tr		2		97					(6)
	DGD		13				tr	tr		7		80					
Spinach (*Spinacia oleracea*)	MGD		tr			30	1	1		1		67					(7)
	DGD		6			3	1	4		3		84					
Spinach lamellae	MGD	tr	tr		1	25		1		2		72					(8)
	DGD	1	3		tr	5		2		2		87					
	TGD[e]	1	9		1	15		1		1		70					
Water forget-me-not (*Myosotis scorpioides*)	MGD	tr	3	tr			tr	1		3	6[b]	42	44[d]			tr	(9) (10)
	DGD	tr	19	2			3	2		11	8[b]	43	12[d]			tr	
Chick weed (*Stellaria media*)	MGD		4	tr	tr	1	tr	tr		3	1[b]	62	29[d]				(11)
	DGD		9	tr	tr	tr	1	1		2	tr[b]	76	10[d]				
Flowering currant (*Ribes sanguineum*)	MGD		3	1	tr	23	tr	1		2		70					(12)
	DGD		6	2	tr	7	1	tr		3		81					
Ivy (*Hedera helix*)	MGD		2	tr	3	36	tr	1		5		53					(12)
	DGD		9	tr	tr	2	1	1		14		73					
Elder (*Sambucus nigra*)	MGD		3	tr	tr	5	tr	tr		1		91					(12)
	DGD		6	tr	tr	3	1	tr		1		90					

Sweet woodruff (*Gallium odoratum*)	MGD		2	tr	tr	35	tr	tr		2		61					(12)
	DGD		8	tr	tr	9	1	1		7		75					
Meadow buttercup (*Ranunculus acirs*)	MGD		1	tr	2	37	tr	1				58					(12)
	DGD		6	tr	tr	4	tr	tr				88					
Montia perfoliata	MGD		1	tr	1	20	tr	tr		1		77					(12)
	DGD		8	tr	1	5	1	1		2		82					
Hog weed (*Heracleum sphondilium*)	MGD		1	tr	1	55	tr	1		1		41					(12)
	DGD		11	tr	tr	8	1	1		5		75					
Tomato (*Lycopersicum esculentum*)	MGD		2	tr	1	32	tr	1		4		59					(12)
	DGD		10	tr	tr	3	2	2		7		75					
Yellow flag (*Iris pseudacorus*)	MGD		1	tr	tr	10	tr	1		1		87					(12)
	DGD		8	tr	tr	1	1	1		6		82					
Sinapis alba	MGD				1	35				2		62					(13)
	DGD		12			3	2			3		77					
Brassica oleracea	MGD				2	32				2		65					(13)
	DGD		12			1	1	tr		11		75					
Ginkgo biloba	MGD		2			11		tr		tr		86				1	(13)
	DGD		26	6				11		10		44				3	
Pteridium aquilinum	MGD		2	tr	1	27				2		66				3	(13)
	DGD		33			1		4		7		49				8	
Equisetum arvense	MGD		1		1	23				1		74				tr	(13)
	DGD		24			2		tr		5		61				9	
Catharinea undulata	MGD		3	2	14	13		1		23		34				11	(13)
	DGD		11	tr	4	2	tr	2		30		46				6	
Picea abies	MGD	1	2	tr	tr	4	1	1	tr	5	1[a]	78	7[c]			1	(14)
	DGD	2	12	tr	tr	2	2	2	tr	6	tr[a]	68	2[c]			3	
Pinus sylvestris	MGD	1	5	tr	1	13	1	2	5	4	2[a]	55	13[c]			1	(14)
	DGD	2	11	tr	tr	1	1	1	4	5	1[a]	63	7[c]			5	
Larix decidua	MGD	tr	2	tr	tr	13	tr	1	tr	3	1[a]	71	9[c]			1	(14)
	DGD	tr	10	tr	tr	3	1	1	tr	4	tr[a]	72	2[c]			7	
Taxa baccata	MGD	tr	5	tr	tr	16	1	2		4		72				tr	(14)
	DGD	1	11	tr	tr	2	1	2		7		73				4	
Moss (*Hypnum cupressiforme*)	MGD		2	1	2	11	tr	1		4		48		29	11	3	(6)
	DGD		6	2	1	2	2	3		5		62		14	4	3	
Anacystis nidulans	MGD	1	43	34			4	20									(15)
	DGD	2	52	28			4	16									
Anabaena variabilis	MGD		27	28	1		tr	12		19		15					(15)
	DGD		26	26	2		2	9		20		17					

Table III (*Continued*)

		14:0 + 14:Un-sat.	16:0	16:1	16:2	16:3	18:0	18:1	18:2		18:3		18:4	20:4	20:5	Oth-ers	Ref.[i]
						$\Delta^{7,10,13}$			$\Delta^{5,9}$	$\Delta^{9,12}$	$\Delta^{5,9,12}$ or $\Delta^{6,9,12}$	$\Delta^{9,12,15}$	$\Delta^{5,9,12,15}$ or $\Delta^{6,9,12,15}$				
Euglena gracilis[f]	MGD		6				1	9		6		41				32[h]	(16)
	DGD		17				0	19		12		26				7[h]	
Chlorella pyrenoidosa	MGD	tr	3	10			tr	41		5		27	3[d]			14	(2)
	DGD	tr	12	10			tr	37		6		27	3[d]			6	
Chlorella vulgaris[g]	MGD		5	2	19	10	2	3		17		45					(14)
	DGD		8	3	6	1	3	3		35		37					
Chlamydomonas mundana	MGD	3	8	8	9	27	tr	10		8		26					(5)
	DGD	1	12	9	14	18	tr	16		10		20					
Chlamydomonas reinhardi	MGD		2				3	13		6		32				33[h]	(16)
	DGD		52				7	22		5		2				0[h]	

[a] $\Delta^{5,9,12}$.
[b] $\Delta^{6,9,12}$.
[c] $\Delta^{5,9,12,15}$.
[d] $\Delta^{6,9,12,15}$.
[e] Trigalactosyl diglyceride.
[f] Grown in light.
[g] Grown in light on inorganic medium.
[h] 16:4 ($\Delta^{4,7,10,13}$).
[i] Key to references: (1) Sastry and Kates (1964b); (2) O'Brien and Benson (1964); (3) Weenink (1964); (4) Roughan (1970); (5) Nichols *et al.* (1967); (6) Nichols (1965b); (7) Allen *et al.* (1964); Gardner (1968); (8) Allen *et al.* (1966a); (9) Allen *et al.* (1966b); (10) Jamieson and Reid (1969); (11) Jamieson and Reid (1971a); (12) Jamieson and Reid (1971b); (13) Auling *et al.* (1971); (14) Jamieson and Reid (1972); (15) Nichols *et al.* (1965); (16) Bloch *et al.* (1967).

Table IV

Fatty Acid Composition (%) of Monogalactosyl Diglyceride (MGD) and Digalactosyl Diglyceride (DGD) of Nonphotosynthetic Tissues

		14:0 + 14:Unsat.	16:0	16:1	16:2 + 16:3	18:0	18:1	18:2	18:3	Others	Ref.[b]
Wheat flour	MGD	1	14	3		1	17	57	2	5	(1)
	DGD		42			4	12	29		13	
	MGD		8	tr		1	8	79	4		(2)
	DGD		16	tr		1	8	72	3		
Briza spicata seeds	MGD		6	tr			86	8			(3)
	DGD		18	2		1	40	34	3		
Apple pulp (preclimacteric)	MGD		2			1	1	5	91		(4)
	DGD		17			4	2	17	60		
(postclimacteric)	MGD		6			1	7	13	73		(4)
	DGD		20			7	7	24	43		
Potato tubers (*Solanum tuberosum*)	MGD		1				1	59	40		(5)
	DGD		14			6	8	47	25		
	TGD[a]		25			11	10	43	12		
Narcissus bulb	MGD		4	2	2	2	5	74	10		(6)
	DGD		13	2	2	2	8	69	5		
Turnip root	MGD		12	1		1	10	20	56		(7)
	DGD		21	2		1	8	14	55		

[a] Trigalactosyl diglyceride.

[b] Key to references: (1) Carter *et al.* (1961a); (2) DeStefanis and Ponte (1969); (3) Smith and Wolff (1966); (4) Galliard (1968b); (5) Galliard (1968a); (6) Nichols and James (1964); (7) Lepage (1967).

hardi, 4,7,10,13-hexadecatetraenoic acid accounts for a substantial amount of the fatty acid residues (Bloch *et al.*, 1967). In some members of the Boraginaceae (*Myosotis scorpioides*) and caryophyllaceae (*Stellaria media*) families, significant amounts of 6,9,12-octadecatrienoic acid (γ-linolenic acid) and 6,9,12,15-octadecatetraenoic acid are encountered as the fatty acid components of glycosyl glycerides (Jamieson and Reid, 1969, 1971a). In conifer leaf glycolipids, while α-linolenic is the major fatty acid, notable quantities of unusual nonmethylene-interrupted C_{18}-polyenoic acids with Δ^5-olefinic unsaturation have been found (Jamieson and Reid, 1972). C_{20}-polyenoic acids have been reported as the major fatty acids of the glycosyl glycerides in the moss, *Hypnum cupressiforme* (Nichols, 1965b). In green algae, glycolipid fatty acids are comprised of mono- and polyunsaturated C_{16} and C_{18} acids. In blue green algae, the fatty acid composition of mono- and digalactosyl diglycerides of *Anabaena variabilis* resembles that of green algae, while *Anacystis nidulans* has palmitic and oleic acids as the principal fatty acid residues with no polyenoic acids at all (Nichols *et al.*, 1965).

From the available data on the fatty acid composition of glycosyl glycerides, some general observations may be made. With the lone exception of *Anacystis nidulans*, all photosynthetic organisms that evolve oxygen contain glycosyl glycerides with large proportions of polyunsaturated fatty acids. The usual fatty acids found in these lipids of higher plant photosynthetic systems are C_{16}- or C_{18}-polyenoic acids where the poly cis double bond system is maximally extended toward the methyl end, leaving only two saturated terminal carbons (Bloch *et al.*, 1967). Considerable differences occur in the fatty acid composition of monogalactosyl and digalactosyl glycerides. The content of polyunsaturated fatty acids in monogalactosyl glycerides is always high. The digalactosyl glycerides are much more saturated and in some algae, such as *Chlamydomonas reinhardi*, contain almost no α-linolenate. The C_{16}-tri- or tetraenoic acids when found in these glycolipids in a plant species, are found in much lesser proportions in the digalactosyl as compared to the monogalactosyl glycerides.

In nonphotosynthetic tissues (Table IV), the fatty acids of glycosyl glycerides are more saturated and linoleate is a predominant fatty acid. Here again, the digalactosyl glycerides are much more saturated with higher amounts of palmitate than the monogalactosyl glycerides.

c. Positional Distribution of Fatty Acids and Molecular Species. As previously noted, α-linolenic acid accounts for more than 90% of the total fatty acids of glycosyl glycerides in most leaves with the result that the major molecular species in many higher plants are mono- and digalactosyl linolenins (Sastry and Kates, 1964b; O'Brien and Benson, 1964). Saturated and monoenoic fatty acids, found as minor constituents in these plant glycolipids, are esterified in position-1, with linoleic or linolenic acids in position-2 of glycerol (Noda and Fujiwara, 1967). However, a more complex fatty acid composition is found in some plants and algae and the positional distribution of different fatty acids on the glycosyl glyceride molecule in these instances is of considerable interest. Such studies on the monogalactosyl diglyceride fractions from a number of plant sources (Table V) show that the positional distribution is influenced more by fatty acid chain length than by their degree of unsaturation; C_{18} acids accumulating preferentially in position-1 and C_{16} and C_{20} acids in position-2 (Safford and Nichols, 1970; Auling *et al.*, 1971). This positional specificity of fatty acids in the monogalactosyl glyceride is found in both higher plants and algae, and contrasts with the distribution in phospholipids where saturated and unsaturated fatty acids predominate in positions-1 and -2, respectively (Sastry and Kates, 1964b; Bajwa and Sastry, 1972a; Safford and Nichols, 1970). In cases where C_{18} acids are almost the only type of fatty acids found, e.g., *Anchusa* leaf (see Table V), the degree of unsaturation and possibly the site of unsaturation confer the specificity with the more highly unsaturated acids concentrating in the 2-position (Safford and Nichols, 1970). Similar studies on digalactosyl glyceride in *Artemisia princeps* leaves showed that saturated acids are esterified in position-1 and unsaturated acids in position-2 (Noda and Fujiwara, 1967). The positional distribution of fatty acids in digalactosyl diglyceride in a variety of leaves has been reported by Tulloch *et al.* (1973), and the only saturated acid, palmitic acid, found here did not show a specific distribution (Table V).

The composition of molecular species of galactosyl glycerides in a number of plants shows that in monogalactoysl diglyceride, molecules having one C_{16} acid and one C_{18} acid are the predominant species, followed by molecules with two C_{18} fatty acid residues. The reverse appears to be the case with digalactosyl diglyceride. Glycolipid molecules with two palmitoyl residues are absent in higher plants (Auling *et al.*, 1971). Similarly in *Chlorella vulgaris*, the major species of monogalactosyl diglyceride are those with C_{18} acid in position-1 and C_{16} acid in position-2 (Safford and Nichols, 1970).

2. *Trigalactosyl and Tetragalactosyl Diglycerides*

Evidence for the occurrence of higher homologs of glycosyl glycerides in plants was reported in a number of studies. Benson *et al.* (1958) identified glycosylgalactotrioside as a deacylation product of labeled lipids of *Chlorella* indicating the presence of trigalactosyl glyceride in algae. Similarly, biosynthetic studies on glycolipids with UDP-galac-

Table V

COMPOSITION OF FATTY ACIDS AT 1- AND 2-POSITIONS OF GLYCEROL MOIETY OF MONOGALACTOSYL DIGLYCERIDE (MGD) AND DIGALACTOSYL DIGLYCERIDE (DGD)

		16:0	16:1	16:2	16:3	18:0	18:1	18:2	18:3 $\Delta^{9,12,15}$	18:3 $\Delta^{6,9,12}$	18:4	20:0	Ref.[a]
Artemisia princeps leaves	MGD 1-	3	1			tr	1	4	92				(1)
	2-	tr	tr				tr	5	95				
	DGD 1-	27	13			5	9	15	31				
	2-	4	tr			1	2	13	81				
Spinach leaves	MGD 1-				5		2	3	90				(2)
	2-				38			2	56				
	DGD total	6			2		2	2	88				(4)
	2-	7			3			2	88				
Anchusa leaves	MGD 1-	5						3	90		3		(2)
	2-	1						2	52	7	38		
Sinapis alba	MGD total			1	35			2	62				(3)
	2-			2	84				15				
	DGD total	8			5			5	84				(4)
	2-	8			9			4	80				

Brassica oleracea	MGD total			2	32		2	65			(3)
	2-			3	73		1	22			
	DGD total	7			2		5	86			(4)
	2-	7			4		3	86			
Vicia faba	DGD total	4					2	94			(4)
	2-						3	97			
Ginkgo biloba	MGD total	2			11	tr	tr	86	1		(3)
	2-	1			20	tr	tr	78	1		
Pteridium acquilinum	MGD total	2	tr	1	27		2	66	3		(3)
	2-	1	tr	3	47		1	38	10		
Equisetum arvense	MGD total	1		1	23		tr	74	tr		(3)
	2-	2	tr	2	46		tr	48	2		
Catharinea undulata	MGD total	3	2	14	13	1	23	34		11	(3)
	2-	1	2	32	25		11	7		22	
Chlorella vulgaris (heterotrophic)	MGD 1-	3	2	3		24	36	32			(2)
	2-	2	20	55	9	4	5	4			
Anabaena cylindrica	MGD 1-	5	6	2	1	4	35	47			(2)
	2-	47	11	19	5	2	6	9			
Anabaena flosaquae	MGD 1-	6	7	2	3	5	9	69			(2)
	2-	28	5	11	26		2	28			

[a] Key to references: (1) Noda and Fujiwara (1967); (2) Safford and Nichols (1970); (3) Auling *et al.* (1971); (4) Tulloch *et al.* (1973).

tose-^{14}C in spinach leaf preparations yielded evidence suggesting the occurrence of tri- and tetragalactosyl glycerides (Neufeld and Hall, 1964; Ongun and Mudd, 1968). Trigalactosyl diglyceride has been tentatively identified in spinach lamellae (Allen *et al.*, 1966b) and in *Sapium sebiferum roxb* leaf lipids (Hirayama, 1965), but its structure was not determined. Only recently, Galliard (1969) isolated a trigalactosyl diglyceride from potato tubers and characterized it as a higher homolog of digalactosyl diglyceride, in which an additional D-galactopyranosyl moiety is linked α-(1 $\rightarrow$ 6) to the terminal galactose unit of digalactosyl diglyceride (Fig. 1). This glycolipid constitutes about 1% by weight of the total lipids in potato tubers (Galliard, 1968a) and occurs in trace amounts in apple pulp (Galliard, 1968b). In potato, the trigalactosyl diglyceride appears to have a more saturated fatty acid composition than the digalactosyl diglyceride (Table III). A component, tentatively identified as tetragalactosyl diglyceride, has been found in spinach chloroplasts and the molar ratio of mono-:di-:tri-:tetragalactosyl diglycerides in this tissue was reported to be 60:30:5:1 (Webster and Chang, 1969).

3. *O-Acylgalactosyl Diglyceride*

Heinz (1967a) isolated a glycolipid from spinach leaf homogenates that was more hydrophobic than monogalactosyl diglyceride and had a composition of glycerol, galactose, and fatty acids in a molar ratio of 1:1:3. This glycolipid appeared to be a mixture of isomers, of which the main component was 1,2-diacyl-3-(6-*O*-acyl-β-D-galactopyranosyl)-*sn*-glycerol (Fig. 1). A similar lipid was isolated from wheat flour, and rigorous structural investigation showed it to be monogalactosyl diglyceride with an additional fatty acid residue esterified at the 6-position of the galactose (Myhre, 1968). Later, Heinz and Tulloch (1969) confirmed this structure for the acylgalactosyl diglyceride of spinach leaves and showed that it is not a mixture of isomers. The acylgalactosyl diglyceride is probably not a normal component of leaf tissues, but is formed on disruption of cell mainly by acyl transfer from di- to monogalactosyl diglyceride (Heinz, 1967b).

4. *Subcellular Distribution*

Only a few studies have been made on the subcellular distribution of glycosyl glycerides and these were mainly with the photosynthetic tissues of higher plants. In leaves, the chloroplasts have high concentrations of mono- and digalactosyl diglycerides and about 45% of the total lipids of spinach chloroplasts is accounted for by these glycolipids (Wintermans, 1963; Zill and Harmon, 1962; Lichtenthaler and Park, 1963). Chloroplasts isolated from beet and tobacco leaves contained 83–100% of the total cellular glycosyl glycerides (Wintermans, 1960; Ongun *et al.*, 1968), while only 62% of total leaf glycolipids were found in the chloroplasts of *Zea mays* and *Antirrhinum majus* (Koenig, 1971). Of the total lipids in avocado and cauliflower chloroplasts, monogalactosyl diglyceride accounted for 9.0% and 19.4%, while digalactosyl diglyceride amounted to 6.7% and 7.4%, respectively (Schwertner and Biale, 1973).

In the chloroplast, glycosyl glycerides have been found as major components in both the envelope membrane and lamellae (Poincelot, 1971). Comparative studies on the molar ratios of mono- and digalactosyl diglycerides to phospholipids in lamellae and whole cells, indicate that a higher ratio of glycolipids than other lipids may exist in portions of chloroplast surrounding the lamellae (Allen *et al.*, 1966a; Hirayama, 1967). It appears that the galactolipid content of a chloroplast is related to its morphology and the ratio of galactolipid to chlorophyll reflects the degree of grana formation. Thus, in the two morphologically distinct types of chloroplasts found in maize and sorghum, the agranal bundle sheath chloroplasts showed a significantly higher amount of galactolipids, on a chlorophyll basis, when compared to the grana-containing mesophyll chloroplasts (Bishop *et al.*, 1971). Regarding the occurrence of galactosyl diglycerides in structures other than the chloroplast, the mitochondria of avocado mesocarp, cauliflower, and sweet potato root showed relatively high galactolipid content, and this was suggested to be a unique feature of plant mitochondria (Biale *et al.*, 1966; Schwertner and Biale, 1973). Mono- and digalactosyl diglycerides have also been detected in potato tuber mitochondria (Abdelkader *et al.*, 1969). However, galactosyl diglycerides have not been found in the lipid extracts of highly purified mitochondria from etiolated mung bean hypocotyls or potato tubers (McCarty *et al.*, 1973). In the diatom, *N. pelliculosa*, monogalactosyl diglyceride was found in both the cell wall and chloroplast lipids, with higher concentrations in the former. In contrast, the digalactosyl diglyceride of this organism is a minor component in the cell wall as compared to the chloroplast (Kates and Volcani, 1968).

B. Bacteria

1. *Discovery, Distribution, and Structural Types*

The occurrence of glycosyl glycerides in bacteria was observed first by Macfarlane (1961) in *Micrococcus lysodiekticus*, where a glycolipid identified as mannosyl glyceride was noticed. Soon after, a lipid containing glucose and tentatively identified as β-glucosyl glyceride was

Table VI

DISTRIBUTION OF GLYCOSYL DIGLYCERIDES IN BACTERIA

Organism	Glycosyl diglycerides[a]	Structure[b]	Dry wt of cells (mg/gm)	% of total lipids	Ref.[g]
Chromatium strain D	-3-*O*-[Glc]-				(1)
	-3-*O*-[Man-Glc]-				
	-3-*O*-[Man-Man-Glc]-				
Chlorobium limicola	-3-*O*-[Gal-Gal]-				(2)
Chloropseudomonas ethylicum	-3-*O*-[Gal]-				(3)
	-3-*O*-[Gal-Rhamnose-unidentified sugar]-				
Pseudomonas rubescens	-3-*O*-[β-D-Glcp][d]-	2b			
	-3-*O*-[β-D-Glucuronop]-	2e		} 15	(4)
Pseudomonas diminuta	-3-*O*-[α-D-Glcp]-	2a			(5)
	-3-*O*-[α-D-Glucuronop]-	2d			
	-3-*O*-[β-D-Glcp-(1 → 4)-*O*-α-D-Glucuronop]-	3f			
Halobacterium cutirubrum	-1-*O*-[Gal SO_4-Man-Glc]-[e] or -1-*O*-[Gal SO_4-Glc-Man]-[e]				(6)
Moderate halophile (unidentified)	-3-*O*-[Glucuronosyl]-[f]			29	(7, 8)
Vibriofetus strains I-17 and V-2673	-3-*O*-[Gal-Gal]-				(9)
Butyrivibrio fibrisolvens	-3-*O*-[Gal]-				(10)
	-3-*O*-[Gal-Gal]-				
Bacterioides symbiosus	-3-*O*-[β-D-Galactofuranosyl]-				(11)
Micrococcus lysodiekticus	-3-*O*-[α-D-Manp-(1 → 3)-*O*-α-D-Manp]-	3e		7.5–15	(12)
Staphylococcus lactis I3	-3-*O*-[β-D-Glcp-(1 → 6)-*O*-β-D-Glcp]-	3b	0.7	2.8	(13)
S. lactis 7944	-3-*O*-[β-D-Glcp-(1 → 6)-*O*-β-D-Glcp]-	3b		1–2	(14, 15)
S. saprophyticus I2	-3-*O*-[β-D-Glcp-(1 → 6)-*O*-β-D-Glcp]-	3b		1–2	(14, 15)
S. aureus	-3-*O*-[β-D-Glcp-(1 → 6)-*O*-β-D-Glcp]-	3b		1–2	(14, 15)

Pneumococcus					
Type I	-3-*O*-[α-D-Glcp]-	2a			(16)
	-3-*O*-[α-D-Galp-(1 → 2)-*O*-α-D-Glcp]-	3d	18.8	34	
Type XIV	-3-*O*-[α-D-Glcp]-	2a			(17)
	-3-*O*-[α-D-Galp-(1 → 2)-*O*-α-D-Glcp]-	3d			
Streptococcus faecalis 9	-3-*O*-[α-D-Glcp-(1 → 2)-*O*-α-D-Glcp]-	3a		1–2	(14, 15)
S. faecalis ATCC 9790	-3-*O*-[Glc]-				(18, 19)
	-3-*O*-[α-D-Glcp-(1 → 2)-*O*-α-D-Glcp]-	3a			
S. pyogenes	-3-*O*-[Glc-Glc]-				(20)
S. MG	-3-*O*-[α-D-Glcp]-	2a			(21)
	-3-*O*-[α-D-Glcp-(1 → 2)-*O*-α-D-Glcp][d]-	3a	1.4[c]		
S. lactis	-3-*O*-[α-D-Glcp-(1 → 2)-*O*-α-D-Glcp]-	3a			(22)
S. hemolyticus D58	-3-*O*-[α-D-Glcp-(1 → 2)-*O*-α-D-Glcp]-	3a		44.3	(23)
	-3-*O*-[α-D-Glcp-(1 → 2)-*O*-α-D-Glcp(1 → 2)-*O*-α-D-Glcp]-	4b		0.9	
Lactobacillus casei ATCC 7469	-3-*O*-[α-D-Galp-(1 → 2)-*O*-α-D-Glcp][d]-	3d }	1.0[c]	17.4	(24)
	-3-*O*-[α-D-Glcp-(1 → 6)-*O*-α-D-Galp(1 → 2)-*O*-α-D-Glcp]-	4a }			
L. buchneri	-3-*O*-[α-D-Galp-(1 → 2)-*O*-α-D-Glcp]-	3d			(25)
L. plantarum	-3-*O*-[α-D-Galp-(1 → 2)-*O*-α-D-Glcp]-	3d			(25)
	-3-*O*-[Glc-Gal-Glc]-				
L. helveticus	-3-*O*-[α-D-Galp-(1 → 2)-*O*-α-D-Glcp]-	3d			(25)
	-3-*O*-[α-D-Glcp-(1 → 6)-*O*-α-D-Galp-(1 → 2)-*O*-α-D-Glcp]-	4a			
	-3-*O*-[Glc-Glc-Gal-Glc]-				
L. acidophilus	-3-*O*-[α-D-Galp-(1 → 2)-*O*-α-D-Glcp]-	3d			(25)
	-3-*O*-[α-D-Glcp-(1 → 6)-*O*-α-D-Galp-(1 → 2)-*O*-α-D-Glcp]-	4a			
	-3-*O*-[Glc-Glc-Gal-Glc]-				
L. fermenti	-3-*O*-[Gal-Glc]-				(26)
Bifidobacterium bifidum	-3-*O*-[Gal]-				(27)
	-3-*O*-[Gal-Gal]-				
	-3-*O*-[Gal-Gal-Gal]-				
Corynebacterium aquaticum	-3-*O*-[Man-Man]-				(28)
Listeria monocytogenes	-3-*O*-[Gal-Glc]-				(29)

Table VI (*Continued*)

Organism	Glycosyl diglycerides[a]	Structure[b]	Dry wt of cells (mg/gm)	% of total lipids	Ref.[g]
Microbacterium lacticum	-3-*O*-[α-D-Manp-(1 → 3)-*O*-α-D-Manp]-	3e		46	(30)
M. thermosphactum	-3-*O*-[Man-Man]-				(31)
Arthrobacter globiformis	-3-*O*-[Gal]-				(32)
	-3-*O*-[β-D-Galp-(1 → 6)-*O*-β-D-Galp]-	3c		13 (3c and 3e together)	
	-3-*O*-[α-D-Manp-(1 → 3)-*O*-α-D-Manp]-	3e			
A. pascens and *A. crystallopoietes*	-3-*O*-[Gal]-				(25)
	-3-*O*-[β-D-Galp-(1 → 6)-*O*-β-D-Galp]-	3c			
	-3-*O*-[α-D-Manp-(1 → 3)-*O*-α-D-Manp]-	3e			
Bacillus subtilis	-3-*O*-[β-D-Glcp-(1 → 6)-*O*-β-D-Glcp]-	3b		1–2	(14, 15, 33)
B. cereus	-3-*O*-[Glc(1 → 6)-Glc]-				(34, 35)
B. megaterium	-3-*O*-[β-glucosaminyl]-	2f		5	(36)
Streptomyces LA 7017	-3-*O*-[α-D-Glcp-(1 → 4)-*O*-α-D-(2 or 3-acyl)-galacturonop]-	3g		4.9	(37)
Treponema pallidum (Kazan 5)	-3-*O*-[α-D-Galp]-	2c			(38)
T. pallidum (Reiter)	-3-*O*-[Gal]-			37	(39)
T. zuelzerae	-3-*O*-[Glc]-			25	(39)

Mycoplasma laidlawii B	-3-*O*-[α-D-Glcp][d]-	2a	45	(40, 41)
	-3-*O*-[α-D-Glcp-(1 → 2)-*O*-α-D-Glcp]-	3a		
Mycoplasma spp. strain J	-3-*O*-[β-D-3,4,6-triacyl-Glcp]-	2g	17.1	(42)
M. pneumoniae	-3-*O*-[Glc-Glc]-			(43)
	-3-*O*-[Gal-Gal]-			
	-3-*O*-[Gal-Gal-Gal]-			
M. mycoides	-3-*O*-[β-D-galactofuranosyl]-			(44)

[a] 1,2-Diacyl-*sn*-glycerols in which the carbohydrate substituents are in position-3. Only the substituents in position-3 are listed here.

[b] Numbers relate to structures in figures.

[c] Milligrams per gram wet cells.

[d] Major component.

[e] 2,3-Di-*O*-phytanyl-*sn*-glycerol in which the carbohydrate substituents are in position-1.

[f] Mixture of two glucuronic acid containing glycolipids representing 28% and 1% of total lipid of the organism. The minor glycolipid seems identical to the glucuronosyl diglyceride of *Pseudomonas* species.

[g] Key to references: (1) Steiner *et al.* (1969); (2) Nichols and James (1965); (3) Constantopoulos and Bloch (1967a); (4) Wilkinson (1968b); (5) Wilkinson (1969); (6) Kates *et al.* (1967); (7) Peleg and Tietz (1971); (8) Stern and Tietz (1971); (9) Tornabene and Ogg (1971); (10) Kunsman (1970); (11) Reeves *et al.* (1964); (12) Lennarz and Talamo (1966); (13) Brundish *et al.* (1967); (14) Brundish *et al.* (1966); (15) Brundish and Baddiley (1968); (16) Brundish *et al.* (1965a,b); (17) Kaufman *et al.* (1965); (18) Vorbeck and Marinetti (1965b); (19) Pieringer (1968); (20) Cohen and Panos (1966); (21) Plackett and Shaw (1967); (22) Fischer and Seyferth (1968); (23) Ishizuka and Yamakawa (1968); (24) Shaw *et al.* (1968a); (25) Shaw (1970); (26) Wincken and Knox (1970); (27) Exterkate and Veerkamp (1969); (28) Khuller and Brennen (1972); (29) Carroll *et al.* (1968); (30) Shaw (1968); (31) Shaw and Stead (1970); (32) Walker and Bastl (1967); (33) Bishop *et al.* (1967); (34) Lang and Lundgren (1970); (35) Saito and Mukoyama (1971); (36) Phizackerley *et al.* (1972); (37) Bergelson *et al.* (1970); (38) Livermore and Johnson (1970); (39) Meyer and Meyer (1971); (40) Shaw and Smith (1967); (41) Shaw *et al.* (1968b); (42) Smith and Mayberry (1968); (43) Plackett *et al.* (1969); (44) Plackett (1967).

found in *Staphylococcus aureus* (Macfarlane, 1962). In the same year, Polonovski *et al.* (1962) reported similar glycolipids in *S. aureus* with glucose as the only sugar component and the major glycolipid was found to be a diglucosyl glyceride. The more general occurrence of glycosyl glycerides in bacteria soon became apparent by the studies of Ikawa (1963) on lactic acid bacteria, and by the studies of Vorbeck and Marinetti (1965a) on *Lactobacillus plantarum* and *Streptococcus faecalis*. A monoglycosyl- and a diglycosyl diglyceride were identified in *S. faecalis* (Vorbeck and Marinetti, 1965b). Brundish *et al.* (1965a, 1966) examined a number of Gram-positive bacteria, and the presence of similar glycolipids was established in all of them. Since then, many other Gram-positive, some Gram-negative, and a few photosynthetic bacteria have been found to contain glycosyl glycerides, and the widespread occurrence of this class of glycolipids in bacteria is now well established.

The first complete structural characterization of a bacterial glycosyl glyceride was carried out in *Pneumococcus* Type I by Brundish *et al.* (1965b,c) and in Type XIV by Kaufman *et al.* (1965); both groups proposed the same structure, 1,2-diacyl-3-*O*-[α-D-galactopyranosyl-(1 → 2)-*O*-α-D-glucopyranosyl]-*sn*-glycerol, for the major glycolipid of this organism. Lennarz and Talamo (1966) established the structure of *M. lysodiekticus* glycolipid as 1,2-diacyl-3-*O*-[α-D-mannopyranosyl-(1 → 3)-*O*-α-D-mannopyranosyl]-*sn*-glycerol. In the past few years, the qualitative and quantitative distribution, as well as the elucidation of structure of glycosyl glycerides, was reported in several bacteria (see Table VI).

Among photosynthetic bacteria, galactosyl diglycerides were found in *Chlorobium limicola* (Nichols and James, 1965), while a monogalactosyl diglyceride and a triglycosyl diglyceride which has not been completely characterized, occur in *Chloropseudomonas ethylicum* (Constantopoulos and Bloch, 1967a). In contrast, *Chromatium* strain D contains a glucosyl diglyceride, a mannosylglucosyl diglyceride, and a triglycosyl diglyceride composed of two mannose residues and glucose (Steiner *et al.*, 1969). However, glycosyl glycerides have not been detected in *Rhodopseudomonas spheroides, R. gelatinosa, R. palustris, R. capsulata,* and in *Rhodospirillum rubrum* (Nichols and James, 1965; Constantopoulos and Bloch, 1967a).

The quantitative distribution of glycosyl glycerides varies widely among bacteria, and this class of glycolipids accounts for about 1–2% of total lipids in several species. In some bacteria, such as *P. rubescens, M. lysodiekticus, Pneumococci, L. casei, A. globiformis,* and *T. pallidum,* the glycosyl diglycerides are the major lipid components. In *Streptococcus hemolyticus* and *Microbacterium lacticum,* nearly half of the total lipid is accounted for by the glycosyl glycerides (Table VI). Monoglycosyl, diglycosyl, and triglycosyl diglycerides have been found in several bacteria. Tetraglycosyl diglycerides have been identified in *Lactobacillus helveticus* and *L. acidophilus* (Shaw, 1970). Except for the monoglucosyl diglyceride in *P. rubescens* (Wilkinson, 1968b) and in *Mycoplasma laidlawii B* (Shaw *et al.*, 1968b) and the monoglucuronosyl diglyceride in an unidentified halophile (Stern and Tietz, 1971), monoglycosyl diglycerides are usually found only as minor components. The lipids of a T strain of *Mycoplasma* contain three glucose-containing glycolipids in trace amounts (Romano *et al.*, 1972). The various types of monoglycosyl diglycerides found in bacteria are shown in Fig. 2. In addition to glucose, galactose, and glucuronic acid-containing glycosyl diglycerides found in several bacterial species, a β-glucosaminyl diglyceride was recently reported in *Bacillus megaterium* (Phizackerley *et al.*, 1972). While the sugars in bacterial glycosyl diglycerides are mostly pyranosides, a β-galactofuranosyl glyceride has been identified in *Bacteroides symbiosus* (Reeves *et al.*, 1964) and in *Mycoplasma mycoides* (Plackett, 1967).

Among the various glycosyl glycerides, diglycosyl diglycerides are the most widespread and appear to be quantitatively the major lipids in bacteria. In Gram-positive bacteria, five structural types of diglycosyl diglycerides, depending upon the nature of the disaccharide residue have been recognized and these are: α-glucosylglucosyl, β-glucosylglucosyl, β-galactosylgalactosyl, α-galactosylglucosyl, and α-mannosylmannosyl diglycerides (Fig. 3). Glucose, galactose, and mannose are the usual sugars found in these glycolipids and the two anomeric centers in the glycosides have the same configuration (Shaw and Baddiley, 1968; Shaw, 1970). In the Gram-negative organisms, *P. rubescens* and *P. diminuta,* glycosyl glycerides containing uronic acids have been reported (Wilkinson, 1968b, 1969). A glucuronosyl diglyceride similar to the glycolipid of *Pseudomonas* species has been recently found in an unidentified moderately halophilic and halotolerent bacterium (Peleg and Tietz, 1971; Stern and Tietz, 1971). Interestingly, in another halophile, *Halobacterium cutirubrum,* which contains unusual phytanyl diether phospholipids (Kates *et al.*, 1965), a glycolipid with galactose sulfate, mannose, and glucose linked to a phytanyl diether glyceride has been found (Kates *et al.*, 1967). Triglycosyl diglycerides, usually present as minor components, have been observed in several bacteria and their structures have been established in *Lactobacillus* and *S. hemolyticus* (Table VI, Fig. 4).

Streptomyces LA 7017 (Bergelson *et al.*, 1970) and *Mycoplasma* spp. strain J (Smith and Mayberry, 1968) contain an acylglucosylgalacturonosyl diglyceride and a triacylglucosyl diglyceride, respectively. Acyl derivatives of monogalactosyl and digalactosyl diglycerides have also

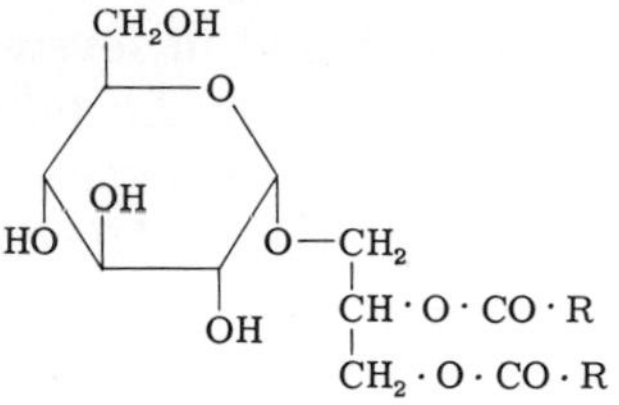

(a) 1,2-diacyl-3-*O*-α-D-glucopyranosyl-*sn*-glycerol

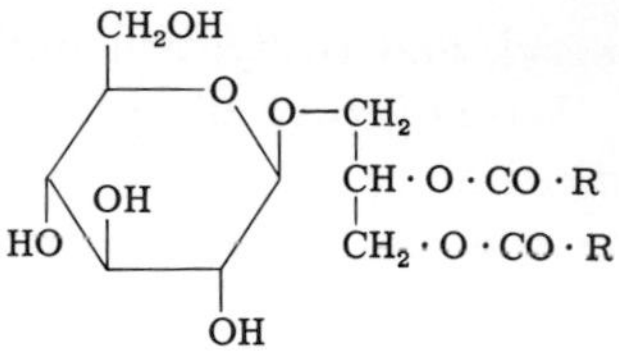

(b) 1,2-diacyl-3-*O*-β-D-glucopyranosyl-*sn*-glycerol

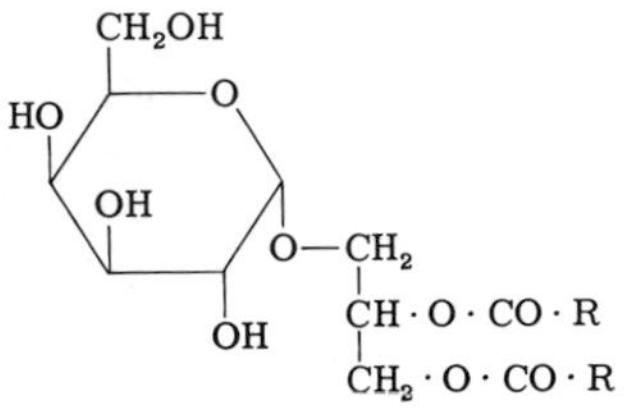

(c) 1,2-diacyl-3-*O*-α-D-galactopyranosyl-*sn*-glycerol

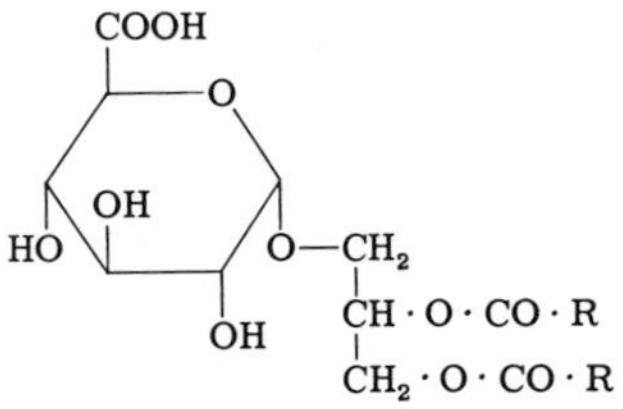

(d) 1,2-diacyl-3-*O*-α-D-glucuronopyranosyl-*sn*-glycerol

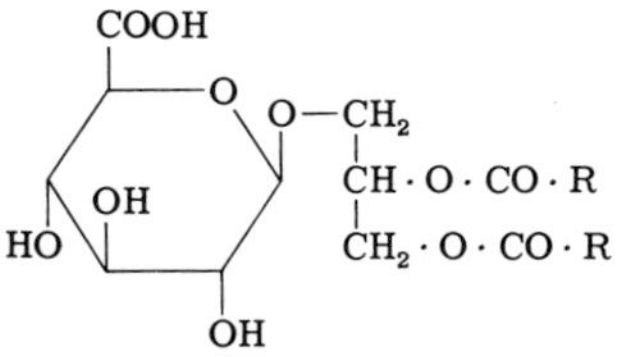

(e) 1,2-diacyl-3-*O*-β-D-glucuronopyranosyl-*sn*-glycerol

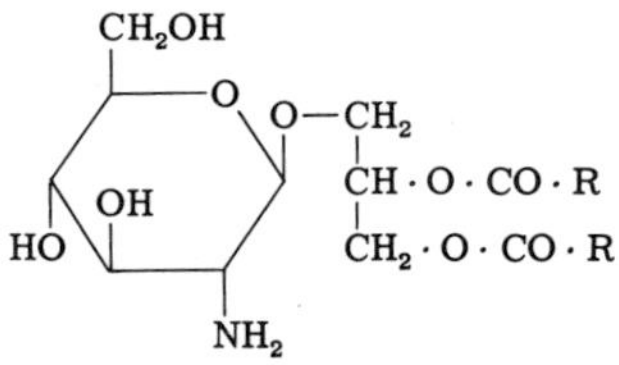

(f) 1,2-diacyl-3-*O*-β-D-glucosaminyl-*sn*-glycerol

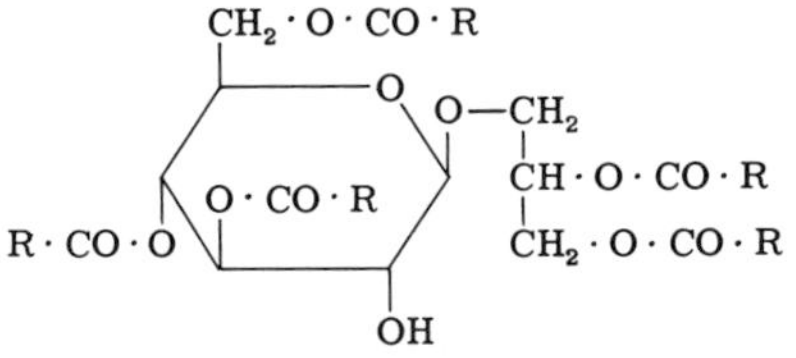

(g) 1,2-diacyl-3-*O*-β-3,4,6-triacyl-D-glucopyranosyl-*sn*-glycerol

FIG. 2. Structures of bacterial monoglycosyl diglycerides.

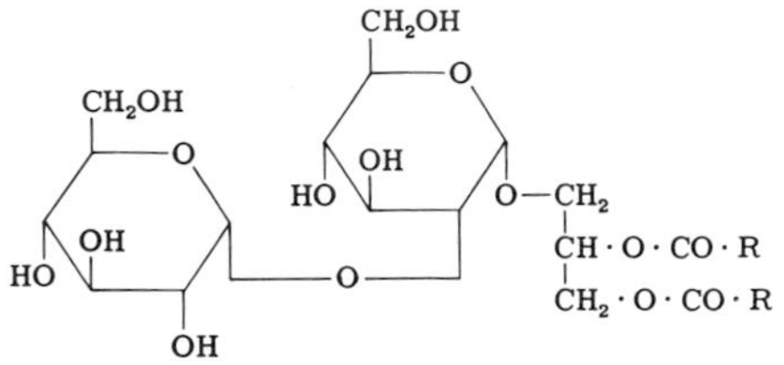

(a) 1,2-diacyl-3-*O*-(α-D-glucopyranosyl-(1 → 2)-*O*-α-D-glucopyranosyl)-*sn*-glycerol

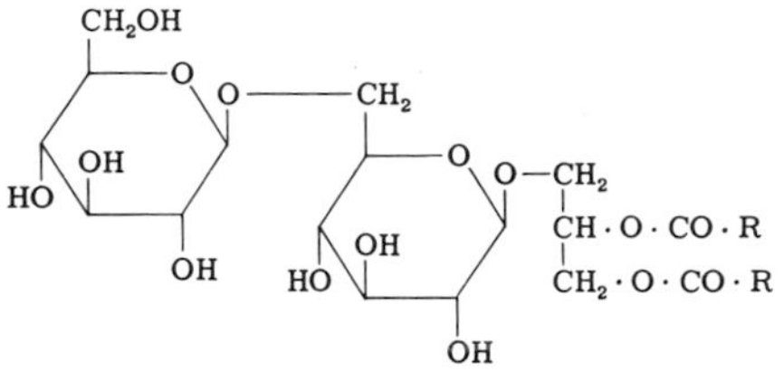

(b) 1,2-diacyl-3-*O*-(β-D-glucopyranosyl-(1 → 6)-*O*-β-D-glucopyranosyl)-*sn*-glycerol

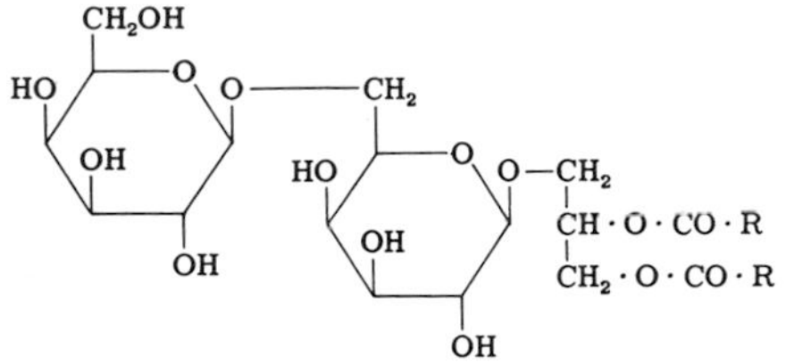

(c) 1,2-diacyl-3-*O*-(β-D-galactopyranosyl-(1 → 6)-*O*-β-D-galactopyranosyl)-*sn*-glycerol

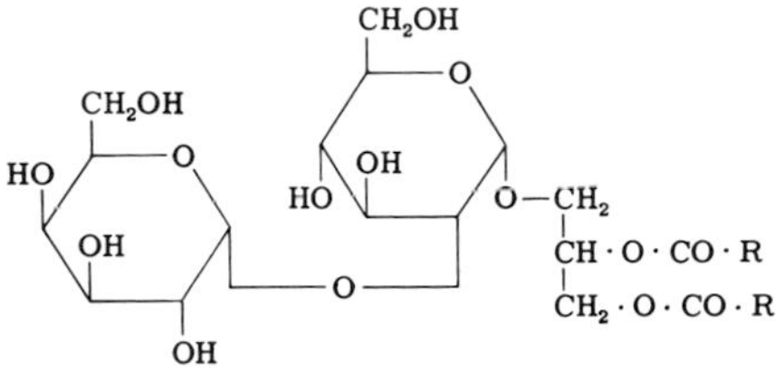

(d) 1,2-diacyl-3-*O*-(α-D-galactopyranosyl (1 → 2)-*O*-α-D-glucopyranosyl)-*sn*-glycerol

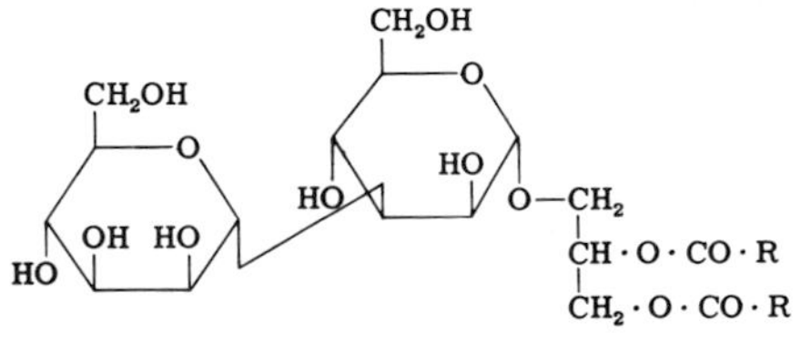

(e) 1,2-diacyl-3-*O*-(α-D-mannopyranosyl-(1 → 3)-*O*-α-D-mannopyranosyl)-*sn*-glycerol

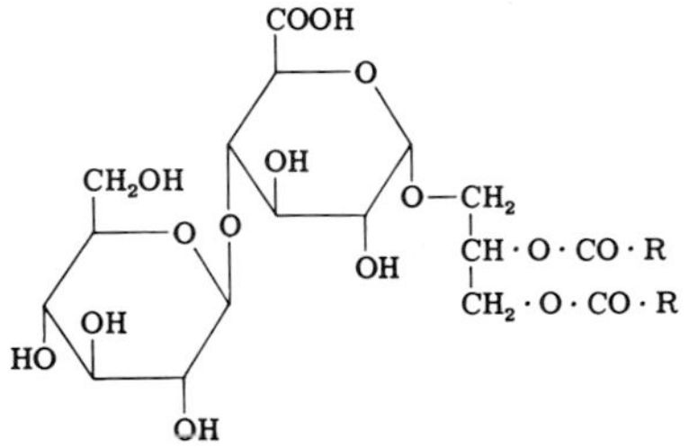

(f) 1,2-diacyl-3-*O*-(β-D-glucopyranosyl-(1 → 4)-*O*-α-D-glucuronopranosyl-)-*sn*-glycerol

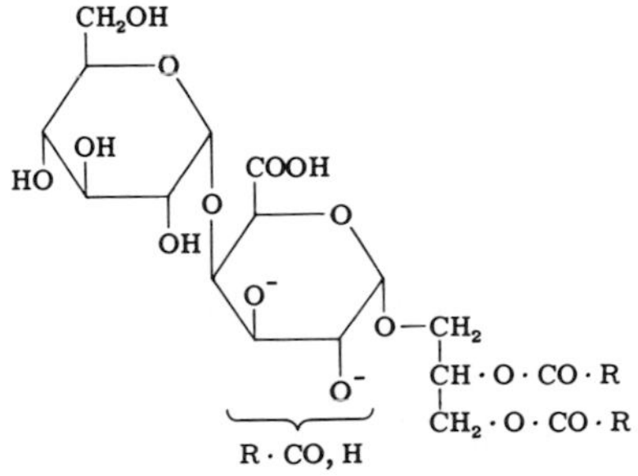

(g) 1,2-diacyl-3-*O*-(α-D-glucopyranosyl-(1 → 4)-*O*-α-2 or 3-acyl-D-galacturonopyranosyl)-*sn*-glycerol

FIG. 3. Structures of bacterial diglycosyl diglycerides.

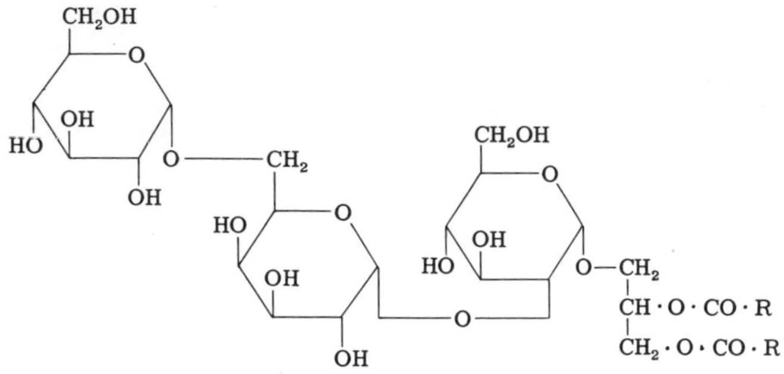

(a) Glucosylgalactosylglucosyl diglyceride

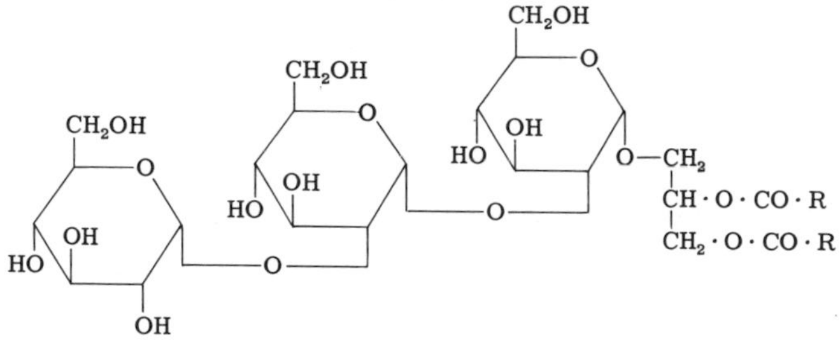

(b) Triglucosyl diglyceride

FIG. 4. Structures of triglycosyl diglycerides found in bacteria.

been detected in *Bifidobacterium bifidum* (Exterkate and Veerkamp, 1969; Veerkamp, 1972). A similar acylgalactosyl diglyceride found in plants is believed to be not a normal component, but formed on cell disruption by acyl transfer from a di- to monogalactosyl diglyceride (Heinz, 1967b). It is not known whether the acylglycosyl diglycerides found in bacteria are also produced by such acyl transfer.

Recently, the occurrence of phosphoglycolipids has been reported in several bacteria (Shaw *et al.*, 1970; Wilkinson and Bell, 1971; Ambrone and Pieringer, 1971; Shaw and Stead, 1972). Though the structures of these lipids have not been completely established, they have been identified as glycosyl diglycerides to which an acylated glycerophosphate is attached by phosphodiester linkage at the C-6 hydroxyls of one of the sugar residues.

2. *Fatty Acid Composition*

The fatty acid composition of glycosyl glycerides has been determined in a number of bacteria (Table VII). In the galactosyl glyceride of *Chloropseudomonas ethylicum*, palmitic and palmitoleic are the predominant fatty acids, with only small amounts of oleic acid; the complete absence of polyunsaturated fatty acids in photosynthetic bacteria is in striking contrast to the fatty acid composition of galactosyl glycerides of photosynthetic tissues of higher plants (Constantopoulos and Bloch, 1967a). In the other bacterial species, normal and branched fatty acids are the predominant acyl residues of glycosyl glycerides. In general, fatty acid composition of bacterial glycosyl glycerides resembles that of the total lipids of the same organism. However, significant differences have been noted in the fatty acid composition of total lipids and the diglucosyl diglyceride of *Streptococcus lactis* (Brundish *et al.*, 1967). A remarkably high content of cyclopropane acids has been reported in the glucuronosyl diglyceride of an unidentified halophile (Peleg and Tietz, 1971).

3. *Correlation of Distribution with Taxonomy*

There appears to exist a correlation between the lipid components found in various bacteria and their taxonomic classification. This has been observed previously with fatty acids and phospholipids (see Kates, 1964a) and may now be extended to glycosyl glycerides (Shaw and Baddiley, 1968; Shaw, 1970).

Glycosyl glycerides are widespread among Gram-positive bacteria, though it is not certain whether their occurrence is universal in this class of organisms. Among the several structural types of diglycosyl diglycerides found in bacteria, organisms belonging to the same genus or closely related species contain the same glycosyl diglycerides. However, the same glycosyl glyceride can be found in bacteria of different families. In the case of *Arthrobacter globiformis* and others of this genus, two unrelated types of diglycosyl glycerides have been found (Table VI), and it is not known whether this is related to the two morphological forms in which these organisms exist (Shaw, 1970).

Glycosyl glycerides have also been found in some Gram-negative bacteria such as photosynthetic bacteria, *Pseudomonas,* halophiles, and *Mycoplasma.* Recently, these glycolipids have been shown to occur in *Vibrio fetus* and *Butyrylvibrio fibrisolvens* (Tornabene and Ogg, 1971; Kunsman, 1970). Thus several Gram-negative bacteria contain the glycosyl glycerides though their occurrence in these organisms appears to be limited.

C. Animals

For the first time in animal tissues, Steim and Benson (1963) detected galactosylglycerol among the deacylation products of lipids from mammalian brain of several species and concluded that galactosyl glyceride

Table VII

FATTY ACID COMPOSITION (%) OF BACTERIAL GLYCOSYL GLYCERIDES

Organism	Glycosyl diglyceride (glycosyl moiety)	12:0 + 14:0	15:0 + 15: Unsat.	16:0	16:1	18:0	18:1	Others	Branched[a]					Cyclopropane		Ref.[f]
									13:br	14:br	15:br	16:br	17:br	17:cy	19:cy	
Chloropseudomonas ethylicum	Gal-			45	49		4	2								(1)
Pseudomonas rubescens	Glc-	1	3	14	34	1	16	17[b]	1	1	10	1	3			(2)
	Glucuronosyl-	1	3	13	35	1	16	18[b]	1	1	9	1	3			
P. diminuta	Glc-			18	3		77	2								(3)
	Glucuronosyl-			23	2		72	3								
	Glc-Glucuronosyl-			24	2		62	12[c]								
Moderate halophile (unidentified)	Glucuronosyl-			28		3	Tr							8	62	(4)
Micrococcus lysodiekticus	Man-Man-			9		9		3			58		12			(5)
Staphylococcus lactis I3	Glc-Glc-	3		14	13	3	2	54								(6)

Pneumococcus															
Type I	Gal-Glc-	28		34	26	3	10								(7)
Type XIV	Glc-	9		38	20	4	29								(8)
	Gal-Glc-	20		43	19	2	16								
Lactobacillus casei ATCC 7469	Gal-Glc- + Glc-Gal-Glc-	2		37	3	3	34							17	(9)
Listeria monocytogenes	Gal-Glc-	3		5						1	41	6	44		(10)
Bacillus cereus	Glc-Glc-	3		10					4	4	44	8	27		(11)
Streptomyces LA 7017	Glc-Acyl galacturonosyl-	3	55	4				39							(12)
Mycoplasma spp. strain J	Triacyl Glc-	1		5	5	8	63	19[d]							(13)
M. mycoides	Galactofuranosyl-	1		18		49	24	8[e]							(14)

[a] Values include both iso and anteiso-isomers.

[b] Contains 17:0, 3%; 17:1, 13%.

[c] Contains 19:1, 11%.

[d] Contains 18:2, 15%.

[e] Contains 18:2, 3%.

[f] Key to references: (1) Constantopoulos and Bloch (1967a); (2) Wilkinson (1968b); (3) Wilkinson (1969); (4) Peleg and Tietz (1971); (5) Macfarlane (1962); (6) Brundish *et al.* (1967); (7) Brundish *et al.* (1965a); (8) Kaufman *et al.* (1965); (9) Shaw *et al.* (1968a); (10) Carroll *et al.* (1968); (11) Saito and Mukoyama (1971); (12) Bergelson *et al.* (1970); (13) Smith and Mayberry (1968); (14) Plackett (1967).

occurs in brain tissue. Its concentration was estimated to be approximately 2% of total glycerophosphatides. This observation was confirmed by a number of workers (Norton and Brotz, 1963; Rouser *et al.*, 1963; Rumsby and Gray, 1965). Monogalactosyl diglyceride was isolated from bovine spinal cord and its structure was established as 1,2-diacyl-3-*O*-β-D-galactopyranosyl-*sn*-glycerol, identical to the plant monogalactolipid (Steim, 1967). Several animal tissues have now been examined for the presence of glycosyl glycerides (Table VIII). Significantly, the occurrence of monogalactosyl diglyceride is confined only to nervous tissues in all the animal species investigated. It occurs, however, in both the central and peripheral nervous systems. This lipid is found only in the white matter of the brain (Steim, 1967) and it is probably a component of myelin lipids. Galactosyl diglyceride could not be detected in liver, spleen, and a variety of other tissues and only trace amounts could be detected in the kidney (Steim, 1967; Inoue *et al.*, 1971). In whole brain,

Table VIII
DISTRIBUTION OF MONOGALACTOSYL GLYCERIDE IN ANIMAL TISSUES
(Values are given as nmoles/gm wet wt*)

Species/tissue	Bovine	Cat	Pig	Rat	Sheep	Mouse	Human
Brain	+[a], 267[d]	+[a]	+[a], 135[d]	+[a], 204[b]	398[d]	438[c]	+[a]
Spinal cord	1810[a]	+		600[b]			
Sciatic nerve				464[b]			
Kidney	+[a]			Ca 0.9[b]			
Liver	−[a]			−[b]	−[e]		
Spleen, intestine	−[a]			−[b]			
Mammary gland	−[a]						
Serum, red and white blood cells, heart, lung, sternal bone, thigh muscle, stomach, skin, testis epididymis and epididymal fat pad				−[b]			

* *a,b,c*: values exclude ether analogs; *d*: values include ether analogs.
Key to symbols: +, Detected; −, not detected.
[a] Calculated data from Steim (1967). Molecular weight of monogalactosyl glyceride was taken as 756.
[b] Inoue *et al.* (1971).
[c] Deshmukh *et al.* (1971). 18-day-old mice used.
[d] Calculated data from Rumsby and Rossiter (1968). Molecular weight of monogalactosyl diglyceride was assumed to be 756.
[e] Rumsby (1967).

Table IX

CHANGE IN CONCENTRATION OF MONOGALACTOSYL DIGLYCERIDE WITH AGE IN RAT BRAIN AND ITS FRACTIONS[a]

			Rat brain fractions[c]					
Age (days)	Whole brain[b]	Whole brain[c]	Total myelin	Large myelin	Small myelin	Micro-somes	Mito-chondria	Synaptic vesi-cles
3	50	—	—	—	—	—	—	—
6	60	23	4	3	3	4	3	3
9	—	28	4	3	3	4	3	3
12	310	—	—	—	—	—	—	—
17	—	291	63	6	58	83	9	54
18	860	—	—	—	—	—	—	—
20	—	1032	92	4	92	417	18	92
23	—	538	187	38	158	92	8	83
24	1290	—	—	—	—	—	—	—
42	1460	—	—	—	—	—	—	—
100	—	288	179	83	92	38	6	31
180	1560	—	—	—	—	—	—	—
330	1620	—	—	—	—	—	—	—
365	—	129	108	58	50	25	3	19

[a] Value in millimoles per gm wet weight. Values exclude ether analogs.
[b] Wells and Dittmer (1967).
[c] Calculated data from Inoue *et al.* (1971).

the concentration of monogalactosyl diglyceride increases with age (Table IX). Wells and Dittmer (1967) reported that this glycolipid occurs at concentrations less than 10% of that found in adult brain up to the onset of myelination, increases rapidly in concentration during the period of active myelination, and the increased levels are maintained in the adult animal. Inoue *et al.* (1971) confirmed the rapid increase of this lipid in brain during myelination, but noted that it reaches a maximum around 20 days after birth in rats and decreases considerably thereafter. Further work is necessary to explain the discrepancy in the two reports. Significantly, the brain of the Jimpy mouse, a mutant with severe deficiency of myelin in the central nervous system, has very low concentrations of monogalactosyl diglyceride (Deshmukh *et al.*, 1971). Studies on subcellular distribution of galactosyl diglyceride in brain have shown that it is associated mainly with microsomes, myelin, and synaptic vesicles (Table IX).

The fatty acid composition of galactosyl diglyceride of nervous tissues is completely different from that found in plant tissues. Palmitic, stearic, and oleic acids are the major fatty acids found in the galactosyl diglyc-

Table X
FATTY ACID COMPOSITION (%) OF MONOGALACTOSYL DIGLYCERIDE IN NERVOUS TISSUES OF VARIOUS SPECIES

Fatty acid	Bovine spinal cord[a]	Sheep brain[b]
10:0	—	Tr
12:0	—	Tr
14:0	2.6	10.3
15:0	0.4	2.6
16:0	53.2	56.4
16:1	2.0	2.6
17:0	2.1	—
18:0	7.9	18.0
18:1	22.3	5.1
18:2	1.0	—
18:3	5.4	—
20:0	0.9	5.1
20:0 (?)	1.9	—

[a] Steim (1967).
[b] Rumsby (1967).

eride of bovine spinal cord and sheep brain (Table X). Unlike cerebrosides and sulfatides, hydroxy fatty acids have not been found in this lipid (Steim, 1967).

A monoalkyl ether analog of monogalactosyl diglyceride has been isolated from bovine, pig, and sheep brains and its structure was shown to be 1-alkyl-2-acyl-3-*O*-β-D-galactopyranosyl-*sn*-glycerol (Fig. 5) (Norton and Brotz, 1963; Rumsby and Rossiter, 1968). The ether analog accounts for about 8–12% of the total galactosyl glyceride of brain tissue in the above species. Chimyl alcohol (C 16:0 in the shorthand system of Wood and Snyder, 1966) accounts for 70–83% of the total alkylglycerol ethers of galactosyl glycerides isolated from the brains of several species (Table XI).

A digalactosyl diglyceride, identical in structure to that found in plants, has been found only as a biosynthetic product in *in vitro* studies with

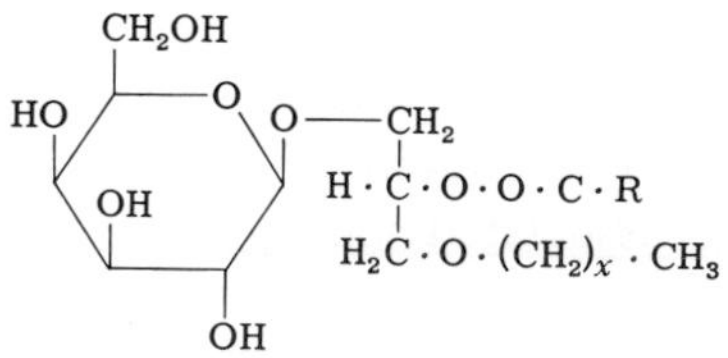

FIG. 5. Structure of 1-alkyl-2-acyl-3-*O*-β-D-galactopyranosyl-*sn*-glycerol found in brain.

Table XI
COMPOSITION (%) OF ALKYL ETHERS ISOLATED FROM MONOGALACTOSYL GLYCERIDE FRACTIONS OF BRAIN TISSUE

Alkyl ether[a]	Bovine[b]	Bovine[c]	Pig[c]	Sheep[c]
10:0	—	2.8	4.2	1.7
11:0	—	1.5	2.1	0.7
12:0	—	0.3	tr	tr
13:0	—	1.0	1.4	1.7
14:0	10.0	8.5	8.1	7.6
15:0	—	2.7	1.4	2.2
16:0	83.0	69.5	71.5	69.7
16:1	—	0.6	1.3	0.7
17:0	—	2.4	1.6	1.6
18:0	2.0	4.7	3.4	7.5
18:Un	2.0	6.1	5.0	6.7

[a] Shorthand system of Wood and Snyder (1966).
[b] Norton and Brotz (1967).
[c] Average data of two (bovine and pig) or three (sheep) analyses (Rumsby and Rossiter, 1968).

brain particulate preparations (Wenger *et al.*, 1970). This lipid has not been detected so far in brain lipid extracts, probably because it occurs in concentrations too low for detection.

V. Chemical Synthesis

A. GLYCOSYLGLYCEROLS

Glycosylglycerols are the water-soluble, deacylation products of glycosyl glycerides. As it is more convenient to separate and identify the glycosylglycerols, a number of these compounds have been synthesized during the structural investigations on naturally occurring glycosyl glycerides. Wickberg (1958b) synthesized *O*-α-D-galactopyranosyl- and *O*-β-D-galactopyranosyl-(1 → 1)-D-glycerols by the condensation of tetra-*O*-acetyl-α-D-galactopyranosyl bromide and methylene bis-2-*O*-(3-*O*-benzoyl-D-glycerol). The corresponding anomeric L-glycerol galactosides were synthesized by reaction with 2,3-di-*O*-benzyl-L-glycerol. By an entirely different procedure, the *O*-α-D-galactopyranosyl- and *O*-β-D-galactopyranosyl-(1 → 2)-glycerols have also been prepared (Charlson *et al.*, 1957). Recently, Brundish and Baddiley (1968) reported the synthesis of *O*-α-D-glucopyranosyl- and *O*-β-D-glucopyranosyl-(1 → 1)-D-glycerols as well as the corresponding anomeric L-glycerol galactosides.

In addition, the four positional isomers of *O*-β-D-glucopyranosyl-(1 → X)-*O*-β-D-glucopyranosyl-(1 → 1)-D-glycerols (X = 2,3,4, or 6) have been synthesized by the condensation of the appropriate hepta-*O*-acetyldisaccharide bromides and methylene bis-2-*O*-(3-*O*-benzoyl-D-glycerol). Using a similar procedure, *O*-α-D-galactopyranosyl-(1 → 2)-*O*-α-D-glucopyranosyl-(1 → 1)-D-glycerol, the deacylation product of the major glycosyl diglyceride of *Pneumococcus*, has also been synthesized (Brundish *et al.*, 1967). From these synthetic studies, physical and chromatographic data (see Section III, C, Table I) are now available, information that should prove useful in the identification of glycosyl glycerides occurring in nature.

B. Glycosyl Glycerides

The complete synthesis of glycosyl diglycerides has been accomplished only recently. Wehrli and Pomeranz (1969) synthesized 1,2-dipalmitoyl- and 1-palmitoyl, 2-linoleoyl-3-*O*-(β-D-galactopyranosyl)-*sn*-glycerols by a procedure that involves acylation of the primary hydroxyl groups of 2,5-methylene-D-mannitol, cleavage of the mannitol moiety between C-3 and C-4 by lead tetraacetate, reduction of the resulting aldehyde, attachment of galactose by the Koenigs-Knorr reaction, hydrolysis of the acetal, acylation of the hydroxyl group, and hydrazinolysis of the acetylated glycolipids. A simplified procedure resulting in the loss of optical activity at C-2 of the glycerol moiety has also been described. Using the orthoester method of synthesis of the diglyceride-carbohydrate glycosidic bond, 1,2-dipalmitoyl-3-*O*-(β-D-glucopyranosyl)-*sn*-glycerol and 1,2-dipalmitoyl-3-*O*-(α-D-mannopyranosyl)-*sn*-glycerol have been obtained in good yield (Bashkatova *et al.*, 1971a). This method has also been used successfully for the synthesis of diglycosyl diglycerides (Bashkatova *et al.*, 1971b; Shvets *et al.*, 1973).

Semisynthetic methods for the preparation of monogalactosyl- and digalactosyl diglycerides having identical or different fatty acids at the 1- and 2-positions of the glycerol moiety have been devised (Heinz, 1971). The procedure here consists of isolation of galactosyl glycerides from natural sources, substitution of the hydroxyl hydrogens of the galactosyl residues by *O*-(1-methoxyethyl) groups, removal of the acyl groups with sodium methoxide, acylation with the desired fatty acyl chloride, and hydrolysis of the protecting groups with boric acid. This procedure may also be used for the preparation of galactosyl monoglycerides (Heisig and Heinz, 1972).

VI. Metabolism in Plants, Bacteria, and Animals

A. Biosynthesis

Studies on the incorporation of acetate-^{14}C into the runner bean leaf lipids (Kates, 1960) and $^{14}CO_2$ into the lipids of *Chlorella pyrenoidosa* (Ferrari and Benson, 1961) during photosynthesis have shown a rapid incorporation of the label into the mono- and digalactosyl diglycerides. In fact, glycosyl glycerides were found to be the most rapidly labeled lipids in *Chlorella* and time course studies indicated that monogalactosyl diglyceride may be the precursor for the digalactosyl diglyceride. Based on these observations, Ferrari and Benson (1961) proposed that the biosynthesis of glycosyl glycerides occurs by stepwise addition of galactose residues to diglyceride from UDP-galactose (reactions 1 and 2).

$$\text{1,2-Diacyl-}sn\text{-glycerol} + \text{UDP-galactose} \rightarrow \text{monogalactosyl diglyceride} \quad (1)$$

$$\text{Monogalactosyl diglyceride} + \text{UDP-galactose} \rightarrow \text{digalactosyl diglyceride} \quad (2)$$

Evidence in support of this biosynthetic pathway was obtained by Neufeld and Hall (1964) who found that isolated spinach chloroplasts catalyze the transfer of galactose from UDP-galactose-^{14}C to an uncharacterized endogenous acceptor yielding mono-, di-, and probably tri-, and tetragalactosyl diglycerides. Of a number of sugar nucleotides tested, only UDP-galactose and UDP-glucose served as the glycosyl donors, and the efficacy of the latter has been attributed to the presence of UDP-galactose epimerase activity in the chloroplasts. More direct experimental proof for the above biosynthetic pathway was provided by Ongun and Mudd (1968). These authors observed in spinach chloroplasts, a 95% incorporation of the label from UDP-galactose-^{14}C into monogalactosyl and digalactosyl diglycerides, and a third compound tentatively identified as trigalactosyl diglyceride. By using acetone powder of chloroplasts, it was demonstrated that diolein is an efficient acceptor for the biosynthesis of monogalactosyl diglyceride, but not for the digalactosyl diglyceride. The biosynthesis of digalactosyl and trigalactosyl diglycerides was shown to involve galactosylation of the mono- and digalactosyl diglycerides, respectively. Evidence was also presented indicating that separate enzymes are responsible for the synthesis of monogalactosyl and digalactosyl diglycerides, the former being more tightly bound to the membranes. It appears likely that two enzymes are involved in the glycolipid biosynthesis, one for the formation of β-glycosidic bond and the other for the α-glycosidic bond. The enzyme system in leaves shows a light-induced increase in activity, but such activity is not confined to chlorophyllous tissues alone. Active glycolipid synthesis has also been found with particles from etiolated pea leaves and other nonchlorophyllous tissues (Ongun and Mudd, 1968). The synthesis of galactosyl diglycerides by spinach chloroplasts is optimal at pH 7.2 and the proportion of monogalactosyl diglyceride decreases while that of digalactosyl diglyceride increases as the pH is lowered. On the other hand, the enzymes are resistant to elevated temperatures, show maximum activity at 45°C, and the proportion of monogalactosyl diglyceride synthesized is more at higher temperature. Diglycerides with a high degree unsaturation serve as the most efficient acceptors in this biosynthetic reaction (Mudd *et al.*, 1969). The chloroplast appears to be the chief site of glycolipid biosynthesis and measures to preserve the integrity of chloroplast result in increased enzyme activity (Helmsing and Barendese, 1970). A soluble subchloroplast fraction from spinach has been obtained that shows active biosynthesis of galactosyl glycerides from UDP-galactose (Chang and Kulkarni, 1970). However, as much as 40% of the glycolipid-synthesizing capability of spinach leaf homogenate is nonparticulate (Mudd *et al.*, 1969). Significant incorporation of galactose into glycolipids from UDP-galactose-^{14}C has also been observed with avocado and cauliflower mitochondria, but not from pea root mitochondria (Ongun and Mudd, 1970). Active incorporation of galactose moieties from UDP-galactose-^{14}C into mono- and digalactosyl diglycerides on illumination of dark-grown maize seedlings was recently reported; experiments with an acetone powder preparation of fully greened up maize chloroplasts showed diolein to be an effective exogenous acceptor of the first galactosylation, and endogenous maize monogalactosyl diglyceride of the second (Bowden and Williams, 1973). It appears likely that monogalactosyl diglyceride molecules, containing little polyunsaturated fatty acids, are selectively utilized in the biosynthesis of digalactosyl diglyceride in plants (Boling and El Baya, 1972). The sulfhydryl nature of the galactosyltransferases has been established with spinach chloroplast preparations (Chang, 1970; Mudd *et al.*, 1971).

Biosynthesis of galactosyl diglycerides from UDP-galactose has also been reported in *Euglena gracilis* chloroplasts (Matson *et al.*, 1970). It has been observed that the chloroplasts obtained from photosynthetic cells, both photoauxotrophic and photoheterotrophic, catalyze the transfer of galactose while the dark-grown cells are essentially devoid of such enzyme activity, implying that the photosynthetic condition is essential in this organism for the biosynthesis of glycolipids. Further, in contrast to spinach chloroplasts, the incorporation of galactose was more into the digalactosyl diglyceride than into monogalactosyl diglyceride with *E. gracilis* chloroplasts. Here again, separate enzymes appear to be involved in the biosynthesis of monogalactosyl and digalactosyl diglycerides (Lin and Chang, 1971), and mercuric salts are strongly inhibitory (Matson *et al.*, 1972).

The aforementioned studies firmly establish the role of diglycerides in the biosynthesis of galactosyl glycerides, but the origin of the diglyceride moiety is not completely understood. This is of particular significance because diglycerides are common precursors for both phospholipids and glycolipids, though the two classes of lipids differ widely in their fatty acid composition. Thus, phosphatidyl choline from runner bean leaf (Sastry and Kates, 1964b) and from leaves of a number of other species (Bajwa and Sastry, 1972a) contains considerable amounts of saturated fatty acids in position-1 of the glycerol moiety while glycosyl glycerides of photosynthetic tissues contain mainly polyunsaturated fatty acids. Studies of Renkonen and Bloch (1969) showed that cell-free extracts of green *E. gracilis* catalyze the transfer of acyl groups from thioesters of acyl carrier protein or coenzyme A to monogalactosyl diglyceride, but not to digalactosyl diglyceride; this reaction was stimulated by *sn*-glycerol-3-phosphate. These experiments suggest that the diglyceride is formed by acylation of glycerophosphate followed by the dephosphorylation of phosphatidic acid. The presence of a microsomal acyl-CoA-glycerophosphate acyltransferase has been shown in plant tissues (Sastry and Kates, 1966). Further support for this pathway is indicated by the observation that plastids (chloroplasts and etioplasts), isolated from spinach leaves, incorporate label from *sn*-glycerol-^{14}C-3-phosphate into monogalactosyl diglyceride (Douce and Guillot-Salomon, 1970). These studies, however, do not account for the characteristic highly unsaturated fatty acid distribution found in glycosyl glycerides. Though Mudd *et al.* (1969) observed that the galactose acceptor capacity of diglycerides increases with increase in unsaturation, detailed studies by Eccleshall and Hawke (1971) on the UDP-galactose: 1,2-di-*O*-acyl-*sn*-glycerol galactosyltransferase in spinach chloroplasts showed no specificity for diglycerides of particular fatty acid composition. It therefore appears likely that the fatty acids residues in glycosyl glycerides are desaturated after *de novo* synthesis. Studies on the incorporation of labeled acetate into monogalactosyl diglyceride of *Chlorella vulgaris* (Nichols and Moorhouse, 1969; Gurr, 1971; Appleby *et al.*, 1971), and the variation observed in the specific activity of a single fatty acid among the various monogalactosyl diglyceride species support this view. Alternatively, a deacylation-reacylation mechanism may bring about the specific fatty acid pattern of glycosyl diglycerides. Evidence in favor of this possibility is the enzymic conversion of monogalactosyl monoglycerides to monogalactosyl diglycerides (reaction 3) recently demonstrated in spinach leaf homogenates (Safford *et al.*, 1971). This reaction has also been found to be catalyzed by New Zealand spinach (*Tetragonia expansa*) chloroplast acetone powders. In this system, unsaturated fatty

$$\text{2-Acyl-3-}(O\text{-}\beta\text{-galactosyl})\text{-}sn\text{-glycerol} + \text{RCOOH} \xrightarrow{\text{CoASH, ATP} + \text{Mg}^{++}} \text{1,2-diacyl-3-}(O\text{-}\beta\text{-galactosyl})\text{-}sn\text{-glycerol} \quad (3)$$

acids were preferentially incorporated and α-linolenic acid was a better substrate than oleate (Bajwa and Sastry, 1973). Incorporation of fatty acids, from fatty acyl-CoA derivatives (Gamini Kannangara and Stumpf, 1971) or in the presence of ATP and coenzyme A (Bajwa and Sastry, 1972b), into monogalactosyl diglycerides has been shown in spinach chloroplasts. Higher incorporations were observed with oleic and α-linolenic acids and this was stimulated by the addition of galactosylglycerol indicating the possibility of acylation of galactosylglycerol in spinach chloroplasts (Bajwa and Sastry, 1972b). It is of interest to note here that an asymmetric transfer of galactose from β-galactosides to glycerol, resulting in the formation of 3-*O*-β-galactosyl-*sn*-glycerol has been found with β-galactosidase from *E. coli* (Boos *et al.*, 1966). The reactions established in plants for the biosynthesis of galactosyl diglycerides are shown in Fig. 6.

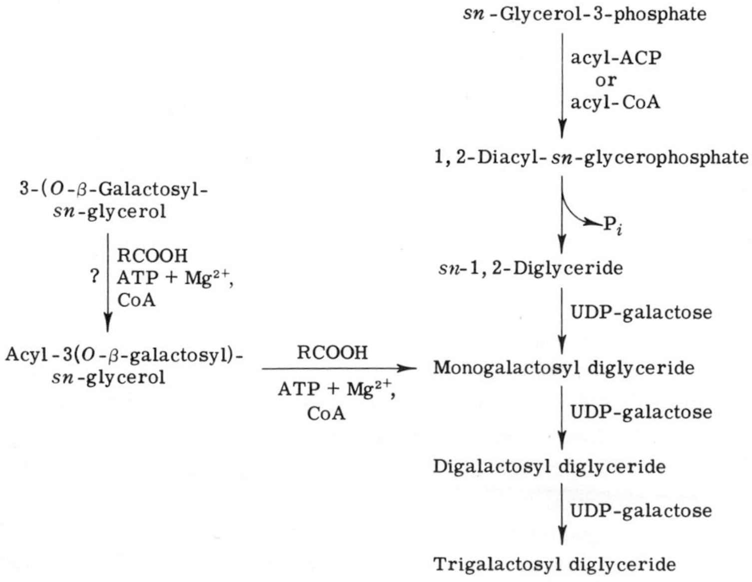

FIG. 6. Biosynthetic pathways of galactosyl diglycerides.

Biosynthesis of glycosyl glycerides in bacteria occurs by reactions analogous to those in plants. In *Pneumococcus* Type XIV, galactosylglucosyl diglyceride is enzymatically synthesized by the transfer of galactose from UDP-galactose to glucosyl diglyceride (Kaufman *et al.*, 1965). Presumably, this organism synthesizes the glucosyl diglyceride from UDP-glucose and diglyceride. The biosynthesis of mannosyl diglycerides in *M. lysodiekticus,* however, involves GDP-mannose as the sugar nucleotide, and two enzymes have been shown to be involved in this process (Lennarz and Talamo, 1966).

$$\text{Diglyceride} + \text{GDP-mannose} \rightarrow \alpha\text{-D-mannosyl-}(1 \rightarrow 3)\text{-diglyceride} \quad (4)$$

$$\xrightarrow{\text{GDP-mannose}} \alpha\text{-D-mannosyl-}(1 \rightarrow 3)\text{-}\alpha\text{-D-mannosyl-}(1 \rightarrow 3)\text{-diglyceride} \quad (5)$$

The enzyme that catalyzes the formation of mannosyl diglyceride (reaction 4) is associated with the particulate fraction, specific for 1,2-diglyceride and shows maximal activity with diglycerides containing branched chain fatty acyl groups. A second enzyme present in soluble fraction catalyzes the synthesis of dimannosyl diglyceride (reaction 5). Pieringer (1968) demonstrated that particulate enzyme preparations of *Streptococcus faecalis* catalyze the synthesis of monoglucosyl and diglucosyl diglycerides as well as a third glycolipid of unknown structure from UDP-glucose and diglyceride. The biosynthetic enzyme(s) are specific toward 1,2-*sn*-diglyceride and the glycolipids appear to be formed sequentially. The biosynthesis of glucuronosyl diglyceride found in an unidentified halophile, was shown to occur by the transfer of glucuronic acid from UDP-glucuronic acid to diglyceride. This reaction was demonstrated with cell-free particles, and the system required the addition of 1,2-diglycerides, which contained cyclopropane fatty acids (Stern and Tietz, 1971, 1973). A similar reaction was also shown for the biosynthesis of glucuronosyl diglyceride with particulate fractions from *Pseudomonas diminuta* (Shaw and Pieringer, 1972).

In animal tissues, the biosynthesis of monogalactosyl and digalactosyl diglycerides has been demonstrated in brain (Wenger *et al.*, 1968, 1970), the only tissue where monogalactosyl diglyceride occurs in significant concentrations. Microsomal preparations of rat brain catalyze the synthesis of monogalactosyl diglyceride from UDP-galactose and diglyceride. The enzyme is localized in microsomes, requires 1,2-*sn*-diglyceride and prefers diglycerides with long-chain fatty acids. Particulate enzyme preparations from rat brain also catalyze the synthesis of digalactosyl diglyceride from UDP-galactose and diglyceride, presumably through the intermediate formation of monogalactosyl diglyceride. Sodium deoxycholate is required in this reaction. There is evidence to show that microsomes are the site of synthesis of the glycolipids though they are primarily deposited in myelin (Inoue *et al.*, 1971). The synthetic ability for both the glycolipids in rat brain varies with the age of the animal. Maximal activities were observed in brains of rats 14–18 days old, the period when myelination occurs at a maximal rate. Significantly, little or no synthesis of glycolipids could be found in the brains of the myelin-deficient Jimpy mice (Deshmukh *et al.*, 1971).

Bossmann (1969) has shown that Triton X-100 extracts of HeLa cells incorporate L-fucosyl and D-mannosyl groups from their respective GDP-esters into endogenous lipid acceptors. Though the products were not fully characterized, distinct glycoglycerolipids were found to be synthesized with each sugar. Furthermore, with an acetone-power preparation, the reaction was shown to be stimulated by diglycerides. Diolein and dipalmitin served as exogenous acceptors in the mannose and fucose systems, respectively, while distearin was ineffective for either sugar.

B. Enzymic Degradation

The enzymic degradation of glycosyl diglycerides was demonstrated first in runner bean leaves, where these enzymes manifest their activity immediately after the leaf cells are disrupted causing the almost complete hydrolysis of the endogenous glycolipids (Sastry and Kates, 1964c). The possible enzymic reactions leading to the complete breakdown of the glycosyl diglycerides are illustrated in Fig. 7 and involve the hydrolysis of the ester bonds (galactolipases) and the glycosidic bonds of the intact lipids or the galactosylglycerols (galactosidases).

In runner bean leaves, Sastry and Kates (1964c) showed that both the chloroplast and cell-sap cytoplasm fractions contain enzymes that catalyze the hydrolysis of mono- and digalactosyl dilinolenins to the corresponding galactosylglycerols and free fatty acids. Though the hydrolysis may involve a stepwise deacylation with the intermediate formation of galactosyl monoglycerides, no evidence for the formation of these compounds was noticed. A partially purified enzyme preparation was inactive toward saturated galactosyl diglycerides and was free of lipase and phospholipase indicating that the enzyme preparation was specific for unsaturated glycolipids. Further, the runner bean enzyme preparation showed different pH optima, Michaelis-Menten constants, and stability (on storage at 4° for several days) in its activity toward mono- and digalactosyl dilinolenins, suggesting that separate enzyme systems may be involved. Cell-sap cytoplasm also showed α- and β-galactosidase activities that catalyzed the hydrolysis of galactosylglycerols to galactose and glycerol, thus establishing that the enzymes necessary for the complete breakdown of glycosyl glycerides exist in leaves.

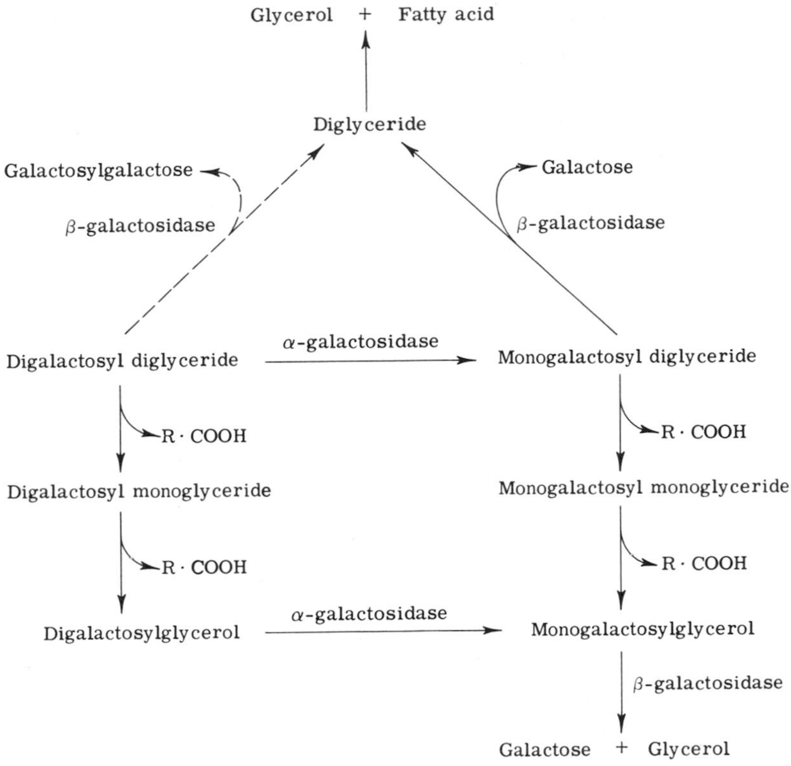

FIG. 7. Enzymic degradation of galactosyl diglycerides.

Leaves from a number of plant species have been examined, but the presence of galactolipases could be demonstrated only in the leaves of *Phaseolus* species; spinach leaves showed very feeble enzyme activity (Sastry and Kates, 1964c). However, Helmsing (1967a) found significant galactolipase activity in an extract from young spinach leaves which varied considerably on storage. This spinach enzyme preparation showed maximal activity toward monogalactosyl diglyceride after 10 days while that toward digalactosyl diglyceride decreased sharply after 4 days of storage at 4°. More recently, Helmsing (1969) isolated a single protein from runner bean leaves that contained both mono- and digalactolipase activities with a specific activity ratio of 2:1. This enzyme is quite stable, activated by strong reductants such as sodium dithionite, completely inhibited by cysteine, and has a molecular weight of 110,000. The formation of galactosyl monoglyceride intermediates has not been detected with the purified runner bean enzyme also. In contrast, an enzyme preparation that catalyzes the deacylation of glycolipids, phospholipids as well as mono- and diglycerides was partially purified from potato tubers (Galliard, 1971). The potato enzyme shows some similarities with the runner bean galactolipase in that it is localized in particle-free supernatant and has a molecular weight of 107,000. However, the potato enzyme is apparently a nonspecific acyl hydrolase and also hydrolyzes monogalactosyl diglyceride with a sequential release of fatty acids (Galliard, 1970). Among algae, *Scenedesmus* extract failed to hydrolyze galactosyl diglyceride (Yagi and Benson, 1962), while *Chlorella vulgaris* homogenates seem to possess galactolipase activity (Safford *et al.*, 1971). An assay method for monogalactosyl and digalactosyl diglyceride acyl hydrolase has been described (Sastry and Kates, 1969).

It has been observed that the photochemical activities of the chloroplasts (Hill reaction and photosynthetic phosphorylation) are impaired when chloroplasts are isolated under conditions where galactolipases manifest their activity and liberate linolenic acid (McCarty and Jagendorf, 1965; Constantopoulos and Kenyon, 1968; Wintermans *et al.*, 1969).

During the breakdown of glycosyl glycerides in leaf homogenates transacylation reactions occur resulting in the formation of 6-*O*-acylgalactosyl diglyceride (see Section IV,A,3). The transacylation was shown to be enzymic with an optimum pH at 4.6 and acylgalactosyl diglyceride is formed by an acyl transfer from monogalactosyl diglyceride by dismutation or from digalactosyl diglyceride or phospholipids (Heinz, 1967b). The enzymic transacylation was also observed when sucrose or mannitol was used in the media for homogenization of leaf tissues (Wintermans *et al.*, 1969).

Purified β-galactosidase from spinach leaves hydrolyzed monogalactosyl diglyceride adsorbed on Celite but neither α- nor β-galactosidase from this source showed hydrolytic activity on digalactosyl diglyceride isolated from *Anacystis nidulans* (Gatt and Baker, 1970). This would suggest that at least monogalactosyl diglyceride may be degraded in leaves by a different pathway (see Fig. 7).

The enzymic breakdown of glycosyl glycerides has been shown in animal tissues. Commercial pancreatic enzyme preparations hydrolyze galactosyl glycerides (Sastry and Kates, 1964c; Noda and Fujiwara, 1967) to the corresponding galactosylglycerols and fatty acids. The intermediate formation of galactosyl monoglycerides with the pancreatic enzymes has been demonstrated (Noda and Fujiwara, 1967). Studies in this laboratory with sheep pancreatic acetone powder confirmed the galactolipase activity in this tissue. A partially purified enzyme from this source catalyzed the hydrolysis of glycosyl glycerides, phosphatidyl choline, methyl oleate, and triglyceride. The pancreatic acetone powder also possessed α- and β-galactosidases resulting in the total hydrolysis of glycolipids. Our results further suggest that the pancreatic α-galactosidase hydrolyzes digalactosyl diglyceride to monogalactosyl diglyceride, and the latter is hydrolyzed by the β-galactosidase to form galactose and diglyceride to a limited extent (Bajwa and Sastry, unpublished data). The presence of lipase and galactosidases catalyzing the hydrolysis of galactosyl glycerides was also shown in the brain tissue. At pH 7.2, brain microsomal fraction shows galactolipase activity toward mono- and digalactosyl diglycerides yielding their respective water-soluble products. In rat brain, this enzyme activity increases with age up to about 40 days, except during the period of active myelination when the galactolipase activity decreases (Subba Rao *et al.*, 1970). At pH 4.4, brain mitochondrial fraction hydrolyzes the terminal galactose moiety of digalactosyl diglyceride by α-galactosidase action and also shows β-galactosidase activity on monogalactosyl diglyceride (Subba Rao *et al.*, 1970; Subba Rao and Pieringer, 1970). It has been reported that the β-galactosidase activity toward monogalactosyl diglyceride is extremely deficient in brain, liver, and skin fibroblasts from patients who died of Krabbe's disease (Wenger *et al.*, 1973).

The occurrence and metabolism of glycosyl glycerides in bacteria would suggest the presence of degradative enzymes in these organisms also, but so far no investigations have been reported.

VII. Biological Function

A. Photosynthetic Tissues

Galactosyl diglycerides are usually absent in photosynthetic bacteria, but are present in all the photosynthetic tissues capable of oxygen evolution under the influence of light (the Hill reaction) (James and Nichols, 1966). Several lines of evidence implicate these lipids in the chloroplast structure and photosynthetic function. The galactosyl diglycerides account for the major lipid fraction of the chloroplast, contain polyunsaturated fatty acids (usually α-linolenic acid), and appear to be integral components of the thylakoid membranes (Bamberger and Park, 1966). The appearance and disappearance of chlorophyll in *E. gracilis* under light and dark conditions is accompanied by the simultaneous appearance or disappearance of galactosyl diglycerides in a relatively fixed ratio. Moreover, light-starved photobiotic *Euglena* show chloroplast shrinkage and a concurrent loss of these lipids (Rosenberg, 1963; Rosenberg and Pecker, 1964; Rosenberg, 1967). *Euglena*, when subjected to higher light intensities, show a decrease in chlorophyll and galactosyl diglycerides and produce cells that are relatively lean, but contain galactosyl diglycerides rich in polyunsaturated fatty acids (Constantopoulos and Bloch, 1967b). Experiments with protein synthesis inhibitors, chloramphenicol and cycloheximide, on chloroplast formation in *Euglena* showed parallel effects on chlorophyll, chlorophyll protein, and galactosyl diglycerides, but not on phospholipids (Bishop and Smillie, 1970). Studies during greening of dark-grown barley seedlings and on chloroplast mutants of barley suggested an association of galactosyl diglycerides enriched in linolenic acid with the formation of chloroplast lamellar systems (Appelqvist *et al.*, 1968a,b). A reduction in galactosyl glycerides paralleling chlorophyll depletion has also been observed in the leaves of a soybean mutant (Keck *et al.*, 1970).

Studies with mustard seedlings showed a phytochrome-mediated increase in glycosyl glycerides and also an enhanced activity of an enzyme that transfers galactose from UDP-galactose-^{14}C to an endogenous acceptor forming monogalactosyl diglyceride, suggesting the involvement of these lipids in thylakoid membrane biogenesis (Unser and Mohr, 1970, 1972).

Erwin and Bloch (1963) proposed that the galactosyl diglycerides with their high α-linolenic acid content play a significant role in photosynthetic oxygen evolution and that α-linolenic acid may be involved chemically in electron transport or may be a necessary physical component. The discovery that the blue-green alga, *Anacystis nidulans*, which can carry out the Hill reaction, contains these lipids associated with monoenoic fatty acids only (Nichols *et al.*, 1965), discounts an essential participation of α-linolenic acid in the photosynthetic process. The role of galactosyl diglycerides thus appears to be one of maintenance of a specific structure in the photosynthetic apparatus. The stearic configuration of α-linolenic acid of galactosyl glycerides and phytol residues of chlorophyll permit a stable lock-and-key fit and may contribute toward the spacing and orientation required for efficient photoreception as well as for the operation of electron transport and primary enzymic reactions involved in photosynthesis (Rosenberg, 1967; Benson, 1966). Specific association of mono- or digalactosyl diglyceride with the domains of photosystem I or II within the chloroplast membrane has not found experimental support (Wintermans, 1971).

A complex, containing manganese-bound galactosyl diglycerides, which may participate in the photosynthetic process has been isolated (Udelnova and Boichenko, 1967). Chang and Lundin (1965) reported that galactosyl diglycerides specifically enhance the photoreduction of cytochrome c by intact spinach chloroplasts.

Based on the rapid metabolism of galactosyl diglycerides in *Chlorella,* Benson (1963b) proposed that these lipids may be involved in sugar transport across chloroplast membranes. In leaves, the galactose moieties of these lipids do not seem to be in equilibrium with the photosynthetic assimilation products and it is unlikely that these lipids participate in sugar transport (Roughan, 1970).

B. Bacteria

The intracellular localization of glycosyl glycerides in Gram-positive bacteria, *S. faecalis* (Vorbeck and Marinetti, 1965b), *B. subtilis* (Bishop *et al.*, 1967), and *S. aureus* (Ward and Perkins, 1968) has been established to be the cytoplasmic membrane. As observed in *Pseudomonas* species (Wilkinson, 1968a), glycosyl glycerides may be localized in the cell walls in Gram-negative organisms. These observations would suggest that the main function of these lipids in bacteria may be to maintain the structural integrity of membranes. It is possible that the acidic glycosyl diglycerides in *Pseudomonas* may replace phospholipids in membrane structures (Wilkinson, 1968a).

It has been suggested that these lipids may be involved in the transfer of sugar residues in bacterial polysaccharide synthesis (Distler and Roseman, 1964). The membrane lipid composition of *S. pyogenes* and derived L-form showed that the latter contained nearly twice as much diglucosyl diglyceride. The accumulation of this glycolipid in the L-form may be related to the L-form's inability to synthesize a rigid cell wall (Cohen and Panos, 1966). It should be remembered, however, that sugar residues linked to C_{55}-isoprenoid alcohols have already been shown to be involved in the biosynthesis of bacterial polysaccharides (Higashi *et al.*, 1967; Scher *et al.*, 1968).

An attractive function for the glycosyl glycerides in the transport phenomena across membranes has been proposed by Brundish *et al.* (1967). From molecular models, these authors pointed out that all bacterial glycolipids can adopt a conformation in which the lipophilic components lie on one side of the molecule and the hydrophilic sugar hydroxyls lie on the other. When a number of glycolipid molecules aggregate, the hydrophilic regions may come together and form a pore through which ions and water-soluble metabolites may pass.

C. Animal Tissues

The occurrence of galactosyl glycerides only in the nervous tissues of animals, and the variation in concentration (Wells and Dittmer, 1967) and biosynthesis (Inoue *et al.*, 1971) observed during the period of active myelination in rat brain, indicate that these lipids are important myelin components. The greatly reduced amount of glycosyl glycerides in the brains of myelin-deficient Jimpy mice (Deshmukh *et al.*, 1971), further suggests that these lipids are involved in the process of myelination.

It is obvious, that glycosyl glycerides function essentially as membrane constituents, but their precise mode of function at a molecular level remains to be understood.

References

Abdelkader, A. B., Mazliak, P., and Catesson, A. M. (1969). *Phytochemistry* **8**, 1121.

Allen, C. F., Good, P., Davis, H. F., and Fowler, S. D. (1964). *Biochem. Biophys. Res. Commun.* **15**, 424.

Allen, C. F., Good, P., Davis, H. F., Chisum, P., and Fowler, S. D. (1966a). *J. Amer. Oil Chem. Soc.* **43**, 223.

Allen, C. F., Hirayama, O., and Good, P. (1966b). *In* "Biochemistry of Chloroplasts" (T. W. Goodwin, ed.), Vol. 1, pp. 195–200. Academic Press, New York.

Allen, C. F., Good, P., and Holton, R. W. (1970). *Plant Physiol.* **46**, 748.

Ambrone, R. T., and Pieringer, R. A. (1971). *J. Biol. Chem.* **246**, 4216.

Appelqvist, L. A. (1972). *J. Amer. Oil Chem. Soc.* **49**, 151.

Appelqvist, L. A., Boynton, J. E., Stumpf, P. K., and von Wettstein, D. (1968a). *J. Lipid Res.* **9**, 425.

Appelqvist, L. A., Boynton, J. E., Henningsen, K. W., Stumpf, P. K., and von Wettstein, D. (1968b). *J. Lipid Res.* **9**, 513.

Appleby, R. S., Safford, R., and Nichols, B. W. (1971). *Biochim. Biophys. Acta* **248**, 205.

Auling, G., Heinz, E., and Tulloch, A. P. (1971). *Hoppe-Seyler's Z. Physiol. Chem.* **352**, 905.

Baddiley, J., Buchanan, J. G., Handschumaker, R. E., and Prescott, J. F. (1956). *J. Chem. Soc.* p. 2818.

Bajwa, S. S., and Sastry, P. S. (1972a). *Indian J. Biochem. Biophys.* **9**, 133.

Bajwa, S. S., and Sastry, P. S. (1972b). *Biochem. J.* **128**, 44P.

Bajwa, S. S., and Sastry, P. S. (1973). *Indian J. Biochem. Biophys.* **10**, 65.

Bamberger, E. S., and Park, R. B. (1966). *Plant Physiol.* **41**, 1591.

Bashkatova, A. I., Smirnova, G. V., Shvets, V. I., and Evstigneeva, R. P. (1971a). *Zh. Org. Khim.* **7**, 1644.

Bashkatova, A. I., Shvets, V. I., and Evstigneeva, R. P. (1971b). *Zh. Org. Khim.* **7**, 2627.

Benson, A. A. (1963a). *Advan. Lipid Res.* **1**, 387.

Benson, A. A. (1963b). *Proc. Int. Congr. Biochem., 5th, Moscow, 1961* **6**, 340–351.

Benson, A. A. (1966). *J. Amer. Oil Chem. Soc.* **43**, 265.

Benson, A. A., Wiser, R., Ferrari, R. A., and Miller, J. A. (1958). *J. Amer. Chem. Soc.* **80**, 4740.

Benson, A. A., Daniel, H., and Wiser, R. (1959a). *Proc. Nat. Acad. Sci. U. S.* **45**, 1582.

Benson, A. A., Wintermans, J. F. G. M., and Wiser, R. (1959b). *Plant Physiol.* **34**, 315.

Bergelson, L. D., Batrakov, S. G., and Pilipenko, T. V. (1970). *Chem. Phys. Lipids* **4**, 181.
Biale, J. B., Yang, S. F., and Benson, A. A. (1966). *Fed Proc., Fed. Amer. Soc. Exp. Biol.* **25**, 405.
Bishop, D. G., and Smillie, R. M. (1970). *Arch. Biochem. Biophys.* **137**, 179.
Bishop, D. G., Rutberg, L., and Samuelson, B. (1967). *Eur. J. Biochem.* **2**, 448.
Bishop, D. G., Anderson, K. S., and Smillie, R. M. (1971). *Biochim. Biophys. Acta* **231**, 412.
Bligh, E. G., and Dyer, W. J. (1959). *Can. J. Biochem. Physiol.* **37**, 911.
Bloch, K., Constantopoulos, G., Kenyon, C., and Nagai, J. (1967). *In* "Biochemistry of Chloroplasts" (T. W. Goodwin, ed.), Vol. 2, pp. 195–211. Academic Press, New York.
Boling, H., and El Baya, A. W. (1972). *Chem. Phys. Lipids* **8**, 102.
Boos, W., Lehmann, J., and Wallenfels, K. (1966). *Carbohyd. Res.* **1**, 419.
Bossmann, H. B. (1969). *Biochim. Biophys. Acta* **187**, 122.
Bowden, B. N., and Williams, P. M. (1973). *Phytochemistry* **12**, 1059.
Brundish, D. E., and Baddiley, J. (1968). *Carbohyd. Res.* **8**, 308.
Brundish, D. E., Shaw, N., and Baddiley, J. (1965a). *Biochem. J.* **95**, 21C.
Brundish, D. E., Shaw, N., and Baddiley, J. (1965b). *Biochem. Biophys. Res. Commun.* **18**, 308.
Brundish, D. E., Shaw, N., and Baddiley, J. (1965c). *Biochem. J.* **97**, 158.
Brundish, D. E., Shaw, N., and Baddiley, J. (1966). *Biochem. J.* **99**, 546.
Brundish, D. E., Shaw, N., and Baddiley, J. (1967). *Biochem. J.* **105**, 885.
Brush, P., and Percival, E. (1972). *Phytochemistry* **11**, 1847.
Carroll, K. K., Cutts, J. H., and Murray, E. G. D. (1968). *Can. J. Biochem.* **46**, 899.
Carter, H. E., McCluer, R. H., and Slifer, E. (1956). *J. Amer. Chem. Soc.* **78**, 3735.
Carter, H. E., Ohno, K., Nojima, S., Tipton, C. L., and Stanacev, N. Z. (1961a). *J. Lipid Res.* **2**, 215.
Carter, H. E., Hendry, R. A., and Stanacev, N. Z. (1961b). *J. Lipid Res.* **2**, 223.
Carter, H. E., Johnson, P., and Weber, E. J. (1965). *Annu. Rev. Biochem.* **34**, 109.
Chang, S. B. (1970). *Phytochemistry* **9**, 1947.
Chang, S. B., and Kulkarni, N. D. (1970). *Phytochemistry* **9**, 927.
Chang, S. B., and Lundin, K. (1965). *Biochem. Biophys. Res. Commun.* **21**, 424.
Charlson, A. J., Gorin, P. A. J., and Perlin, A. S. (1957). *Can. J. Chem.* **35**, 365.
Clayton, T. A., McMurray, T. A., and Morrison, W. R. (1970). *J. Chromatogr.* **47**, 277.
Cohen, M., and Panos, C. (1966). *Biochemistry* **5**, 2385.
Colin, H., and Gueguen, E. (1930). *C. R. Acad. Sci.* **191**, 163.
Constantopoulos, G., and Bloch, K. (1967a). *J. Bacteriol.* **93**, 1788.
Constantopoulos, G., and Bloch, K. (1967b). *J. Biol. Chem.* **242**, 3538.
Constantopoulos, G., and Kenyon, C. N. (1968). *Plant Physiol.* **43**, 531.
Dawson, R. M. C. (1967). *In* "Lipid Chromatographic Analysis" (G. V. Marinetti, ed.), Vol. 1, pp. 163–189. Dekker, New York.
Deshmukh, D. S., Inoue, T., and Pieringer, R. A. (1971). *J. Biol. Chem.* **246**, 5695.
DeStefanis, V. A., and Ponte, J. G. (1969). *Biochim. Biophys. Acta* **176**, 198.
Distler, J., and Roseman, S. (1964). *Proc. Nat. Acad. Sci. U. S.* **51**, 897.
Douce, R., and Guillot-Salomon, T. (1970). *FEBS (Fed. Eur. Biochem. Soc.), Lett.* **11**, 121.
Dubois, M., Gillies, K. A., Hamilton, J. K., Rebers, P. A., and Smith, F. (1956). *Anal. Chem.* **28**, 350.

Eccleshall, T. R., and Hawke, J. C. (1971). *Phytochemistry* **10**, 3035.
Erwin, J., and Bloch, K. (1963). *Biochem. Z.* **338**, 496.
Exterkate, F. A., and Veerkamp, J. H. (1969). *Biochim. Biophys. Acta* **176**, 65.
Ferrari, R. A., and Benson, A. A. (1961). *Arch. Biochem. Biophys.* **93**, 185.
Fischer, W., and Seyferth, W. (1968). *Hoppe-Seyler's Z. Physiol. Chem.* **349**, 1662.
Folch, J., Lees, M., and Sloane-Stanley, G. H. (1957). *J. Biol. Chem.* **226**, 497.
Galliard, T. (1968a). *Phytochemistry* **7**, 1907.
Galliard, T. (1968b). *Phytochemistry* **7**, 1915.
Galliard, T. (1969). *Biochem. J.* **115**, 335.
Galliard, T. (1970). *Phytochemistry* **9**, 1725.
Galliard, T. (1971). *Biochem. J.* **121**, 379.
Gamini Kannangara, C., and Stumpf, P. K. (1971). *Biochem. Biophys. Res. Commun.* **44**, 1544.
Gardner, H. W. (1968). *J. Lipid Res.* **9**, 139.
Gatt, S., and Baker, E. A. (1970). *Biochim. Biophys. Acta* **206**, 125.
Gurr, M. I. (1971). *Lipids* **6**, 266.
Heinz, E. (1967a). *Biochim. Biophys. Acta* **144**, 321.
Heinz, E. (1967b). *Biochim. Biophys. Acta* **144**, 333.
Heinz, E. (1971). *Biochim. Biophys. Acta* **231**, 537.
Heinz, E., and Tulloch, A. P. (1969). *Hoppe-Seyler's Z. Physiol. Chem.* **350**, 493.
Heisig, O. M. R. A., and Heinz, E. (1972). *Phytochemistry* **11**, 815.
Helmsing, P. J. (1967a). *Biochim. Biophys. Acta* **144**, 470.
Helmsing, P. J. (1967b). *J. Chromatogr.* **28**, 131.
Helmsing, P. J. (1969). *Biochim. Biophys. Acta* **178**, 519.
Helmsing, P. J., and Barendese, G. W. M. (1970). *Acta Bot. Neer.* **19**, 567.
Higashi, Y., Strominger, J. L., and Sweeley, C. C. (1967). *Proc. Nat. Acad. Sci. U. S.* **57**, 1878.
Hirayama, O. (1965). *J. Biochem. (Tokyo)* **57**, 581.
Hirayama, O. (1967). *J. Biochem. (Tokyo)* **61**, 179.
Ikawa, M. (1963). *J. Bacteriol.* **85**, 772.
Inoue, T., Deshmukh, D. S., and Pieringer, R. A. (1971). *J. Biol. Chem.* **246**, 5688.
Ishizuka, I., and Yamakawa, T. (1968). *J. Biochem. (Tokyo)* **64**, 13.
James, A. T. (1960). *Methods Biochem. Anal.* **8**, 1.
James, A. T., and Nichols, B. W. (1966). *Nature (London)* **210**, 372.
Jamieson, G. R., and Reid, E. H. (1969). *Phytochemistry* **8**, 1489.
Jamieson, G. R., and Reid, E. H. (1971a). *Phytochemistry* **10**, 1575.
Jamieson, G. R., and Reid, E. H. (1971b). *Phytochemistry* **10**, 1837.
Jamieson, G. R., and Reid, E. H. (1972). *Phytochemistry* **11**, 269.
Kates, M. (1959). *Biochem. Biophys. Res. Commun.* **1**, 238.
Kates, M. (1960). *Biochim. Biophys. Acta* **41**, 315.
Kates, M. (1964a). *Advan. Lipid Res.* **2**, 17.
Kates, M. (1964b). *J. Lipid Res.* **5**, 132.
Kates, M. (1967). *In* "Lipid Chromatographic Analysis" (G. V. Marinetti, ed.), pp. 1–39. Dekker, New York.
Kates, M. (1970). *Advan. Lipid Res.* **8**, 225.
Kates, M., and Eberhardt, F. M. (1957). *Can. J. Bot.* **35**, 895.
Kates, M., and Volcani, B. E. (1966). *Biochim. Biophys. Acta* **116**, 264.
Kates, M., and Volcani, B. E. (1968). *Z. Pflanzenphysiol.* **60**, 19.
Kates, M., Yengoyan, L. S., and Sastry, P. S. (1965). *Biochim. Biophys. Acta* **98**, 252.

Kates, M., Palameta, B., Perry, M. P., and Adams, G. A. (1967). *Biochim. Biophys. Acta* **137,** 213.
Kaufman, B., Kundig, F. D., Distler, J., and Roseman, S. (1965). *Biochem. Biophys. Res. Commun.* **18,** 312.
Keck, R. W., Dailey, R. A., Allen, C. F., and Biggs, A. (1970). *Plant Physiol.* **46,** 692.
Khuller, G. K., and Brennen, P. J. (1972). *Biochem. J.* **127,** 369.
Kinsella, J. E. (1971). *J. Food Sci.* **36,** 865.
Kleinschmidt, M. G., and McMahon, V. A. (1970). *Plant Physiol.* **46,** 290.
Koenig, F. (1971). *Z. Naturforsch. B* **26,** 1180.
Kunsman, J. E. (1970). *J. Bacteriol.* **103,** 104.
Lang, D. R., and Lundgren, D. G. (1970). *J. Bacteriol.* **101,** 483.
Lennarz, W. J., and Talamo, B. (1966). *J. Biol. Chem.* **241,** 2707.
Lepage, M. (1964). *J. Chromatogr.* **13,** 99.
Lepage, M. (1967). *Lipids* **2,** 244.
Levin, E., Lennarz, W. J., and Bloch, K. (1964). *Biochim. Biophys. Acta* **84,** 471.
Lichtenthaler, H. K., and Park, R. B. (1963). *Nature (London)* **198,** 1070.
Lin, M. F., and Chang, S. B. (1971). *Phytochemistry* **10,** 1543.
Livermore, B. P., and Johnson, R. C. (1970). *Biochim. Biophys. Acta* **210,** 315.
McCarty, R. E., and Jagendorf, A. T. (1965). *Plant Physiol.* **40,** 725.
McCarty, R. E., Douce, R., and Benson, A. A. (1973). *Biochim. Biophys. Acta* **316,** 266.
Macfarlane, M. G. (1961). *Biochem. J.* **80,** 45P.
Macfarlane, M. G. (1962). *Biochem. J.* **82,** 40P.
McKillican, M. E. (1966). *J. Amer. Oil Chem. Soc.* **43,** 461.
Mason, L. H., and Johnston, A. E. (1958). *Cereal Chem.* **35,** 435.
Matson, R. S., Fei, M., and Chang, S. B. (1970). *Plant Physiol.* **45,** 531.
Matson, R. S., Mustoe, G. E., and Chang, S. B. (1972). *Environ. Sci. Technol.* **6,** 158.
Maxwell, J. P., and Williams, J. P. (1968a). *J. Chromatogr.* **31,** 62.
Maxwell, J. P., and Williams, J. P. (1968b). *J. Chromatogr.* **35,** 223.
Meyer, H., and Meyer, F. (1971). *Biochim. Biophys. Acta* **231,** 93.
Miyano, M., and Benson, A. A. (1962). *J. Amer. Chem. Soc.* **84,** 57.
Morris, O. L. (1948). *Science* **107,** 254.
Mudd, J. B., Van Vliet, H. H. D. M., and Van Deenen, L. L. M. (1969). *J. Lipid Res.* **10,** 623.
Mudd, J. B., McManus, T. T., Ongun, A., and McCullogh, T. E. (1971). *Plant Physiol.* **48,** 335.
Myhre, D. V. (1968). *Can. J. Chem.* **46,** 3071.
Neufeld, E. F., and Hall, C. W. (1964). *Biochem. Biophys. Res. Commun.* **14,** 503.
Nichols, B. W. (1963). *Biochim. Biophys. Acta* **70,** 417.
Nichols, B. W. (1964). *In* "New Biochemical Separations" (A. T. James and L. J. Morris, eds.), p. 321. Van Nostrand, New York.
Nichols, B. W. (1965a). *Biochim. Biophys. Acta* **106,** 274.
Nichols, B. W. (1965b). *Phytochemistry* **4,** 769.
Nichols, B. W., and James, A. T. (1964). *Fette, Seifen, Anstrichm.* **66,** 1003.
Nichols, B. W., and James, A. T. (1965). *Biochem. J.* **94,** 22P.
Nichols, B. W., and Moorhouse, R. (1969). *Lipids* **4,** 311.
Nichols, B. W., Harris, R. V., and James, A. T. (1965). *Biochem. Biophys. Res. Commun.* **20,** 256.

Nichols, B. W., Stubbs, J. M., and James, A. T. (1967). *In* "Biochemistry of Chloroplasts" (T. W. Goodwin, ed.), Vol. 2, pp. 677–690. Academic Press, New York.
Noda, M., and Fujiwara, N. (1967). *Biochim. Biophys. Acta* **137**, 199.
Norton, W. T., and Brotz, M. (1963). *Biochem. Biophys. Res. Commun.* **12**, 198.
Norton, W. T., and Brotz, M. (1967). *Fed. Proc., Fed. Amer. Soc. Exp. Biol.* **26**, 675.
Obara, T., and Miyata, N. (1969). *Nippon Nogei Kagaku Kaishi* **43**, 95.
O'Brien, J. S., and Benson, A. A. (1964). *J. Lipid Res.* **5**, 432.
Ongun, A., and Mudd, J. B. (1968). *J. Biol. Chem.* **243**, 1558.
Ongun, A., and Mudd, J. B. (1970). *Plant Physiol.* **45**, 255.
Ongun, A., Thomson, W. W., and Mudd, J. B. (1968). *J. Lipid Res.* **9**, 409.
Patton, S., Fuller, G., Loeblich, A. R., and Benson, A. A. (1966). *Biochim. Biophys. Acta* **116**, 577.
Peleg, E., and Tietz, A. (1971). *FEBS (Fed. Eur. Biochem. Soc.), Lett.* **15**, 309.
Phizackerley, P. J. R., MacDougall, J. C., and Moore, R. A. (1972). *Biochem. J.* **126**, 499.
Pieringer, R. A. (1968). *J. Biol. Chem.* **243**, 4894.
Plackett, P. (1967). *Biochemistry* **6**, 2746.
Plackett, P., and Shaw, E. J. (1967). *Biochem. J.* **104**, 61C.
Plackett, P., Marmion, B. P., Shaw, E. J., and Lemcke, R. M. (1969). *Aust. J. Exp. Biol. Med. Sci.* **47**, 171.
Pohl, P., Glarl, H., and Wagner, H. (1970). *J. Chromatogr.* **49**, 488.
Poincelot, R. P. (1971). *Biochim. Biophys. Acta* **239**, 57.
Polonovski, J., Wald, R., and Paysant Diament, M. (1962). *Ann. Inst. Pasteur, Paris* **103**, 32.
Pruthi, T. D., and Bhatia, I. S. (1970). *J. Sci. Food Agr.* **21**, 419.
Putman, E. W., and Hassid, W. Z. (1954). *J. Amer. Chem. Soc.* **76**, 2221.
Radunz, V. A. (1969). *Hoppe-Seyler's Z. Physiol. Chem.* **350**, 411.
Reeves, R. E., Latour, N. G., and Lousteau, R. J. (1964). *Biochemistry* **3**, 1248.
Renkonen, O., and Bloch, K. (1969). *J. Biol. Chem.* **244**, 4899.
Renkonen, O., and Varo, P. (1967). *In* "Lipid Chromatographic Analysis" (G. V. Marinetti, ed.), Vol. 1, pp. 41–98. Dekker, New York.
Romano, N., Smith, P. F., and Mayberry, W. R. (1972). *J. Bacteriol.* **109**, 565.
Rosenberg, A. (1963). *Biochemistry* **2**, 1148.
Rosenberg, A. (1967). *Science* **157**, 1191.
Rosenberg, A., and Gouaux, J. (1967). *J. Lipid Res.* **8**, 80.
Rosenberg, A., and Pecker, M. (1964). *Biochemistry* **3**, 254.
Roughan, P. G. (1970). *Biochem. J.* **117**, 1.
Roughan, P. G., and Batt, R. D. (1968). *Anal. Biochem.* **22**, 74.
Roughan, P. G., and Batt, R. D. (1969). *Phytochemistry* **8**, 363.
Rouser, G., Kritchevsky, G., Heller, D., and Lieber, E. (1963). *J. Amer. Oil Chem. Soc.* **40**, 425.
Rouser, G., Kritchevsky, G., and Yamamoto, A. (1967). *In* "Lipid Chromatographic Analysis" (G. V. Marinetti, ed.), Vol. 1, pp. 99–162. Dekker, New York.
Rumsby, M. G. (1967). *J. Neurochem.* **14**, 733.
Rumsby, M. G., and Gray, I. K. (1965). *J. Neurochem.* **12**, 1005.
Rumsby, M. G., and Rossiter, R. J. (1968). *J. Neurochem.* **15**, 1473.
Safford, R., and Nichols, B. W. (1970). *Biochim. Biophys. Acta* **210**, 57.

Safford, R., Appleby, R. S., and Nichols, B. W. (1971). *Biochim. Biophys. Acta* **239**, 509.
Saito, K., and Mukoyama, K. (1971). *J. Biochem. (Tokyo)* **69**, 83.
Sastry, P. S., and Kates, M. (1963). *Biochim. Biophys. Acta* **70**, 214.
Sastry, P. S., and Kates, M. (1964a). *Biochim. Biophys. Acta* **84**, 231.
Sastry, P. S., and Kates, M. (1964b). *Biochemistry* **3**, 1271.
Sastry, P. S., and Kates, M. (1964c). *Biochemistry* **3**, 1280.
Sastry, P. S., and Kates, M. (1965). *Can. J. Biochem.* **43**, 1445.
Sastry, P. S., and Kates, M. (1966). *Can. J. Biochem.* **44**, 459.
Sastry, P. S., and Kates, M. (1969). *In* "Methods in Enzymology" (J. M. Lowenstein, ed.), Vol. 14, pp. 204–208. Academic Press, New York.
Scher, M., Lennarz, W. J., and Sweeley, C. C. (1968). *Proc. Nat. Acad. Sci. U. S.* **59**, 1313.
Schwertner, H. A., and Biale, J. B. (1973). *J. Lipid Res.* **14**, 235.
Shaw, J. M., and Pieringer, R. A. (1972). *Biochem. Biophys. Res. Commun.* **46**, 1201.
Shaw, N. (1968). *Biochim. Biophys. Acta* **152**, 427.
Shaw, N. (1970). *Bacteriol. Rev.* **34**, 365.
Shaw, N., and Baddiley, J. (1968). *Nature (London)* **217**, 142.
Shaw, N., and Smith, P. F. (1967). *Bacteriol. Proc.* p. 108.
Shaw, N., and Stead, D. (1970). *J. Appl. Bacteriol.* **33**, 470.
Shaw, N., and Stead, A. (1972). *FEBS (Fed. Eur. Biochem. Soc.), Lett.* **21**, 249.
Shaw, N., Heatherington, K., and Baddiley, J. (1968a). *Biochem. J.* **107**, 491.
Shaw, N., Smith, P. F., and Koostra, W. L. (1968b). *Biochem. J.* **107**, 329.
Shaw, N., Smith, P. F., and Verheij, H. M. (1970). *Biochem. J.* **120**, 439.
Shvets, V. I., Bashkatova, A. I., and Evstigneeva, R. P. (1973). *Chem. Phys. Lipids* **10**, 267.
Singh, H., and Privett, O. S. (1970). *Lipids* **5**, 692.
Smith, C. R., and Wolff, I. A. (1966). *Lipids* **1**, 123.
Smith, P. F., and Mayberry, W. R. (1968). *Biochemistry* **7**, 2706.
Steim, J. M. (1967). *Biochim. Biophys. Acta* **144**, 118.
Steim, J. M., and Benson, A. A. (1963). *Fed. Proc., Fed. Amer. Soc. Exp. Biol.* **22**, 299.
Stein, R. A., Slawson, V., and Mead, J. F. (1967). *In* "Lipid Chromatographic Analysis" (G. V. Marinetti, ed.), Vol. 1, pp. 361–400. Dekker, New York.
Steiner, S., Conti, S. F., and Lester, R. L. (1969). *J. Bacteriol.* **98**, 10.
Stern, N., and Tietz, A. (1971). *FEBS (Fed. Eur. Biochem. Soc.), Lett.* **19**, 217.
Stern, N., and Tietz, A. (1973). *Biochim. Biophys. Acta* **296**, 136.
Subba Rao, K., and Piéringer, R. A. (1970). *J. Neurochem.* **17**, 483.
Subba Rao, K., Wenger, D. A., and Pieringer, R. A. (1970). *J. Biol. Chem.* **245**, 2520.
Thompson, A. C., and Hedin, P. A. (1965). *Crop Sci.* **5**, 133.
Thompson, A. C., Henson, R. D., Minyard, J. P., and Hedin, P. A. (1968). *Lipids* **3**, 373.
Tornabene, T. G., and Ogg, J. E. (1971). *Biochim. Biophys. Acta* **239**, 133.
Tulloch, A. P., Heinz, E., and Fischer, W. (1973). *Hoppe-Seyler's Z. Physiol. Chem.* **354**, 879.
Udelnova, T. M., and Boichenko, E. A. (1967). *Biokhimiya* **32**, 779.
Unser, G., and Mohr, H. (1970). *Naturwissenschaften* **57**, 358.
Unser, G., and Mohr, H. (1972). *Naturwissenschaften* **57**, 39.
Van der Veen, J., Hirota, K., and Olcott, H. S. (1967). *Lipids* **2**, 406.

Veerkamp, J. H. (1972). *Biochim. Biophys. Acta* **273**, 359.
Vorbeck, M. L., and Marinetti, G. V. (1965a). *J. Lipid Res.* **6**, 3.
Vorbeck, M. L., and Marinetti, G. V. (1965b). *Biochemistry* **4**, 296.
Wagner, H., Hörhammer, L., and Wolff, P. (1961). *Biochem. Z.* **334**, 175.
Walker, R. W., and Bastl, C. P. (1967). *Carbohyd. Res.* **4**, 49.
Walter, M. W., Jr., Hansen, A. P., and Purcell, A. E. (1971). *J. Food. Sci.* **36**, 795.
Ward, J. B., and Perkins, H. R. (1968). *Biochem. J.* **106**, 391.
Webster, D. E., and Chang, S. B. (1969). *Plant Physiol.* **44**, 1523.
Webster, G. R., and Folch, J. (1961). *Biochim. Biophys. Acta* **49**, 399.
Weenink, R. O. (1959). *N. Z. J. Sci. Technol.* **2**, 273.
Weenink, R. O. (1961). *J. Sci. Food Agr.* **12**, 34.
Weenink, R. O. (1964). *Biochem. J.* **93**, 606.
Wehrli, H. P., and Pomeranz, Y. (1969). *Chem. Phys. Lipids* **3**, 357.
Wells, M. A., and Dittmer, J. C. (1963). *Biochemistry* **2**, 1259.
Wells, M. A., and Dittmer, J. C. (1967). *Biochemistry* **6**, 3169.
Wenger, D. A., Petitpas, J. W., and Pieringer, R. A. (1968). *Biochemistry* **7**, 3700.
Wenger, D. A., Subba Rao, K., and Pieringer, R. A. (1970). *J. Biol. Chem.* **245**, 2513.
Wenger, D. A., Sattler, M., and Markey, S. P. (1973). *Biochem. Biophys. Res. Commun.* **53**, 680.
Wickberg, B. (1958a). *Acta Chem. Scand.* **12**, 1183.
Wickberg, B. (1958b). *Acta Chem. Scand.* **12**, 1187.
Wilkinson, S. G. (1968a). *Biochim. Biophys. Acta* **152**, 227.
Wilkinson, S. G. (1968b). *Biochim. Biophys. Acta* **164**, 148.
Wilkinson, S. G. (1969). *Biochim. Biophys. Acta* **187**, 492.
Wilkinson, S. G., and Bell, M. E. (1971). *Biochim. Biophys. Acta* **248**, 293.
Willemot, C., and Boll, W. G. (1967). *Can. J. Bot.* **45**, 1863.
Wincken, A. J., and Knox, K. W. (1970). *J. Gen. Microbiol.* **60**, 293.
Wintermans, J. F. G. M. (1960). *Biochim. Biophys. Acta* **44**, 49.
Wintermans, J. F. G. M. (1963). *Colloq. Int. Cent. Nat. Rech. Sci.* **119**, 381.
Wintermans, J. F. G. M. (1971). *Biochim. Biophys. Acta* **248**, 530.
Wintermans, J. F. G. M., Helmsing, P. J., Polman, B. J. J., Van Gisbergen, J., and Collard, T. (1969). *Biochim. Biophys. Acta* **189**, 95.
Wood, R., and Snyder, F. (1966). *Lipids* **1**, 62.
Yagi, T., and Benson, A. A. (1962). *Biochim. Biophys. Acta* **57**, 601.
Zill, L. P., and Harmon, A. E. (1962). *Biochim. Biophys. Acta* **57**, 573.

Inhibition of Fatty Acid Oxidation by Biguanides: Implications for Metabolic Physiopathology

SERGIO MUNTONI

Department of Pharmacology and Chemotherapy, University of Cagliari; Second Division of Medicine, and Center for Metabolic Diseases and Arteriosclerosis, SS. Trinita Hospital of Calgliari, Italy

I. Introduction

A series of indicative elements, suitably correlated and interpreted, supplied the clue to the identification of the mechanism of action of antidiabetic biguanides (Muntoni, 1968). The first step was the hypothesis that biguanides inhibit fatty acid oxidation in tissues utilizing these fuels, in particular muscle and liver (Muntoni, 1968). The next step consisted in verifying experimentally the exactness of the original hypothesis: in rats under different experimental conditions, all characterized by increased fatty acid oxidation, a single dose of phenformin was found to reduce fatty acid utilization (Muntoni *et al.*, 1969, 1970).

Subsequent *in vitro* experiments (Muntoni *et al.*, 1973a,b; Corsini *et al.*, 1974) demonstrated that nontoxic concentrations of phenformin or metformin depressed the $^{14}CO_2$ production from palmitic-U-^{14}C acid, but not from glucose-U-^{14}C, by rat diaphragm homogenate; moreover, the inhibition of glucose-U-^{14}C oxidation by unlabeled palmitic acid was partly removed by biguanides. The most typical and best known pharmacological effects of biguanides may thus be attributed to this basic mechanism of action: this subject has been fully discussed elsewhere (Muntoni, 1968; Muntoni *et al.*, 1970; Muntoni and Sirigu, 1971). Yet, on surveying the extensive literature concerning these drugs, many of the experimental data still appear contradictory or scarcely compatible, giving the impression that a single interpretation of the complex mechanism of action of biguanides is impossible. I believe, however, that with the above-mentioned mechanism as a starting point, we may now reconsider all the effects of biguanides on metabolism, identifying and differentiating specific from toxic effects, and finally interpreting the meaning of the metabolic changes induced by biguanides in the healthy and the diabetic organism. Many contradictions in the experimental data will then prove to be only apparent and the value of these drugs, both as research and therapeutic means, will be better assessed.

The greatest difficulties are met in trying to interpret and reconcile the data in literature relative to the effects on carbohydrate metabolism, this being the most investigated aspect of the subject. The property of biguanides that lowers hyperglycemia in diabetic subjects while failing to modify the blood glucose levels in normal subjects although known for a long time (Fajans *et al.*, 1960; Madison and Unger, 1960), appeared at once as very peculiar. It certainly stimulated the interest of many investigators, but probably led to the misunderstanding that lack of hypoglycemic effect corresponded to lack of any effect on the carbohydrate metabolism of normal subjects. This misunderstanding has now been cleared up as the result of conclusive experimental data (see Sections II, III), proving that biguanides do in fact influence carbohydrate metabolism in normal subjects and in animal species considered as "poorly sensitive" to biguanides. The fact that phenformin induces hypoglycemia in normal subjects fasted for 40 hours (Lyngsöe and Trap-Jensen, 1969) further confirms this point.

The problem of the different effect of biguanides on the blood glucose level of normal versus diabetic hyperglycemic subjects is closely correlated with a whole series of effects on intermediary metabolism. Very thorough investigations have been carried out in this field, but the results, at first sight, seem difficult to interpret univocally. In my opinion, these investigations deserve careful consideration because it is possible to assess their results critically and to include them in a comprehensive view of the metabolic effects of biguanides. In order to do this, however, it is first necessary to discuss and define some pharmacological and biological criteria to be adopted for the interpretation of rather heterogeneous experimental data.

II. Preliminary Pharmacobiological Criteria

A suggestion in favor of adopting the previously mentioned criteria stems from the inhibition of gluconeogenesis and from the hypoglycemia observed in the guinea pig. It is known that in some systems and under certain experimental conditions, biguanides inhibit gluconeogenesis while in other cases, as in normal human subjects, biguanides fail to prevent its increase secondary to the increased utilization of glucose (Searle and Cavalieri, 1968) (see Section III). The effect of biguanides on gluconeogenesis is likely to be conditioned by complex factors.

The *in vivo* (Tyberghein and Williams, 1957; Altschuld and Kruger, 1968) and *in vitro* (Altschuld and Kruger, 1968) inhibition of gluconeogenesis in guinea pig liver is closely related to the reduction of hepatic ATP levels and to the increase in AMP, resulting from inhibition of oxidative phosphorylation (Altschuld and Kruger, 1968). In fact, guanidine and its derivatives are known to produce such an inhibition (Wick *et al.*, 1958; Steiner and Williams, 1958, 1959; Pressman, 1963; Jangaard *et al.*, 1968; Schäfer, 1969). The low ATP levels are insufficient for the ATP-requiring steps of gluconeogenesis; moreover, AMP is a strong allosteric inhibitor of fructose-1,6-diphosphatase (Newsholme, 1963), one of the key enzymes of gluconeogenesis.

The fact, that of all the animals studied, biguanides induce hypoglycemia at a dose as low as 10 mg/kg only in the guinea pig, must be of some significance since 100 mg/kg have no effect on blood glucose, hepatic ATP levels, and gluconeogenesis (Altschuld and Kruger, 1968), in the rat. On the other hand, the absence of effect on glycemia in the normal rat does not imply that biguanides have no effect on glucose metabolism, since Losert *et al.* (1971) found that the production of $^{14}CO_2$ from glucose-U-^{14}C was increased.

It is obvious that the guinea pig is special among other animal species, inasmuch as it is not only less capable of inactivating phenformin (see Section IV), but its oxidative phosphorylation processes are also highly sensitive to inhibition by low doses of biguanides. In the guinea pig, moreover, gluconeogenesis is particularly sensitive to inhibitory influences: this is demonstrated by another hypoglycemic compound, hypoglycine, which is much more active in the guinea pig than in the rat (Sherratt, 1969). A compound analogous to hypoglycine, namely cyclopropanecarboxylic acid, also exerts a hypoglycemic effect in the guinea pig, but not in the rat or other animal species (Sherratt, 1969).

The low sensitivity threshold of the guinea pig respiratory chain to guanidine derivatives is a phenomenon, which instead of misleading us, may in fact contribute to the solution of our problem. Thus, in the normal guinea pig we observe that the inhibition of oxidative phosphorylation is automatically associated with a reduction in hepatic ATP, an arrest in gluconeogenesis, and a fall of the blood glucose below normal values. If all these changes do not occur in the normal rat with doses ten times higher, it must mean that oxidative phosphorylation in the rat is not inhibited by doses, which, on the other hand, enhance glucose utilization (Losert *et al.*, 1971) evidently by a different mechanism.

Many misunderstandings have certainly arisen from research on biguanides carried out in the guinea pig. Even the statement that the guinea pig is the only animal species in which these drugs cause hypoglycemia is only true if we do not take into account the extraordinary sensitivity of this animal to biguanides. Losert *et al.* (1971) demonstrated that the guinea pig behaves just like the rat when the dose of biguanide is reduced in proportion to the sensitivity of the animal. Thus, while a dose of 25 mg/kg of phenformin or buformin produces hypoglycemia, 2.5 mg/kg does not. Nevertheless, this last dose markedly stimulates the production of $^{14}CO_2$ from glucose-U-^{14}C also in the guinea pig. This proves beyond a doubt that the two effects of biguanides may be dissociated in this animal also, as glucose oxidation is enhanced in the absence of any inhibition of oxidative phosphorylation.

Hence many of the guinea pig investigations carried out so far are of greater toxicological than pharmacological significance since the doses used were out of proportion to the sensitivity of this species. This contributed to the confusion that arose in searching for the mechanism of "antidiabetic" action of biguanides; in fact, even in animal species least sensitive to the toxic effects of biguanides, the antidiabetic effect occurs at doses considerably lower than those inducing hypoglycemia in healthy animals.

Hence, for each animal species, it is necessary to define (for biguanides, as for any other drug) the active dose versus the toxic dose, since large differences are known to exist among different species. In the specific case of biguanides it is essential, however, to define pharmacological effects as opposed to toxic effects. From these considerations, it seems clear that hypoglycemia in the normal animal cannot be considered as a specific effect, but rather as the obvious consequence of the toxic effect, namely the inhibition of oxidative phosphorylation. Those who tried to determine the therapeutic index of biguanides on the basis of the hypoglycemic effect obviously found it to be very low, but they committed a conceptual error since this cannot represent the therapeutic index.

Final agreement on this point is desirable. In my opinion, we should consider as specific effects of biguanides only those that occur in the healthy, normally fed animal in the absence of hypoglycemia, the same effects that lower hyperglycemia in the diabetic organism. It will then become clear how great is the distance between "antidiabetic" and hypoglycemic doses, i.e., between therapeutically effective and toxic doses, even though this difference may vary in the different animal species, guinea pig included.

Hence, while Söling and Ditschuneit's (1970) statement that the therapeutic and toxic doses of biguanides are quite close would seem to be inexact, I am in full agreement with the same authors when they state that to understand the therapeutic action of guanidine derivatives on blood glucose, the only important metabolic effects are those which do not yet cause inhibition of oxidative phosphorylation.

These concepts certainly apply also to man: a considerable difference has been found between a hypoglycemic dose in normal subjects (normally fed) and a dose, therapeutically effective in types of diabetes sensitive to biguanides. It seems likely that in man as well, the mechanism responsible for the antidiabetic action is different from the one causing the toxic effects. Supporting this belief is the fact that biguanides do not induce hypoglycemia even in men or animals suffering from diabetes sensitive to these drugs; they simply normalize the hyperglycemia. The diabetic condition, therefore supplies the best measure of the therapeutic index of these drugs.

To conclude, it may be stated that the confusion in this field stems from the fact that hypoglycemia is one of the most evident toxic effects of biguanides; hence it seemed logical, but isn't, that their antidiabetic activity should come from their capability to induce hypoglycemia. According to this view guanidine should also be an antidiabetic drug, because of this well-known hypoglycemic activity (Watanabe, 1918) and its capability to block the transfer of electrons along the respiratory chain (Pressman, 1963).

Having dealt with these necessary definitions, we shall now find it easier to examine critically the different metabolic effects of biguanides; the most important and complex of these are the effects on glucose turnover and on gluconeogenesis.

III. Glucose Turnover and Oxidation

Searle and Cavalieri (1968) studied the effects of 2 days treatment with phenformin on the turnover and oxidation to $^{14}CO_2$ of glucose-U-^{14}C (uniformly labeled glucose) in diabetic patients and glucose turnover in healthy subjects. In the healthy subjects no changes were observed in blood glucose level, but the glucose turnover was significantly increased by the treatment. The diabetic subjects showed a fall in blood glucose level and an increase both in glucose turnover and in the amount of expired $^{14}CO_2$, indicating an increase in the amount of glucose oxidized to CO_2.

The authors excluded the hypothesis of a raised anaerobic glucose utilization secondary to inhibition of aerobic glycolysis, since on the contrary, the oxidation of glucose to CO_2 was increased. The rise in blood lactate after phenformin, an inconstant and negligible effect in these subjects, cannot result from inhibition of the Krebs cycle, as they previously believed (Searle *et al.*, 1966) but might, in their view, be simply the expression of increased entry of lactate into the Cori cycle, to be explained by a mechanism different from the inhibition of the Krebs cycle.

Since biguanides in normal subjects do not lower the blood glucose and moreover were shown to increase the hepatic glucose output (Searle *et al.*, 1966), Searle and Cavalieri (1968) concluded that while in normal subjects, the increased peripheral utilization of glucose is balanced by an increased rate of glucose release by the liver, in the diabetic, in whom hepatic glucose production is maximal, the increased glucose oxidation induced by phenformin cannot be balanced by a further increase in hepatic glucose production: this would result in a lowering of the hyperglycemia.

Note that Searle and Cavalieri (1968), who supplied quite a logical explanation of the different effects of phenformin on the blood glucose level of normal and diabetic subjects, did not refer to any direct effect of biguanides on liver gluconeogenesis, but postulated an increase in the latter (evidently not hindered by the drug) in response to the increased peripheral glucose utilization.

In a subsequent paper, Searle *et al.* (1969) completed this research by studying glucose oxidation after phenformin in normal subjects using glucose-6-^{14}C. They found that also in these subjects, the oxidation of glucose to CO_2 was enhanced, though to a lesser extent than in the previous diabetic group. Their determinations, based on the appearance of ^{14}C into positions 1–5 of glucose, confirmed once more that after phenformin, the Cori cycle is more active in normal subjects also. This would in fact indicate an increased recycling of lactate into glucose. Moreover, since the increase in glucose turnover was found to be double the increase in glucose production from lactate (Cori cycle), Searle *et al.* (1969) concluded that the administration of phenformin to normal subjects also stimulates gluconeogenesis from other substrates.

A series of experiments by Kreisberg supplied results which at first sight seem discordant. In an investigation on normal and obese subjects (including 4 subjects with chemical diabetes), Kreisberg (1968a), using glucose-U-^{14}C, found that the glucose pool, taken as an absolute quantity, was larger in the obese than in the normal subjects; if referred to the body weight, the pool was equal in the two groups, but if referred to the metabolically active body mass (exchangeable potassium), it was in fact larger in the obese. Glucose turnover was apparently lower in the obese; nevertheless, if glucose-lactate-glucose recycling was taken into account by means of glucose-1-^{14}C, it was found to be equal in the two groups. Recycling was in fact increased in obese subjects, thus showing that gluconeogenesis is increased in the obese condition. This had already been suggested by indirect arguments (Kreisberg *et al.*, 1967). Glucose oxidation to CO_2 in obese subjects was not significantly different from what it is in normal subjects (glucose-U-^{14}C).

After 10–14 days of treatment with phenformin, obese subjects (not stated if also diabetic) showed a reduction in the absolute amount of recycled glucose (glucose-1-^{14}C); the amount of glucose-1-^{14}C oxidized to $^{14}CO_2$ varied: it was reduced in 4 subjects and increased in 2 subjects.

Although according to Kreisberg (1968a), the effects of phenformin on glucose oxidation could not be deduced from his data, he concluded that the drug might be considered to act both by inhibiting gluconeogenesis and by enhancing glucose oxidation. The fact that after phenformin treatment more ^{14}C is present in lactate, is compatible according to the author, with a reduced lactate utilization, consequent to the inhibition of gluconeogenesis. The interruption of the excessive glucose neoproduction could lead, according to Kreisberg (1968a), to a reduction in insulin resistance [perhaps caused by excessive endogenous glucose production, as by prolonged glucose infusion (Kreisberg *et al.*, 1967)] and induce as a secondary phenomenon, a more active peripheral glucose utilization and oxidation, without necessarily postulating a direct effect of the drug at this level.

In a subsequent experiment, Kreisberg (1968b) found that in normal subjects phenformin caused an increase in glucose turnover due entirely to glucose-lactate recycling, with a rise in blood lactate. Phenformin reduced the oxidation of glucose-1-^{14}C to $^{14}CO_2$ in normal subjects. In obese subjects, the effects on glucose turnover and recycling were the same but less marked; the effects on the oxidation of glucose to CO_2 were not unequivocal.

In contrast with his previous statements, Kreisberg (1968b) concluded that phenformin increases glucose utilization by diverting its metabolism in peripheral tissues along a nonoxidative pathway. The rise in lactate, more marked in normal than in obese subjects, was no longer interpreted as an expression of reduced gluconeogenesis, but as the result of hyperproduction secondary to enhanced anaerobic glucose catabolism. Finally, since the total amount of CO_2 (labeled plus nonlabeled) remained unchanged, the author concluded that other substrates must have been oxidized to an extent corresponding to the amount of glucose diverted toward anaerobic pathways.

More recently, Kreisberg *et al.* (1970) confirmed the results and conclusions of their previous paper: using lactate-U-^{14}C and glucose-1-^{14}C, they found that in obese subjects phenformin increased glucose turnover, entirely as a result of recycling through lactate, while it did not increase the oxidation of glucose to CO_2 (discordant results).

In research carried out by nonisotopic methods in normal and diabetic subjects, Gomez *et al.* (1970) found that buformin increased glucose uptake and oxidation, with an associated increase in respiratory quotient up to almost 1.

Losert *et al.* (1971) recently studied the effects of phenformin, metformin, and buformin on the oxidation of glucose-U-^{14}C to $^{14}CO_2$ in normal rats: they found that all three biguanides induced a marked and statistically significant increase in expired $^{14}CO_2$, with a clear dose-effect ratio. Blood lactate increased in parallel: while the increase was modest in blood taken from the aorta and vena cava, it was quite marked in portal blood.

Finally Davies *et al.* (1971), using glucose-6-^{14}C and glucose-6-^{3}H, observed in normal rats and dogs that pretreatment with phenformin or buformin enhanced glucose turnover and its recycling in the Cori cycle, as demonstrated by the more rapid reduction of plasma ^{3}H versus ^{14}C. The total expired CO_2 remained unchanged. The liver glycogen content also remained unchanged; the $^{3}H/^{14}C$ ratio of liver glycogen fell: this proved that hepatic gluconeogenesis was not inhibited.

In practice, the results and interpretations of different authors coincide only in some points while they disagree in others. Even individual authors (e.g., Kreisberg, 1968a,b; Kreisberg *et al.*, 1970) modified their conclusions in the course of their studies. Moreover, the different authors give discordant interpretations when they try to identify the primary metabolic effect of biguanides. There is general agreement on one point:

biguanides influence glucose metabolism in normal man and rat, though without causing hypoglycemia. There is no agreement, however, on the interpretation of these effects.

Thus Searle and Cavalieri (1968) believe that the primary effect is the stimulation of oxidative glucose utilization in peripheral tissues with resulting increase in the activity of the Cori cycle and of glucose turnover (liver gluconeogenesis) in the normal subject.

The same authors (Searle *et al.*, 1969) state moreover that in normal subjects, the primary enhancement of peripheral glucose oxidation is followed, as a consequence, by increased gluconeogenesis from substrates other than lactate.

According to Kreisberg (1968a), the primary effect consists in the inhibition of gluconeogenesis with the following consequences: increased lactate due to its reduced utilization for gluconeogenesis (reduced total glucose-lactate recycling); a possible, but not certain, increased peripheral glucose utilization and oxidation, due to reduced insulin resistance.

The next interpretation suggested by Kreisberg (1968b) is still different: the primary effect is now envisaged as an inhibition of glucose oxidation with the following consequences: increased anaerobic glycolysis, increased glucose-lactate recycling without inhibition of gluconeogenesis; increased oxidation of substrates other than glucose, since the total amount of CO_2 produced does not fall.

More recently, Kreisberg *et al.* (1970) again concluded that the primary effect consists in stimulation of the conversion of glucose into lactate (anaerobic glycolysis), without, however, any reduction in glucose oxidation. According to Gomez *et al.* (1970), the effect consists in increased peripheral glucose uptake and oxidation. Losert *et al.* (1971) conclude that in the rat, the primary effect is the increased oxidation of glucose to CO_2 with simultaneous increase in blood lactate, particularly in portal blood. Finally Davies *et al.* (1971) conclude that in the dog and rat, the primary effect is the increased glucose turnover and recycling in the Cori cycle, without inhibition of gluconeogenesis and without any reduction in the amount of expired CO_2.

Since the aforementioned experiments were carried out by techniques beyond criticism, there may be two possible explanations for such discordant conclusions: (a) the differences in experimental design (method of drug administration, differences among subjects studied, metabolic differences between man and rat) and the necessarily limited number of human subjects studied resulted in an excessive variability of effects; or (b) the effects were correctly detected but their interpretation must be reconsidered. Since within single experiments, the results were significantly coherent, I tend to exclude the first possibility and rather think that the disagreements are to a large extent only apparent: it seems to me in fact that the results may be interpreted univocally.

I consider as fundamental the position of the ^{14}C atom in the molecule of glucose employed. The experiments in which the oxidation of glucose to CO_2 was found to be increased had been carried out with glucose-U-^{14}C (uniformly labeled glucose) (Searle and Cavalieri, 1968; Losert *et al.*, 1971) or with glucose-6-^{14}C (Searle *et al.*, 1969); those in which glucose oxidation was reduced or unchanged had been performed with glucose-1-^{14}C (Kreisberg, 1968a,b; Kreisberg *et al.*, 1970). Since biguanides are known to inhibit the pentose phosphate pathway in adipose tissue (Wick *et al.*, 1958; Söling *et al.*, 1967) and since it is also known that only the C-1 of glucose oxidized via this pathway is recovered in CO_2, the results obtained with glucose-1-^{14}C must be considered as confirmation of the inhibition of the direct glucose oxidation pathway and not indicative of an inhibition of glucose oxidation via the Krebs cycle (this suspicion was also put forth by Kreisberg, 1968b).

The activity of the Embden-Meyerhof-Krebs (EMK) pathway is determined more reliably using glucose-U-^{14}C: in this case, in fact, there is a higher probability that $^{14}CO_2$ will be formed right from the entry of glucose (as pyruvate) into the Krebs cycle, since the first atoms to appear in CO_2 are C-3 and C-4, subsequently C-2 and C-5, and lastly C-1 and C-6 (Javillier *et al.*, 1969a). Hence, should there be a diversion from the pentose cycle to the tricarboxylic acid cycle, glucose-1-^{14}C might underestimate the activity of the Krebs cycle, as compared to glucose-U-^{14}C, because it is possible that some intermediate compounds of this cycle, containing ^{14}C, may leave it and enter the synthetic pathway (aspartate, glutamate) (Harper, 1965), without any production of $^{14}CO_2$ from ^{14}C. This cannot occur when the ^{14}C is in position 3 or 4, because these atoms give rise to CO_2 right from the first step of the cycle.

This possibility must be kept in mind in evaluating Kreisberg's results (Kreisberg, 1968a,b; Kreisberg *et al.*, 1970), obtained with glucose-1-^{14}C and, for different reasons, in assessing the results of Searle *et al.* (1969) obtained with glucose-6-^{14}C. In this case, the authors observed only a slight increase in glucose oxidation, lower than the one previously observed using glucose-U-^{14}C (Searle and Cavalieri, 1968). This difference might depend either upon the differences in types of subjects studied [i.e. diabetic in one case (Searle and Cavalieri, 1968) and normal in the other (Searle *et al.*, 1969)] or it might depend upon the different fate of the first three versus the last three carbon atoms of glucose. When the pentose cycle is active, more triose phosphate is formed from C-4, C-5, and C-6 than from C-1, C-2, and C-3: thus the pentose cycle enhances the specific activity of triose phosphates generated from glucose-6-^{14}C, as compared with those formed from glucose-

U-^{14}C (Landau and Katz, 1965). Inhibition of the pentose cycle can therefore reduce to a greater extent, the production of triose phosphates containing the C-6 glucose, as compared to those not containing it and as a result, reduce the production of $^{14}CO_2$ from ^{14}C-6 in the Krebs cycle.

It may be concluded that while there is no reason to doubt the results obtained with glucose-U-^{14}C, there are reasons for believing that experiments with glucose-1-^{14}C (and perhaps also with glucose-6-^{14}C) have underestimated the degree of glucose oxidation via the Krebs cycle after phenformin treatment. Hence we can agree with Searle and Cavalieri (1968) and Losert *et al.* (1971) that phenformin stimulates the oxidation of glucose to CO_2.

Since after phenformin treatment, larger amounts of C-2, C-3, C-4, C-5 of glucose arc found in CO_2, it is clear that the entire glycolytic EMK cycle has been activated. Presumably, it also utilizes glucose made available by inhibition of the pentose cycle. If this phenomenon also involves districts which produce lactate aerobically as well, by utilizing glucose via the EM pathway (kidneys, erythrocytes, intestinal mucosa) (Moruzzi *et al.*, 1966), there will be a resulting increase in lactate production. The fact (to be discussed later) that biguanides induce a more marked "district" production of lactate in the splanchnic area (Losert *et al.*, 1971) further explains why the Cori cycle was found to be more active after phenformin.

According to Kreisberg (1968b), the increase in glucose-lactate recycling corresponds to the proportion of glucose not oxidized. It should be mentioned, however, that blood lactate was also raised when the increase in glucose oxidation was quite marked (Searle and Cavalieri, 1968; Losert *et al.*, 1971). Hence, in disagreement with the repeated claims of Tyberghein and Williams (1957), Wick *et al.* (1958), Jangaard *et al.* (1968), Kreisberg (1968b), the phenomenon cannot be ascribed to the fact that guanidine and its derivatives may, under certain conditions and given concentrations, inhibit oxidative phosphorylation (Steiner and Williams, 1958, 1959; Schäfer, 1969; Pressman, 1963; Jangaard *et al.*, 1968), or at least cannot be ascribed to a "systemic" inhibition of oxidative phosphorylation; on the other hand, it cannot be excluded—and is even very likely—that an effect of this type may occur in special areas (see Section VII). The fact that total CO_2 production does not decrease (Kreisberg, 1968b; Davies *et al.*, 1971) is also against any inhibition in the Krebs cycle; on the contrary, the increase in respiratory quotient (Gomez *et al.*, 1970) demonstrates that glucose is oxidized to a greater extent in place of other substrates. Hence Kreisberg's (1968b) results need another interpretation. Since they were obtained with glucose-1-^{14}C, the author is likely to have found in lactate a fair proportion of the ^{14}C of the glucose diverted from the direct oxidative route (inhibited by phenformin) to the EMK pathway: the part converted into lactate (kidneys, erythrocytes, splanchnic area) may contain the ^{14}C while the part oxidized to CO_2 via the Krebs cycle is not likely to contain it since we are dealing with glucose-1-^{14}C (see above).

To conclude, we may state that the disagreement between the experimental data of the aforementioned authors is only apparent if the results are interpreted critically. Thus, one may easily deduce that biguanides increase the proportion of glucose oxidized to CO_2 via the EMK cycle, while reducing the amount oxidized via the pentose cycle. One may also deduce that the increased amount of glucose entering the EMK cycle is associated, according to a certain ratio, with increased lactate production; the latter may represent a significant fraction of the increased lactate-glucose recycling found after biguanides.

IV. Gluconeogenesis

To apply the pharmacobiological criteria initially discussed to this complex problem, it is first essential to consider in which animal species and at which local concentrations (in tissues or *in vitro*) biguanides exert their effects. The chief animal species generally used in this field of research have already been discussed. Much more difficult is the task of defining the therapeutically active or "toxic" concentrations (also in relation to the animals species employed), reached *in vivo* in liver and kidneys, and to compare them to those used *in vitro* by different authors.

The plasma levels induced in man by therapeutic doses of biguanides are known. After 100 mg of oral phenformin, the plasma level is 0.1–0.2 μg/ml (Beckmann, 1968; Mehnert, 1969a), equivalent to concentrations ranging between 0.5 and $1 \times 10^{-6}\ M$; after 100 mg buformin, the level is below 0.6 μg/ml (Mehnert, 1969a), i.e., below $3.8 \times 10^{-6}\ M$; after 1–2 gm of metformin, the levels range between 3 and 8 μg/ml (Mehnert, 1969a), equivalent to concentrations of 2.3 to $6.1 \times 10^{-5}\ M$. These plasma levels are short-lived; the biological half-life of the three biguanides corresponds to about 3 hours (Mehnert, 1969a). It is also known that in certain organs (e.g., liver and kidney) these compounds reach concentrations higher than in plasma. The experiments carried out on animals to establish tissue concentrations are incomplete and difficult to compare. They are nevertheless sufficient to suggest the order of magnitude of these concentrations.

According to a study of Beckmann (1965) on the rat, the maximum hepatic concentration of a drug after a 50 mg/kg oral dose of buformin is reached at about the first or second hour, the values ranging between 50 and 60 μg/gm (i.e., about $4 \times 10^{-4}\ M$). In my opinion, this concentration is hardly indicative of an elective storage in the liver, since it is of the same order as the dose:bodyweight ratio. After the second hour, the drug's concentration in the liver falls rapidly and in the sixth hour, it does not exceed one-sixth of the initial value. The concentrations in the kidneys are quite similar to those observed in the liver.

In the mouse, at equal dose per kilogram, Yoh (1967) found considerably lower second hour concentrations then those observed by Beckmann (1965), namely 17 μg/gm (little more than $1 \times 10^{-4}\,M$) in the liver and 23 μg/gm (i.e., $1.5 \times 10^{-4}\,M$) in the kidney.

With regard to phenformin, in an experiment with ^{14}C-labeled drug, Hall *et al.* (1968) confirmed its early concentration in rat liver (even more, if alloxan diabetic) and guinea pig liver and its subsequent rapid fall within 6 hours. The same phenomenon is observed in the kidneys, but with lower absolute values. One important fact emerges from this experiment: in the rat, most liver radioactivity is due to *p*-hydroxyphenethylbiguanide, chief metabolite of phenformin and devoid of any hypoglycemic activity (Mehnert, 1969a); on the contrary, in the guinea pig at equal levels of total liver radioactivity, the proportion of hydroxy derivative is much lower (Hall *et al.*, 1968). This may help to explain the specific sensitivity of the guinea pig to phenformin. In this regard, it must be remembered that man behaves like the rat, metabolizing and eliminating phenformin as the *p*-hydroxy derivative (Beckmann, 1968).

In practice, the above experiments show that biguanides reach clearly detectable but not particularly high concentrations in the liver, contrary to what is commonly stated. To estimate the hepatic concentrations of biguanides as 10 times higher than the plasma levels (Berger, 1970) would seem excessive. In the case of phenformin, moreover, the concentrations of "active," namely nonhydroxylated, drug in rat liver are certainly much lower than the values determined by radioisotopic methods, since the inactive *p*-hydroxy derivative contributes to the total radioactivity. This can very likely be applied also to man.

These preliminary remarks are necessary to evaluate critically the results obtained using liver fragments surviving *in vitro*, results which in any case must be accepted with some reservations.

In interpreting the *in vitro* effects, a point of reference might be the possible concomitant depletion in liver glycogen. This depletion occurs *in vivo* after acute doses of guanidine or sintaline, or after high doses of biguanides; it is due, besides the component mediated by adrenergic stimulation, to a direct action of the drug, inasmuch as it is also reproducible in rat liver slices *in vitro* (Söling, 1969). This effect, however, appears only at high concentrations of biguanides ($1 \times 10^{-3}\,M$ of phenformin) and is associated with the overall picture of increased anaerobic glycolysis with marked lactate production, with fall in ATP

ADP ratio (Söling, 1969), and in practice, with inhibition of oxidative phosphorylation, just as in the guinea pig with low doses of phenformin (Altschuld and Kruger, 1968). On the contrary since no reduction in liver glycogen nor any sign of inhibition of oxidative phosphorylation is observed in patients treated effectively with phenformin or buformin and in rat liver perfused *in vitro* with buformin at concentrations (2.55×10^{-5} *M*) not exceeding ten times the plasma level for therapeutic doses (Söling, 1969), it follows that the reduction in ATP and the glycogen depletion indicate the production of toxic effects of the guanidine type; the specific pharmacological effects of biguanides must hence be sought in the absence of such phenomena.

For these reasons, the demonstration in the guinea pig of the inhibition of liver gluconeogenesis caused by biguanides (Altschuld and Kruger, 1968; Jangaard *et al.*, 1968; Haeckel and Haeckel, 1968; Williams *et al.*, 1957; Meyer *et al.*, 1967) does not contribute to the understanding of the problem, since the fall in hepatic ATP itself inhibits gluconeogenesis (Altschuld and Kruger, 1968).

An *in vitro* experiment of Sandler *et al.* (1968) on rabbit liver slices deserves special mention: it shows that phenformin inhibits gluconeogenesis from alanine-^{14}C. The high concentration of drug used (0.8×10^{-3} *M*) leads one to suspect that the changes observed may once again be due to reduction in liver ATP, a conclusion reached by the authors themselves. Moreover in these experiments, the ^{14}C of triglyceride-glycerol was considerably reduced, yet when ethanol was used instead of phenformin, ^{14}C was present in normal amounts in spite of the fact that ethanol also inhibited gluconeogenesis. This difference between the effects of phenformin and ethanol corresponds to the different effects of the two compounds on liver ATP generation, which is reduced by high concentrations of phenformin (Söling, 1969) and remains unchanged (Ammon and Estler, 1967) or is even increased (Haeckel and Haeckel, 1968) by high concentrations of ethanol. It is known that ATP is necessary for the esterification of fatty acids (Tietz and Shapiro, 1956). Hence the inhibition of gluconeogenesis by ethanol found by Sandler *et al.* (1968) should be attributed, as known (Kaden *et al.*, 1969; Toews *et al.*, 1970; Madison *et al.*, 1967; Calandra *et al.*, 1968) to a reduction in NAD $NADH_2$ ratio, with resulting inhibition of NAD-dependent steps.[1]

---

[1] Note that unlike Sandler *et al.* (1968), Kaden *et al.* (1969) found that ethanol does not inhibit gluconeogenesis from alanine, but only from substrates requiring NAD-dependent reactions. It is not unlikely, however, that an excess of $NADH_2$ may, under special conditions, also convert the pyruvate which is forming from alanine into lactate, thus diverting the pyruvate from the gluconeogenetic pathway.

This mechanism cannot be attributed to phenformin, even if high concentrations of the latter are known to also lower the NAD/$NADH_2$ ratio (Jangaard *et al.*, 1968) because additional $NADH_2$ enhances the formation of α-glycerophosphate from dihydroxyacetone phosphate and cannot therefore explain the reduction in ^{14}C-triglyceride-glycerol, observed by Sandler *et al.* (1968). Hence in these experiments, the inhibition of gluconeogenesis by phenformin was caused, as already mentioned, by the reduction in hepatic ATP. With previous remarks in mind, however, this effect should be attributed to the high concentration of the compound and does not fulfill the requirements for the status of "pharmacological effect." Note that in the course of preliminary tests, this was the minimum concentration capable of inhibiting gluconeogenesis (Sandler *et al.*, 1968).

To conclude, the previously discussed experiments of Sandler *et al.* (1968) show that phenformin inhibits hepatic gluconeogenesis from alanine, only at concentrations which are so high as to reduce liver ATP production.

The experiments carried out by various investigators on the rat seem to be more easily interpretable. Altschuld and Kruger (1968) perfused isolated rat liver with phenformin $2.5 \times 10^{-3}\,M$ and observed a weak and fairly insignificant inhibition of gluconeogenesis from glycerol, no inhibition of gluconeogenesis from lactate after 1 hour of perfusion, and scanty inhibitory effect after a second hour of perfusion. On the contrary, in guinea pig liver, the same authors observed inhibition of gluconeogenesis from glycerol and lactate at concentrations 5 times lower ($0.5 \times 10^{-3}\,M$): these concentrations are capable of reducing the ATP content of guinea pig liver, but not of rat liver (Altschuld and Kruger, 1968).

The effects on gluconeogenesis from glycerol (inhibited in the guinea pig but not in the rat) are very interesting because they involve metabolic steps that do not concern pyruvate carboxylase, while substrates such as alanine and lactate have to pass through this enzymatic step which, as will be shown later, is a key point in the action of biguanides on gluconeogenesis. The findings of Altschuld and Kruger (1968) contribute proof that the inhibition of gluconeogenesis from glycerol occurs only in presence of lowered ATP:ADP ratio and NAD:$NADH_2$ ratio (guinea pig, but not rat):NAD is essential for the step α-glycerophosphate-dihydroxyacetonephosphate. Hence any nontoxic, specific effect of biguanides on gluconeogenesis must be sought among NAD-independent steps.

Patrick (1966) also failed to observe any inhibition of gluconeogenesis from pyruvate or from glucose 6-phosphate in rat liver slices in the presence of phenformin ($4 \times 10^{-4}\,M$), while he found partial inhibition in rat kidney. Only by prolonging the incubation beyond 1 hour was it possible to observe partial inhibition of gluconeogenesis from fructose 1,6-diphosphate, attributed by the author to allosteric inhibition of fructose-1,6-diphosphatase by AMP. It cannot therefore be excluded that on prolonging Patrick's (1966) experimental conditions beyond the first hour, ATP may have started to fall: with regard to this point, it should be mentioned that the organs were taken from fasted animals (see later).

Meyer *et al.* (1967) studied *in vivo* and *in vitro* the effects of phenformin and metformin on gluconeogenesis in rat liver and kidney. A 30–80 mg/kg dose of metformin administered to rats fasted for 24 hours significantly inhibited gluconeogenesis from alanine and cortisol-stimulated gluconeogenesis from either alanine or pyruvate. The latter was inhibited even more strongly by 30 mg/kg of phenformin. Moreover, in the case of rat kidney slices, gluconeogenesis from a series of substrates (pyruvate, alanine, oxaloacetate, glutamate) was partially inhibited by concentrations of metformin (up to 10^{-4} *M*) or phenformin (up to 5×10^{-5} *M*) not much higher than 10 times the plasma levels produced in man by therapeutic doses, and hence probably close to the hepatic and renal concentrations actually resulting from these doses: these concentrations do not inhibit oxidative phosphorylation either in the rat or in man. The two biguanides also differed, in relation to glucogenetic substrates, in their inhibitory effectiveness: these differences are not easily explained if we assume a common action mechanism and I will not try to interpret them at this stage. However, we may conclude that Meyer *et al.* (1967) have shown both *in vivo* and *in vitro* that inhibition of gluconeogenesis is a specific pharmacological effect of biguanides.

In practice, however, it is necessary to analyze these results in greater detail. When speaking of gluconeogenesis we must remember that it does not take place according to a single rigid model. On the contrary, it is known that the modalities of gluconeogenesis activation vary considerably with regard to metabolic routes, substrates, and to physiopathological conditions and hence to experimental conditions.

In the experiments of Meyer *et al.* (1967), the *in vivo* inhibition of gluconeogenesis was quite evident, but in this case it was a question of gluconeogenesis stimulated by cortisol or alanine in fasted animals.

The *in vitro* inhibition caused by biguanides (apart from general reservations, always appropriate in such cases, and the fact that the concentrations of biguanides were not always low) was quite evident when gluconeogenesis was stimulated by a variety of substrates, while there was no inhibition of basal gluconeogenesis (or in many cases none was reported). Furthermore, in both *in vivo* and *in vitro* experiments on gluconeogenesis from alanine, the control results were compared with those of treatment with alanine alone or alanine + biguanides, while those relative to biguanides alone were missing. In any case, in the presence of alanine + biguanides, gluconeogenesis was lower than with alanine alone, but was always higher than in the controls (without either biguanides or alanine). This means that biguanides do not inhibit the glucogenetic process as such (on the contrary, they allow it to increase to some extent when more substrate is available), but depress the high gluconeogenetic activity induced by cortisol or by excess of some substrates. These different aspects of gluconeogenesis in relation to the effects of biguanides will be discussed later.

Söling's (1969) results are very interesting. He perfused isolated livers of normal or alloxan diabetic rats with buformin (2.55×10^{-5} *M*) and observed a reduction in net production of inorganic phosphate, incompatible with the hypothesis of an inhibition of oxidative phosphorylation; in normal liver, no change occurred in the lactate:pyruvate ratio, a fact also incompatible with the same hypothesis. In diabetic liver, the following occurred: normalization of the initially raised lactate:pyruvate ratio, normalization of the pathologically increased release of potassium, normalization of the increased urea production, and return to a positive amino acid balance. If the concentration of buformin was increased to 1.02×10^{-4} *M*, the above effects stopped and were replaced by an increase in lactate:pyruvate ratio. This demonstrates that the inhibition of oxidative phosphorylation is a characteristic property of the higher concentrations, a property that can replace the specific pharmacobiological effects of low concentrations of biguanides. In any case, Söling (1969) did not detect any inhibition of hepatic glucose production from endogenous substrates with either concentration.

Connon (1971) perfused the livers of normal or streptozotocin diabetic rats with phenformin. In the latter group, the initial gluconeogenesis was 30% higher than in normal rats. When the concentration of phenformin in the perfusate was high (40 mg/100 ml = 2×10^{-3} *M*), gluconeogenesis was completely inhibited in normal and diabetic livers. When, however, the phenformin concentration was lower (12 mg/100 ml = 6×10^{-4} *M*), only gluconeogenesis in diabetic liver was completely inhibited, while in normal liver it was only slightly affected.

Davies *et al.* (1971) studied *in vivo* in normal rats and dogs, the effects of a dose of phenformin or buformin (60 mg / kg in the rat and 20 mg / kg in the dog) on liver gluconeogenesis, using intravenous glucose-6-^{3}H and glucose-6-^{14}C. They found that after biguanides were administered, the liver glycogen content was unchanged, the ^{3}H:^{14}C ratio of liver glycogen was reduced, and the activity of the Cori cycle was increased. Their conclusion was that in the normal animal, hepatic gluconeogenesis is not inhibited by biguanides.

Summarizing the results of the experiments so far discussed, we may state that "therapeutic" concentrations of biguanides do not inhibit gluconeogenesis indiscriminately. They do not inhibit gluconeogenesis in normal liver, but selectively inhibit only some modalities of the same, e.g., gluconeogenesis activated by cortisol or by excess of some substrates (but even in these cases without abolishing all residual gluconeogenetic activity) and gluconeogenesis taking place in diabetic liver.

Careful analysis of some well-known basic aspects of gluconeogenesis will allow us to delineate, and reconcile the discordant experimental data discussed so far and to explain them on the basis of the fundamental action mechanism of biguanides, i.e., the inhibition of fatty acid oxidation. This analysis could begin with an answer to the following question: how can we reconcile the fact (already analyzed in Section III) that biguanides cause, or allow, an increase in the activity of the Cori cycle with the fact that they may inhibit gluconeogenesis?

It must be admitted that lactate-glucose recycling within the normal Cori cycle must take place via pathways or modalities different from those followed by other gluconeogenetic processes. It is necessary therefore to analyze in greater detail, the process of gluconeogenesis and its regulation, at least those steps concerning biguanides.

Insulin is known to inhibit hepatic gluconeogenesis (Söling, 1970). This action of insulin fits into the more general rules of both hormonal and nonhormonal regulation of specific metabolic pathways by acting on key enzymes (Krebs, 1964). A coarse control is achieved by stimulation or inhibition of enzyme synthesis, i.e., by modifying the concentrations of the enzyme: this mechanism is carried out exclusively by hormones. A fine control is achieved by activating or inhibiting the enzyme, without influencing its concentration: certain enzymes are regulated, not only by their respective substrates, but also by special metabolites operating by an allosteric mechanism (Monod *et al.*, 1963). Hormones, inasmuch as they are capable of modifying the availability or distribution of these metabolites, also play a part in fine control. The latter, due to its characteristics, rapidly adjusts the activity of the specific metabolic step requiring regulation (Krebs, 1964).

Insulin inhibits liver gluconeogenesis both by preventing the synthesis (induced by glucocorticoids) of the key enzymes of gluconeogenesis (Weber and Srivastava, 1965), and by exerting an "acute" effect, presumably secondary to its activity on lipid metabolism (antilipolytic activity) (Söling, 1970).

The activity of the enzyme, pyruvate carboxylase, is a critical step of gluconeogenesis from pyruvate and from substrates that must pass through pyruvate (lactate, alanine, and other amino acids, with the exception of those which can form intermediary products of the Krebs cycle and be converted into oxaloacetate). Pyruvate can actually generate phosphoenolpyruvate (PEP) by different metabolic routes involving either pyruvate kinase, malic enzyme, or pyruvate carboxylase. The three pathways are not, however, equally efficient.

The first direct pathway is rather inefficient due to difficulties in overcoming the energy barrier existing in this direction (Seubert, 1970), which drives its activity almost entirely in the direction PEP-pyruvate; nevertheless, the direct step pyruvate-PEP is possible in the presence of a high ATP:ADP ratio (Seubert, 1970).

The indirect malic enzyme pathway (pyruvate-malate-oxaloacetate-PEP) although more suitable for overcoming the energy gradient and therefore considered as the most important pathway, now appears of limited physiological importance, after the demonstration that the malic enzyme functions prevalently as decarboxylase, hence in the opposite direction (malate-pyruvate) (Seubert, 1970).

Therefore, the basic pathway of gluconeogenesis from pyruvate is the shortest indirect route involving pyruvate carboxylase (with subsequent steps involving PEP carboxykinase) (Utter, 1963; Seubert, 1970). The activity of this pathway is increased in diabetes and during fasting, as an effect of corticosteroids (Seubert, 1970), and in all conditions associated with increased fatty acid oxidation (Krebs *et al.*, 1963).

In its role, as the key enzyme of gluconeogenesis, pyruvate carboxylase is subjected both to coarse and fine regulation. The latter is based essentially on the fact that acetyl-CoA in an essential activator of the enzyme (Utter and Keech, 1963). There are valid reasons for believing that mitochondria contain two acetyl-CoA pools of different origin; the acetyl-CoA generated from fatty acid oxidation is probably present in a functionally separate compartment from acetyl-CoA derived from pyruvate (Fritz, 1967). Equally reliable data indicate that pyruvate carboxylase is closely related to the oxidase complex of fatty acids (Fritz, 1967). Hence only acetyl-CoA generated from fats and not the one formed from pyruvate, seems capable of activating the enzyme and of promoting gluconeogenesis (Fritz, 1967).

Hormonal mechanisms also play a part in the fine regulation of pyruvate carboxylase activity. Some hormones, such as epinephrine and glucagon, increase the production of cyclic 3′,5′-AMP, promote lipolysis, and stimulate gluconeogenesis from alanine and lactate; insulin has opposite effects (Exton *et al.*, 1966; Williamson *et al.*, 1966a; Williamson, 1967; Ball and Jungas, 1964; Ruderman *et al.*, 1969). Cyclic 3′,5′-AMP stimulates the activity of pyruvate carboxylase, since its addition to the fluid perfusing isolated liver enhances gluconeogenesis from lactate (Exton *et al.*, 1966). According to Williamson *et al.* (1966b), however, cyclic 3′,5′-AMP does not activate the enzyme directly: its effect on pyruvate carboxylase is believed to be secondary to the increased production of acetyl-CoA it causes (Williamson *et al.*, 1966b; Fritz, 1967). This hypothesis is not fully accepted by all authors since some experimental observations of Exton *et al.* (1970) do not seem to confirm it as the sole mechanism. Nevertheless, even taking into account these observations, Lefebvre and Luyckx (1972) consider it as tempting because it allows a single interpretation of the action of glucagon on liver cells. In any case, other mechanisms do not exclude this one.

The stimulation of pyruvate carboxylase activity by gluconeogenetic hormones is likely to be mediated by their capacity to activate, by increasing the formation of cyclic 3′,5′-AMP, the lipase of cellular triglycerides (both in adipose tissue and in liver cells themselves) (Bewsher and Ashmore, 1966), thus making available by lipolysis larger amounts of fatty acids for oxidation and acetyl-CoA production. It is the latter that activates pyruvate carboxylase. Insulin influences the same series of events but in the opposite direction.

If we keep in mind these mechanisms that regulate gluconeogenesis from pyruvate, it may be useful to compare the antigluconeogenetic action of insulin with that of biguanides. The inhibitory effects of insulin, either endogenous or possibly exogenous, on gluconeogenesis induced by fasting, diabetes, glucocorticoids, or increased FFA oxidation require no further comment.

One might ask, however, how endogenous insulin acts physiologically when gluconeogenesis from pyruvate occurs within the Cori cycle, activated for example, by intensive muscular work under relatively anaerobic conditions. Muscular exercise actually induces complex neurohormonal and metabolic modifications tending to produce an "anti-insulin" effect, namely: increased plasma levels of growth hormone (Schwarz *et al.*, 1969), catecolamines (Kärki, 1957), glucagon (Assan, 1972), FFA and ketone bodies (Johnson *et al.*, 1969; Schwarz, *et al.*, 1969), while blood insulin is mostly reduced (Johnson *et al.*, 1969; Schwarz, *et al.*, 1969), but may at times be raised in obese subjects (Schwarz *et al.*, 1969) and in coronary patients (Nikkilä *et al.*, 1968). Glucose tolerance may consequently be lowered (Johnson *et al.*, 1969) or, more often, is increased due to "peripheral" mechanisms, apparently independent of plasma insulin behavior (Conard, 1965; Pruett and Oseid, 1970; Nikkilä *et al.*, 1968). One such mechanism worthy of note was described in the hind limbs of the dog during muscular exercise, namely an increase in glucose utilization and an increase of NSILA[2] in lymph returning from the limbs, while the plasma levels of NSILA and IRI[3] remained unchanged (Couturier *et al.*, 1970). Taken as a whole, these changes would tend to favor simultaneous muscular glucose utilization and hepatic reconversion of lactate into glucose.

If muscular exercise takes place after meals, namely after the onset of hyperglycemia and hyperinsulinemia, there will still be at least two possibilities allowing the Cori cycle to function. The first is that the same neurohormonal and metabolic mechanisms activated by muscular exercise may be able to overcome the effect of insulin on the tissues involved in the specific metabolic condition, namely adipose tissue and liver. The situation in this case is similar to the previous one and pyruvate carboxylase may be activated.

The second possibility is that the accumulation of lactate-pyruvate may force the two alternative pathways from pyruvate to PEP, bypassing the obstacle set at the level of pyruvate carboxylase. This second possibility may only be accepted in relation to the "acute" effects of insulin on gluconeogenesis, effects as previously mentioned, due to insufficient production of acetyl-CoA for pyruvate carboxylase; it cannot be valid, however, when insulin exerts its overall effects ("coarse" and "fine") on gluconeogenesis.

Let us now consider the interference of biguanides on these processes. We know that biguanides inhibit gluconeogenesis induced by fasting, cortisol, or diabetes. On the other hand, they do not inhibit the Cori cycle, whose activity is even enhanced in normal subjects receiving biguanides. Moreover, there is no evidence that biguanides exert any direct inhibitory effect on the enzymes of carbohydrate metabolism, even when they inhibit the relative metabolic steps. For example, in the guinea pig, phenformin was shown to have no direct effect on pyruvate dehydrogenase (Jangaard *et al.*, 1968) or phosphoglycerokinase (Haeckel and Haeckel, 1968), although it inhibits the reactions catalyzed by these two enzymes.

The effects of biguanides on gluconeogenesis may be explained in terms of their capability to inhibit fatty acid oxidation and hence the generation of acetyl-CoA of lipid origin. Like insulin, the antilipolytic effect exerted by biguanides *in vitro* (Stone and Brown, 1968) could, if present *in vivo*, reduce the production of acetyl-CoA due to reduced availability of FFA for oxidation. In practice, this mechanism is unlikely to apply to biguanides, since in acute experiments the plasma levels of FFA increase because the inhibition of their oxidation prevails (Muntoni *et al.*, 1970; Sirigu *et al.*, 1973).

---

[2] Nonsuppressible Insulin-Like Activity.

[3] Immunologically Reactive Insulin.

Inhibition of fatty acid oxidation is hence responsible for the effects of biguanides on gluconeogenesis at the level of pyruvate carboxylase. These effects are therefore similar to the "acute" effects of insulin. The analogy depends on the fact that the active sites of insulin and biguanides in this process correspond with two steps of the same metabolic pathway generating acetyl-CoA from fats: insulin acts proximally (inhibition of lipolysis) and biguanides distally (inhibition of FFA oxidation). This is a fine example of how a drug may exert fine control on a metabolic step, just like a hormone, although unrelated to it in either structure or mechanism of action.

The differences between insulin and biguanides on the overall process of gluconeogenesis depend upon the fact that insulin is also responsible for the "coarse" regulation of other steps in gluconeogenesis. The effects of insulin and of biguanides coincide when pyruvate carboxylase is the rate-limiting step: in such a case, the inhibitory effect of biguanides is practically selective.

The effects of biguanides on gluconeogenesis are now more easily understood. At "toxic" doses or concentrations, biguanides inhibit gluconeogenesis indiscriminately, due to reduced ATP production caused by inhibition of oxidative phosphorylation. This is hence an aspecific toxic effect. At "pharmacological" doses or concentrations, biguanides selectively inhibit *only* gluconeogenesis depending upon the activity of pyruvate carboxylase. This is their specific pharmacological effect.

In the light of these conclusions, it is now possible to interpret coherently, the effects of biguanides in different physiopathological conditions. All the following considerations are based on the borderline hypothesis that fatty acid oxidation is totally inhibited by biguanides. However, since there is evidence suggesting that the inhibition is only partial (Muntoni *et al.*, 1970, 1973a,b; Corsini *et al.*, 1974), the interpretation of the metabolic consequences remains qualitatively but not quantitatively valid.

Inhibition of gluconeogenesis stimulated by cortisol, diabetes, obesity, and excess FFA is due to the fact that in all these conditions, the limiting step is the activity of pyruvate carboxylase, which acts as the driving wheel of the gluconeogenetic works. Hence inhibition of fatty acid oxidation blocks the process.

The slight reduction of gluconeogenesis, stimulated by excess of alanine and lactate, may be explained by the fact that these substrates force the routes alternative to pyruvate carboxylase; the driving force in this case is the substrate, while the gluconeogenetic mechanism moves rather passively. As already mentioned in commenting on the data of Meyer *et al.* (1967), biguanides do not prevent the increase in gluconeogenesis induced by excess alanine, even though this increase is still greater in the absence of biguanides: the difference between the two increases, may be attributed to inhibition of pyruvate carboxylase activity.

The absence of hypoglycemic effect in the normal subject can be explained, with regard to the hepatic component, by the fact that there are no changes in gluconeogenesis from substrates between PEP and glucose nor in the stores of liver glycogen or the activity of the Cori cycle. With regard to the Cori cycle, we can apply what has been said for gluconeogenesis due to excess substrate, which in this case is lactate.

The hypoglycemia induced by biguanides in normal subjects after prolonged fasting is due to reduced stores of liver glycogen and also to the decrease in both acetyl-CoA of lipid origin (biguanides) and metabolites for the Krebs cycle (fasting): in these conditions, the production of oxaloacetate is likely to be reduced. In fact, since oxaloacetate, essential for the activity of the Krebs cycle, cannot be generated from the pyruvate carboxylase reaction due to inhibition of fatty acid oxidation, it may only be formed via the indirect malic enzyme route (if plenty of pyruvate producing substrates are available) and from amino acids capable of yielding Krebs-cycle intermediates without passing through pyruvate. However, since the formation of pyruvate from carbohydrates is scanty, (due to fasting) the residual possibilities of forming oxaloacetate still depend on (a) regeneration of the same oxaloacetate via the Krebs cycle (condition that occurs only if no intermediary compounds leave the cycle and which is not compatible therefore with gluconeogenesis from oxaloacetate-PEP); (b) the amino acids yielding Krebs-cycle intermediates through any route. Of course, gluconeogenesis from substrates included between PEP and glucose (glyceraldehyde phosphate, dihydroxyacetone phosphate, fructose) should continue to the extent allowed by the availability of the substrates.

However, to complete the picture, it is necessary to take into account the thermodynamic and energetic aspects of the process. Since fatty acid oxidation is inhibited by biguanides and since practically no carbohydrates are available due to prolonged fasting, ATP production will be reduced. Moreover, gluconeogenesis uses up more ATP than is produced by glycolysis in the opposite direction and may hence be regarded as a pathway directed against the energy gradient. When amino acids produce intermediates of the Krebs cycle, which otherwise is so poorly supplied, it is more likely that these will continue to cycle as substrates for the production of energy, rather than leave as oxaloacetate for endoergonic gluconeogenesis. In practice, therefore, the combination of fasting + biguanides could also block gluconeogenesis from amino acids. Gluconeogenesis from substrates situated between PEP and glucose might also be inhibited for the same energy reasons.

These phenomena cannot occur when the Krebs cycle is normally supplied with available carbohydrates; thus, there is justification for the gluconeogenesis from substrates not passing through lactate ⇄ pyruvate and also for the increased activity of the Cori cycle in normal subjects treated with phenformin (Searle *et al.*, 1969); and for the preserved gluconeogenesis from (a) fructose in man treated with biguanides (Beckmann, 1969) and (b) glycerol in rat liver perfused with phenformin (Altschuld and Kruger, 1968).

To conclude, therapeutic doses of biguanides selectively inhibit a specific mechanism of hepatic (and renal) gluconeogenesis, namely the mechanism depending upon the activation of pyruvate carboxylase by increased fatty acid oxidation. This mechanism functions in diabetes, obesity, hypercortisolism, and in other pathological conditions characterized by a high FFA supply to the liver. It is the mechanism which, according to Randle *et al.* (1963, 1965) mostly accounts for the alterations in hepatic glucose-fatty acid cycle. Biguanides act by shifting these changes. The definition "drugs of the Randle cycle" (Muntoni, 1968; Muntoni *et al.*, 1970) appears therefore to be fully justified.

V. Peripheral Glucose Utilization

In present-day terminology, "peripheral" glucose utilization refers chiefly to muscular utilization, even though other organs or tissues (e.g., nervous tissue) depend mainly on glucose for their metabolism. This is simply because striated muscles as a whole represent the largest fraction of the metabolically active body mass, and in particular they constitute the quantitatively most important insulin-dependent system.

With regard to the effects of biguanides on muscular tissue incubated *in vitro* (generally rat diaphragm), the same reservations apply here as were mentioned with reference to *in vitro* studies on gluconeogenesis. In fact with muscle, it is difficult to establish which concentrations are toxic and which produce specific effects.

Williams *et al.* (1957) reported an effect of phenformin on glucose uptake by rat diaphragm *in vitro*, comparable to the effect of insulin. This effect was subsequently confirmed (Bolinger *et al.*, 1960; Ditschuneit and Hoff, 1964); it occurs at phenformin concentrations of 2.10×10^{-5} *M* and buformin concentrations of 1.02×10^{-4} *M* and roughly corresponds to the effect of 500 μU/ml of insulin.

In many papers, mentioned by Söling and Ditschuneit (1970), the results on this point are discordant. Some do not confirm the increase in glucose uptake; others state that, unlike insulin, glucose taken up in the presence of biguanides is not stored as glycogen, but is mostly converted into lactate. Since many of these experiments were conducted using phenformin concentrations ranging between $1 \times 10^{-4}\,M$ and $1 \times 10^{-3}\,M$, it is difficult to distinguish toxic from pharmacological effects and, among the latter, the "insulin-like" effects from those that occur only in the presence of insulin.

More reliable and indicative results were obtained by *in vivo* studies. One of these, deserving special attention, was performed by Butterfield (1968, 1969), who studied muscular metabolism in man by catheterizing a forearm artery and vein. Briefly, these investigations demonstrated that:

(1) The muscular glucose uptake after oral load is significantly reduced in diabetic and obese subjects; in the latter, weight loss obtained by a hypocaloric diet causes an increase in glucose uptake.

(2) Muscular insulin clearance is proportionately reduced in the same cases: the ratio $1{:}2 \times 10^6$ between fixed insulin molecules and glucose molecules transported from plasma to muscle is equal to that in normal subjects. Hence in diabetes and obesity the ability of muscle to clear insulin from the circulation is impaired, while its metabolic response (glucose transport) to the cleared insulin is not.

(3) In diabetic subjects sensitive to phenformin, after 10 days treatment, the muscular threshold to glucose is reduced just as after insulin treatment.

(4) Phenformin injected in the forearm artery of fasting normal or diabetic subjects has no insulin-like effect; when injected after an oral glucose load, it potentiates locally the effects of endogenous insulin (glucose uptake): this effect is particularly evident in mild forms of diabetes associated with obesity and hyperinsulinemia, while it is less marked in normal subjects and is entirely absent in severe diabetes.

(5) Conversely, oral phenformin treatment potentiates the local effects of small doses of insulin injected intraarterially.

(6) All the previously described effects of phenformin are associated with an increase in muscular clearance of plasma insulin, while the ratio $1{:}2 \times 10^6$ between molecules of cleared insulin and molecules of transported glucose remains unchanged.

(7) The possibility that phenformin may induce glycolysis in anaerobic conditions can be excluded.

(8) The possibility that phenformin may displace insulin from carrier proteins can also be excluded.

Butterfield's (1968, 1969) studies contribute decisively to an understanding of the effects of biguanides on peripheral glucose utilization and supply a basis for interpreting the increase in the K coefficient of glucose observed in man by Lavieuville (1967) and by us (Muntoni *et al.*, 1968) after metformin and confirmed by other authors (Ghionni *et al.*, 1968; Mirouze *et al.*, 1969; Fratino *et al.*, 1970) for the other two biguanides, with the exception of Czyzyk (1969) (man) and Lorch (1971) (rat).

The significance of the increase in *K* coefficient is debatable inasmuch as the physiological meaning of the *K* of glucose is questionable. Conard (1965), in fact assumes that hyperglycemia induced by rapid glucose infusion inhibits the release of glucose from the liver: hence the blood glucose reduction constant is the direct index of cellular glucose uptake. This assumption is acceptable for normal subjects, but not for diabetic subjects in whom gluconeogenesis and glucose release from the liver are unlikely to be inhibited by the induced hyperglycemia (Bernier *et al.*, 1968). In this case, the low value of *K* is partly due to the release of glucose from the liver: cellular glucose uptake must be higher than indicated by the *K* in these conditions. If this is the situation, the increase in *K* in diabetics after biguanides may be attributed both to inhibition of gluconeogenesis and to the increase in cellular glucose uptake. On the other hand, the increase in *K* coefficient found in normal subjects after biguanides (Fratino *et al.*, 1970) should be attributed entirely to the increase in peripheral glucose uptake.

To conclude, a series of investigations, in particular those of Butterfield (1968, 1969) demonstrate that biguanides stimulate muscular glucose utilization by a mechanism requiring the presence of insulin. This mechanism is in good agreement with clinical results showing that biguanides are effective in forms of diabetes in which the blood insulin levels are not excessively low.

At this stage we may still ask whether the changes in glucose-fatty acid cycle and the effects of biguanides on these changes may be correlated in some way with the previously discussed phenomena.

In the muscle of alloxan-diabetic rats, Randle *et al.* (1965) found several abnormalities of glucose metabolism, as well as reduced glucose transport through the cell membrane, which is the direct consequence of a lack of insulin. These abnormalities included a weaker effect on glucose transport of physiological concentrations of insulin, reduced hexokinase activity, inhibition of phosphofructokinase, and of pyruvate dehydrogenase. Taken as a whole, these alterations suggest a condition of relative insensitivity of the muscle to insulin. Insulin succeeds in overcoming this insensitivity only after a certain time, a period of time which corresponds to the delay in onset of the hypoglycemic effect of insulin in special metabolic conditions of diabetes.

According to Randle *et al.* (1965), analogous metabolic modifications may be induced in the myocardium and diaphragm of normal rats by perfusing these muscles with a medium containing palmitate or other fatty acids. In these experimental conditions and in the presence of physiological concentrations of insulin, the transport of glucose through the cell membrane is also partially inhibited.

The mechanism whereby long-chain fatty acids induce a relative insensitivity to insulin in muscle, although complex, is based on the increased production of acetyl-CoA. The latter in its turn starts a series of metabolic changes, partly through allosteric mechanisms, briefly consisting of: inhibition of pyruvate dehydrogenase; increased production of citrate, an inhibitor of phosphofructokinase; consequent increase in glucose 6-phosphate, which in turn inhibits hexokinase (Randle *et al.*, 1965).

A large number of experimental and clinical observations confirm the fundamental part played by long-chain fatty acids in the metabolic changes occurring in diabetes, obesity, and other conditions characterized by high plasma levels and increased utilization of FFA. After triglyceride infusion in normal man, Felber and Vannotti (1964) observed an increase in blood insulin level with reduced glucose tolerance, namely a state of reduced sensitivity to insulin. Schalch and Kipnis (1964) obtained similar results. Gomez *et al.* (1971) found in these conditions that the production of CO_2 from fats increases while its production from glucose decreases: they concluded that increased fatty acid oxidation inhibits glucose oxidation and induces insulin insensitivity. In human pathology, high plasma levels of FFA in maturity onset diabetes and in obesity are also associated with high blood insulin levels and reduced glucose tolerance, with reduced sensitivity to insulin (Yalow *et al.*, 1965; Kreisberg *et al.*, 1967).

Compounds capable of reducing the plasma FFA levels, such as sodium salicylate (Randle *et al.*, 1965), nicotinic acid (Carlson and Ostman, 1965, 1966; Balasse and Ooms, 1973) and its analogs (Froesch *et al.*, 1967; Gomez *et al.*, 1971) induce opposite modifications in glucose metabolism. The improvement in glucose tolerance is even more marked when these compounds are administered to rats in a state of acute insulin deficiency induced by anti-insulin serum (Froesch *et al.*, 1967; Gross and Carlson, 1968), namely when the cellular enzymes are still intact.

Besides exerting its direct effects on glucose metabolism, insulin also acts indirectly, through its antilipolytic activity, by lowering plasma FFA levels: the delay in its hypoglycemic activity in maturing onset diabetes is attributed to the fact that insulin has to lower the plasma FFA levels before achieving its effect on muscle glucose metabolism (Randle *et al.*, 1965).

With these phenomena in mind, it is not difficult to understand how they may be influenced by biguanides. By inhibiting fatty acid oxidation, with consequent reduction in acetyl-CoA production, these drugs abolish in muscle the changes in glucose transport and metabolism or, in other words, insulin resistance. The following is an experimental example of the effectiveness of this mechanism: 2-bromostearate, an inhibitor of fatty acid oxidation, abolishes the *in vitro* insulin resistance of alloxan-diabetic myocardium: the effects of insulin on the uptake, metabolism, and oxidation of glucose-U-^{14}C are restored by bromostearate (Randle, 1969). Further support to these findings has been provided by recent investigations (Bihler and Sawh, 1972): insulin-stimulated membrane transport of 3-*O*-methyl-D-glucose in the rat hemidiaphragm is strongly inhibited by palmitic acid; this inhibitory effect is abolished by 2-bromostearate, which by itself is devoid of any effect on sugar transport.

To conclude, the effects of biguanides on the peripheral utilization and muscular metabolism of glucose are a direct consequence of their activity on the Randle cycle, where they abolish the changes induced by excessive fatty acid oxidation.

The question whether the influence of biguanides on muscular insulin clearance demonstrated by Butterfield (1968) is correlated or not with the activity of these drugs on lipid metabolism remains still to be clarified. This problem will be discussed in Section XIII.

VI. Secondary Hyperinsulinemia

While the relationships between lipid and carbohydrate metabolism in the context of the Randle cycle are sufficiently clear, no single interpretation is yet possible for the hyperinsulinemia associated with raised plasma FFA levels in obesity, maturity onset diabetes, and experimental conditions in which FFA are increased by various means.

The insulin insensitivity of muscle and the reduced glucose tolerance may justify a compensatory increase in insulin production when the blood glucose levels tend to exceed normal values. When, however, the glucose level is normal, even in the presence of a reduced *K* coefficient of glucose a direct effect of FFA on insulin secretion may be envisaged. This effect was demonstrated in the dog by oleate infusion (Crespin *et al.*, 1969), in rat islets using short-chain fatty acids (Montague and Taylor, 1968), and in sheep islets using long-chain fatty acids (Jordan and Hopwood, 1970). The same phenomenon was thought to occur also in man (Jenkins, 1967), and was recently demonstrated by Balasse and Ooms (1973). Hence, according to Ruderman *et al.* (1969) and Balasse and Ooms (1973), increased fatty acid metabolism could induce both the insulin resistance and the hyperinsulinemia in obese subjects with high plasma FFA levels.

The fact that in normal subjects after prolonged fasting, plasma levels of FFA are high and their oxidation is increased in association with low plasma insulin levels (Cahill *et al.*, 1966) does not exclude that FFA may all the same stimulate insulin secretion: Madison *et al.* (Mebane and Madison, 1964; Seyffert and Madison, 1967) believe that in the absence of the stimulating effect of FFA and ketone bodies on insulin secretion, the blood insulin level during fasting could fall so low as to induce acute ketoacidosis instead of the gradual orderly transition from carbohydrate to lipid combustion that normally occurs during fasting.

No satisfactory explanation is yet available for the mechanism inducing hyperinsulinemia in obesity and in conditions of insulin resistance with normal blood glucose levels.

According to Butterfield (1968), when the muscular insulin clearance is reduced and hence muscular glucose uptake is also reduced, larger amounts of insulin must be produced to ensure adequate glucose uptake in adipose tissue, which is physiologically less sensitive than muscle to this effect of insulin, in order to maintain the blood glucose level within normal limits.

On the other hand, the fact that raised blood insulin levels fail to inhibit high plasma FFA levels led some authors to think that adipose tissue is also insulin resistant (Randle *et al.*, 1965; Salans *et al.*, 1968; Cahill, 1971), while others disagree on this point (Yalow *et al.*, 1965). Some authors (Salans *et al.*, 1968; Cahill, 1971; Guy-Grand and Bour, 1972) associated this special type of insulin resistance observed in adipose tissue with overdistension of the fat cells laden with triglycerides, in other words, with the increase in their size. Björntorp (1972) disagrees with the above authors: since in obese subjects, the raised insulin levels may be normalized by physical exercise before any reduction in the mass of adipose tissue, he considers the increase in volume of fat cells as secondary to hyperinsulinemia and to its effects on adipose tissue. In any case, the fact that weight loss normalizes glucose tolerance and the plasma levels of FFA and insulin is worthy of note (Karam *et al.*, 1965; Doar, 1968).

Many authors, including Cahill (1971), ask themselves which is the signal starting from the overstretched fat cells that simultaneously induces hypersecretion of insulin and insulin resistance in the other sites of insulin activity (muscle, liver). From the previous discussion, it would seem that FFA released in large amounts from the enlarged fat cells and oxidized to a high degree in the various tissues utilizing them, constitute at the same time the cause (or one of the causes) of insulin resistance and the signal (or one of the signals) for the hypersecretion of insulin.

The increase in muscular insulin clearance and in peripheral glucose utilization, together with the reduction in gluconeogenesis, all caused by biguanides, should reduce the hyperinsulinemia.

Phenformin is known in fact to lower the insulin levels after glucose load (Grodsky *et al.*, 1963) and this effect occurs only in obese latent diabetic "hypersecretors" (Boshell *et al.*, 1968). Biguanides, however, also normalize hyperinsulinemic patterns in obese subjects with normal glucose tolerance (Boshell *et al.*, 1968). In this case, the signal for hyperinsulinemia is unlikely to be glucose. How then can biguanides normalize the blood insulin levels? Which signal do they abolish? For the time being we can only answer with a hypothesis that refers again to the role of FFA in insulin hypersecretion: it is possible that, by depressing fatty acid oxidation also in β-cells, biguanides may abolish one of the stimuli for the hypersecretion of insulin.

VII. Intestinal Glucose Absorption

In man and in several animal species, biguanides decrease the intestinal absorption of glucose and other substances. Biro *et al.* (1961) demonstrated that phenformin reduces intestinal glucose absorption in the rat. After 3 days treatment with phenformin, Czyzyk (1969; Czyzyk *et al.*, 1968) observed a reduction in the intestinal absorption of glucose introduced by the intraduodenal route in man. The same authors showed that buformin reduces intestinal glucose absorption in the dog. Berchtold *et al.* (1969) found a reduction in the intestinal absorption of xylose and vitamin B_{12} in man during treatment with metformin.

The extent to which this effect of biguanides may contribute to their therapeutic activity in diabetes has been differently assessed. Obviously the authors who believe that biguanides improve the oral glucose tolerance test, but not the *K* coefficient after intravenous load (Czyzyk, 1969; Czyzyk *et al.*, 1968), tend to enhance the significance of the reduction in intestinal absorption; on the other hand, those who observed a marked increase in the *K* coefficient (Lavieuville, 1967; Muntoni *et al.*, 1968; Ghionni *et al.*, 1968; Mirouze *et al.*, 1969; Fratino *et al.*, 1970; Gomez *et al.*, 1970) consider the effects on intestinal absorption to play only an accessory role in the therapeutic activity.

The reduction in intestinal glucose absorption does not seem to be correlated in any way to the fundamental action of biguanides on lipid metabolism. This effect may instead result from the particularly high concentrations reached by biguanides in the intestinal mucosa (Wick *et al.*, 1960; Cohen and Costerousse, 1961); these concentrations have been estimated to be 30–100 times higher than the plasma levels (Berger, 1970) and are hence certainly capable of inhibiting oxidative phosphorylation (the effects of high concentrations of biguanides have been discussed in Section IV). Taking into account the essential role that ATP present in intestinal epithelium plays in the absorption of glucose (Crane, 1960), one can agree with Czyzyk (1969) that the reduction in glucose absorption caused by biguanides may be attributed to inhibition of oxidative phosphorylation and hence of ATP generation in the intestinal cells.

It is worthy to note that in isolated rat intestine, the onset of anaerobic conditions causes a simultaneous net reduction in glucose transport and a marked increase in lactate production (Cappelli *et al.*, 1969). Analogous metabolic effects may be attributed to biguanides since Losert *et al.* (1971) found that the increase in blood lactate, induced by these drugs in the rat, originates in the splanchnic area. Although the intestinal mucosa is known to produce lactate under aerobic conditions (Moruzzi *et al.*, 1966) as well, high concentrations of biguanides within the mucosa are likely to enhance anaerobic glycolysis.

To conclude, an effect, probably "toxic" in nature, localized for pharmacokinetic reasons in a single tissue contributes, together with the specific pharmacological effects on other tissues, to the complex overall action of biguanides on metabolism.

VIII. Lactate Metabolism

Under certain conditions, the administration of guanidine derivatives is followed by an increase in blood lactate both in animals (Tyberghein and Williams, 1957) and in man (Craig *et al.*, 1960; Söling *et al.*, 1963). This observation led to the belief that the activity of biguanides on carbohydrate metabolism depends on inhibition at the level of the respiratory chain (Tyberghein and Williams, 1957; Wick *et al.*, 1958; Jangaard *et al.*, 1968; Kreisberg, 1968b).

Of the various biguanides, only phenformin was actually found to be capable of increasing blood lactate (Bigelow-Sherman and Foà, 1969), while buformin may increase it exceptionally (Söling and Ditschuneit, 1970) even when the treatment is effective (Beckmann, 1969), and metformin, never (Debry *et al.*, 1964). Such differences are attributable to the different ways in which the three drugs are metabolized in the body. Phenformin could give rise to a free monoguanidine derivative (Wick *et al.*, 1960, 1963), responsible for the effect (this is not confirmed however by more recent research of Beckmann, 1968), while in man, the other two biguanides are eliminated unchanged or metabolized to a negligible extent (Beckmann, 1968).

The fact that not all biguanides active in carbohydrate metabolism induce an increase in blood lactate already challenges the hypothesis that the basis of this activity may be an inhibition of the respiratory processes. The fact that an increase in lactate occurs in association with the increase in glucose oxidation to CO_2 (Losert *et al.*, 1971; Searle and Cavalieri, 1968) is another argument against this theory.

The hypothesis that the increase in blood lactate results from its reduced utilization in the liver, due to the inhibition of gluconeogenesis (Kreisberg, 1968a; Meyer *et al.*, 1967) is contradicted by the demonstration that biguanides increase glucose-lactate-glucose recycling (Searle and Cavalieri, 1968; Kreisberg, 1968b; Davies *et al.*, 1971).

With regard to the problem of lactate metabolism, just as for gluconeogenesis, it is necessary to distinguish the "pharmacological" from the "toxic" effects of biguanides. It is understandable how toxic effects of the "guanidine" type involving the respiratory chain may cause an increase in lactate production and in lactate:pyruvate ratio. The following are thus justified: the *in vitro* increase in lactate produced by high concentrations of phenformin (Tyberghein and Williams, 1957) or buformin (Söling and Ditschuneit, 1970); the marked production of lactate in the intestine (see Section VII); the lactic acidosis caused by phenformin when its catabolism in the liver is decreased or diverted due to severe hepatic failure, or coexisting renal failure or conditions capable of causing tissue anoxia (Bigelow-Sherman and Foà, 1969).

In all these cases, there is no doubt that lactate overproduction is the expression of "local" or "systemic" toxic effects. The activity of biguanides on carbohydrate metabolism, however, is not associated with these effects since it is also present when oxidative phosphorylation is not inhibited, as was extensively discussed in previous sections. What significance must then be assigned to any increase in blood lactate in relation to the pharmacological effects of biguanides?

The concept that lactacidemia and plasma lactate:pyruvate ratio are a reliable index of anaerobic conditions, valid in the past decades, must now be revised especially with regard to muscle metabolism (Alpert, 1965). In muscle, the state of the Redox systems and in particular of the $NADH_2/NAD$ system may be out of balance with respect to the lactate:pyruvate ratio, due to the existence of a functional compartmentalization in the above system (Hohorst *et al.*, 1965); even under aerobic conditions in muscle at rest, it would thus be possible to have glycolysis with production of lactate, which on reaching the liver or renal cortex would contribute to the Cori cycle (Hohorst *et al.*, 1965). A mechanism of this type presumably plays a part in the overproduction of lactate in muscle at rest, induced by insulin in the presence of hyperglycemia (Houghton *et al.*, 1971).

It is known, moreover, that other cells and tissues (erythrocytes, renal medulla, intestinal mucosa) also produce lactate by utilizing glucose under aerobic conditions (Moruzzi *et al.*, 1966). Obviously this lactate also contributes to the Cori cycle. On the basis of the aforementioned physiological data, it is conceivable that the increased peripheral glucose utilization, induced by pharmacological concentrations of biguanides, without any inhibition of respiration, may cause an increase in lactate production and in the activity of the Cori cycle.

Since the fundamental mechanism of biguanide action consists in the inhibition of fatty acid oxidation, this section cannot be concluded without examining the relationship between FFA and lactate metabolism.

An increase in fatty acid oxidation in the liver should cause an increase in $NADH_2$:NAD ratio (Wieland and Loeffler, 1962). In agreement with this, an absolute fat diet causes an increase in lactate:pyruvate ratio in rat liver (Wieland and Loeffler, 1962). This phenomenon, however, seems to represent an acute effect of FFA utilization in the liver because as this utilization proceeds, the modifications in $NADH_2$:NAD ratio and lactate:pyruvate ratio regress (Hohorst *et al.*, 1965). According to these authors, the amount of FFA utilized in the liver has only a negligible effect on the oxidoreductive state of the $NADH_2$/NAD system in diabetes and fasting. In this context a lowering of fatty acid oxidation caused by biguanides in diabetes should not influence the $NADH_2$:NAD and lactate:pyruvate ratios.

To conclude, the basic mechanism of biguanide action on fatty acid oxidation has only indirect consequences on lactate metabolism. The increased production of lactate and the consequent increase in the activity of the Cori cycle depend on the increased peripheral glucose utilization, which in its turn, is caused by the decreased production of acetyl-CoA from fats, fully discussed in the previous sections. It is possible, however, that under special conditions already examined, increased lactate production may be caused by toxic effects of the "guanidine" type.

IX. Adipose Tissue Metabolism

Biguanides exert complex metabolic effects on adipose tissue. In isolated rat adipose tissue, phenformin concentrations of 2.10×10^{-5} *M* (Tranquada and Beigelman, 1960) or buformin concentrations of 2.55×10^{-5} *M* (Daweke and Bach, 1963) stimulate glucose uptake. The fate of glucose in fat cells is influenced differently by biguanides than by insulin: while the former reduce its incorporation into glycogen, the latter increases it (Tranquada and Bender, 1962). Moreover, $2.10 \times 10^{-5}\, M$ phenformin inhibits the effect of as much as 1000 μU/ml of insulin on the same process (Söling *et al.*, 1967).

The further fate of glucose taken up by fat cells, but not incorporated into glycogen due to the presence of biguanides, may be deduced with some difficulty from other experimental studies. In isolated fat cells, high concentrations of phenformin ($2.10 \times 10^{-3}\, M$) lower CO_2 production, while lower concentrations ($1.05 \times 10^{-4}\, M$) increase the same and also potentiate the effects of 20 μU/ml of insulin on the same phenomenon (Correa and Marques, 1964). Conversely, phenformin or buformin concentrations even lower than the above (2 to $3 \times 10^{-5}\, M$) clearly inhibit the effect of 1000 μU/ml of insulin on the oxidation of glucose-1-^{14}C via the pentose shunt (Ditschuneit and Hoff, 1964; Söling *et al.*, 1967), while they do not significantly influence the basal activity of this metabolic pathway (Tranquada and Bender, 1962; Daweke and Bach, 1963).

Another important effect of biguanides, probably related to the previous one, consists in inhibiting liposynthesis. The antilipogenetic activity of phenformin in rat adipose tissue is evident at concentrations of $5 \times 10^{-4}\, M$ (Pereira *et al.*, 1967). In isolated fat cells, the same effect is produced by even lower concentrations of buformin ($5 \times 10^{-6}\, M$), which also inhibit lipogenesis stimulated by 25 μU/ml of insulin (Ditschuneit *et al.*, 1967). Note that these concentrations are of the same order as serum levels produced by a therapeutic dose of buformin in man.

The inhibiting action of biguanides on lipogenesis and on the pentose cycle stimulated by insulin deserves consideration because it may explain, at least in part, the weight-reducing effect exerted by these drugs on obese diabetic subjects. Since the antilipogenetic activity of biguanides is very likely to be produced also in liver (see Sections X and XIII), no questions should be raised, as far as the weight-reducing effect is concerned, from the fact that the lipogenic capacity of human adipose tissue is scanty (less than 5% of glucose carbons are converted to fatty acids) (Rudman and DiGirolamo, 1967). We were among the first investigators to observe the weight-reducing effect of metformin (Muntoni *et al.*, 1965) and the same was also observed by several authors using the other biguanides (Pedersen, 1964; Patel and Stowers, 1964; Mirsky and Schwartz, 1966; Duncan *et al.*, 1968; Alterman and Lopez-Gomez, 1968; Meinert and Schwartz, 1968; Roginsky and Sandler, 1968; Mirsky, 1968; Gershberg *et al.*, 1968).

In view of the physiological relationships between pentose cycle and lipogenesis in adipose tissue, it is conceivable that biguanides inhibit both processes by acting on some metabolic step involving both of them. The actual point at which biguanides interfere with these processes has not yet been demonstrated experimentally and can therefore only be presumed. Also Ditschuneit *et al.* (1967) believe in a close correlation between biguanide-induced inhibition of the pentose cycle and inhibition of lipogenesis, but in the absence of clear-cut experimental proof the problem of the primary site of action is left open.

The hypothesis that the inhibition of lipogenesis is secondary to the inhibition of the pentose cycle, although tempting, is not entirely convincing if we consider that biguanides have no inhibitory effect on the pentose cycle of erythrocytes even at the highest concentrations (phenformin 2.10×10^{-3} *M*) (Krebs *et al.*, 1965). This is an indirect argument against a primary effect of biguanides on the pentose cycle of adipose tissue. Moreover, there is valid evidence supporting the possibility that the inhibition of the pentose cycle may be secondary to the inhibition of lipogenesis. The relationships between pentose cycle, $NADPH_2$:NADP ratio, and lipogenesis are very complex and not yet completely clear. Some experimental data reported in the recent literature appear very hard to reconcile, but nevertheless indicate, though by different interpretations, that lipogenetic activity and pentose-phosphate cycle influence each other and constitute a true metabolic cycle subject to a rather complicated regulation.

Some experimental observations demonstrate that the flow of glucose via the pentose cycle is controlled in a determining way by the Redox state of the NADP system which, in turn, is determined by the degree of activity of the lipogenetic processes (Gumaa and McLean, 1971). In metabolic conditions characterized by inhibited lipogenesis, as in starvation, the reduced activity of the pentose cycle is secondary to the increase in $NADPH_2$:NADP ratio which, in turn, is the result of reduced lipogenesis; in fact, the presence of an electron acceptor capable of reoxidizing $NADPH_2$, restores the glucose flow through the pentose cycle while in spite of this, lipogenesis remains depressed (Gumaa and McLean, 1971).

On the other hand, the activity of glucose 6-phosphate dehydrogenase (G-6-PDH), which controls the entry of glucose into the pentose cycle, is subjected to metabolic regulation when the pentose cycle works in association with lipogenesis; under these conditions the long-chain acyl-CoA inhibit the activity of G-6-PDH through a feedback mechanism (Eger-Neufeldt *et al.*, 1965). Hence lipogenesis appears as a self-limiting process. In metabolic conditions, characterized by an increase in cellular thioesters of long-chain acyl-CoA (namely starvation and lipid diet), the acyl-CoA are believed to inhibit G-6-PDH, the generation of $NADPH_2$, and hence lipogenesis (Hohorst, 1970).

The most evident contrast between this model of regulation and the previous one concerns the $NADPH_2$:NADP ratio, which is raised in one model and lowered in the other. An increase in this ratio may result from reduced lipogenesis and hence from a reduced utilization of $NADPH_2$; a lowering, on the contrary, could indicate that lipogenesis is depressed due to inhibition of G-6-PDH and of the pentose cycle. As previously mentioned, long-chain acyl-CoA are feedback inhibitors of this enzyme. They also inhibit, however, by a feedback mechanism, the enzyme acetyl-CoA carboxylase (Tubbs and Garland, 1963). It is conceivable that when the inhibition of G-6-PDH prevails, the $NADPH_2$: NADP ratio falls, while conversely, when the inhibition of acetyl-CoA carboxylase prevails the above ratio increases. It is thus possible to suggest different ways whereby lipogenesis may be inhibited, explaining the discordant experimental data on the behavior of the NADP system. In any case, even though different mechanisms are involved, the degree of lipogenetic activity is likely to influence the activity of the pentose cycle more than it is influenced by it; in other words, in adipose tissue the pentose cycle subserves lipogenesis. This statement also seems valid in the case of hepatic lipogenesis: the generation of $NADPH_2$ from direct oxidation of glucose does not seem to constitute the limiting factor (Shamoian *et al.*, 1964; Söling, 1970).

With regard to the effect of biguanides, they are known to increase the $NADPH_2$:NADP ratio in adipose tissue (Ditschuneit and Hoff, 1964); this increase is attributed to inhibition of $NADPH_2$ oxidation; the addition of methylene blue, as a hydrogen acceptor, abolishes this change and restores the flow of glucose along the pentose shunt (Ditschuneit and Hoff, 1964). These data do not demonstrate that biguanides inhibit lipogenesis by inhibiting the pentose cycle, since the $NADPH_2$:NADP ratio is increased and not lowered. Rather, they recall the above-mentioned data of Gumaa and McLean (1971), in which the primary phenomenon is the depression of lipogenesis, so that the reoxidation of $NADPH_2$, achieved by means of an electron acceptor, restores the activity of the pentose cycle, but not lipogenesis.

Of the previously described models of lipogenesis inhibition, the most suitable for explaining the effects of biguanides is the one produced by inhibition of acetyl-CoA carboxylase. In the absence of direct experimental proof, it may be suggested that biguanides favor, through a mechanism to be discussed in Section XIII, the inhibition of acetyl-CoA carboxylase by long-chain acyl-CoA. The effects on the pentose cycle and on the NADP system would be a consequence of the inhibition of lipogenesis. This would also explain the previously mentioned fact that biguanides, prevent pentose cycle activation induced by insulin, but have no effect on the basal activity of this pathway. Insulin, in fact, stimulates the activity of acetyl-CoA carboxylase by both coarse and fine control mechanisms (Gellhorn and Benjamin, 1964; Masoro, 1962). Inhibition of this step, brought about indirectly by biguanides, should as a consequence, prevent the effects of insulin on lipogenesis and on the pentose cycle. Finally, this mechanism of biguanide action would also explain the absence of effects on the erythrocyte pentose cycle. As known, this cycle is not as closely associated with lipogenetic processes as it is in adipose tissue and has a different physiological role.

Another effect of biguanides (or at least of phenformin) on adipose tissue is the inhibition of lipolysis (Stone and Brown, 1968; Brown *et al.*, 1969). This effect is induced by rather high concentrations of phenformin (2×10^{-4} *M*) on isolated rat fat cells. Hence it is justifiable to doubt whether therapeutic doses cause such an effect in man. In any case, the investigations of Stone *et al.* (Stone and Brown, 1968; Brown *et al.*, 1969) deserve careful consideration because they clarify many aspects of the antilipolytic activity of phenformin.

This drug significantly reduces the basal release of FFA and glycerol when the incubation medium also contains no glucose. Moreover, it inhibits lipolysis stimulated by norepinephrine, ACTH, glucagon, dexamethasone, growth hormone (GH), and theophylline (Stone and Brown, 1968). The stimulation of lipolysis induced by the combination dexamethasone-GH, which is due to new synthesis of lipase, is also inhibited by phenformin (Stone and Brown, 1968). Anti-insulin serum (AIS), which abolishes the antilipolytic effect of insulin, does not abolish that of phenformin. Stone and Brown (1968) conclude that phenformin does not liberate insulin bound to proteins, does not potentiate the action of free insulin, and has no action on NSILA.

Subsequent experiments carried out by stimulating lipolysis with cyclic dibutyril-AMP plus theophylline (Brown *et al.*, 1969) demonstrated that while insulin inhibits lipolysis by inhibiting the adenylcyclase system, phenformin acts at a late stage either by inhibiting lipase activation by cyclic AMP or by directly inhibiting the lipase system.

To conclude, biguanides have several important effects on carbohydrate and lipid metabolism in adipose tissue. At present, these effects cannot be traced back to a single point of attack or a single mechanism of action, even if some evidence suggests that the antilipogenetic effect is in some way correlated with the primary mechanism of biguanide action, responsible in other tissues for the reduced oxidation of fatty acids. This possible correlation will be discussed in Section XIII. In any case, all or some of the effects with regard to adipose tissue metabolism are likely to play an important role in the action of biguanides in diabetes and obesity.

X. Hyperlipoproteinemia

The effects of biguanides on plasma lipids are complex. They are still difficult to interpret because they have not yet been studied systematically in relation to the different types of hyperlipoproteinemia (as classified by Fredrickson *et al.*, 1967), and in particular to carbohydrate induced lipemias (Ahrens *et al.*, 1961). The recent study of Gustafson *et al.* (1971) is an exception: these authors treated some well-defined types of hyperlipoproteinemia (type II, type IV, and mixed type II + IV) with metformin. After 4 months treatment with metformin, they found that the serum cholesterol values decreased significantly only in type IV patients. Roberts (1969) treated chemical diabetes patients with phenformin and observed a reduction both in basal cholesterolemia and in the "paradox" hypercholesterolemia induced by a glucose load. Other authors found that phenformin treatment reduced blood cholesterol in diabetic (Schwartz *et al.*, 1966; Mirsky, 1968; Gershberg *et al.*, 1968) and in coronary patients with abnormal glucose tolerance (Tzagournis *et al.*, 1968). Phenformin is known to exert inhibitory effects on several steps of cholesterol synthesis, chiefly on the conversion of $\Delta^{5,7}$-cholestanediol into cholesterol, by inhibiting Δ^7-reductase (Dempsey, 1968). Dempsey (1968) attributes the lowering of blood cholesterol induced by phenformin in obese diabetics to these effects. However, since the phenformin concentrations which induce these inhibitions *in vitro* (10^{-3} to $10^{-4}\,M$) are very high, doubts are raised about the possibility that therapeutic doses of phenformin may act in man by the same mechanism. On the other hand, since the intestinal mucosa is considered to be the most important extrahepatic site of cholesterol synthesis in the body (Wilson *et al.*, 1968), and since biguanides accumulate electively at this site (Wick *et al.*, 1960; Cohen and Costerousse, 1961; Berger, 1970), the mechanism described by Dempsey (1968) might contribute to lower blood cholesterol in man. Note, however, that phenformin lowers blood cholesterol only in maturity onset diabetes and not in nondiabetic subjects with high blood cholesterol (Schaefer, 1968). This phenomenon, which agrees with the more recent observation of Gustafson *et al.* (1971) mentioned previously, induces us to exclude the possibility that in man, the direct mechanism of inhibition of Δ^7-reductase may be responsible for the hypocholesterolemic action of phenformin.

Parallel effects of biguanides were observed by the same authors on plasma triglycerides, the high levels of which were lowered by phenformin in obese diabetic subjects (Schwartz *et al.*, 1966; Mirsky, 1968), and in patients with early coronary atherosclerosis (Tzagournis *et al.*,

1968; Negri *et al.*, 1971), but not in nondiabetic subjects with high blood triglyceride levels (Schaefer, 1968). High plasma triglyceride levels were also lowered by metformin, but only in type IV hyperlipoproteinemia in which pre-β-lipoproteins also disappeared (Gustafson *et al.*, 1971). More recently, Stout and Bierman (1972) reported that in endogenous hypertriglyceridemia, a 5-day course of phenformin lowered plasma triglyceride and cholesterol levels: these effects were accompanied by a reduction in plasma triglyceride turnover rate, suggesting reduced input of triglycerides into plasma.

The simultaneous effects of phenformin on blood cholesterol and triglyceride levels in diabetic subjects is a point in favor of a single mode of action on the respective aspects of metabolism. The previously quoted authors attribute the two effects to the reduction of the hyperinsulinemia, which they consider the cause of the increased lipid synthesis. One should recall in this regard that, according to Roginsky and Sandler (1968), phenformin reduces body weight only in obese subjects with abnormal glucose tolerance and high blood insulin levels (Yalow *et al.*, 1965; Kreisberg *et al.*, 1967).

The effects of biguanides on plasma FFA levels have been studied little so far. From the scanty data concerning diabetic patients treated with biguanides, it may be deduced that in general, there is an initial increase in plasma FFA levels, followed by a progressive reduction down to values below the initial ones (Mehnert, 1969b). The acute effect of a dose of biguanide has been only studied in a few cases. After 1 or 2 mg / kg of intravenous buformin, normal subjects show no changes while the plasma FFA in diabetics behave in a noncharacteristic manner (Wahl and Sanwald, 1967). In contrast with these results, we (Sirigu *et al.*, 1973) found that after a 15 mg / kg intravenous dose of metformin, both in normal and in insulin-independent diabetic subjects, the plasma FFA levels frequently (but not constantly) increased without any corresponding increase in plasma glycerol. In this regard, one should recall that in the rat in basal conditions, a dose of phenformin causes a slight and transient increase in plasma FFA levels; the increase is much more marked when the animal is in a condition of increased fatty acid utilization; in this case, the increase in plasma FFA is an expression of reduced utilization caused by phenformin (Muntoni *et al.*, 1969, 1970). Moreover, further investigations carried out in our Institutes (Tagliamonte *et al.*, 1973) have shown that a 5-day phenformin treatment in man produces a marked reduction in FFA turnover.

Finally, with regard to the effects on ketonemia and ketonuria, therapeutic doses of biguanides generally exert an antiketotic action (Sterne, 1969). An opposite effect, sometimes attributed to phenformin, is occasionally caused by one of its toxic metabolites and not by the pharmacological antidiabetic action, since neither metformin nor buformin ever produce ketosis (Sterne, 1969).

The overall action of phenformin on plasma lipids (triglycerides and cholesterol) and on blood insulin in latent diabetic subjects with early coronary atherosclerosis is considered by Tzagournis *et al.* (1968) to be a basis for the prophylaxis of atherosclerosis (through modifications of the humoral components of atherogenesis). According to these authors, phenformin could prevent both the possible lipogenetic and antilipolytic effect of high insulin concentrations on the arterial wall, and the excessive accumulation of lipids in the same resulting from filtration favored by the high blood lipid levels.

It is certainly premature to say that phenformin and the other biguanides are really effective on the early stages of atherogenesis, but the preliminary data appear all the more convincing, because biguanides not only influence lipid metabolism, but they activate fibrinolysis (Back *et al.*, 1968; Fearnley *et al.*, 1968) as well. The activation of fibrinolysis becomes important in light of Duguid's (1946) theory on the role of the deposition of lipids and fibrin in the arterial intima and of Astrup's theory (1956) on the opposite role of the fibrinolytic process at the same site.

A discussion concerning the way in which biguanides influence the modifications in blood lipids presupposes a precise knowledge of the pathogenesis of these modifications and of the relations between these modifications, carbohydrate metabolism, and insulin. This subject is, however, still controversial and cannot constitute a reliable point of reference; on the contrary, biguanides and what is known of their other metabolic effects may become helpful in investigating such a complex field. The recent research of Owen *et al.* (1971), which will be discussed later, is based on this criterion.

Most authors agree that in carbohydrate-induced hypertriglyceridemias, the hyperinsulinemia is secondary to peripheral insulin resistance. There is no agreement, however, on the role of hyperinsulinemia in the pathogenesis of hypertriglyceridemia.

According to Reaven *et al.* (1967), a correlation exists between blood insulin levels and triglyceride response to high-carbohydrate diet; this is in accordance with the previous hypothesis of Farquhar *et al.* (1966) of increased hepatic triglyceride synthesis resulting from high blood insulin levels. Debry *et al.* (1970) point out that hyperinsulinemia causes hypertriglyceridemia only when it is secondary to peripheral insulin resistance; the simultaneous supply of glucose and insulin to the liver stimulates triglyceride synthesis; conversely, primary hyperinsulinism (insuloma) results in obesity with increased carbohydrate tolerance, but not hyperlipemia. Davidson and Albrink (1966) believe that hypertriglyceridemia induces peripheral insulin resistance, with secondary compensatory hyperinsulinemia. According to Avogaro *et al.* (1967), increased triglyceride synthesis in liver and adipose tissue is caused by a diversion of glucose metabolism towards lipogenesis, induced by hyperinsulinemia; the high blood triglyceride level could, in turn, induce an abnormal carbohydrate tolerance, by a mechanism analogous to that of FFA, as suggested by the previous authors (Davidson and Albrink, 1966). According to Butturini (1970), the defect in peripheral glucose utilization leading to hypertriglyceridemia may be either primary or secondary: the further course of the blood insulin level is determined by the ability of β-cells to respond to this metabolic situation, to dietary carbohydrate loads, and to insulin-antagonist factors. This endocrine-metabolic situation is improved by reducing food intake and body weight, but not by lowering plasma FFA levels with nicotinic acid. Thus, according to Butturini (1970), a high-carbohydrate diet and/or insulin-antagonist factors stimulate β-cells: if these respond adequately, the result is hyperinsulinemia which induces obesity; obesity, in turn, causes insulin resistance, reduction of carbohydrate tolerance, and hypertriglyceridemia. The idea of a vicious circle, obesity/insulin resistance, is shared by other authoritative investigators such as Karam *et al.* (1965) and Vague *et al.* (1969). The close connection between obesity, diabetes, and hypertriglyceridemia is stressed also by Crepaldi *et al.* (1972) who view diabetes both as "genetic basis" and "final conclusion" of the complex pathogenesis of these dysmetabolic conditions.

The relations between insulinemia and hypertriglyceridemia have been studied by other authors. Glueck *et al.* (1969) did not find any correlation between blood insulin levels and hypertriglyceridemia induced by a high-carbohydrate diet. According to Nikkilä (1969), the magnitude of plasma insulin response to oral glucose is not correlated to plasma triglyceride levels; but this fact does not exclude the possibility that hyperinsulinemia might be involved in the pathogenesis of hyperglyceridemia, at least in particular cases (Nikkilä, 1969). In agreement with these conclusions, more recently Bagdade *et al.* (1971) found that basal hyperinsulinemia correlated more closely with body weight than with plasma triglyceride levels. Owen *et al.* (1971) also failed to find any correlation between insulinemia and hypertriglyceridemia. Moreover, they used phenformin as a means of exploring the correlations between the different humoral modifications: the drug was found capable of preventing hypertriglyceridemia induced by a high-carbohydrate diet, without causing any reduction in blood insulin levels [the experimental subjects were neither obese nor hyperinsulinemic, and Boshell *et al.* (1968) had shown that in such subjects, phenformin does not modify the blood insulin levels]. Owen *et al.* (1971) exclude the possibility that the drug may have hindered intestinal glucose absorption because the subjects' weight remained constant. According to these authors, excessive stimulation of hepatic triglyceride synthesis in the endogenous hypertriglyceridemias of obese subjects is not caused by high blood insulin levels, themselves secondary to peripheral insulin resistance; in their opinion, this theory would imply that insulin-resistance does not involve the liver, a fact which they consider unlikely; moreover in their normoinsulinemic subjects, phenformin prevented carbohydrate-induced hypertriglyceridemia without modifying the blood insulin levels. In any case, Owen *et al.* (1971) conclude that it is not yet possible to explain the mechanism of phenformin action on triglyceride synthesis.

I believe that with the help of available data on the mechanism of biguanide action and also with the help of recent findings concerning the relationships between carbohydrate and lipid metabolism, some progress may be made in understanding carbohydrate-induced hypertriglyceridemia and the effects of biguanides on this metabolic abnormality.

The effects of insulin on lipid metabolism in the liver are very complex and have not yet been completely clarified. In insulin-deficient diabetes, increased hepatic ketogenesis is associated with reduced fatty acid synthesis, chiefly due to reduced acetyl-CoA carboxylase activity, this constituting the rate-limiting step in the extramitochondrial pathway of fatty acid synthesis (Wieland *et al.*, 1963). This enzyme is subject to direct metabolic control: it is activated by citrate (Martin and Vagelos, 1962) and conversely, it is inhibited by coenzyme-A acyl-derivatives (Tubbs and Garland, 1963). Increased fatty acid esterification, induced by α-glycerophosphate, causes a reduction in the concentration of acyl-CoA and hence in the inhibition of acetyl-CoA carboxylase (Howard and Lowenstein, 1965). Insulin exerts both a coarse and a fine control on this enzyme. The coarse control is achieved by promoting the synthesis of the new enzyme (this effect is prevented by actinomycin D) (Gellhorn and Benjamin, 1964). The fine control is obtained through increased fatty esterification, increased ATP synthesis, and probably also by inhibition of ATPase (Masoro, 1962). These mechanisms explain the increase in hepatic fatty acid synthesis induced by insulin in pancreatectomized rats (Fain *et al.*, 1965).

In any case, even in the absence of insulin effects, lipid production in the liver can proceed to some extent and partly contribute to two phenomena associated with the metabolic imbalance present in human insulin-dependent diabetes, namely steatosis and hyperlipemia.

Hepatic steatosis, which depends to a large extent on modifications in lipid transport (Savage *et al.*, 1960), is partly caused by the increased FFA supply to the liver (oxidation, resynthesis of triglycerides). In this metabolic condition, the hyperlipemia is of two main types (Patrassi and Crepaldi, 1971): (a) hyperchylomicronemia, which represents a defect in the removal of chylomicrons from plasma due to reduced post heparin plasma lipolytic activity (PHLA), that is promptly corrected by insulin administration; (b) hypertriglyceridemia in the course of ketosis (Harris *et al.*, 1953), attributed not only to impaired removal of triglycerides from plasma (Bagdade *et al.*, 1968, 1970; Mancini *et al.*, 1972), but also to a true increase in hepatic triglyceride and cholesterol synthesis, paralleled by an increase in pre-β and β-lipoproteins (Patrassi and Crepaldi, 1971).

In these metabolic conditions, hepatic lipid production is backed-up by the increased supply of fatty acids deriving from adipose tissue and by the persistence to some extent of lipogenesis from acetate (Shamoian *et al.*, 1964), even when glucose utilization and NADPH generation from direct glucose oxidation are lowered due to the diabetic condition (Söling, 1970). The capability to esterify fatty acids is not seriously impaired since the liver can produce α-glycerophosphate even in absence of insulin (Chernick and Scow, 1964): in fact glycerol, taken up from plasma, can be phosphorylated by hepatic glycerokinase (Harper, 1965), the required ATP generated from fatty acid oxidation. Under these circumstances, cholesterol synthesis also continues and even increases due to increased fatty acid oxidation in the liver (Hotta and Chaikoff, 1952) and hence to increased availability of acetyl-CoA for this biosynthetic pathway (Söling, 1970) as well.

The increased ketogenesis observed in diabetic liver is chiefly due to the increased FFA supply, namely to the absence of extrahepatic insulin effects, and does not differ from ketosis caused by fasting or a high-fat diet (Söling, 1970).

Insulin suppresses hepatic ketogenesis both by depressing lipolysis in adipose tissue and by acting directly on the liver where insulin: (a) favors esterification of part of the FFA derived from plasma and thus prevents their oxidation to acetyl-CoA,[4] (b) stimulates the activity of acetyl-CoA carboxylase and thus diverts acetyl-CoA away from keto-

---

[4] Such an effect is still debated: in fact Nikkilä (1969) brought evidence from literature and from his own data against any regulatory role of insulin on the esterification of fatty acids taken up from plasma by liver; on the other hand, more recently McGarry and Foster (1972) showed that insulin can prevent ketosis from long-chain fatty acids (delivered to liver by infusion of chylomicrons and heparin), but not from infused octanoate, which is known not to be utilized directly for triglyceride biosynthesis: these investigators then concluded that insulin stimulates triglyceride biosynthesis from long-chain fatty acids.

genesis in favor of lipogenesis; (c) stimulates the activity of the Krebs cycle and hence oxidation of acetyl-CoA to CO_2; (d) promotes the synthesis of fatty acids from acetoacetate (Harper, 1965).

The critical metabolite in this hepatic metabolic picture is acetyl-CoA. In conditions of increased FFA supply to the liver, the increased production of acetyl-CoA may simultaneously supply all its possible metabolic pathways, namely oxidation via the Krebs cycle, formation of ketone bodies, fatty acid and cholesterol synthesis; a collateral effect is the stimulation of gluconeogenesis. The availability of insulin determines the choice of pathways. Briefly, insulin not only partly opposes the formation of acetyl-CoA, but also diverts it away from ketogenesis while creating suitable conditions for its utilization in the Krebs cycle, in the synthesis of fatty acids (and their esterification) and, at least indirectly (Söling, 1970), in the synthesis of cholesterol.

It is in this context that one must view the opposing metabolic conditions characteristic of the liver, on the one hand in insulin-deficient diabetes and on the other in latent diabetes with insulin-resistance and hyperinsulinemia. The two conditions share a common factor, namely an increased supply of FFA to liver, although this results from different causes. In the first case, it is basically due to insulin deficiency in adipose tissue. In the second case, it is attributed to persisting excessive lipolysis in the presence of insulin, in spite of the fact that the latter, as demonstrated by Pozza *et al.* (1972) in human adipose tissue, exerts an antilipolytic effect even at concentrations still insufficient to stimulate liposynthesis. Excessive lipolysis could take place in muscle since its lipase might be less sensitive to insulin (Randle *et al.*, 1965), or in the mesenteric region, which is believed to supply FFA to liver directly via the portal route (Nikkilä, 1969; Boyer, 1970), or most probably in the enlarged fat cells themselves (Salans *et al.*, 1968; Cahill, 1971). According to Zinder and Shapiro, (1971) the lipolytic activity of fat cells is in fact proportional to the cell surface. This correlation is supported by the research of Knittle and Ginsberg-Fellner (1972) and of Guy-Grand and Bour (1972), who found that in human fat cells the lipolytic activity, both basal and stimulated by catecholamines, is proportional to the cell size, namely to the degree of hypertrophic obesity.

The consequences of increased fatty acid supply and oxidation in the liver in the two conditions are different due to the different availability of insulin. In insulin-deficient diabetes most of the acetyl-CoA produced is used for ketogenesis, cholesterol synthesis, and to a lesser extent, for lipogenesis (see before).

In conditions characterized by hyperinsulinemia, secondary to peripheral insulin resistance, two processes take place in parallel. The first consists in increased triglyceride production by direct esterification of FFA taken up from plasma: this process tends to prevent the oxidation of fatty acids to acetyl-CoA. In contrast, the second process consists in increased generation of acetyl-CoA from fatty acids and in the resulting increase in lipogenesis (see as follows) due to activation of insulin-sensitive extramitochondrial system, and in cholesterol synthesis; this process is also involved in the stimulation of gluconeogenesis. The respective role of these two processes in the causation of hypertriglyceridemia will be discussed later. In any case, one of the causes of the carbohydrate-dependence of hypertriglyceridemia in these conditions is connected with the effects of insulin on hepatic metabolism. It is fairly easy to understand why fructose stimulates hepatic triglyceride synthesis and induces hepatic steatosis more than glucose (MacDonald, 1970; Butturini, 1970): fructose produces glycerophosphate more easily, which can be utilized for fatty acid esterification and abolishes inhibition of acetyl-CoA carboxylase. This is because the production of glycerophosphate from glucose, even in the presence of insulin, is partly hindered just by the increase in fatty acid oxidation to acetyl-CoA and by the increased concentration of citrate (Randle *et al.*, 1965). Finally, it is understandable how carbohydrate-induced hypertriglyceridemia may be frequently induced by ethanol through a similar mechanism (Debry *et al.*, 1970): one of the metabolic effects of ethanol is to induce, via acetaldehyde, a net increase in hepatic acetyl-CoA levels (Forsander and Lindros, 1967). Besides, ethanol was shown to increase the glycerol phosphate content of the liver (Nikkilä, 1971), a factor that might contribute to ethanol-induced triglyceride production.

In my opinion, there are reasons for believing that increased acetyl-CoA production from fats may be even more important in the pathogenesis of carbohydrate-induced hyperlipemias than direct esterification of FFA taken up from plasma.

One of these reasons is that increased FFA supply to the liver, without their further oxidation, could only explain the increased triglyceride production (by direct esterification), but not the associated metabolic phenomena, namely, increased cholesterol synthesis and gluconeogenesis, characteristic of obesity and diabetes, so frequently associated with endogenous hypertriglyceridemia. Both cholesterol synthesis and stimulation of gluconeogenesis depend in fact on the availability of acetyl-CoA. Gluconeogenesis, in particular, depends on the generation of acetyl-CoA from fats since acetyl-CoA produced from pyruvate has no access to the active site of pyruvate carboxylase (Fritz, 1967).

Another reason is that in endogenous hypertriglyceridemias, biguanides simultaneously influence plasma triglycerides, cholesterol, and pre-β-lipoproteins (Gustafson *et al.*, 1971). They inhibit, moreover, gluconeogenesis dependent upon pyruvate carboxylase (see Section IV). Since we now know that biguanides depress fatty acid oxidation, their effectiveness in endogenous hypertriglyceridemia is further proof of the important part played in these dysmetabolic conditions by increased FFA oxidation and not simply by their increased supply to the liver (Muntoni, 1972). In fact, while in normal subjects, large amounts of fatty acids and insulin are never presented simultaneously to liver, and therefore, acetyl-CoA carboxylase is activated only when acetyl-CoA is being generated from pyruvate (i.e., in a fed state), in hyperinsulinemia, secondary to peripheral insulin-resistance, the "coarse" and "fine" effects of insulin on acetyl-CoA carboxylase persist to some extent even in a fasted state, when acetyl-CoA is being generated from fatty acids. It follows that the latter could enter a pathway that under physiological conditions is active only during carbohydrate utilization. Therefore, in endogenous hyperglyceridemia, hepatic lipogenesis is conceivably maximal after carbohydrate load, but, paradoxically, it can persist to a certain extent in the fasting state, because of the recycling of acetyl-CoA generated from fatty acid breakdown.

The essence of metabolic derangement in endogenous hyperglyceridemia consists, in my opinion, in failure of the mechanism that normally shifts the hepatic metabolism from a "fed" to "fasted state" pattern. In my opinion, both the persistence of high hepatic triglyceride production, in either starved or high-fat fed type IV subjects, and the high rate of hepatic fatty acid synthesis, in fasted obese-hyperglycemic hyperinsulinemic mice, as reported by Nikkilä (1969), can be accounted for by such an abnormality.

Therefore, I think that this metabolic disturbance could properly be considered a particular case of "anomalous interconversion of substrates" according to definition proposed by Adezati and Prando (1972). But while these authors referred this definition to quantitative alterations (i.e., to decreased efficiency of substrate-transforming reactions), the aforementioned metabolic derangement might rather represent a qualitative change in the hepatic metabolic pattern.

To conclude, there are valid reasons for believing that increased acetyl-CoA production from fats plays an important role in carbohydrate-induced hyperlipemias. Hyperinsulinemia may be viewed as a phenomenon secondary to peripheral insulin resistance, which is itself a consequence of the same basic phenomenon, namely of the increased production of acetyl-CoA in other tissues, such as muscle (Randle *et al.*, 1965). Hyperinsulinemia, in turn, drives hepatic metabolism toward a further enhancement of lipogenesis, even at the expense of ketogenesis.

Hence hyperinsulinemia may be viewed at the same time as a consequence of the increased extrahepatic and hepatic FFA metabolism and as an accessory cause of the hyperlipemia. Not all authors agree about the role of increased fatty acid utilization in the causation of insulin-resistance, because their plasma levels are not always markedly increased. It should be recalled, however, that the increase in hepatic and muscular fatty acid utilization may be proportional not so much to their plasma levels as to their turnover, which was found to be increased in diabetes (Mancini *et al.*, 1972) and in obesity (Birkenhäger and Tjabbes, 1969). Note, moreover, that hepatic fatty acid uptake may be increased in patients with endogenous hypertriglyceridemia in the presence of normal plasma FFA levels (Havel, 1969; Bagdade *et al.*, 1971). Finally, it is possible, as shown by Schonfeld and Kipnis (1968), that the alterations in glucose-fatty acid cycle may be correlated, at least in muscle, more with intracellular than with plasma FFA levels.

The complex physiopathological picture of carbohydrate-induced hyperlipoproteinemia is still debated. In my opinion, the aforementioned pathogenetic concept has the merit both of identifying a key-point common to the different endocrine-metabolic alterations typical of this condition, and of supplying a coherent interpretation of the effects of biguanides on the same alterations. The ability of biguanides to depress FFA oxidation and hence acetyl-CoA production explains, independently from the effects on the insulin level, the reduction in hepatic triglyceride and cholesterol synthesis and the lowering of their plasma levels. This fact suggests that in carbohydrate-induced hyperlipemias, a considerable share of FFA taken up by the liver is not directly esterified, but must be oxidized to acetyl-CoA in order to produce the complete series of effects on hepatic lipid and carbohydrate metabolism. The reduction of high blood insulin levels could further favor the effects of biguanides on blood lipids, in proportion to the still controversial role of hyperinsulinemia in the genesis of hyperlipemias, previously discussed.

Hence, the influence of biguanides on fatty acid oxidation also explains their effects on hepatic lipid synthesis. With regard to the production of these effects, however, besides the fundamental mechanism, an accessory mechanism consisting in the enhancement of the feedback inhibition of acetyl-CoA carboxylase by long-chain acyl-CoA may also be suggested. This mechanism, already mentioned in Section IX with reference to inhibition of lipogenesis in adipose tissue, will be discussed in Section XIII. Conceivably, this inhibitory mechanism should be maximally effective in the fed state, when biguanides cannot prevent large amounts of acetyl-CoA from being available for hepatic lipogenesis, since in this case it is derived from pyruvate.

Another effect of biguanides may possibly be related to their activity in liver metabolism, since Adezati (1968) found a reduction in insulin fixation by rat liver slices in the presence of metformin. The significance of this interesting observation must be established. Taking into account the effects of insulin on hepatic lipid synthesis, it cannot be overlooked that the phenomenon described by Adezati (1968) may be a component of the action of biguanides on hepatic lipid metabolism.

We must finally discuss a possible objection. Inhibition of fatty acid oxidation could increase the share of FFA available for direct esterification in liver cells, without the step through acetyl-CoA formation. This should result in increased triglyceride synthesis and reduced cholesterol synthesis. Experimental conditions, in which fatty acid oxidation is depressed, as in the case of methyl groups or choline deficiency or administration of diphtheria toxin, are in effect associated with an accumulation of triglyerides in the cells (Bressler, 1970). These conditions are unlikely, however, to represent models qualitatively or quantitatively comparable to the metabolic changes induced by biguanides. In any case, I think the following two considerations may answer the aforementioned objection.

The first concerns some aspects, still imperfectly understood, of fatty acid metabolism in the liver. The complex mechanisms controlling it are based essentially on the existence of separate intracellular compartments (Spector, 1968) and thus of several cellular FFA pools: hence the variation in size of one compartment need not immediately influence the others. In any case, since the overall intracellular FFA concentration is in equilibrium with the extracellular concentration (without necessarily being equal to it) and since the rate of equilibration between the extracellular and cell FFA pools exceeds by far the rate of utilization of cell FFA (Spector, 1968), it is not necessary to postulate a cellular accumulation of FFA as an automatic consequence of its reduced utilization. Hence there should not be any reasons for an increase in their esterification. On the other hand, the fact that under particular experimental conditions, biguanides prevent hepatic steatosis (Sterne, 1969) and the fact that they lower plasma triglyceride levels even more than cholesterol levels (Gustafson *et al.*, 1971), demonstrate that reduced fatty acid oxidation does not cause an increase in triglyceride synthesis. It has exactly the opposite effect.

The second consideration regards the overall effects of biguanides on lipid metabolism. These drugs (see Section IX) also influence several steps preceding fatty acid oxidation: in fact, they hinder lipogenesis and inhibit lipolysis in adipose tissue (the latter effect was demonstrated only *in vitro*). Hence biguanides influence lipid metabolism by causing an overall slowing down of the same. This is probably the main reason why, during prolonged biguanide therapy, no lipid accumulation occurs above the single steps (liver, plasma, adipose tissue) of the long metabolic pathway of lipids. An interpretation of this effect, which might be defined as "lipostatic," will be discussed in Section XIII.

To conclude, biguanides reduce liver triglyceride overproduction in endogenous hypertriglyceridemia through at least four mechanisms: (1) through depression of fatty acid oxidation, thus preventing fat-generated acetyl-CoA from being abnormally directed to resynthesis of fatty acyl-CoA and triglycerides during fasting; (2) through lowering hyperinsulinemia and reducing hepatic fixation of insulin, thus depressing hepatic lipogenesis in the fed state; (3) through direct antilipogenetic effect even in the presence of insulin; (4) through inhibition of lipolysis in adipose tissue and hence reduced FFA presentation to liver, thus preventing fatty acids from being available in larger amounts for esterification, due to their depressed oxidation.

XI. Nitrogen Metabolism

The effects of biguanides on protein metabolism are not so marked and important as those on carbohydrate and lipid metabolism. In any case, they seem to be secondary to the other metabolic effects so far discussed.

In the isolated and perfused livers of diabetic rats, buformin concentrations of $2.55 \times 10^{-5}\ M$ normalize the increased urea production and restore a positive amino acid balance (Söling, 1969). This effect is probably secondary to the reduction in gluconeogenesis and is incompatible with the hypothesis of an inhibition of oxidative phosphorylation since it is associated with normalization of the increased release of inorganic phosphate and potassium, as well as with normalization of the raised lactate:pyruvate ratio (Söling, 1969). If the concentration of buformin is increased to $1.02 \times 10^{-4}\ M$, the amino acid balance is no longer positive (Söling, 1969). In this case, the high concentration of biguanide probably induces the well-known toxic effects on oxidative phosphorylation, since the effects on lactate:pyruvate ratio and on the release of inorganic phosphate and potassium are also reversed (Söling, 1969).

The effects of biguanides on purine metabolism are still little-known. Worthy of note are the studies of Roberts (1969), who found that 2-weeks of phenformin treatment reduces the basal uricemia and the hyperuricemia induced by a glucose load in over 50% of cases of initial chemical diabetes. A discussion on the mechanism of these effects is premature; Roberts himself (1969) avoids it. Nevertheless, in view of the close relationships among diabetes, obesity, and hyperuricemia (Butturini *et al.*, 1971), it is likely that biguanides act on purine metabolism by influencing some alteration common to the three conditions. One of these could be the increased activity of the pentose-phosphate cycle leading, among other things, to increased synthesis of purine rings due to increased formation of the precursor phosphoribosyl-pyrophosphate (PRPP). Hyperuricemia present in type I glycogenosis and the one induced by a fructose load are other examples of increased purine synthesis consequent to enhanced activity of the pentose-phosphate cycle (Butturini *et al.*, 1971). The previously discussed effects of biguanides on this metabolic pathway (see Sections IX, X, and XIII) suggest the hypothesis that these drugs reduce overproduction of purine rings in diabetes and obesity, as a consequence of inhibiting the enhanced activity of the pentose cycle.

XII. Relationships between Biguanides and Insulin

The problem of the relationships between biguanides and insulin is far from new. In view of the many complex interferences between the biological effects of insulin and those of biguanides, it is understandable why this problem has often been only partially examined and why it has given rise to several, often contradictory hypotheses.

The fact that biguanides are ineffective, both in experimental and in clinical cases of diabetes due to absolute insulin deficiency (Söling and Ditschuneit, 1970) and the fact that under these same conditions, biguanides can reduce the requirement for exogenous insulin (Muntoni *et al.*, 1965) demonstrates that the presence of insulin is necessary for at least some effects of biguanides.

On the other hand, it has been established that these drugs do not increase insulin secretion in the guinea pig, mouse, and dog (Söling and Ditschuneit, 1970) but, on the contrary, lower the high insulin levels present after a glucose load in human "hypersecretor" subjects (Grodsky *et al.*, 1963; Boshell *et al.*, 1968) (see Section VI). In contrast with these well-known data, there is only the observation of Loubatières *et al.* (1971) that metformin and phenformin stimulate insulin secretion in the whole dog, and in isolated and perfused rat pancreas. In the absence of further confirmation, it is difficult to discuss these findings that appear at present to disagree with the entire literature of the past ten years on biguanides.

Knowledge of the mechanism of biguanide action now allows us to reexamine the relationships between these drugs and insulin. The different metabolic effects of biguanides so far discussed indicate four different possible relations between the activity of biguanides and that of insulin: dependence, independence, synergism, and antagonism.

A. Dependence

The increased glucose uptake induced by biguanides in striated muscle is an effect that seems to depend upon the presence of insulin. In fact, some of the earlier investigations performed on rat diaphragm incubated *in vitro* (Williams *et al.*, 1957; Bolinger *et al.*, 1960; Ditschuneit and Hoff, 1964) demonstrated increased glucose uptake in the presence of buformin or phenformin. These results must, however, be accepted with many reservations for different reasons, including the frequently high concentrations of drug used and the discrepancies between them and analogous experiments carried out by other investigators (these experiments are reported and fully discussed by Söling and Ditschuneit, 1970). In any case, an increase in glucose uptake in these experimental models does not demonstrate an "insulin-like effect" of biguanides since the presence of insulin fixed to muscle cannot be excluded.

Conversely, *in vivo* research, and in particular those experiments of Butterfield (1968, 1969) (see Section V) demonstrate that phenformin has no insulin-like effects and that it promotes muscular glucose uptake only in the presence of insulin.

The absence of any direct effects on glucose transport through the cellular membrane explains the ineffectiveness of biguanides on hyperglycemia in insulin-deficiency diabetes. The previously discussed effects of these drugs on muscular lipid and carbohydrate metabolism, which result in an increased tendency to metabolize glucose, find a limiting factor in the process of glucose supply to the cell: only in the presence of insulin, which can ensure glucose transport, can such drug-induced metabolic attitude of muscle result in an actual increase in glucose utilization.

B. Independence

The inhibition of hepatic gluconeogenesis, discussed in Section IV, is an effect of biguanides independent of insulin: biguanides prevent activation of pyruvate carboxylase through their ability to decrease acetyl-CoA formation from fats. This effect is similar to the "acute" effect of insulin on the same step involving pyruvate carboxylase. The analogy between the two effects does not imply that biguanides have an "insulin-like" effect, but simply that they act on a metabolic path which is subject to "fine" control by insulin: the latter acts "above' (inhibition of lipolysis) while biguanides act "below" (inhibition of fatty acid oxidation).

The analogy between thc effects of biguanides and insulin on the hepatic (and renal) metabolic processes is not an accidental coincidence, but the logical consequence of the fact that biguanides act primarily on fatty acid oxidation and that insulin plays an important role in the regulation of lipid metabolism.

Another effect exerted by biguanides independently of insulin, is the inhibition of lipolysis in adipose tissue. The significance and the mechanism of this effect have been discussed in Section IX. Suffice to recall here that insulin inhibits lipolysis by acting on an earlier step (adenylcyclase system) than the one influenced by biguanides (lipase system).

C. Synergism

The potentiation of exogenous or endogenous insulin and the decrease in insulin resistance induced by biguanides have been given different interpretations, often lacking experimental support.

Knowledge of the mechanism of biguanide action now allows us to also face this complex problem more rationally. As specified in previous sections, reduced fatty acid oxidation in liver and muscle results in both reduction of gluconeogenesis and increase in glucose utilization. According to Kreisberg (1968a), reduced gluconeogenesis would, by itself, be sufficient to cause a decrease in insulin resistance, since excessive glucose production is considered to be one of the possible causes of such a resistance, as are prolonged glucose infusions (Kreisberg *et al.*, 1967).

The effects on muscle metabolism should be considered as even more important. As was fully reported in Section V, increased fatty acid oxidation in muscle causes a state of relative insulin resistance (Randle *et al.*, 1965). Insulin may modify this situation only by an indirect mechanism, namely by reducing the FFA supply to muscle through its antilipolytic action in adipose tissue: the delay in hypoglycemic effect, observed in maturity onset diabetes, is attributed to the absence of any direct effects of insulin on muscle metabolism thus oriented (Randle *et al.*, 1965). 2-Bromostearate, which inhibits the oxidation of long-chain fatty acids, abolishes insulin resistance in the myocardium of alloxan-diabetic animals (Randle, 1969). It is understandable how biguanides, which also inhibit fatty acid oxidation, can reduce muscle insulin resistance and hence potentiate the effects of insulin. Biguanides direct muscle metabolism toward preferential glucose utilization, but, as mentioned previously, in fact this will only take place in the presence of insulin, which allows glucose uptake by the cell.

At this stage one may ask what is the relation if any, between this metabolic trend toward carbohydrate utilization and the increased muscular insulin clearance, induced by phenformin. Butterfield (1968, 1969) considers the increased fixation of insulin to muscle as the primary effect of the drug since the increase in glucose uptake is proportional to the amount of cleared insulin. In my opinion, this proportionality does not prove that the primary effect of phenformin is the one suggested by Butterfield (1968, 1969): since insulin, in any case (except for the merely theoretical case of a biguanide action on the glucose carrier) is the limiting factor for cellular glucose uptake, there must be an obvious proportion between quantity of insulin cleared and quantity of glucose transported and hence metabolized, just as found by Butterfield (1968, 1969). Counter to this insufficiently demonstrated but neither to be excluded interpretation, I should like to suggest the following hypothesis. By inverting the terms of the problem, I propose that the cellular metabolic trend toward glucose utilization induced by biguanides makes more insulin-receptors available and thus allows the cells to obtain more glucose through greater insulin fixation. This hypothesis, which allows one to interpret the effects of biguanides on the Randle cycle and on muscular insulin clearance by the same mechanism, opens up interesting perspectives for speculation and research. One may postulate that, in addition to the known influences of the membrane receptor stimulation on cell metabolism, the reverse may also occur, that is, cell metabolism could modify the receptor affinity (or availability) for its specific hormone(s).

Apart from this last hypothesis, which remains to be proved, we may hence conclude that the potentiation of insulin activity on muscle glucose metabolism is a direct consequence of the fundamental action of biguanides on fatty acid utilization in the same tissue. Thus Sterne's (1964) suggestive hypothesis of a liberation of insulin bound to a plasma protein carrier must be excluded for it was not demonstrated and is no longer necessary. This hypothesis, put forward again five years later by the same author (Sterne, 1969) without any new experimental data, is opposed by Butterfield (1969) (research on muscular tissue) who excludes the possibility that phenformin may liberate insulin from carrier proteins. Stone and Brown (1968) (research on adipose tissue), also conclude that phenformin does not liberate insulin bound to proteins and has no action on NSILA.

D. Antagonism

The opposing influence of insulin and biguanides on hepatic triglyceride synthesis was discussed in Section X. The antagonism between biguanides and insulin on liposynthesis and on the activity of the pentose cycle in adipose tissue was analyzed in Section IX.

Although in both cases insulin increases and biguanides reduce lipid synthesis, the mechanism of these opposing effects seems to be substantially different in the two cases. The reduction in synthesis of hepatic triglycerides induced by biguanides may be ascribed once again to decreased acetyl-CoA formation, as demonstrated in Section X. The reduced availability of acetyl-CoA for acetyl-CoA carboxylase, an enzyme stimulated by insulin, prevents the effects of the latter on lipid synthesis. The fact that insulin and biguanides have opposite effects on this process, while potentiating each other in muscle, depends only on the particular physiological role of insulin on hepatic lipid metabolism, while biguanides act on the latter through their basic mechanism of action.

In the case of liposynthesis in adipose tissue and its relations with the pentose cycle, the mechanism of the biguanide-induced inhibition, which antagonizes insulin, has not yet been sufficiently investigated. In Section IX, I suggested the possibility that biguanides may favor feedback inhibition of acetyl-CoA carboxylase by long-chain acyl-CoA. A hypothesis on the mechanism of this phenomenon may be put forward in the context of a single interpretation of the basic action mechanism of biguanides, which will be discussed in Section XIII.

To conclude, the relationships between biguanides and insulin now appear less complex and more understandable than previously believed. The fact that synergism is the rule in some cases and antagonism in others, that some effects are insulin-dependent while others are not, no longer obliges us to postulate many scarcely convincing action mechanisms for biguanides. These drugs exert all their effects through a single mechanism. The relations between biguanides and insulin appear to be so variable and complex due to the manifold effects and roles played by insulin in the body.

XIII. A Further Hypothesis

In previous sections, I discussed the various experimental data demonstrating how most of the metabolic effects of biguanides depend upon a single mechanism, namely the inhibition of fatty acid oxidation. The experimental data now available do not bring us any nearer to an understanding of how this inhibition is brought about; nevertheless, several indications seem to suggest a working hypothesis.

A first suggestion stems from the inhibition of lipogenesis (and from the corresponding inhibition of the pentose cycle) in adipose tissue, which is the only effect of biguanides not ascribable to the action on fatty acid oxidation.

Other suggestions arise from knowledge of the mechanism through which other compounds inhibit fatty acid oxidation. As known, hypoglycine, 4-pentenoic acid, and other analogous hypoglycemic compounds depress the oxidation of long-chain fatty acids (Sherratt, 1969; Corredor *et al.*, 1967). In treated animals, the hypoglycemia caused by these compounds is preceded by a reduction of palmitate oxidation in the myocardium (Entman and Bressler, 1967) and by an increase in plasma fatty acid levels due to their reduced utilization (Sherratt, 1969). The hypoglycemia is due to inhibition of gluconeogenesis and to an increase in glucose oxidation, these phenomena being secondary to decreased fatty acid oxidation (Corredor *et al.*, 1967). The essential action mechanism of these compounds is based on the formation of nonmetabolizable acyl-carnitine. In this way, less carnitine will be available to form acyl-carnitine with the natural long-chain fatty acids (Corredor *et al.*, 1967). Hence the latter cannot be transported to the sites of mitochondrial oxidation, although the activity of palmityl-carnitine acyltransferase is not inhibited (Corredor *et al.*, 1967).

The physiological role of carnitine in fatty acid oxidation and in the control of lipid and carbohydrate metabolism is sufficiently well known and was excellently reviewed by Fritz (1967). The rate of long-chain fatty acid oxidation is controlled by their transport through the mitochondrial barrier, which is impermeable to them; this transport is possible in the presence of carnitine, through the formation of acyl-carnitine, which is transported through the mitochondrial membrane by carnitine acyltransferase (Fritz, 1967). These facts justify the ability of carnitine to restore a normal rate of palmitate oxidation in myocardium homogenate from animals treated with hypoglycine (Entman and Bressler, 1967) and to stimulate gluconeogenesis from alanine-^{14}C in rabbit liver slices (Benmiloud and Freinkel, 1967).

Carnitine also influences fatty acid synthesis. The activity of acetyl-CoA carboxylase is physiologically subjected to feedback inhibition by the final products of lipogenesis, namely long-chain acyl-CoA (Tubbs and Garland, 1963). Carnitine and its long-chain acyl-derivatives, such as palmityl-carnitine, release the inhibition of acetyl-CoA carboxylase induced by palmityl-CoA or by starvation (Fritz, 1967). This effect is attributed to competition between palmityl-carnitine and palmityl-CoA for the sites of the enzyme acetyl-CoA carboxylase (Fritz, 1967). Thus carnitine actually plays an important physiological role in favoring both synthesis and oxidation of long-chain fatty acids. The search for a single point of attack, capable of accounting for all the metabolic effects of biguanides, must consider the hypothesis that such a point coincides with the carnitine system.

My hypothesis is that since the chemical structure of biguanides, which to be metabolically active, must not be tetrasubstituted on the terminal nitrogen atoms of the guanidine residues (Elpern, 1968), the capability to influence some metabolic step important for the availability of carnitine is implied. It is interesting that the inhibitory action of guanidine on poliovirus replication is antagonized by some molecules, of which the most active was found to be choline: this action is attributed to a direct interaction with the guanidine molecule (Loddo *et al.*, 1967). It is conceivable that an analogous interaction may occur between the partially free guanidine group of biguanides and carnitine, which has the same trimethylammonium group as choline, or its immediate precursor γ-butyrobetaine (Javillier *et al.*, 1969b), which is structurally similar to carnitine. In view of the analogy between carnitine and γ-butyrobetaine, it is conceivable that biguanides may influence both of them.

A direct action on the available carnitine may explain the immediate effect of a single dose of biguanide on the plasma FFA levels (increased) and on the oxidation of fatty acids (reduced) and of glucose (increased) (see relevant sections). An effect on γ-butyrobetaine could explain why several days are necessary for therapeutic doses of biguanides to produce a full effect: an action at the levels of this precursor could enhance carnitine deficiency by reducing its synthesis. It is also possible that the dose and route of biguanide administration will determine whether the prevailing effect will be on carnitine or on its precursor.

From a purely conceptual point of view, a direct interference of biguanides with the enzyme carnitine acyl transferase cannot be excluded *a priori*, even though this mechanism would seem to be less probable.

The hypothesis of an interference of biguanides with the carnitine system must now be verified experimentally: such studies are in progress in our laboratories with some positive preliminary results. In my opinion, this hypothesis is as promising theoretically as the one I suggested six years ago (Muntoni, 1968), which allowed us to demonstrate experimentally the fundamental action of biguanides on fatty acid oxidation (Muntoni *et al.*, 1969, 1970, 1973a,b; Corsini *et al.*, 1974).

The present hypothesis has the advantage of ascribing to a single mechanism of action both the inhibition of fatty acid oxidation and the inhibition of lipogenesis and the pentose cycle. A block in the carnitine system would, in fact, cause feedback inhibition of acetyl-CoA carboxylase by long-chain acyl-CoA, due to the previously discussed role of carnitine on lipogenesis. The reduced lipogenesis results in an increase in $NADPH_2$:NADP ratio (Gumaa and McLean, 1971), which in turn, can inhibit the activity of the pentose cycle (Gumaa and McLean, 1971). All these effects are really produced by biguanides, at least in rat adipose tissue; their reciprocal relationships have been discussed in Section IX, in which I presented evidence demonstrating that inhibition of the pentose cycle, stimulated by insulin cannot be considered as a direct effect of biguanides (because it is associated with an increased $NADPH_2$: NADP ratio and because it does not take place in erythrocytes), but must be considered as secondary to inhibition of lipogenesis at the level of acetyl-CoA carboxylase. The same mechanism suggested here might be an important component of the effect of biguanides on hepatic lipid synthesis, discussed in Section X. The consequent reduction in the activity of the pentose cycle may account for the effect of biguanides on the hyperuricemia present in diabetes and obesity (see Section XI).

The hypothesis of an interference biguanides-carnitine also permits a coherent interpretation of this chain of effects and, more generally, of the overall slowing down of both anabolic and catabolic components of lipid metabolism ("lipostatic" effect) discussed at the end of Section X.

If proved experimentally, the present hypothesis could open up stimulating prospects regarding a possible role of the carnitine system in diabetes, obesity, and hyperlipoproteinemias. The physiological mechanism regulating lipid and carbohydrate metabolism, attributed by Fritz (1967) to carnitine, would thus have its pathological counterpart.

XIV. Conclusions

Biguanides act fundamentally by depressing fatty acid oxidation in the main utilizing tissues, such as striated muscle and liver.

In the previous sections, I reviewed the metabolic effects of biguanides and was able to demonstrate that the most important and most typical effects are the direct consequence of the same mechanism of action. Inhibition of fatty acid oxidation and of acetyl-CoA generation induces the following: increase in glucose turnover and oxidation; inhibition of hepatic gluconeogenesis at the level of pyruvate carboxylase; increase in peripheral glucose utilization and in carbohydrate tolerance; reduction of hepatic production of cholesterol and triglycerides and of their plasma levels; "potentiation" of endogenous and exogenous insulin. The effects on insulinemia and on lactate metabolism may depend directly, and partly indirectly, upon the same mechanism. Inhibition of lipogenesis and of the pentose cycle are the only effects that cannot be ascribed to inhibition of fatty acid oxidation. The attempt to identify a single mechanism also capable of inducing these effects, leads to the hypothesis of a more general inhibition of fatty acid transport to and from cellular metabolic compartments, with resulting consequences both on fatty acid oxidation and synthesis. The carnitine-dependent transport system may thus be suspected of being the target of biguanides. Whether the antilipogenetic mechanism is this or another one, inhibition of the pentose cycle seems to be more its consequence than its cause. The reduced activity of the pentose pathway may in turn play a role in the action of biguanides on purine metabolism.

The greater knowledge we now have of the action of biguanides obviously favors both research and clinical applications. In the field of research on metabolism physiopathology, biguanides proved to be a useful exploratory tool. In previous sections, I discussed some still controversial problems and made use of the effects of biguanides to understand these problems more clearly. In Section IV, I reviewed the modalities of hepatic gluconeogenesis activation, demonstrating that the inhibitory effects of biguanides support the concept of Randle *et al.* (1963, 1965) on the role of increased fatty acid oxidation in pyruvate carboxylase activation: biguanides selectively inhibit this mechanism, which operates in diabetes, obesity, and hypercortisolism, while they do not interfere with other mechanisms of gluconeogenesis activation. In Section X, I discussed the complex problem of the pathogenesis of carbohydrate-induced hyperlipemias in relation to the metabolic effects of biguanides. In this case, it was possible to conclude that of the different mechanisms involved in hepatic overproduction of triglycerides and cholesterol, the one based on increased acetyl-CoA production from fatty acids during fasting probably plays a more important role than direct reesterification of FFA taken up from plasma. Other problems concerning the origin of hyperinsulinemia in states of insulin-resistance (Section VI) and of hyperuricemia in diabetes and obesity (Section XI) can be better understood, if discussed in relation to the efforts of biguanides.

The usefulness of these drugs as research tools is not limited only to the above examples but also extends to the speculative field. In the previous sections, two working hypotheses were suggested. The first (Section XII) concerns the possibility that cellular metabolism may be capable of influencing the availability of insulin receptors. The second (Section XIII), concerns the role of the carnitine system in the pathology of the glucose-fatty acid cycle, and consequently the relationships between this system and the pharmacological action of biguanides.

Even if these two hypotheses should not be confirmed experimentally I believe that the problems raised by the biguanides' peculiar mechanism of action will in any case, direct pharmacological research toward the study of new molecules capable of interfering with FFA transport and oxidation. Biguanides, in fact, demonstrate, on the one hand, that Randle's concept (Randle *et al.*, 1963, 1965) can coherently explain many pathogenetic features of diabetes, obesity, and several associated metabolic abnormalities; on the other hand, biguanides indicate that pharmacological control of complex metabolic cycles, such as the glucose-fatty acid cycle, is not only conceivable but already obtainable.

In the field of clinical applications, more thorough knowledge of the action mechanism of biguanides supplies a solid pharmacological and physiopathological basis for the indications and rational use of these drugs, not only in the treatment, but also in the prophylaxis of overt diabetes. For many years now, we have stated and demonstrated (Muntoni *et al.*, 1965, 1966, 1968; Muntoni and Sirigu, 1971) that biguanide treatment: (a) in latent diabetes prevents the evolution of the condition to overt diabetes; (b) in diabetes of recent onset brings the condition back to the latent stage, normalizing or improving the oral glucose tolerance test (OGTT) and the tolbutamide test (TT). These results agree with those of Wilansky and Sochat (1968).

We now also understand the pharmacological mechanism through which the above results are obtained. The previous hypotheses on the mechanism of action of biguanides (inhibition of oxidative phosphorylation, stimulation of anaerobic glycolysis, reduction in intestinal glucose absorption, liberation of insulin from protein inhibitors) were not able to explain them; moreover they have proved inconsistent. We now know that inhibition of enhanced fatty acid oxidation, obtained with biguanides, is their key point of action in the prophylaxis and therapy of diabetes. Since increased fatty acid oxidation is, in turn, the key point for the changes in glucose-fatty acid cycle in latent diabetes and obesity, treatment with biguanides satisfies the requirements of a specific therapy at a pathogenetic level and constitutes a rational specific pharmacological prophylaxis of overt diabetes.

XV. Summary

Biguanides exert their metabolic effects through a single basic mechanism, namely inhibition of fatty acid oxidation. This mechanism has no connection with the inhibition of oxidative phosphorylation which is rather a toxic effect produced by concentrations too high with respect to the sensitivity of the treated animal, a factor which varies from species to species.

Knowledge of the action mechanism of biguanides allows us not only to interpret univocally their metabolic and therapeutic effects, but also to exploit these drugs as research tools in the field of metabolic physiopathology. Several problems that are still being debated may thus be reexamined, in particular, the role of the glucose-fatty acid cycle in diabetes and obesity.

Biguanides increase glucose utilization via the EMK pathway, with consequent increase both in the activity of the Cori cycle and in CO_2 production from glucose. Some apparently contrasting experimental data are not actually so; since they were obtained using glucose-1-^{14}C, they only reveal the already known inhibition of the pentose-phosphate pathway.

Biguanides do not inhibit gluconeogenesis indiscriminately: by depressing fatty acid oxidation they exert an inhibitory effect only when pyruvate carboxylase, activated by acetyl-CoA, is the rate-limiting step of gluconeogenesis.

Glucose uptake and oxidation in muscle, hindered by increased fatty acid oxidation, are stimulated by biguanides.

Hyperinsulinemia, secondary to peripheral insulin-resistance is normalized by biguanides, which are capable of abolishing the "signal" for hypersecretion.

The reduction in intestinal glucose absorption, which plays a fairly negligible role in the antidiabetic action of biguanides, depends upon a local "toxic" effect, resulting from the high concentrations reached by these drugs in the intestinal mucosa.

The increased lactate production does not necessarily indicate inhibition of respiration, but depends to a large extent on increased glycolysis both in tissues that physiologically produce lactate aerobically and in striated muscle, in which the Redox systems are distributed in functional compartments.

Inhibition of lipogenesis is the cause, and not the consequence, of inhibition of the pentose-phosphate pathway. The effects of biguanides lead to some considerations on the relationships between liposynthesis and the pentose shunt.

The effects of biguanides on hyperlipoproteinemias lead to a reexamination of the pathogenetic problem of carbohydrate-induced hyperlipemias and suggest that hepatic acetyl-CoA production from fatty acids probably plays an important role in the overproduction of triglycerides during fasting.

The reduced production of uric acid may be a consequence of the inhibition of the pentose-phosphate pathway.

The relationships between biguanides and insulin are manifold. Some effects are insulin-dependent while others are not: some effects imply synergism between biguanides and insulin and others antagonism. The multiplicity of these relations can now be interpreted more easily: it is not due to biguanides, which produce their effects through a single mechanism of action, but to insulin, which exerts a polymorphic physiological role.

Finally, a comprehensive view of the metabolic effects of biguanides suggests the hypothesis that in diabetes, obesity, and other dysmetabolic conditions a common pathogenetic component may operate at the level of the carnitine-dependent system of long-chain fatty acid transport.

Thanks to our present knowledge of the mechanism of biguanide action, it is now possible not only to reexamine some controversial problems of metabolic physiopathology, but also to supply with a rational pharmacobiological basis, the clinical use of these drugs for therapy and especially, for prophylaxis of maturity onset diabetes.

References

Adezati, L. (1968). Personal communication.

Adezati, L., and Prando, R. (1972). *In* "La Via Metabolica dell'Aterogenesi" (G. Labò, L. Barbara, and N. Melchionda, eds.), p. 15. Patron, Bologna.

Ahrens, E. H., Hirsch, J., Oette, K., Farquhar, J. W., and Stein, Y. (1961). *Trans. Ass. Amer. Physicians* **74,** 134.

Alpert, N. R. (1965). *Ann. N. Y. Acad. Sci.* **119,** 995.

Alterman, S. L., and Lopez-Gomez, A. A. (1968). *Ann. N. Y. Acad. Sci.* **148,** 884.

Altschuld, R. A., and Kruger, F. A. (1968). *Ann. N. Y. Acad. Sci.* **148,** 612.

Ammon, H. P. T., and Estler, C. J. (1967). Quoted in Sandler *et al.* (1968).

Assan, R. (1972). *Eur. Meet. Metab. 1st, Padua* Abstr. p. 43.

Astrup, T. (1956). *Blood* **11,** 781.

Avogaro, P., Crepaldi, G., Enzi, G., and Tiengo, A. (1967). *Acta Diabet. Lat.* **4,** 572.

Back, N., Wilkens, H., Barlow, B., and Czarnecki, J. (1968). *Ann. N. Y. Acad. Sci.* **148,** 691.

Bagdade, J. D., Porte, D., Jr., and Bierman, E. L. (1968). *Diabetes* **17,** 127.

Bagdade, J. D., Porte, D., Jr., and Bierman, E. L. (1970). *Journees Annu. Diabetol. Hotel-Dieu, Paris* p. 221.

Bagdade, J. D., Bierman, E. L., and Porte, D., Jr. (1971). *Diabetes* **20,** 664.

Balasse, E. O., and Ooms, H. A. (1973). *Diabetologia* **9,** 145.

Ball, E. G., and Jungas, R. L. (1964). *Recent Progr. Horm. Res.* **20,** 183.

Beckmann, R. (1965). *Arzneim.-Forsch.* **15,** 761.

Beckmann, R. (1968). *Ann. N. Y. Acad. Sci.* **148,** 820.

Beckmann, R. (1969). *Arzneim.-Forsch.* **19,** 628.

Benmiloud, M., and Freinkel, N. (1967). *Metab. Clin. Exp.* **16,** 658.

Berchtold, P., Bolli, P., Arbenz, U., and Keiser, G. (1969). *Diabetologia* **5,** 405.

Berger, W. (1970). *Actua, Med. Hyg.* **2,** 10.

Bernier, J. J., Modigliani, R., and Vidon, N. (1968). *Journees Annu. Diabetol. Hotel-Dieu, Paris* p. 357.

Bewsher, P. D., and Ashmore, J. (1966). *Biochem. Biophys. Res. Commun.* **24,** 431.

Bigelow-Sherman, J. D., and Foà, P. P. (1969). *Acta Diabet. Lat.* **6,** 507.

Bihler, I., and Sawh, P. C. (1972). *Fed. Proc., Fed. Amer. Soc. Exp. Biol.* **31**, 287. (Abstr.)
Birkenhäger, J. C., and Tjabbes, T. (1969). *Metab. Clin. Exp.* **18**, 18.
Biro, L., Banyasz, T., Kovacs, M. B., and Bajor, M. (1961). *Klin. Wochenschr.* **39**, 760.
Björntorp, P. (1972). *Euro. Meet. Metab. 1st, Padua* Abstr. p. 5.
Bolinger, R. E., McKee, W. P., and Davis, J. W. (1960). *Metab. Clin. Exp.* **9**, 30.
Boshell, B. R., Roddam, R. F., and McAdams, G. L. (1968). *Ann. N. Y. Acad. Sci.* **148**, 756.
Boyer, J. (1970). *Journees Annu. Diabetol. Hotel-Dieu, Paris* p. 161.
Bressler, R. (1970). *Compr. Biochem.* **18**, 331.
Brown, J. D., Stone, D. B., and Steele, A. A. (1969). *Metab. Clin. Exp.* **18**, 926.
Butterfield, W. J. H. (1968). *Ann. N. Y. Acad. Sci.* **148**, 724.
Butterfield, W. J. H. (1969). *Acta Diabet. Lat.* **6**, Suppl. 1, 644.
Butturini, U. (1970). *Journees Annu. Diabetol. Hotel-Dieu, Paris* p. 297.
Butturini, U., Coscelli, C., and Palmari, V. (1971). *Recenti Progr. Med.* **51**, 359.
Cahill, G. F. (1971). *New Engl. J. Med.* **284**, 1268.
Cahill, G. F., Jr., *et al.* (1966). *J. Clin. Invest.* **45**, 1751.
Calandra, S., Zeneroli, M. L., and Ventura, E. (1968). *Acta Diabet. Lat.* **5**, 391.
Cappelli, V., Pietra, P., and Panagia, V. (1969). *Boll. Soc. Ital. Biol. Sper.* **45**, 1588.
Carlson, L. A., and Ostman, J. (1965). *Acta Med. Scand.* **178**, 71.
Carlson, L. A., and Ostman, J. (1966). *Diabetologia* **2**, 127.
Chernick, S. S., and Scow, R. O. (1964). *J. Biol. Chem.* **239**, 2416.
Cohen, Y., and Costerousse, O. (1961). *Therapie* **16**, 109.
Conard, V. (1965). *Acta Diabet. Lat.* **2**, 447.
Connon, J. J. (1971). *Annu. Meet. Eur. Ass. Study Diabetes, 7th, Southampton, Engl.* Abstr. No. 42.
Correa, P. R., and Marques, M. (1964). *Metab. Clin. Exp.* **13**, 496.
Corredor, C., Brendel, K., and Bressler, R. (1967). *Proc. Nat. Acad. Sci. U. S.* **58**, 2299.
Corsini, G. U., Sirigu, F., Tagliamonte, P., and Muntoni, S. (1974). *Pharmacol. Res. Commun.* (in press).
Couturier, E., Camu, F., Rasio, F., and Conard, V. (1970). *Annu. Meet. Eur. Ass. Study Diabetes, 6th, Warsaw* Abstr. No. 43.
Craig, J. E., Miller, M., Woodward, H., Merik, J. R., and Merik, E. (1960). *Diabetes* **9**, 186.
Crane, R. K. (1960). *Physiol. Rev.* **40**, 789.
Crepaldi, G., Muggeo, M., Tiengo, A., Fedele, D., Bagnariol, G., Fellin, R., Enzi, G., and Briani, G. (1972). *Congr. Naz. Soc. Ital. Diabetol. 4th, Catania* Abstr. p. 27.
Crespin, S. R., Greenough, W. B., and Steinberg, D. (1969). *J. Clin. Invest.* **48**, 1934.
Czyzyk, A. (1969). *Acta Diabet. Lat.* **6**, Suppl. 1, 636.
Czyzyk, A., Tawecki, J., Sadowski, J., Ponikowska, I., and Szczepanik, Z. (1968). *Diabetes* **17**, 492.
Davidson, P. D., and Albrink, M. J. (1966). *J. Clin. Invest.* **45**, 1000.
Davies, V. H., Martin, L. E., Mills, J. G., and Vardey, C. J. (1971). *Annu. Meet. Eur. Ass. Study Diabetes, 7th, Southampton, Engl.* Abstr. No. 45.
Daweke, H., and Bach, I. (1963). *Metab. Clin. Exp.* **12**, 319.
Debry, G., Anziani, Cherrier, and Laurent, J. (1964). *Diabete* **12**, 295.
Debry, G., Laurent, J., Guisard, D., Gonand, J. P., Mejean, L., and Drouin, P. (1970). *Journees Annu. Diabetol. Hotel-Dieu, Paris* p. 229.

Dempsey, M. E. (1968). *Ann. N. Y. Acad. Sci.* **148,** 631.
Ditschuneit, H., and Hoff, F. (1964). *New Istanbul Contrib. Clin. Sci.* **7,** 106.
Ditschuneit, H., Rott, W. H., and Faulharber, J. D. (1967). *Int. Biguanid-Symp., 2nd, Stuttgart* Abst. p. 62.
Doar, J. W. H. (1968). *Minerva Med.* **59,** 1786.
Duguid, J. B. (1946). *J. Pathol. Bacteriol.* **58,** 207.
Duncan, G. G., Duncan, T. G., and Schatanoff, J. (1968). *Ann. N. Y. Acad. Sci.* **148,** 906.
Eger-Neufeldt, I., Teinzer, A., Weiss, L., and Wieland, O. (1965). *Biochem. Biophys. Res. Commun.* **19,** 43.
Elpern, B. (1968). *Ann. N. Y. Acad. Sci.* **148,** 577.
Entman, M., and Bressler, R. (1967). *Mol. Pharmacol.* **3,** 333.
Exton, J. H., Jefferson, R. W., Butcher, R. W., and Park, C. R. (1966). *Amer. J. Med.* **40,** 709.
Exton, J. H., Mallette, L. E., Jefferson, L. S., Wong, E. H. A., Friedmann, N., Miller, T. B., Jr., and Park, C. R. (1970). *Recent Progr. Horm. Res.* **26,** 411.
Fain, J. N., Scow, R. O., Urgui-Otti, E. J., and Chernick, S. S. (1965). *Endocrinology* **77,** 137.
Fajans, S. S., Moorhouse, J. A., Doorenbos, H., Louis, H. L., and Conn, J. W. (1960). *Diabetes* **9,** 194.
Farquhar, J. W., Frank, A., Gross, R. C., and Reaven, G. M. (1966). *J. Clin. Invest.* **45,** 1648.
Fearnley, G. R., Chakrabarti, R., Hocking, E., and Evans, J. (1968). *Ann. N. Y. Acad. Sci.* **148,** 840.
Felber, J. P., and Vannotti, A. (1964). *Med. Exp.* **10,** 153.
Forsander, O. A., and Lindros, K. O. (1967). *Acta Chem. Scand.* **21,** 2568.
Fratino, P., Barosi, G., and Pozzoli, E. (1970). *Atti Congr. Naz. Soc. Ital. Diabetologia, 3rd, Modena* p. 273.
Fredrickson, D. S., Levy, R. I., and Lees, R. S. (1967). *New Engl. J. Med.* **276,** 273.
Fritz, I. B. (1967). *Perspect. Biol. Med.* **10,** 643.
Froesch, E. R., *et al.* (1967). *Mol. Pharmacol* **3,** 442.
Gellhorn, A., and Benjamin, W. (1964). *Science* **146,** 1166.
Gershberg, H., Javier, Z., Hulse, M., and Hecht, A. (1968). *Ann. N. Y. Acad. Sci.* **148,** 914.
Ghionni, A., Esposito, E., and Giuliani, G. (1968). *Int. Symp. Antidiabet. Biguanides, Rimini. Abstr.* p. 20.
Glueck, C. J., Levy, R. I., and Fredrickson, D. S. (1969). *Diabetes* **18,** 739.
Gomez, F., Jéquier, E., Rüedi, B., and Felber, J. P. (1970). *Annu. Meet. Eur. Ass. Study Diabetes, 6th, Warsaw* Abstr.
Gomez, F., Jéquier, E., Chabot, V., Büber, V., and Felber, J. P. (1971). *Annu. Meet. Eur. Ass. Study Diabetes, 7th, Southampton, Engl.* Abstr. No. 65.
Grodsky, G. M., Karam, J. H., Pavlatos, F. C., and Forsham, P. H. (1963). *Meta., Clin. Exp.* **12,** 278.
Gross, R. C., and Carlson, L. A. (1968). *Diabetes* **17,** 353.
Gumaa, K. A., and McLean, P. (1971). *Postgrad. Med. J.* **47,** 403.
Gustafson, A., Björntorp, P., and Fahlén, M. (1971). *Acta Med. Scand.* **190,** 491.
Guy-Grand, B., and Bour, H. (1972). *Journees Annu. Diabetol. Hotel-Dieu, Paris* p. 81.
Haeckel, R., and Haeckel, H. (1968). Quoted in Söling (1969). p. 667.

Hall, H., Ramachander, G., and Glassman, J. M. (1968). *Ann. N. Y. Acad. Sci.* **148**, 601.

Harper, H. A. (1965). "Chimica Fisiologica e Patologica". Piccin, Padua.

Harris, L. V. D., van Eck, W. F., Man, E. B., and Peters, J. B. (1953). *Metab., Clin. Exp.* **2**, 120.

Havel, R. J. (1969). *In* "Advances in Internal Medicine" (G. H. Stollerman, ed.), Vol. XV, p. 117. Yearbook Publ., Chicago, Illinois.

Hohorst, H. J. (1970). *In* "Il Diabete Mellito" (E. F. Pfeiffer, ed.), Vol. I, p. 315. Il Ponte, Milan.

Hohorst, H. J., Arese, P., Bartels, H., Stratmann, D., and Talke, H. (1965). *Ann. N. Y. Acad. Sci.* **119**, 974.

Hotta, S., and Chaikoff, I. L. (1952). *J. Biol. Chem.* **198**, 895.

Houghton, C. R. S., Caterson, I. D., and Williamson, D. H. (1971). *Annu. Meet. Euro. Ass. Study Diabetes, 7th, Southampton, Engl.* Abstr. No. 90.

Howard, C. F., Jr., and Lowenstein, J. M. (1965). *J. Biol. Chem.* **240**, 4170.

Jangaard, N. O., Pereira, J. N., and Pinson, R. (1968). *Diabetes* **17**, 96.

Javillier, M., Polonovski, M., Florkin, M., Boulanger, P., Lemoigne, M., Roche, J., and Wurmser, R. (1969a). *Traite Biochim. Gen.* **3**, Part 2, 3.

Javillier, M., Polonovski, M., Florkin, M., Boulanger, P., Lemoigne, M., Roche, J., and Wurmser, R. (1969b). *Traite Biochim. Gen.* **3**, Part 2, 524.

Jenkins, D. J. A. (1967). *Lancet* **ii**, 340.

Johnson, R. H., Walton, J. L., Krebs, H. A., and Williamson, D. H. (1969). *Lancet* **ii**, 1383.

Jordan, H. H., and Hopwood, M. L. (1970). *Fed. Proc., Fed. Amer. Soc. Exp. Biol.* **29**, 379.

Kaden, M., Oakley, N. W., and Field, J. B. (1969). *Amer. J. Physiol.* **216**, 756.

Kärki, N. (1957). *Acta Physiol. Scand., Suppl.* **39**, 132.

Karam, J. H., Grodsky, G. M., and Forsham, P. H. (1965). *Ann. N. Y. Acad. Sci.* **131**, 374.

Knittle, J. L., and Ginsberg-Fellner, F. (1972). *Diabetes* **21**, 754.

Krebs, H. A. (1964). *Proc. Roy. Soc., Ser. B* **19**, 545.

Krebs, H. A., Hems, R., and Gasocoyne, T. (1963). *Acta Biol. Med. Ger.* **11**, 607.

Krebs, R., Ditschuneit, H., and Fritzsche, W. (1965). *Gastroenterologia* **104**, 204.

Kreisberg, R. A. (1968a). *Ann. N. Y. Acad. Sci.* **148**, 743.

Kreisberg, R. A. (1968b). *Diabetes* **17**, 481.

Kreisberg, R. A., Boshell, B. R., Diplacido, J., and Roddam, R. F. (1967). *New Engl. J. Med.* **276**, 314.

Kreisberg, R. A., Pennington, L. F., and Boshell, B. R. (1970). *Diabetes* **19**, 64.

Landau, B. R., and Katz, J. (1965). *In* "Adipose Tissue" (A. E. Renold and G. F. Cahill, Jr., eds.), Handbook of Physiology, Sect. 5, p. 253. Amer. Physiol. Soc., Washington, D. C.

Lavieuville, M. (1967). *Journees Annu. Diabetol. Hotel-Dieu, Paris* p. 441.

Lefebvre, P., and Luyckx, A. (1972). *Journees Annu. Diabetol. Hotel-Dieu, Paris* p. 93.

Loddo, B., Gessa, G. L., Tagliamonte, A., and Ferrari, W. (1967). *Experientia* **23**, 1047.

Lorch, E. (1971). *Diabetologia* **7**, 195.

Losert, W., Kraaz, W., Jahn, P., and Rilke, A. (1971). *Naunyn-Schmiedebergs Arch. Pharmakol. Exp. Pathol.* **269**, 459.

Loubatières, A., Mariani, M. M., and Jallet, F. (1971). *Annu. Meet. Euro. Ass. Study Diabetes, 7th, Southampton, Engl.* Abstr. No. 113.
Lyngsöe, J., and Trap-Jensen, J. (1969). *Brit. Med. J.* **ii**, 224.
MacDonald, I. (1970). *Journees Annu. Diabetol. Hotel-Dieu, Paris* p. 241.
McGarry, J. D., and Foster, D. W. (1972). *Metab., Clin. Exp.* **21**, 471.
Madison, L. L., and Unger, R. H. (1960). *Diabetes* **9**, 202.
Madison, L. L., Lochner, A., and Wulff, J. (1967). *Diabetes* **16**, 252.
Mancini, M., Lewis, B., and De Ritis, F. (1972). *Congr. Naz. Soc. Ital. Diabetol., 4th, Catania* Abstr. p. 30.
Martin, D. B., and Vagelos, P. R. (1962). *J. Biol. Chem.* **237**, 1787.
Masoro, E. J. (1962). *J. Lipid Res.* **3**, 149.
Mebane, D., and Madison, L. L. (1964). *J. Lab. Clin. Med.* **63**, 177.
Mehnert, H. (1969a). *Acta Diabet. Lat.* **6**, *Suppl. 1*, 137.
Mehnert, H. (1969b). *Acta Diabet. Lat.* **6**, *Suppl. 1*, 678.
Meinert, C. L., and Schwartz, T. B. (1968). *Ann. N. Y. Acad. Sci.* **148**, 875.
Meyer, F., Ipaktchi, M., and Clauser, H. (1967). *Journees Annu. Diabetol. Hotel-Dieu, Paris* p. 341.
Mirouze, J., Bernard, R., and Isnard, F. (1969). *Journees Med. Montpellier* **4**, 337.
Mirsky, S. (1968). *Ann. N. Y. Acad. Sci.* **148**, 937.
Mirsky, S., and Schwartz, M. J. (1966). *J. Mt. Sinai Hosp., New York* **33**, 180.
Monod, J., Changeux, J. P., and Jacob, F. (1963). *J. Mol. Biol.* **6**, 306.
Montague, W., and Taylor, K. W. (1968). *Nature (London)* **217**, 853.
Moruzzi, G., Rossi, C. A., and Rabbi, A. (1966). "Principi di Chimica Biologica," Tiranelli, Bologna.
Muntoni, S. (1968). *Int. Symp. Antidiabet. Biguanides, Rimini.* Abstr. p. 19.
Muntoni, S. (1972). *In* "La Via Metabolica dell'Aterogenesi" (G. Labò, L. Barbara, and N. Melchionda, eds.), p. 529. Patron, Bologna.
Muntoni, S., and Sirigu, F. (1971). *Rass. Med. Sarda* **74**, 241.
Muntoni, S., Boero, A., Corona, M., and Floris, M. (1965). *Clin. Ter.* **35**, 227.
Muntoni, S., Boero, A., and Floris, M. (1966). *Congr. Naz. Soc. Ital. Diabetol., 1st, Catania* p. 555.
Muntoni, S., Sirigu, F., Floris, M., and Boero, A. (1968). *Minerva Med. Giuliana* **8**, 256.
Muntoni, S., Duce, M., and Corsini, G. U. (1969). *Congr. Soc. Ital. Farmacol., 15th, Milan* Abstr. p. 76.
Muntoni, S., Duce, M., and Corsini, G. U. (1970). *Life Sci.* **9**, Part II, 241.
Muntoni, S., Tagliamonte, P., Sirigu, F., and Corsini, G. U. (1973a). *Le Progrès Médical* **101**, 277.
Muntoni, S., Tagliamonte, P., Sirigu, F., and Corsini, G. U. (1973b). *Acta Diabet. Lat.* **10**, 1300.
Negri, A. U., Matteoli, E., Zaini, G. F., and Riva, D. (1971). *Minerva Med.* **62**, 4405.
Newsholme, E. A. (1963). *Biochem. J.* **89**, 388.
Nikkilä, E. A. (1969). *Advan. Lipid Res.* **7**, 63.
Nikkilä, E. A. (1971). *Progr. Biochem. Pharmacol.* **6**, 102.
Nikkilä, E. A., Taskinen, M. R., Miettinen, T. A., Pelkonen, R., and Poppius, H. (1968). *Diabetes* **17**, 209.
Owen, W. C., Kreisberg, R. A., and Siegal, A. M. (1971). *Diabetes* **20**, 739.
Patel, D. P., and Stowers, J. M. (1964). *Lancet* **ii**, 282.
Patrassi, G., and Crepaldi, G. (1971). "Le Iperlipoproteinemie." Pozzi, Rome.

Patrick, S. J. (1966). *Can. J. Biochem.* **44**, 27.
Pedersen, J. (1964). *Lancet* **ii**, 281.
Pereira, J. N., Jangaard, N. O., and Pinson, E. R. (1967). *Diabetes* **16**, 869.
Pozza, G., Sanesi, E., Ghidoni, A., Pappalettera, E., and Melogli, O. (1972). *Euro. Meet. Metab., 1st, Padua.* Abstr. p. 9.
Pressman, B. C. (1963). *J. Biol. Chem.* **238**, 401.
Pruett, E. D. R., and Oseid, S. (1970). *Scand. J. Clin. Lab. Invest.* **26**, 277.
Randle, P. J. (1969). *Nature (London)* **221**, 777.
Randle, P. J., Garland, P. B., Newsholme, E. A., and Hales, C. N. (1963). *Lancet* **1**, 785.
Randle, P. J., Garland, P. B., Newsholme, E. A., and Hales, C. N. (1965). *Ann. N. Y. Acad. Sci.* **131**, 324.
Reaven, G. M., Lerner, R. L., Stern, M. P., and Farquhar, J. W. (1967). *J. Clin. Invest.* **46**, 1756.
Roberts, H. J. (1969). *Acta Diabet. Lat.* **6**, 728.
Roginsky, M. S., and Sandler, J. (1968). *Ann. N. Y. Acad. Sci.* **148**, 892.
Ruderman, N. B., Toews, C. J., and Shafrir, E. (1969). *Arch. Int. Med.* **123**, 299.
Rudman, D., and DiGirolamo, M. (1967). *Advan. Lipid Res.* **5**, 35.
Salans, L. P., Knittle, J. L., and Hirsch, J. (1968). *J. Clin. Invest.* **47**, 153.
Sandler, R., Vinnick, L., and Freinkel, N. (1968). *Life Sci.* **7**, Part II, 459.
Savage, N., Gillman, J., and Gilbert, C. (1960). *Nature (London)* **185**, 168.
Schaefer, L. E. (1968). *Ann. N. Y. Acad. Sci.* **148**, 925.
Schäfer, G. (1969). *Biochim. Biophys. Acta* **172**(2), 334.
Schalch, D. S., and Kipnis, D. M. (1964). *J. Clin. Invest.* **43**, 1283.
Schonfeld, G., and Kipnis, D. M. (1968). *Diabetes* **17**, 422.
Schwartz, M. J., Mirsky, S., and Schaefer, L. E. (1966). *Metab., Clin. Exp.* **15**, 808.
Schwarz, F., ter Haar, J. D., van Riet, H. G., and Thijssen, J. H. H. (1969). *Metab., Clin. Exp.* **18**, 1013.
Searle, G. L., and Cavalieri, R. R. (1968). *Ann. N. Y. Acad. Sci.* **148**, 734.
Searle, G. L., Shilling, S., Porte, D., Jr., Barbaccia, J., Degrazia, J., and Cavalieri, R. R. (1966). *Diabetes* **15**, 173.
Searle, G. L., Gulli, R., and Cavalieri, R. R. (1969). *Metab., Clin. Exp.* **18**, 148.
Seubert, W. (1970). *In* "Il Diabete Mellito" (E. F. Pfeiffer, ed.), Vol. I, p. 327. Il Ponte, Milan.
Seyffert, W. S., and Madison, L. L. (1967). *Diabetes* **16**, 765.
Shamoian, C. A., Masoro, E. J., Derrow, A., and Canzanelli, A. (1964). *Endocrinology* **74**, 21.
Sherratt, H. S. A. (1969). *Brit. Med. Bull.* **25**(3), 250.
Sirigu, F., Tagliamonte, P., Corsini, G. U., and Muntoni, S. (1973). *Riv. Farmacol. Ter.* **4**, 235.
Söling, H. D. (1969). *Acta Diabet. Lat.* **6**, Suppl. 1, 656.
Söling, H. D. (1970). *In* "Il Diabete Mellito" (E. F. Pfeiffer, ed.), Vol. I, p. 529. Il Ponte, Milan.
Söling, H. D., and Ditschuneit, H. (1970). *In* "Il Diabete Mellito" (E. F. Pfeiffer, ed.), Vol. I, p. 713. Il Ponte, Milan.
Söling, H. D., Werchau, H., and Creutzfeld, W. (1963). *Naunyn-Schmiedebergs Arch. Exp. Pathol. Pharmakol.* **244**, 290.
Söling, H. D., Zahlten, R., Böttcher, M., and Willms, B. (1967). *Diabetologia* **3**, 377.
Spector, A. A. (1968). *Ann. N. Y. Acad. Sci.* **149**, 768.
Steiner, D. F., and Williams, R. H. (1958). *Biochim. Biophys. Acta* **30**, 329.

Steiner, D. F., and Williams, R. H. (1959). *Diabetes* **8**, 154.
Sterne, J. (1964). *Metab., Clin. Exp.* **13**, 791.
Sterne, J. (1969). *In* "Oral Hypoglycemic Agents" (G. D. Campbell, ed.), pp. 193–245. Academic Press, New York.
Stone, D. B., and Brown, J. D. (1968). *Ann. N. Y. Acad. Sci.* **148**, 623.
Stout, R. W., and Bierman, E. L. (1972). *Diabetes* **21**, Suppl. 1, 380.
Tagliamonte, P., Sirigu, F., Corsini, G. U., and Muntoni, S. (1973). *Riv. Farmacol. Ter.* **4**, 151.
Tietz, A., and Shapiro, B. (1956). *Biochim. Biophys. Acta* **19**, 374.
Toews, C. J., Lowy, C., and Ruderman, N. B. (1970). *J. Biol. Chem.* **245**, 818.
Tranquada, R. E., and Beigelman, P. M. (1960). *Clin. Res.* **8**, 248.
Tranquada, R. E., and Bender, A. B. (1962). *Clin. Res.* **10**, 90.
Tubbs, P. K., and Garland, P. B. (1963). *Biochem. J.* **89**, 250.
Tyberghein, J. M., and Williams, R. H. (1957). *Proc. Soc. Exp. Biol. Med.* **96**, 29.
Tzagournis, M., Seidensticker, J. F., and Hamwi, G. J. (1968). *Ann. N. Y. Acad. Sci.* **148**, 945.
Utter, M. F. (1963). *Iowa St. J. Sci.* **38**, 97.
Utter, M. F., and Keech, D. B. (1963). *J. Biol. Chem.* **238**, 2603.
Vague, P., Boeuf, G., Depieds, R., and Vague, J. (1969). *In* "Physiopathology of Adipose Tissue" (J. Vague, ed.), p. 203. Excerpta Med. Found. Amsterdam.
Wahl, P., and Sanwald, R. (1967). *Int. Congr. Diabetes Fed., 6th, Stockholm* Abstr. No. 385.
Watanabe, C. K. (1918). *J. Biol. Chem.* **33**, 253.
Weber, G., and Srivastava, S. K. (1965). *Proc. Nat. Acad. Sci. U. S.* **53**, 96.
Wick, A. N., Larson, E. R., and Serif, G. S. (1958). *J. Biol. Chem.* **233**, 296.
Wick, A. N., Steward, C. J., and Serif, G. S. (1960). *Diabetes* **9**, 163.
Wick, A. N., Walton, G., Drury, D. R., and Copp, E. F. F. (1963). *Biol. Pharmacol.* **12**, Suppl., 83.
Wieland, O., and Loeffler, G. (1962). Quoted in Hohorst *et al.* (1965), p. 987.
Wieland, O., Neufeld, I., Numa, S., and Lynen, F. (1963). *Biochem. Z.* **336**, 445.
Wilansky, D. L., and Sochat, G. (1968). *Ann. N. Y. Acad. Sci.* **148**, 848.
Williams, R. H., Tyberghein, J. M., Hyde, P. M., and Nielsen, R. L. (1957). *Metab., Clin. Exp.* **6**, 311.
Williamson, J. R. (1967). *Advan. Enzyme Regul.* **5**, 229.
Williamson, J. R., Kreisberg, R. A., and Felts, P. W. (1966a). *Proc. Nat. Acad. Sci. U. S.* **52**, 247.
Williamson, J. R., Wright, P. H., Malaisse, W. J., and Ashmore, J. (1966b). *Biochem. Biophys. Res. Commun.* **24**, 765.
Wilson, J. D., Lindsey, C. A., and Dietschy, M. (1968). *Ann. N. Y. Acad. Sci.* **149**, 808.
Yalow, R. S., Glick, S., Roth, J., and Berson, S. A. (1965). *Ann. N. Y. Acad. Sci.* **131**, 357.
Yoh, Y. (1967). *Jap. J. Pharmacol.* **17**, 439.
Zinder, O., and Shapiro, B. (1971). *J. Lipid Res.* **12**, 91.

Author Index

Numbers in italics refer to the pages on which the complete references are listed.

D

G

M

S

T

Subject Index

D

E

M

A 4
B 5
C 6
D 7
E 8
F 9
G 0
H 1
I 2
J 3